PHILIP'S

GEOGRAPHICAL

DIGEST

1998–99

PHILIP'S

GEOGRAPHICAL

DIGEST

1998–99

Published in Great Britain in 1998
by Heinemann Educational
a division of Reed Educational and Professional Publishing Limited
Halley Court
Jordan Hill
Oxford OX2 8EJ

**OXFORD FLORENCE MADRID ATHENS
PRAGUE CHICAGO MELBOURNE KUALA LUMPUR
MEXICO CITY AUCKLAND SINGAPORE TOKYO
SÃO PAULO NAIROBI IBADAN GABORONE KAMPALA
JOHANNESBURG PORTSMOUTH NH (USA)**

in association with
George Philip Limited
an imprint of Reed Consumer Books Limited
Michelin House
81 Fulham Road
London SW3 6RB
and Auckland and Melbourne

© 1998 George Philip Limited

Cartography by Philip's

Front cover photograph © NRSC

ISBN 0–435–35022–6

A CIP catalogue record for this book is available from the British Library.

Compiled and edited by
Caroline Rayner, Simon G. Roberts, Patricia Willett and B.M. Willett

Design Karen Ferguson, Stephen Scanlan

Printed in Great Britain by Butler and Tanner Limited, Frome, Somerset

Contents

Introduction

This edition of *Philip's Geographical Digest* is formed of three parts: a statistical section; a text section, listing the more important geographical changes of the last two years; and a section on the European Union with statistical information and a map of the current union and applicant countries.

The statistical part of *Philip's Geographical Digest* consists of world lists for a variety of topics, including various aspects of demography and agriculture and over 100 tables showing the production of many agricultural, mineral and manufactured products. A special new table in this edition provides information on global tourism, as well as information on new world heritage sites.

The world lists include as many countries as possible. Please note that *Philip's Geographical Digest* uses the transcriptions recommended by the PCGN (Permanent Committee for Geographical Names) for some of the newly independent countries in the former USSR. For example, Belarus is used instead of Belorussia, Moldova for Moldavia and Kazakstan for Kazakhstan. Where the only data available are for the former USSR, Czechoslovakia and Yugoslavia, this information appears in italics. What is generally called Serbia is listed under Yugoslavia (Serbia), and Bosnia-Herzegovina is often abbreviated to Bosnia.

In addition, in lists of percentages, the sum of the individual figures may not equal 100 due to rounding.

For a number of countries the traditional English conventional name form has been used: Brunei (Brunei Darussalam), Burma (Myanmar), Ivory Coast (Côte d'Ivoire), Surinam (Suriname). The data for Belgium often includes that of Luxembourg. In figures for 1950, Bangladesh is included in the totals for Pakistan.

The latest figures available have been given, usually for the years 1994–97. The most recent figure is often provisional and all world totals should be used cautiously and should be taken to indicate a year-on-year trend. A country is included in the production lists if it has for at least two of the years of the series produced over one-thousandth part of the world total.

Where applicable, we have used the measure and spelled it 'tonnes' to indicate that the statistics are recorded in metric tons.

In the production statistics the top ten producers are indicated with the percentage of world total formed by each. This is calculated for the latest year shown.

The contents list gives the first page of each section. The production statistics are arranged alphabetically within the broad groupings of agriculture, forest and fishing products, and minerals and manufactured products.

Over the years, *Philip's Geographical Digest* has aimed to cover all of the European countries with regard to census information. In this edition, new data for Finland and Poland, as well as data for Canada, Guatemala, Indonesia, Japan, Morocco and New Zealand, are included.

The symbol ... indicates that the relevant figures are not available, or are not applicable to a particular country. The symbol – means that although there was production for a particular year it was very small.

The following are the official sources that have been used in the compilation of *Philip's Geographical Digest*.

United Nations: Demographic Yearbook 1995, Energy Yearbook 1994, Monthly Bulletin of Statistics (various), Population and Vital Statistics Report (various), Industrial Commodity Statistics Yearbook 1995, International Trade Yearbook 1995, World Population Projections 1992/3, Human Development Report 1997.

Food and Agricultural Organization: Fertilizer Yearbook 1996, Yearbook of Fishery Statistics 1995, Yearbook of Forest Products 1997, Production Yearbook 1996.

World Bank: Development Report 1997, World Tables 1997.

Metallgesellschaft Aktiengesellschaft: Metal Statistics 1985–95.

Office of Population, Censuses and Surveys: Population estimates (various).

Ministry of Agriculture: Digest of Agricultural Census Statistics 1995.

Eurostat: Basic Statistics of the Community 1996.

Country-by-country summary

These profiles aim to give a brief statistical picture of each country. Many of the figures have been expressed in, it is hoped, a more meaningful and helpful way by showing, for example, the value per inhabitant or a measure in relation to the size of the country. The tables are standard for all countries except the very small; for these the basic facts are shown. If a usual item is omitted from a country list, the information is not available or not applicable. The total area is shown and this includes water areas. If the water area is larger than 1% of the total, then the land area is shown in parentheses. The population figure is an estimate for mid-1997. The population change is a yearly average for the period 1990–97. The fertility rate is a broad indication of the number of children born live to a woman in her lifetime; it is an estimate for 1995. Wealth is the 1995 GNP (Gross National Product) of a country divided by its population. The GNP is a rough measure of the value of the country's production of goods and services and also the net balance of the import and export of services. Where it is available, the average annual change in this total, 1985–95, is given after the total. The energy data refer to the amount of energy produced or consumed per person, expressed in tonnes of coal. The official language(s) of a country is given in italics, with others listed if numerically significant.

Afghanistan

CAPITAL CITY: Kabul
AREA: 652,090 sq km
POPULATION: 23,000,000 people
POPULATION DENSITY: 35 people per sq km
POPULATION CHANGE: 4.8% per year
BIRTH RATE: 43 per 1,000 people
DEATH RATE: 18 per 1,000 people
LIFE EXPECTANCY: Males 47, females 46 years
INFANT MORTALITY: 147 per 1,000 live births
URBAN POPULATION: 20% of population
FERTILITY RATE: 7 children per female
AGE GROUPS: 0–14 yrs 42%, 15–59 yrs 53%, 60+ yrs 5%
ETHNIC GROUPS: Pashtun 52%, Tajik 20%, Uzbek 9%, Hazara 9%, Chahar, Turkmen, Baluchi
LANGUAGES: *Pashto, Dari Persian*, Uzbek, Turkmen
RELIGIONS: Sunni Muslim 84%, Shiite Muslim 15%
LAND USE: Arable 12%, grass 46%, forest 3%
EMPLOYMENT: Agric. 61%, ind. 14%, services 25%
ANNUAL INCOME: $300 per person, –6%
ORIGIN OF WEALTH: Agriculture 52%, industry 33%, services 15%
ENERGY: Prod. 0.30 tonnes, consump. 0.04 tonnes
TRADE: $48 per person
CURRENCY: Afghani = 100 puls
ROADS: 27 km per 1,000 sq km of land
ADULT LITERACY: 29%
EDUCATIONAL EXPENDITURE: 2.0% of GNP
MILITARY EXPENDITURE: 8% of GNP
AID RECEIVED: $10 per person

Albania

CAPITAL CITY: Tirana
AREA: 28,750 sq km (Land area 27,400 sq km)
POPULATION: 3,600,000 people
POPULATION DENSITY: 131 people per sq km
POPULATION CHANGE: 1.5% per year
BIRTH RATE: 22 per 1,000 people
DEATH RATE: 8 per 1,000 people
LIFE EXPECTANCY: Males 65, females 72 years
INFANT MORTALITY: 47 per 1,000 live births
URBAN POPULATION: 37% of population
FERTILITY RATE: 3 children per female
AGE GROUPS: 0–14 yrs 33%, 15–59 yrs 59%, 60+ yrs, 8%
ETHNIC GROUPS: Albanian 96%, Greek 2%, Romanian, Macedonian, Montenegrin, Gypsy
LANGUAGES: *Albanian*
RELIGIONS: Sunni Muslim 65%, Albanian Orthodox 23%, Roman Catholic 10%
LAND USE: Arable 26%, grass 15%, forest 38%
EMPLOYMENT: Agric. 56%, ind. 19%, services 25%
ANNUAL INCOME: $670 per person, –7%
ORIGIN OF INCOME: Agriculture 37%, industry 18%, services 46%
ENERGY: Prod. 1.41 tonnes, consump. 0.30 tonnes
TRADE: $177 per person
CURRENCY: Lek = 100 qindars
ROADS: 566 km per1,000 sq km of land
RAILWAYS: 26 km per 1,000 sq km of land
ADULT LITERACY: 85%
AID RECEIVED: $21 per person

Algeria

CAPITAL CITY: Algiers
AREA: 2,381,740 sq km
POPULATION: 29,300,000 people
POPULATION DENSITY: 12 people per sq km
POPULATION CHANGE: 2.3% per year
BIRTH RATE: 28 per 1,000 people
DEATH RATE: 6 per 1,000 people
LIFE EXPECTANCY: Males 68, females 70 years
INFANT MORTALITY: 47 per 1,000 live births
URBAN POPULATION: 56% of population
FERTILITY RATE: 4 children per female
AGE GROUPS: 0–14 yrs 44%, 15–59 yrs 51%, 60+ yrs 5%
ETHNIC GROUPS: Arab 83%, Berber 16%
LANGUAGES: *Arabic*, French, Berber
RELIGIONS: Sunni Muslim 99%
LAND USE: Arable 3%, grass 13%, forest 2%
EMPLOYMENT: Agric. 18%, ind. 33%, services 49%
ANNUAL INCOME: $1,600 per person, –2.6%
ORIGIN OF INCOME: Agriculture 13%, industry 43%, services 43%
ENERGY: Prod. 6.04 tonnes, consump. 1.59 tonnes
TRADE: $757 per person
CURRENCY: Algerian dinar = 100 centimes
ROADS: 42 km per 1,000 sq km of land
RAILWAYS: 2 km per 1,000 sq km of land
POPULATION PER DOCTOR: 1,064 people
ADULT LITERACY: 57%
EDUCATIONAL EXPENDITURE: 9.4% of GNP
MILITARY EXPENDITURE: 1.9% of GNP
AID RECEIVED: $11 per person

American Samoa

CAPITAL CITY: Pago Pago
AREA: 200 sq km
POPULATION: 62,000 people
POPULATION DENSITY: 310 people per sq km
POPULATION CHANGE: 7.2% per year
BIRTH RATE: 35 per 1,000 people
DEATH RATE: 4 per 1,000 people
LIFE EXPECTANCY: Males 71, females 75 years
INFANT MORTALITY: 19 per 1,000 live births
FERTILITY RATE: 5 children per female
ETHNIC GROUPS: Samoan 90%, Caucasian 2%, Tongan 2%
LANGUAGES: *Samoan, English*
RELIGIONS: Congregational, Roman Catholic
LAND USE: Arable 10%, forest 70%
EMPLOYMENT: Agric. 2%, ind. 34%, services 64%
ANNUAL INCOME: $3,500 per person
ENERGY: Consumption 2.88 tonnes per person
TRADE: $13,320 per person
CURRENCY: US currency
ROADS: 1,750 km per 1,000 sq km of land
ADULT LITERACY: 42%

Andorra

CO-PRINCIPALITY OF SPAIN AND FRANCE
CAPITAL CITY: Andorra La Vella
AREA: 453 sq km
POPULATION: 75,000 people
POPULATION DENSITY: 166 people per sq km
POPULATION CHANGE: 6.9% per year
BIRTH RATE: 10 per 1,000 people
DEATH RATE: 3 per 1,000 people
LIFE EXPECTANCY: Males 86, females 95 years
INFANT MORTALITY: 2 per 1,000 live births
FERTILITY RATE: 1 child per female
ETHNIC GROUPS: Spanish 46%, Andorran 28%, Portuguese 11%, French 8%
LANGUAGES: *Catalan*, French, Castilian
RELIGIONS: Roman Catholic 90%
LAND USE: Arable 2%, grass 56%, forest 22%
ANNUAL INCOME: $14,000 per person
TRADE: $952 per person
CURRENCY: French and Spanish currency
ROADS: 598 km per 1,000 sq km of land

Angola

CAPITAL CITY: Luanda
AREA: 1,246,700 sq km
POPULATION: 11,200,000 people
POPULATION DENSITY: 9 people per sq km
POPULATION CHANGE: 1.6% per year
BIRTH RATE: 44 per 1,000 people
DEATH RATE: 17 per 1,000 people
LIFE EXPECTANCY: Males 45, females 50 years
INFANT MORTALITY: 136 per 1,000 live births
URBAN POPULATION: 32% of population
FERTILITY RATE: 7 children per female
AGE GROUPS: 0–14 yrs 45%, 15–59 yrs 50%, 60+ yrs 5%
ETHNIC GROUPS: Ovimbundu 37%, Mbundu 23%, Kongo, Luimbe, Humbe, Chokwe
LANGUAGES: *Portuguese*, Ovimbundu, Mbundu, Kongo, other Bantu languages
RELIGIONS: Roman Catholic 44%, Traditionalist 34%, Protestant 20%
LAND USE: Arable 2%, grass 23%, forest 42%
EMPLOYMENT: Agric. 73%, ind. 10%, services 17%
ANNUAL INCOME: $410 per person, –6.1%
ORIGIN OF INCOME: Agriculture 12%, industry 43%, services 45%
ENERGY: Prod. 3.63 tonnes, consump. 0.09 tonnes
TRADE: $475 per person
CURRENCY: Kwanza = 100 lwei
ROADS: 58 km per 1,000 sq km of land
RAILWAYS: 2 km per 1,000 sq km of land
POPULATION PER DOCTOR: 25,000 people
ADULT LITERACY: 43%
EDUCATIONAL EXPENDITURE: 7.3% of GNP
MILITARY EXPENDITURE: 35.5% of GNP
AID RECEIVED: $40 per person

Anguilla

DEPENDENT TERRITORY OF UK
CAPITAL CITY: The Valley
AREA: 96 sq km
POPULATION: 10,000 people
POPULATION DENSITY: 65 people per sq km
POPULATION CHANGE: 5.2% per year
BIRTH RATE: 17 per 1,000 people
DEATH RATE: 5 per 1,000 people
LIFE EXPECTANCY: Males 74, females 80 years
INFANT MORTALITY: 22 per 1,000 live births
FERTILITY RATE: 3 children per female
ETHNIC GROUPS: Of African descent
LANGUAGES: *English*, Creole
RELIGIONS: Protestant
ANNUAL INCOME: $3,300 per person
CURRENCY: East Caribbean $ = 100 cents
ADULT LITERACY: 95%

Antigua and Barbuda

CAPITAL CITY: St John's
AREA: 440 sq km
POPULATION: 66,000 people
POPULATION DENSITY: 150 people per sq km
POPULATION CHANGE: –2.0% per year
BIRTH RATE: 17 per 1,000 people
DEATH RATE: 5 per 1,000 people
LIFE EXPECTANCY: Males 72, females 76 years
INFANT MORTALITY: 17 per 1,000 live births
URBAN POPULATION: 37% of population
FERTILITY RATE: 2 children per female
ETHNIC GROUPS: Of African descent
LANGUAGES: *English*, local dialects
RELIGIONS: Protestant 80%
LAND USE: Arable 18%, grass 9%, forest 11%
EMPLOYMENT: Agric. 9%, ind. 57%, services 34%
ANNUAL INCOME: $7,000 per person, 2.7%
ORIGIN OF INCOME: Agriculture 4%, industry 20%, services 76%
ENERGY: Consumption 2.09 tonnes per person
CURRENCY: East Caribbean $ = 100 cents
ROADS: 2,639 km per 1,000 sq km of land
RAILWAYS: 0 km per 1,000 sq km of land
ADULT LITERACY: 96%
EDUCATIONAL EXPENDITURE: 2.7% of GNP
AID RECEIVED: $46 per person

Argentina

CAPITAL CITY: Buenos Aires
AREA: 2,766,890 sq km (Land area 2,736,690 sq km)
POPULATION: 35,400,000 people
POPULATION DENSITY: 13 people per sq km
POPULATION CHANGE: 1.3% per year
BIRTH RATE: 20 per 1,000 people
DEATH RATE: 8 per 1,000 people
LIFE EXPECTANCY: Males 71, females 78 years
INFANT MORTALITY: 19 per 1,000 live births
URBAN POPULATION: 88% of population
FERTILITY RATE: 3 children per female
AGE GROUPS: 0–14 yrs 30%, 15–59 yrs 57%, 60+ yrs 13%
ETHNIC GROUPS: European 85%, Mestizo, Amerindian
LANGUAGES: *Spanish*, Italian, Guarani
RELIGIONS: Roman Catholic 93%, Protestant 2%
LAND USE: Arable 9%, grass 52%, forest 22%
EMPLOYMENT: Agric. 13%, ind. 34%, services 53%
ANNUAL INCOME: $8,030 per person, 1.9%
ORIGIN OF INCOME: Agriculture 6%, industry 31%, services 63%
ENERGY: Prod. 2.36 tonnes, consump. 1.99 tonnes
TRADE: $877 per person
CURRENCY: Peso = 10,000 australs
ROADS: 79 km per 1,000 sq km of land
RAILWAYS: 12 km per 1,000 sq km of land
POPULATION PER DOCTOR: 329 people
ADULT LITERACY: 96%
EDUCATIONAL EXPENDITURE: 3.1% of GNP
MILITARY EXPENDITURE: 1.7% of GNP
AID RECEIVED: $7 per person

Armenia

CAPITAL CITY: Yerevan
AREA: 29,800 sq km
POPULATION: 3,800,000 people
POPULATION DENSITY: 134 people per sq km
POPULATION CHANGE: 1.9% per year
BIRTH RATE: 17 per 1,000 people
DEATH RATE: 8 per 1,000 people
LIFE EXPECTANCY: Males 65, females 74 years
INFANT MORTALITY: 39 per 1,000 live births
URBAN POPULATION: 69% of population
FERTILITY RATE: 3 children per female
AGE GROUPS: 0–14 yrs 30%, 15–59 yrs 59%, 60+ yrs 11%
ETHNIC GROUPS: Armenian 93%, Azerbaijani 3%, Russian 2%, Kurd 2%
LANGUAGES: *Armenian*, Azerbaijani, Russian
RELIGIONS: Armenian Orthodox 90%
LAND USE: Arable 22%, grass 54%, forest 14%
EMPLOYMENT: Agric. 11%, ind. 32%, services 57%
ANNUAL INCOME: $730 per person, –15.1%
ORIGIN OF INCOME: Agriculture 48%, industry 30%, services 22%
ENERGY: Consumption 0.75 tonnes per person
TRADE: $500 per person
CURRENCY: Dram = 100 couma
ROADS: 271 km per 1,000 sq km of land
RAILWAYS: 29 km per 1,000 sq km of land
POPULATION PER DOCTOR: 260 people
ADULT LITERACY: 99%
EDUCATIONAL EXPENDITURE: 3.9% of GNP
MILITARY EXPENDITURE: 2.5% of GNP
AID RECEIVED: $27 per person

Aruba

SELF-GOVERNING DUTCH TERRITORY
CAPITAL CITY: Oranjestad
AREA: 193 sq km
POPULATION: 70,000 people
POPULATION DENSITY: 368 people per sq km
POPULATION CHANGE: 2.2% per year
BIRTH RATE: 14 per 1,000 people
DEATH RATE: 6 per 1,000 people
LIFE EXPECTANCY: Males 73, females 81 years
INFANT MORTALITY: 8 per 1,000 live births
FERTILITY RATE: 2 children per female
ETHNIC GROUPS: Mixed European/Caribbean Indian 80%
LANGUAGES: *Dutch*, Papiamento, English, Spanish
RELIGIONS: Roman Catholic 82%, Protestant 8%
LAND USE: Arable 11%
EMPLOYMENT: Industry 11%, services 89%
ANNUAL INCOME: $16,000 per person, 6%
CURRENCY: Aruban florin = 100 cents
ROADS: 2,000 km per 1,000 sq km of land

Ascension

DEPENDENT TERRITORY OF UK
CAPITAL CITY: Georgetown
AREA: 88 sq km
POPULATION: 1,500 people
POPULATION DENSITY: 17 people per sq km

Australia

CAPITAL CITY: Canberra
AREA: 7,686,850 sq km
POPULATION: 18,400,000 people
POPULATION DENSITY: 2 people per sq km
POPULATION CHANGE: 1.2% per year
BIRTH RATE: 14 per 1,000 people
DEATH RATE: 7 per 1,000 people
LIFE EXPECTANCY: Males 77, females 83 years
INFANT MORTALITY: 5 per 1,000 live births
URBAN POPULATION: 86% of population
FERTILITY RATE: 2 children per female
AGE GROUPS: 0–14 yrs 22%, 15–59 yrs 63%, 60+ yrs 15%
ETHNIC GROUPS: White 94%, Asian 2%, Aboriginal 1%
LANGUAGES: *English*, aboriginal languages
RELIGIONS: Roman Catholic 26%, Anglican 24%, other Christian 22%, Muslim, Jewish, Buddhist
LAND USE: Arable 7%, grass 54%, forest 14%
EMPLOYMENT: Agric. 6%, ind. 24%, services 70%
ANNUAL INCOME: $18,720 per person, 1.4%
ORIGIN OF INCOME: Agriculture 3%, industry 29%, services 68%
ENERGY: Prod. 13.16 tonnes, consump. 7.38 tonnes
TRADE: $4,993 per person
CURRENCY: Australian $ = 100 cents
ROADS: 107 km per 1,000 sq km of land
RAILWAYS: 5 km per 1,000 sq km of land
POPULATION PER DOCTOR: 400 people
ADULT LITERACY: 99%
EDUCATIONAL EXPENDITURE: 5.5% of GNP
MILITARY EXPENDITURE: 2.4% of GNP
AID GIVEN: $62 per person

Austria

CAPITAL CITY: Vienna
AREA: 83,850 sq km (Land area 82,730 sq km)
POPULATION: 8,200,000 people
POPULATION DENSITY: 99 people per sq km
POPULATION CHANGE: 1.1% per year
BIRTH RATE: 11 per 1,000 people
DEATH RATE: 10 per 1,000 people
LIFE EXPECTANCY: Males 74, females 80 years
infant mortality: 6 per 1,000 live births
URBAN POPULATION: 65% of population
FERTILITY RATE: 2 children per female
AGE GROUPS: 0–14 yrs 17%, 15–59 yrs 62%, 60+ yrs 20%
ETHNIC GROUPS: Austrian 94%, Slovene 2%, Turkish, German
LANGUAGES: *German*, Slovene, Croat, Turkish, Slovak, Hungarian
RELIGIONS: Roman Catholic 78%, Protestant 6%, Muslim 2%
LAND USE: Arable 17%, grass 24%, forest 39%
EMPLOYMENT: Agric. 7%, ind. 37%, services 56%
ANNUAL INCOME: $26,890 per person, 1.9%
ORIGIN OF INCOME: Agriculture 2%, industry 35%, services 62%
ENERGY: Prod. 1.13 tonnes, consump. 4.17 tonnes

Austria continued
TRADE: $11,126 per person
CURRENCY: Schilling = 100 Groschen
ROADS: 1,563 km per 1,000 sq km of land
RAILWAYS: 68 km per 1,000 sq km of land
POPULATION PER DOCTOR: 230 people
ADULT LITERACY: 99%
EDUCATIONAL EXPENDITURE: 5.4% of GNP
MILITARY EXPENDITURE: 0.9% of GNP
AID GIVEN: $82 per person

Azerbaijan
CAPITAL CITY: Baku
AREA: 86,600 sq km
POPULATION: 7,650,000 people
POPULATION DENSITY: 89 people per sq km
POPULATION CHANGE: 1.0% per year
BIRTH RATE: 22 per 1,000 people
DEATH RATE: 9 per 1,000 people
LIFE EXPECTANCY: Males 60, females 70 years
INFANT MORTALITY: 74 per 1,000 live births
URBAN POPULATION: 56% of population
FERTILITY RATE: 3 children per female
AGE GROUPS: 0–14 yrs 33%, 15–59 yrs 58%, 60+ yrs 9%
ETHNIC GROUPS: Azerbaijani 83%, Russian 6%, Armenian 6%, Lezgin 2%
LANGUAGES: *Azerbaijani*, Russian, Armenian
RELIGIONS: Shiite Muslim 70%, Sunni Muslim 20%, Russian Orthodox, Armenian Orthodox
EMPLOYMENT: Agric. 15%, ind. 21%, services 64%
ANNUAL INCOME: $480 per person, –16.3%
ORIGIN OF INCOME: Agriculture 22%, industry 52%, services 26%
ENERGY: Prod. 3.58 tonnes, consump. 2.2 tonnes
TRADE: $4,000 per person
CURRENCY: Manat = 100 gopik
ROADS: 671 km per 1,000 sq km of land
RAILWAYS: 24 km per 1,000 sq km of land
POPULATION PER DOCTOR: 250 people
ADULT LITERACY: 96%
EDUCATIONAL EXPENDITURE: 3.9% of GNP
MILITARY EXPENDITURE: 1.9% of GNP
AID RECEIVED: $3 per person

Azores
PORTUGUESE AUTONOMOUS REGION
CAPITAL CITY: Ponta Delgada
AREA: 2,247 sq km
POPULATION: 280,000 people
POPULATION DENSITY: 125 people per sq km

Bahamas
CAPITAL CITY: Nassau
AREA: 13,880 sq km (Land area 10,010 sq km)
POPULATION: 280,000 people
POPULATION DENSITY: 28 people per sq km
POPULATION CHANGE: 1.5% per year
BIRTH RATE: 18 per 1,000 people
DEATH RATE: 6 per 1,000 people
LIFE EXPECTANCY: Males 69, females 77 years
INFANT MORTALITY: 22 per 1,000 live births
URBAN POPULATION: 85% of population
FERTILITY RATE: 2 children per female
ETHNIC GROUPS: Black 80%, Mixed 10%, White 10%
LANGUAGES: *English*, Creole
RELIGIONS: Protestant 75%, Roman Catholic 20%
LAND USE: Arable 1%, forest 32%
EMPLOYMENT: Agric. 5%, ind. 4%, services 91%
ANNUAL INCOME: $11,940 per person, –1%
ORIGIN OF INCOME: Agriculture 2%, industry 14%, services 83%
ENERGY: Consumption 3.26 tonnes per person
TRADE: $12,762 per person
CURRENCY: Bahamian $ = 100 cents
ROADS: 240 km per 1,000 sq km of land
POPULATION PER DOCTOR: 7500 people
ADULT LITERACY: 98%
EDUCATIONAL EXPENDITURE: 4.4% of GNP
MILITARY EXPENDITURE: 2.3% of GNP
AID RECEIVED: $15 per person

Bahrain
CAPITAL CITY: Manama (Al Manamah)
AREA: 678 sq km
POPULATION: 605,000 people
POPULATION DENSITY: 890 people per sq km
POPULATION CHANGE: 2.3% per year
BIRTH RATE: 23 per 1,000 people
DEATH RATE: 3 per 1,000 people
LIFE EXPECTANCY: Males 72, females 77 years
INFANT MORTALITY: 16 per 1,000 live births
URBAN POPULATION: 89% of population
FERTILITY RATE: 4 children per female
AGE GROUPS: 0–14 yrs 33%, 15–59 yrs 64%, 60+ yrs 3%
ETHNIC GROUPS: Bahraini Arab 68%, Persian, Indian and Pakistani 25%, other Arab 4%, European 3%
LANGUAGES: *Arabic*, English
RELIGIONS: Shiite Muslim 60%, Sunni Muslim 25%
LAND USE: Arable 1%, grass 6%
EMPLOYMENT: Agric. 3%, ind. 14%, services 83%
ANNUAL INCOME: $7,840 per person, 0.6%
ORIGIN OF INCOME: Agriculture 1%, industry 42%, services 57%
ENERGY: Prod. 19.56 tonnes, consump. 14.78 tonnes
TRADE: $13,915 per person
CURRENCY: Bahrain dinar = 1,000 fils
ROADS: 4,144 km per 1,000 sq km of land
POPULATION PER DOCTOR: 775 people
ADULT LITERACY: 84%
EDUCATIONAL EXPENDITURE: 5.0% of GNP
MILITARY EXPENDITURE: 5.6% of GNP

Bangladesh
CAPITAL CITY: Dhaka
AREA: 144,000 sq km (Land area 130,170 sq km)
POPULATION: 124,000,000 people
POPULATION DENSITY: 953 people per sq km
POPULATION CHANGE: 1.0% per year
BIRTH RATE: 30 per 1,000 people
DEATH RATE: 11 per 1,000 people
LIFE EXPECTANCY: Males 56, females 56 years
INFANT MORTALITY: 100 per 1,000 live births
URBAN POPULATION: 18% of population
FERTILITY RATE: 4 children per female
AGE GROUPS: 0–14 yrs 44%, 15–59 yrs 52%, 60+ yrs 5%
ETHNIC GROUPS: Bengali 98%, Bihari, tribal
LANGUAGES: *Bengali, English*, nearly 100 tribal dialects
RELIGIONS: Sunni Muslim 87%, Hindu 12%
LAND USE: Arable 68%, grass 5%, forest 15%
EMPLOYMENT: Agric. 59%, ind. 13%, services 28%
ANNUAL INCOME: $240 per person, 2.1%
ORIGIN OF INCOME: Agriculture 30%, industry 17%, services 52%
ENERGY: Prod. 0.06 tonnes, consump. 0.08 tonnes
TRADE: $54 per person
CURRENCY: Taka = 100 paisas
ROADS: 1,485 km per 1,000 sq km of land
RAILWAYS: 21 km per 1,000 sq km of land
POPULATION PER DOCTOR: 12,500 people
ADULT LITERACY: 36%
EDUCATIONAL EXPENDITURE: 2.0% of GNP
MILITARY EXPENDITURE: 1.3% of GNP
AID RECEIVED: $11 per person

Barbados
CAPITAL CITY: Bridgetown
AREA: 430 sq km
POPULATION: 265,000 people
POPULATION DENSITY: 616 people per sq km
POPULATION CHANGE: 0.6% per year
BIRTH RATE: 15 per 1,000 people
DEATH RATE: 8 per 1,000 people
LIFE EXPECTANCY: Males 72, females 77 years
INFANT MORTALITY: 18 per 1,000 live births
URBAN POPULATION: 46% of population
FERTILITY RATE: 2 children per female
AGE GROUPS: 0–14 yrs 25%, 15–59 yrs 60%, 60+ yrs 15%
ETHNIC GROUPS: Black 80%, White 4%, Mixed 16%
LANGUAGES: *English*, Creole
RELIGIONS: Protestant 65%, Roman Catholic 4%
LAND USE: Arable 37%, grass 5%
EMPLOYMENT: Agric. 7%, ind. 11%, services 82%
ANNUAL INCOME: $6,560 per person, –0.2%
ORIGIN OF INCOME: Agric. 7%, ind. 21%,services 73%
ENERGY: Prod. 0.46 tonnes, consump. 1.81 tonnes
TRADE: $2,986 per person
CURRENCY: Barbados $ = 100 cents
ROADS: 3,658 km per 1,000 sq km of land
POPULATION PER DOCTOR: 1,000 people
ADULT LITERACY: 99%
EDUCATIONAL EXPENDITURE: 8% of GNP
MILITARY EXPENDITURE: 0% of GNP
AID RECEIVED: $417 per person

Belarus
CAPITAL CITY: Minsk
AREA: 207,600 sq km
POPULATION: 10,500,000 people
POPULATION DENSITY: 51 people per sq km
POPULATION CHANGE: 0.3% per year
BIRTH RATE: 11 per 1,000 people
DEATH RATE: 13 per 1,000 people
LIFE EXPECTANCY: Males 64, females 74 years
INFANT MORTALITY: 13 per 1,000 live births
URBAN POPULATION: 69% of population
FERTILITY RATE: 2 children per female
AGE GROUPS: 0–14 yrs 23%, 15–59 yrs 60%, 60+ yrs 17%
ETHNIC GROUPS: Belarusian 78%, Russian 14%, Polish 4%, Ukrainian 3%, Jewish 1%
LANGUAGES: *Belarusian, Russian*
RELIGIONS: Belarusian Orthodox 85%, Roman Catholic 10%, Evangelical
LAND USE: Arable 45%, grass 15%, forest 33%
EMPLOYMENT: Agric. 20%, ind. 62%, services 18%
ANNUAL INCOME: $2,070 per person, –5.2%
ORIGIN OF INCOME: Agriculture 17%, industry 54%, services 29%
ENERGY: Prod. 0.54 tonnes, consump. 5.1 tonnes
TRADE: $6,458 per person
CURRENCY: Rouble = 100 kopeks
ROADS: 243 km per 1,000 sq km of land
RAILWAYS: 27 km per 1,000 sq km of land
POPULATION PER DOCTOR: 280 people
ADULT LITERACY: 98%
EDUCATIONAL EXPENDITURE: 3.9% of GNP
MILITARY EXPENDITURE: 4.5% of GNP
AID RECEIVED: $11 per person

Belgium
CAPITAL CITY: Brussels
AREA: 33,100 sq km
POPULATION: 10,225,000 people
POPULATION DENSITY: 335 people per sq km
POPULATION CHANGE: 0.5% per year
BIRTH RATE: 12 per 1,000 people
DEATH RATE: 10 per 1,000 people
LIFE EXPECTANCY: Males 74, females 81 years
INFANT MORTALITY: 6 per 1,000 live births
URBAN POPULATION: 97% of population
FERTILITY RATE: 2 children per female
AGE GROUPS: 0–14 yrs 18%, 15–59 yrs 62%, 60+ yrs 21%
ETHNIC GROUPS: Fleming 55%, Walloon 34%, Italian 3%
LANGUAGES: *Flemish (Dutch), Walloon (French), German*
RELIGIONS: Roman Catholic 72%, Protestant
LAND USE: Arable 23%, grass 21%, forest 21%
EMPLOYMENT: Agric. 3%, ind. 28%, services 69%
ANNUAL INCOME: $24,710 per person, 2.2%
ORIGIN OF INCOME: Agriculture 2%, industry 30%, services 68%
ENERGY: Prod. 1.69 tonnes, consump. 6.87 tonnes
TRADE: $24,748 per person
CURRENCY: Belgian franc = 100 centimes
ROADS: 4,669 km per 1,000 sq km of land
RAILWAYS: 111 km per 1,000 sq km of land
POPULATION PER DOCTOR: 298 people
ADULT LITERACY: 99%
EDUCATIONAL EXPENDITURE: 5.4% of GNP
MILITARY EXPENDITURE: 1.8% of GNP
AID GIVEN: $81 per person

Belize
CAPITAL CITY: Belmopan
AREA: 22,960 sq km
POPULATION: 228,000 people
POPULATION DENSITY: 10 people per sq km
POPULATION CHANGE: 2.9% per year
BIRTH RATE: 32 per 1,000 people
DEATH RATE: 6 per 1,000 people
LIFE EXPECTANCY: Males 67, females 71 years
INFANT MORTALITY: 33 per 1,000 live births
URBAN POPULATION: 53% of population
FERTILITY RATE: 5 children per female
AGE GROUPS: 0–14 yrs 20%, 15–59 yrs 77%, 60+ yrs 3%
ETHNIC GROUPS: Mestizo 44%, Creole 30%, Mayan Indian 11%, Carib Indian 7%, White 4%
LANGUAGES: *English*, Creole, Spanish, Carib, Mayan languages
RELIGIONS: Roman Catholic 58%, Protestant 34%
LAND USE: Arable 2%, grass 2%, forest 44%
EMPLOYMENT: Agric. 18%, ind. 72%, services 10%
ANNUAL INCOME: $2,630 per person, 4.4%
ORIGIN OF INCOME: Agric. 19%
ENERGY: Consumption 0.64 tonnes per person
TRADE: $1,967 per person
CURRENCY: Belize $ = 100 cents
ROADS: 119 km per 1,000 sq km of land
POPULATION PER DOCTOR: 1,500 people
ADULT LITERACY: 96%
EDUCATIONAL EXPENDITURE: 6.0% of GNP
MILITARY EXPENDITURE: 2.6% of GNP
AID RECEIVED: $137 per person

Benin
CAPITAL CITY: Porto-Novo
AREA: 112,620 sq km (Land area 110,620 sq km)
POPULATION: 5,800,000 people
POPULATION DENSITY: 52 people per sq km
POPULATION CHANGE: 2.9% per year
BIRTH RATE: 46 per 1,000 people
DEATH RATE: 13 per 1,000 people
LIFE EXPECTANCY: Males 51, females 55 years
INFANT MORTALITY: 103 per 1,000 live births
URBAN POPULATION: 36% of population
FERTILITY RATE: 6 children per female
AGE GROUPS: 0–14 yrs 47%, 15–59 yrs 49%, 60+ yrs 5%
ETHNIC GROUPS: Fon 66%, Bariba 10%, Yoruba 9%, Somba 5%
LANGUAGES: *French*, Fon, Yoruba, Adja, Aizo
RELIGIONS: Traditional beliefs (Voodoo) 61%, Roman Catholic 23%, Sunni Muslim 15%
LAND USE: Arable 17%, grass 4%, forest 31%
EMPLOYMENT: Agric. 70%, ind. 7%, services 23%
ANNUAL INCOME: $370 per person, –0.4%
ORIGIN OF INCOME: Agric. 37%, ind. 14%, services 49%
ENERGY: Prod. 0.09 tonnes, consump. 0.05 tonnes
TRADE: $156 per person
CURRENCY: CFA franc = 100 centimes
ROADS: 55 km per 1,000 sq km of land
RAILWAYS: 5 km per 1,000 sq km of land
POPULATION PER DOCTOR: 15,000 people
ADULT LITERACY: 23%
EDUCATIONAL EXPENDITURE: 3.5% of GNP
MILITARY EXPENDITURE: 1.9% of GNP
AID RECEIVED: $53 per person

Bermuda
BRITISH COLONY
CAPITAL CITY: Hamilton
AREA: 53 sq km
POPULATION: 65,000 people
POPULATION DENSITY: 1,300 people per sq km
POPULATION CHANGE: 1.6% per year
BIRTH RATE: 15 per 1,000 people
DEATH RATE: 7 per 1,000 people
LIFE EXPECTANCY: Males 73, females 77 years
INFANT MORTALITY: 13 per 1,000 live births
URBAN POPULATION: 100% of population
FERTILITY RATE: 2 children per female
ETHNIC GROUPS: Black 61%, White 37%
LANGUAGES: *English*
RELIGIONS: Anglican 37%, Methodist 15%, Roman Catholic 14%
LAND USE: Forest 20%
EMPLOYMENT: Agric. 2%, ind. 14%, services 84%
ANNUAL INCOME: $27,000 per person, –1.2%
ENERGY: Consumption 1.96 tonnes per person
TRADE: $9,750 per person
CURRENCY: Bermudan $ = 100 cents
ROADS: 4,500 km per 1,000 sq km of land
ADULT LITERACY: 98%

Bhutan
TREATY RELATIONSHIP WITH INDIA
CAPITAL CITY: Thimphu
AREA: 47,000 sq km
POPULATION: 1,790,000 people
POPULATION DENSITY: 38 people per sq km
POPULATION CHANGE: 2.4% per year
BIRTH RATE: 38 per 1,000 people
DEATH RATE: 15 per 1,000 people
LIFE EXPECTANCY: Males 52, females 51 years
INFANT MORTALITY: 114 per 1,000 live births
URBAN POPULATION: 6% of population
FERTILITY RATE: 6 children per female
AGE GROUPS: 0–14 yrs 40%, 15–59 yrs 55%, 60+ yrs 6%
ETHNIC GROUPS: Bhote 60%, Nepalese 25%
LANGUAGES: *Dzongkha*, Nepali dialects
RELIGIONS: Buddhist 70%, Hindu 25%
LAND USE: Arable 3%, grass 6%, forest 56%
EMPLOYMENT: Agric. 92%, ind. 3%, services 5%
ANNUAL INCOME: $420 per person, 4%
ORIGIN OF INCOME: Agriculture 43%, industry 27%, services 30%
CURRENCY: Ngultrum = 100 chetrum
ROADS: 51 km per 1,000 sq km of land
POPULATION PER DOCTOR: 13,110 people
ADULT LITERACY: 38%
EDUCATIONAL EXPENDITURE: 3.7% of GNP
AID RECEIVED: $44 per person

Bolivia
CAPITAL CITY: La Paz/Sucre
AREA: 1,098,580 sq km (Land area 1,084,380 sq km)
POPULATION: 7,650,000 people
POPULATION DENSITY: 7 people per sq km
POPULATION CHANGE: 0.6% per year
BIRTH RATE: 32 per 1,000 people
DEATH RATE: 10 per 1,000 people
LIFE EXPECTANCY: Males 57, females 63 years
INFANT MORTALITY: 66 per 1,000 live births
URBAN POPULATION: 62% of population
FERTILITY RATE: 5 children per female
AGE GROUPS: 0–14 yrs 44%, 15–59 yrs 51%, 60+ yrs 5%
ETHNIC GROUPS: Mestizo 31%, Quechua 25%, Aymara 17%, White 15%
LANGUAGES: *Spanish, Aymara, Quechua*
RELIGIONS: Roman Catholic 94%
LAND USE: Arable 2%, grass 25%, forest 51%
EMPLOYMENT: Agric. 47%, ind. 19%, services 34%
ANNUAL INCOME: $800 per person, 1.7%
ORIGIN OF INCOME: Agriculture 24%, industry 30%, services 46%
ENERGY: Prod. 0.77 tonnes, consump. 0.23 tonnes
TRADE: $237 per person
CURRENCY: Boliviano = 100 centavos
ROADS: 39 km per 1,000 sq km of land
RAILWAYS: 3 km per 1,000 sq km of land
POPULATION PER DOCTOR: 1,500 people
ADULT LITERACY: 78%
EDUCATIONAL EXPENDITURE: 2.3% of GNP
MILITARY EXPENDITURE: 3.9% of GNP
AID RECEIVED: $96 per person

Bosnia-Herzegovina
CAPITAL CITY: Sarajevo
AREA: 51,129 sq km
POPULATION: 3,600,000 people
POPULATION DENSITY: 70 people per sq km
POPULATION CHANGE: –2.7% per year
BIRTH RATE: 6 per 1,000 people
DEATH RATE: 15 per 1,000 people
LIFE EXPECTANCY: Males 55, females 65 years
INFANT MORTALITY: 36 per 1,000 live births
URBAN POPULATION: 41% of population
ETHNIC GROUPS: Muslim 44%, Serb 33%, Croat 17%
LANGUAGES: *Serbo-Croat*
RELIGIONS: Sunni Muslim 40%, Serbian Orthodox 31%, Roman Catholic 15%
LAND USE: Arable 16%, grass 31%, forest 48%

EMPLOYMENT: Agric. 4%, ind. 51%, services 46%
ANNUAL INCOME: $2,600 per person, 1.8%
ORIGIN OF INCOME: Agriculture 15%, industry 61%, services 24%
TRADE: $900 per person
CURRENCY: Dinar = 100 paras
ROADS: 413 km per 1,000 sq km of land
RAILWAYS: 20 km per 1,000 sq km of land
POPULATION PER DOCTOR: 600 people
ADULT LITERACY: 86%

Botswana

CAPITAL CITY: Gaborone
AREA: 581,730 sq km (Land area 566,730 sq km)
POPULATION: 1,510,000 people
POPULATION DENSITY: 3 people per sq km
POPULATION CHANGE: 2.2% per year
BIRTH RATE: 33 per 1,000 people
DEATH RATE: 18 per 1,000 people
LIFE EXPECTANCY: Males 44, females 46 years
INFANT MORTALITY: 55 per 1,000 live births
URBAN POPULATION: 31% of population
FERTILITY RATE: 5 children per female
AGE GROUPS: 0–14 yrs 49%, 15–59 yrs 46%, 60+ yrs 5%
ETHNIC GROUPS: Tswana 76%, Shana 12%, San (Bushmen) 3%
LANGUAGES: *English*, Setswana, Shishona, San, Hottentot
RELIGIONS: Traditional beliefs 50%, Protestant 30%
LAND USE: Arable 2%, grass 58%, forest 19%
EMPLOYMENT: Agric. 28%, ind. 11%, services 61%
ANNUAL INCOME: $3,020 per person, 6%
ORIGIN OF INCOME: Agriculture 5%, industry 54%, services 41%
TRADE: $2,500 per person
CURRENCY: Pula = 100 thebe
ROADS: 32 km per 1,000 sq km of land
RAILWAYS: 2 km per 1,000 sq km of land
POPULATION PER DOCTOR: 51,590 people
ADULT LITERACY: 74%
EDUCATIONAL EXPENDITURE: 8.2% of GNP
MILITARY EXPENDITURE: 1.9% of GNP
AID RECEIVED: $64 per person

Brazil

CAPITAL CITY: Brasília
AREA: 8,511,970 sq km
POPULATION: 159,500,000 people
POPULATION DENSITY: 19 people per sq km
POPULATION CHANGE: 0.8% per year
BIRTH RATE: 20 per 1,000 people
DEATH RATE: 9 per 1,000 people
LIFE EXPECTANCY: Males 57, females 66 years
INFANT MORTALITY: 53 per 1,000 live births
URBAN POPULATION: 78% of population
FERTILITY RATE: 3 children per female
AGE GROUPS: 0–14 yrs 35%, 15–59 yrs 58%, 60+ yrs 7%
ETHNIC GROUPS: White 53%, Mulatto 22%, Mestizo 12%, Black 11% (Indian 0.1%)
LANGUAGES: *Portuguese*, Amerindian languages
RELIGIONS: Roman Catholic 87%, Protestant 8%
LAND USE: Arable 7%, grass 22%, forest 58%
EMPLOYMENT: Agric. 25%, ind. 25%, services 50%
ANNUAL INCOME: $3,640 per person, –0.7%
ORIGIN OF INCOME: Agriculture 10%, industry 39%, services 51%
ENERGY: Prod. 0.53 tonnes, consump. 0.44 tonnes
TRADE: $343 per person
CURRENCY: Cruzeiro real = 100 centavos
ROADS: 216 km per 1,000 sq km of land
RAILWAYS: 4 km per 1,000 sq km of land
POPULATION PER DOCTOR: 1,000 people
ADULT LITERACY: 81%
EDUCATIONAL EXPENDITURE: 3.7% of GNP
MILITARY EXPENDITURE: 1.2% of GNP
AID RECEIVED: $2 per person

British Indian Ocean Territory

TERRITORY OF UK
AREA: 60 sq km
No permanent civilian population; UK–US military base

Brunei

CAPITAL CITY: Bandar Seri Begawan
AREA: 5,770 sq km (Land area 5,270 sq km)
POPULATION: 300,000 people
POPULATION DENSITY: 57 people per sq km
POPULATION CHANGE: 1.7% per year
BIRTH RATE: 25 per 1,000 people
DEATH RATE: 5 per 1,000 people
LIFE EXPECTANCY: Males 70, females 73 years
INFANT MORTALITY: 24 per 1,000 live births
URBAN POPULATION: 68% of population
FERTILITY RATE: 4 children per female
AGE GROUPS: 0–14 yrs 33%, 15–59 yrs 61%, 60+ yrs 6%
ETHNIC GROUPS: Malay 69%, Chinese 18%, Indian
LANGUAGES: *Malay*, English, Chinese
RELIGIONS: Muslim 63%, Buddhist 14%, Christian 10%
LAND USE: Arable 1%, grass 1%, forest 43%
EMPLOYMENT: Agric. 2%, ind. 22%, services 76%
ANNUAL INCOME: $14,500 per person, –1%
ORIGIN OF INCOME: Agriculture 2%, industry 45%, services 53%
ENERGY: Consumption 2.18 tonnes per person
TRADE: $11,108 per person
CURRENCY: Brunei $ (ringgit) = 100 cents
ROADS: 459 km per 1,000 sq km of land
RAILWAYS: 4 km per 1,000 sq km of land
POPULATION PER DOCTOR: 1,500 people
ADULT LITERACY: 86%
MILITARY EXPENDITURE: 7.7% of GNP

Bulgaria

CAPITAL CITY: Sofia
AREA: 110,910 sq km
POPULATION: 8,560,000 people
POPULATION DENSITY: 77 people per sq km
POPULATION CHANGE: –0.7% per year
BIRTH RATE: 8 per 1,000 people
DEATH RATE: 14 per 1,000 people
LIFE EXPECTANCY: Males 67, females 75 years
INFANT MORTALITY: 15 per 1,000 live births
URBAN POPULATION: 71% of population
FERTILITY RATE: 2 children per female
AGE GROUPS: 0–14 yrs 20%, 15–59 yrs 61%, 60+ yrs 19%
ETHNIC GROUPS: Bulgarian 85%, Turkish 9%, Gypsy 3%, Macedonian 3%, Armenian, Romanian, Greek
LANGUAGES: *Bulgarian*, Turkish, Romany
RELIGIONS: Eastern Orthodox 80%, Sunni Muslim
LAND USE: Arable 38%, grass 18%, forest 35%
EMPLOYMENT: Agric. 17%, ind. 38%, services 46%
ANNUAL INCOME: $1,330 per person, –2.2%
ORIGIN OF INCOME: Agriculture 13%, industry 63%, services 24%
ENERGY: Prod. 1.98 tonnes, consump. 3.77 tonnes
TRADE: $2,000 per person
CURRENCY: Lev (leva) = 100 stotinki
ROADS: 334 km per 1,000 sq km of land
RAILWAYS: 59 km per 1,000 sq km of land
POPULATION PER DOCTOR: 320 people
ADULT LITERACY: 93%
MILITARY EXPENDITURE: 4.4% of GNP
AID RECEIVED: $6 per person

Burkina Faso

CAPITAL CITY: Ouagadougou
AREA: 274,200 sq km
POPULATION: 10,900,000 people
POPULATION DENSITY: 40 people per sq km
POPULATION CHANGE: 2.8% per year
BIRTH RATE: 46 per 1,000 people
DEATH RATE: 20 per 1,000 people
LIFE EXPECTANCY: Males 42, females 42 years
INFANT MORTALITY: 117 per 1,000 live births
URBAN POPULATION: 27% of population
FERTILITY RATE: 7 children per female
AGE GROUPS: 0–14 yrs 44%, 15–59 yrs 51%, 60+ yrs 5%
ETHNIC GROUPS: Mossi 48%, Mande 8%, Fulani 8%, Bobo 7%, Gourounsi 7%, Gourmantche 7%
LANGUAGES: *French*, Fulani, Mossi, 20 others
RELIGIONS: Traditional beliefs 45%, Sunni Muslim 43%, Roman Catholic 12%
LAND USE: Arable 13%, grass 37%, forest 24%
EMPLOYMENT: Agric. 87%, ind. 4%, services 9%
ANNUAL INCOME: $230 per person, –0.1%
ORIGIN OF INCOME: Agriculture 44%, industry 20%, services 36%
ENERGY: Consumption 0.03 tonnes per person
TRADE: $48 per person
CURRENCY: CFA franc = 100 centimes
ROADS: 48 km per 1,000 sq km of land
RAILWAYS: 2 km per 1,000 sq km of land
POPULATION PER DOCTOR: 57,320 people
ADULT LITERACY: 18%
EDUCATIONAL EXPENDITURE: 2.3% of GNP
MILITARY EXPENDITURE: 2.8% of GNP
AID RECEIVED: $48 per person

Burma (Myanmar)

CAPITAL CITY: Rangoon (Yangon)
AREA: 676,577 sq km (Land area 657,540 sq km)
POPULATION: 47,500,000 people
POPULATION DENSITY: 72 people per sq km
POPULATION CHANGE: 1.9% per year
BIRTH RATE: 30 per 1,000 people
DEATH RATE: 11 per 1,000 people
LIFE EXPECTANCY: Males 55, females 58 years
INFANT MORTALITY: 79 per 1,000 live births
URBAN POPULATION: 27% of population
FERTILITY RATE: 4 children per female
AGE GROUPS: 0–14 yrs 37%, 15–59 yrs 56%, 60+ yrs 6%
ETHNIC GROUPS: Burmese 69%, Shan 9%, Karen 6%, Rakhine 5%, Mon 2%, Chin 2%, Kachin 1%
LANGUAGES: *Burmese*, English, Shan, Karen, Rakhine, Mon, Chin, Kachin, Kayah
RELIGIONS: Buddhist 85%, Christian 5%, Muslim 4%, Hindu, animist
LAND USE: Arable 15%, grass 1%, forest 49%
EMPLOYMENT: Agric. 70%, ind. 9%, services 21%
ANNUAL INCOME: $1,000 per person, 0.4%
ORIGIN OF INCOME: Agriculture 51%, industry 12%, services 37%
ENERGY: Prod. 0.07 tonnes, consump. 0.06 tonnes
TRADE: $24 per person
CURRENCY: Kyat = 100 pyas
ROADS: 37 km per 1,000 sq km of land
RAILWAYS: 8 km per 1,000 sq km of land
POPULATION PER DOCTOR: 3,700 people
ADULT LITERACY: 81%
EDUCATIONAL EXPENDITURE: 2.2% of GNP
MILITARY EXPENDITURE: 3.1% of GNP
AID RECEIVED: $3 per person

Burundi

CAPITAL CITY: Bujumbura
AREA: 27,830 sq km (Land area 25,650 sq km)
POPULATION: 6,250,000 people
POPULATION DENSITY: 243 people per sq km
POPULATION CHANGE: 2.0% per year
BIRTH RATE: 42 per 1,000 people
DEATH RATE: 15 per 1,000 people
LIFE EXPECTANCY: Males 48, females 50 years
INFANT MORTALITY: 101 per 1,000 live births
URBAN POPULATION: 7% of population
FERTILITY RATE: 7 children per female
AGE GROUPS: 0–14 yrs 45%, 15–59 yrs 50%, 60+ yrs 5%
ETHNIC GROUPS: Hutu 85%, Tutsi 14%, Twa 1%
LANGUAGES: *French, Rundi*
RELIGIONS: Roman Catholic 62%, traditional beliefs 30%, Protestant 5%
LAND USE: Arable 52%, grass 36%, forest 3%
EMPLOYMENT: Agric. 92%, ind. 2%, services 6%
ANNUAL INCOME: $160 per person, –1.3%
ORIGIN OF INCOME: Agriculture 55%, industry 16%, services 29%
ENERGY: Consumption 0.01 tonnes per person
TRADE: $60 per person
CURRENCY: Burundi franc = 100 centimes
ROADS: 564 km per 1,000 sq km of land
POPULATION PER DOCTOR: 21,000 people
ADULT LITERACY: 50%
EDUCATIONAL EXPENDITURE: 3.2% of GNP
MILITARY EXPENDITURE: 2.6% of GNP
AID RECEIVED: $46 per person

Cambodia

CAPITAL CITY: Phnom Penh
AREA: 181,040 sq km (Land area 176,520 sq km)
POPULATION: 10,500,000 people
POPULATION DENSITY: 59 people per sq km
POPULATION CHANGE: 3.5% per year
BIRTH RATE: 43 per 1,000 people
DEATH RATE: 15 per 1,000 people
LIFE EXPECTANCY: Males 49, females 52 years
INFANT MORTALITY: 106 per 1,000 live births
URBAN POPULATION: 21% of population
FERTILITY RATE: 4 children per female
AGE GROUPS: 0–14 yrs 35%, 15–59 yrs 60%, 60+ yrs 5%
ETHNIC GROUPS: Khmer 93%, Vietnamese 4%, Chinese 3%
LANGUAGES: *Khmer*, Vietnamese, Cham
RELIGIONS: Buddhist 88%, Muslim 2%
LAND USE: Arable 17%, grass 3%, forest 76%
EMPLOYMENT: Agric. 74%, ind. 7%, services 19%
ANNUAL INCOME: $270 per person, 2%
TRADE: $25 per person
CURRENCY: Riel = 100 sen
ROADS: 70 km per 1,000 sq km of land
RAILWAYS: 3 km per 1,000 sq km of land
POPULATION PER DOCTOR: 25,000 people
ADULT LITERACY: 35%
AID RECEIVED: $57 per person

Cameroon

CAPITAL CITY: Yaoundé
AREA: 475,440 sq km (Land area 465,400 sq km)
POPULATION: 13,800,000 people
POPULATION DENSITY: 30 people per sq km
POPULATION CHANGE: 2.6% per year
BIRTH RATE: 42 per 1,000 people
DEATH RATE: 14 per 1,000 people
LIFE EXPECTANCY: Males 51, females 53 years
INFANT MORTALITY: 78 per 1,000 live births
URBAN POPULATION: 45% of population
FERTILITY RATE: 6 children per female
AGE GROUPS: 0–14 yrs 47%, 15–59 yrs 48%, 60+ yrs 5%
ETHNIC GROUPS: Fang 20%, Bamileke and Mamum 19%, Duala, Luanda and Basa 15%, Fulani 10%
LANGUAGES: *French, English*, Sudanic and Bantu languages
RELIGIONS: Animist 25%, Sunni Muslim 22%, Roman Catholic 21%, Protestant 18%
LAND USE: Arable 15%, grass 18%, forest 53%
EMPLOYMENT: Agric. 79%, ind. 7%, services 14%
ANNUAL INCOME: $650 per person, –7%
ORIGIN OF INCOME: Agriculture 27%, industry 22%, services 51%
ENERGY: Prod. 1.05 tonnes, consump. 0.07 tonnes
TRADE: $310 per person
CURRENCY: CFA franc = 100 centimes
ROADS: 104 km per 1,000 sq km of land
RAILWAYS: 2 km per 1,000 sq km of land
POPULATION PER DOCTOR: 12,190 people
ADULT LITERACY: 54%
EDUCATIONAL EXPENDITURE: 3.3% of GNP
MILITARY EXPENDITURE: 2.1% of GNP
AID RECEIVED: $35 per person

Canada

CAPITAL CITY: Ottawa
AREA: 9,976,140 sq km (Land area 9,220,970 sq km)
POPULATION: 30,200,000 people
POPULATION DENSITY: 3 people per sq km
POPULATION CHANGE: 1.9% per year
BIRTH RATE: 13 per 1,000 people
DEATH RATE: 7 per 1,000 people
LIFE EXPECTANCY: Males 76, females 83 years
INFANT MORTALITY: 6 per 1,000 live births
URBAN POPULATION: 77% of population
FERTILITY RATE: 2 children per female
AGE GROUPS: 0–14 yrs 21%, 15–59 yrs 63%, 60+ yrs 16%
ETHNIC GROUPS: British 40%, French 27%, other European 20%, Asiatic 2%, Amerindian/Inuit (Eskimo) 2%
LANGUAGES: *English, French*, Inuktitut
RELIGIONS: Roman Catholic 47%, Protestant 41%, Eastern Orthodox, Jewish, Muslim, Hindu
LAND USE: Arable 5%, grass 3%, forest 39%
EMPLOYMENT: Agric. 5%, ind. 23%, services 72%
ANNUAL INCOME: $19,380 per person, 0.4%
ORIGIN OF INCOME: Agriculture 3%, industry 21%, services 76%
ENERGY: Prod. 13.75 tonnes, consump. 8.81 tonnes
TRADE: $9,355 per person
CURRENCY: Canadian $ = 100 cents
ROADS: 111 km per 1,000 sq km of land
RAILWAYS: 8 km per 1,000 sq km of land
POPULATION PER DOCTOR: 450 people
ADULT LITERACY: 99%
EDUCATIONAL EXPENDITURE: 7.2% of GNP
MILITARY EXPENDITURE: 2% of GNP
AID GIVEN: $73 per person

Canary Islands

SPANISH AUTONOMOUS REGION
CAPITAL CITY: Las Palmas/Santa Cruz
AREA: 7,273 sq km
POPULATION: 1,700,000 people
POPULATION DENSITY: 234 people per sq km

Cape Verde

CAPITAL CITY: Praia
AREA: 4,030 sq km
POPULATION: 410,000 people
POPULATION DENSITY: 102 people per sq km
POPULATION CHANGE: 1.8% per year
BIRTH RATE: 35 per 1,000 people
DEATH RATE: 7 per 1,000 people
LIFE EXPECTANCY: Males 67, females 73 years
INFANT MORTALITY: 50 per 1,000 live births
URBAN POPULATION: 44% of population
FERTILITY RATE: 4 children per female
AGE GROUPS: 0–14 yrs 45%, 15–59 yrs 49%, 60+ yrs 6%
ETHNIC GROUPS: Mixed 71%, Black 28%, White 1%
LANGUAGES: *Portuguese*, Crioulo
RELIGIONS: Roman Catholic 95%
LAND USE: Arable 10%, grass 6%
EMPLOYMENT: Agric. 31%, ind. 6%, services 63%
ANNUAL INCOME: $960 per person, 2.1%
ORIGIN OF INCOME: Agriculture 14%, industry 25%, services 61%
ENERGY: Consumption 0.05 tonnes per person
TRADE: $331 per person
CURRENCY: Escudo = 100 centavos
ROADS: 272 km per 1,000 sq km of land
POPULATION PER DOCTOR: 5,800 people
ADULT LITERACY: 53%
EDUCATIONAL EXPENDITURE: 2.9% of GNP
MILITARY EXPENDITURE: 11% of GNP
AID RECEIVED: $214 per person

Cayman Islands

BRITISH COLONY
CAPITAL CITY: George Town
AREA: 259 sq km
POPULATION: 35,000 people
POPULATION DENSITY: 135 people per sq km
POPULATION CHANGE: 4.9% per year
BIRTH RATE: 14 per 1,000 people
DEATH RATE: 5 per 1,000 people
LIFE EXPECTANCY: Males 75, females 79 years
INFANT MORTALITY: 8 per 1,000 live births
URBAN POPULATION: 100% of population
FERTILITY RATE: 1 child per female
ETHNIC GROUPS: Mixed 40%, White 20%, Black 20%
LANGUAGES: *English*
RELIGIONS: Christian
LAND USE: Grass 8%, forest 23%
ANNUAL INCOME: $13,670 per person
ENERGY: Consumption 2.1 tonnes per person
TRADE: $5,000 per person
CURRENCY: Caymanian $ = 100 cents
ROADS: 463 km per 1,000 sq km of land

Cayman Islands continued
POPULATION PER DOCTOR: 700 people
ADULT LITERACY: 98%

Central African Republic
CAPITAL CITY: Bangui
AREA: 622,980 sq km
POPULATION: 3,400,000 people
POPULATION DENSITY: 5 people per sq km
POPULATION CHANGE: 1.8% per year
BIRTH RATE: 40 per 1,000 people
DEATH RATE: 18 per 1,000 people
LIFE EXPECTANCY: Males 44, females 46 years
INFANT MORTALITY: 110 per 1,000 live births
URBAN POPULATION: 39% of population
FERTILITY RATE: 6 children per female
AGE GROUPS: 0–14 yrs 45%, 15–59 yrs 49%, 60+ yrs 6%
ETHNIC GROUPS: Banda 29%, Baya 25%, Ngbandi 11%, Azanda 10%
LANGUAGES: *French, Sango*, Banda, Baya
RELIGIONS: Traditional beliefs 57%, Christian 35%, Sunni Muslim 8%
LAND USE: Arable 3%, grass 5%, forest 57%
EMPLOYMENT: Agric. 81%, ind. 3%, services 16%
ANNUAL INCOME: $340 per person, –2%
ORIGIN OF INCOME: Agriculture 41%, industry 16%, services 43%
TRADE: $70 per person
CURRENCY: CFA franc = 100 centimes
ROADS: 39 km per 1,000 sq km of land
POPULATION PER DOCTOR: 25,930 people
ADULT LITERACY: 38%
EDUCATIONAL EXPENDITURE: 2.9% of GNP
MILITARY EXPENDITURE: 1.7% of GNP
AID RECEIVED: $50 per person

Chad
CAPITAL CITY: Ndjamena
AREA: 1,284,000 sq km (Land area 1,259,200 sq km)
POPULATION: 6,750,000 people
POPULATION DENSITY: 5 people per sq km
POPULATION CHANGE: 2.5% per year
BIRTH RATE: 44 per 1,000 people
DEATH RATE: 17 per 1,000 people
LIFE EXPECTANCY: Males 45, females 50 years
INFANT MORTALITY: 119 per 1,000 live births
URBAN POPULATION: 22% of population
FERTILITY RATE: 6 children per female
AGE GROUPS: 0–14 yrs 43%, 15–59 yrs 52%, 60+ yrs 6%
ETHNIC GROUPS: Bagirmi, Sara and Kreish 31%, Sudanic Arab 26%, Teda 7%
LANGUAGES: *French, Arabic*, 15 others
RELIGIONS: Sunni Muslim 44%, animist 38%, various Christian 17%
LAND USE: Arable 3%, grass 36%, forest 10%
EMPLOYMENT: Agric. 83%, ind. 5%, services 12%
ANNUAL INCOME: $180 per person, 0.5%
ORIGIN OF INCOME: Agriculture 43%, industry 18%, services 39%
ENERGY: Consumption 0.02 tonnes per person
TRADE: $104 per person
CURRENCY: CFA franc = 100 centimes
ROADS: 26 km per 1,000 sq km of land
POPULATION PER DOCTOR: 30,030 people
ADULT LITERACY: 30%
EDUCATIONAL EXPENDITURE: 2% of GNP
MILITARY EXPENDITURE: 3.8% of GNP
AID RECEIVED: $38 per person

Chile
CAPITAL CITY: Santiago
AREA: 756,950 sq km (Land area 748,800 sq km)
POPULATION: 14,700,000 people
POPULATION DENSITY: 20 people per sq km
POPULATION CHANGE: 1.6% per year
BIRTH RATE: 18 per 1,000 people
DEATH RATE: 6 per 1,000 people
LIFE EXPECTANCY: Males 72, females 78 years
INFANT MORTALITY: 13 per 1,000 live births
URBAN POPULATION: 85% of population
FERTILITY RATE: 3 children per female
AGE GROUPS: 0–14 yrs 31%, 15–59 yrs 61%, 60+ yrs 9%
ETHNIC GROUPS: Mestizo 79%, European 20%, Amerindian 1%
LANGUAGES: *Spanish*, Araucanian
RELIGIONS: Roman Catholic 80%, Protestant 6%
LAND USE: Arable 6%, grass 18%, forest 12%
EMPLOYMENT: Agric. 19%, ind. 26%, services 55%
ANNUAL INCOME: $4,160 per person, 6.1%
ORIGIN OF INCOME: Agriculture 8%, industry 30%, services 62%
ENERGY: Prod. 0.57 tonnes, consump. 1.15 tonnes
TRADE: $1,221 per person
CURRENCY: Peso = 100 centavos
ROADS: 106 km per 1,000 sq km of land
RAILWAYS: 9 km per 1,000 sq km of land
POPULATION PER DOCTOR: 2,150 people
ADULT LITERACY: 93%
EDUCATIONAL EXPENDITURE: 3.6% of GNP
AID RECEIVED: $11 per person

China
CAPITAL CITY: Beijing
AREA: 9,596,960 sq km (Land area 9,326,410 sq km)
POPULATION: 1,210,000,000 people
POPULATION DENSITY: 130 people per sq km
POPULATION CHANGE: 0.9% per year
BIRTH RATE: 17 per 1,000 people
DEATH RATE: 7 per 1,000 people
LIFE EXPECTANCY: Males 69, females 72 years
INFANT MORTALITY: 38 per 1,000 live births
URBAN POPULATION: 29% of population
FERTILITY RATE: 2 children per female
AGE GROUPS: 0–14 yrs 27%, 15–59 yrs 65%, 60+ yrs 9%
ETHNIC GROUPS: Han (Chinese) 93%, 55 others
LANGUAGES: *Mandarin*, Cantonese, local languages and dialects
RELIGIONS: Confucian 20%, Buddhist 6%, Taoist 2%, Muslim 2%, Christian
LAND USE: Arable 10%, grass 43%, forest 14%
EMPLOYMENT: Agric. 73%, ind. 14%, services 13%
ANNUAL INCOME: $620 per person, 8%
ORIGIN OF INCOME: Agriculture 27%, industry 42%, services 31%
ENERGY: Prod. 0.88 tonnes, consump. 0.35 tonnes
TRADE: $137 per person
CURRENCY: Renminbi yuan= 10 jiao = 100 fen
ROADS: 120 km per 1,000 sq km of land
RAILWAYS: 8 km per 1,000 sq km of land
POPULATION PER DOCTOR: 1,000 people
ADULT LITERACY: 70%
EDUCATIONAL EXPENDITURE: 2.4% of GNP
MILITARY EXPENDITURE: 3.7% of GNP
AID RECEIVED: $3 per person

Christmas Island
TERRITORY OF AUSTRALIA
CAPITAL CITY: The Settlement
AREA: 135 sq km
POPULATION: 2,000 people

Cocos (Keeling) Islands
TERRITORY OF AUSTRALIA
CAPITAL CITY: West Island
AREA: 14 sq km
POPULATION: 1,000 people

Colombia
CAPITAL CITY: Bogotá
AREA: 1,138,910 sq km (Land area 1,038,700 sq km)
POPULATION: 35,900,000 people
POPULATION DENSITY: 35 people per sq km
POPULATION CHANGE: 1.2% per year
BIRTH RATE: 21 per 1,000 people
DEATH RATE: 5 per 1,000 people
LIFE EXPECTANCY: Males 70, females 76 years
INFANT MORTALITY: 25 per 1,000 live births
URBAN POPULATION: 73% of population
FERTILITY RATE: 3 children per female
AGE GROUPS: 0–14 yrs 36%, 15–59 yrs 58%, 60+ yrs 6%
ETHNIC GROUPS: Mestizo 68%, White 20%, Amerindian 7%, Black 5%
LANGUAGES: *Spanish*, Amerindian languages and dialects
RELIGIONS: Roman Catholic 95%
LAND USE: Arable 5%, grass 39%, forest 48%
EMPLOYMENT: Agric. 2%, ind. 21%, services 77%
ANNUAL INCOME: $1,910 per person, 2.8%
ORIGIN OF INCOME: Agriculture 17%, industry 35%, services 48%
ENERGY: Prod. 1.77 tonnes, consump. 0.61 tonnes
TRADE: $364 per person
CURRENCY: Peso = 100 centavos
ROADS: 103 km per 1,000 sq km of land
RAILWAYS: 3 km per 1,000 sq km of land
POPULATION PER DOCTOR: 1,000 people
ADULT LITERACY: 87%
EDUCATIONAL EXPENDITURE: 2.9% of GNP
MILITARY EXPENDITURE: 2.2% of GNP
AID RECEIVED: $6 per person

Comoros
CAPITAL CITY: Moroni
AREA: 2,230 sq km
POPULATION: 630,000 people
POPULATION DENSITY: 283 people per sq km
POPULATION CHANGE: 2.1% per year
BIRTH RATE: 45 per 1,000 people
DEATH RATE: 10 per 1,000 people
LIFE EXPECTANCY: Males 57, females 62 years
INFANT MORTALITY: 73 per 1,000 live births
URBAN POPULATION: 29% of population
FERTILITY RATE: 7 children per female
AGE GROUPS: 0–14 yrs 48%, 15–59 yrs 48%, 60+ yrs 4%
ETHNIC GROUPS: Arab, Bantu, Malagasy
LANGUAGES: *Comorian, Arabic, French*, Malagasy
RELIGIONS: Sunni Muslim 86%, Roman Catholic 14%
LAND USE: Arable 45%, grass 7%, forest 16%
EMPLOYMENT: Agric. 83%, ind. 6%, services 11%
ANNUAL INCOME: $470 per person, –1.4%

ORIGIN OF INCOME: Agriculture 41%, industry 10%, services 49%
ENERGY: Consumption 0.04 tonnes per person
TRADE: $120 per person
CURRENCY: CFA franc = 100 centimes
ROADS: 382 km per 1,000 sq km of land
POPULATION PER DOCTOR: 12,000 people
ADULT LITERACY: 61%
EDUCATIONAL EXPENDITURE: 6.5% of GNP
MILITARY EXPENDITURE: 3% of GNP
AID RECEIVED: $78 per person

Congo
CAPITAL CITY: Brazzaville
AREA: 342,000 sq km
POPULATION: 2,730,000 people
POPULATION DENSITY: 8 people per sq km
POPULATION CHANGE: 2.9% per year
BIRTH RATE: 39 per 1,000 people
DEATH RATE: 17 per 1,000 people
LIFE EXPECTANCY: Males 44, females 47 years
INFANT MORTALITY: 106 per 1,000 live births
URBAN POPULATION: 59% of population
FERTILITY RATE: 7 children per female
AGE GROUPS: 0–14 yrs 46%, 15–59 yrs 49%, 60+ yrs 5%
ETHNIC GROUPS: Kongo 52%, Teke 17%, Mboshi 12%, Mbete 5%
LANGUAGES: *French*, Monokutuba Kongo, Teke
RELIGIONS: Roman Catholic 54%, Protestant 24%
LAND USE: Grass 29%, forest 62%
EMPLOYMENT: Agric. 62%, ind. 12%, services 26%
ANNUAL INCOME: $680 per person, –3.2%
ORIGIN OF INCOME: Agriculture 12%, industry 37%, services 51%
ENERGY: Prod. 5.1 tonnes, consump. 0.15 tonnes
TRADE: $694 per person
CURRENCY: CFA franc = 100 centimes
ROADS: 37 km per 1,000 sq km of land
RAILWAYS: 2 km per 1,000 sq km of land
POPULATION PER DOCTOR: 8,300 people
ADULT LITERACY: 57%
EDUCATIONAL EXPENDITURE: 5.1% of GNP
MILITARY EXPENDITURE: 3.6% of GNP
AID RECEIVED: $50 per person

Congo (Zaïre)
CAPITAL CITY: Kinshasa
AREA: 2,344,860 sq km (Land area 2,267,500 sq km)
POPULATION: 47,200,000 people
POPULATION DENSITY: 21 people per sq km
POPULATION CHANGE: 4.1% per year
BIRTH RATE: 48 per 1,000 people
DEATH RATE: 17 per 1,000 people
LIFE EXPECTANCY: Males 45, females 49 years
INFANT MORTALITY: 106 per 1,000 live births
URBAN POPULATION: 29% of population
FERTILITY RATE: 7 children per female
AGE GROUPS: 0–14 yrs 46%, 15–59 yrs 50%, 60+ yrs 4%
ETHNIC GROUPS: Luba 18%, Kongo 16%, Mongo 14%, Rwanda 10%, Azandi 6%, Bangi and Ngale 6%
LANGUAGES: *French*, Lingala, Swahili, Kikongo, Azande, Luba, Mongo, Rwanda, Boa, Rundi
RELIGIONS: Roman Catholic 48%, Protestant 29%, indigenous Christian 17%, traditional beliefs 3%
LAND USE: Arable 3%, grass 7%, forest 77%
EMPLOYMENT: Agric. 71%, ind. 13%, services 16%
ANNUAL INCOME: $120 per person, –8.5%
ORIGIN OF INCOME: Agriculture 30%, industry 33%, services 36%
ENERGY: Prod. 0.07 tonnes, consump. 0.06 tonnes
TRADE: $18 per person
CURRENCY: Congolese franc
ROADS: 68 km per 1,000 sq km of land
RAILWAYS: 2 km per 1,000 sq km of land
POPULATION PER DOCTOR: 14,250 people
ADULT LITERACY: 74%
EDUCATIONAL EXPENDITURE: 0.9% of GNP
MILITARY EXPENDITURE: 2.9% of GNP
AID RECEIVED: $4 per person

Cook Islands
FREE ASSOCIATION WITH NEW ZEALAND
CAPITAL CITY: Avarua
AREA: 240 sq km
POPULATION: 20,000 people

Costa Rica
CAPITAL CITY: San José
AREA: 51,100 sq km
POPULATION: 3,500,000 people
POPULATION DENSITY: 69 people per sq km
POPULATION CHANGE: 2.2% per year
BIRTH RATE: 23 per 1,000 people
DEATH RATE: 4 per 1,000 people
LIFE EXPECTANCY: Males 73, females 78 years
INFANT MORTALITY: 13 per 1,000 live births
URBAN POPULATION: 50% of population
FERTILITY RATE: 3 children per female
AGE GROUPS: 0–14 yrs 36%, 15–59 yrs 57%, 60+ yrs 6%

ETHNIC GROUPS: White 87%, Mestizo 7%
LANGUAGES: *Spanish*, Creole
RELIGIONS: Roman Catholic 92%
LAND USE: Arable 10%, grass 46%, forest 32%
EMPLOYMENT: Agric. 25%, ind. 27%, services 48%
ANNUAL INCOME: $2,610 per person, 2.9%
ORIGIN OF INCOME: Agriculture 18%, industry 25%, services 57%
ENERGY: Prod. 0.14 tonnes, consump. 0.37 tonnes
TRADE: $1,110 per person
CURRENCY: Colón = 100 céntimos
ROADS: 697 km per 1,000 sq km of land
RAILWAYS: 19 km per 1,000 sq km of land
POPULATION PER DOCTOR: 1,030 people
ADULT LITERACY: 93%
EDUCATIONAL EXPENDITURE: 4.4% of GNP
MILITARY EXPENDITURE: 0.4% of GNP
AID RECEIVED: $8 per person

Croatia
CAPITAL CITY: Zagreb
AREA: 56,538 sq km
POPULATION: 4,850,000 people
POPULATION DENSITY: 86 people per sq km
POPULATION CHANGE: 0.2% per year
BIRTH RATE: 10 per 1,000 people
DEATH RATE: 11 per 1,000 people
LIFE EXPECTANCY: Males 69, females 77 years
INFANT MORTALITY: 10 per 1,000 live births
URBAN POPULATION: 55% of population
ETHNIC GROUPS: Croat 78%, Serb 12%, Muslim 1%
LANGUAGES: *Serbo-Croat*
RELIGIONS: Roman Catholic 77%, Serbian Orthodox 11%, Sunni Muslim 1%
LAND USE: Arable 24%, grass 36%, forest 36%
EMPLOYMENT: Agric. 5%, ind. 42%, services 54%
ANNUAL INCOME: $3,250 per person, –20%
ORIGIN OF INCOME: Agriculture 14%, industry 50%, services 36%
TRADE: $1,500 per person
CURRENCY: Kuna = 100 lipas
ROADS: 477 km per 1,000 sq km of land
RAILWAYS: 48 km per 1,000 sq km of land
POPULATION PER DOCTOR: 500 people
ADULT LITERACY: 96%

Cuba
CAPITAL CITY: Havana
AREA: 110,860 sq km
POPULATION: 11,250,000 people
POPULATION DENSITY: 102 people per sq km
POPULATION CHANGE: 0.8% per year
BIRTH RATE: 13 per 1,000 people
DEATH RATE: 7 per 1,000 people
LIFE EXPECTANCY: Males 73, females 78 years
INFANT MORTALITY: 9 per 1,000 live births
URBAN POPULATION: 75% of population
FERTILITY RATE: 2 children per female
AGE GROUPS: 0–14 yrs 23%, 15–59 yrs 66%, 60+ yrs 12%
ETHNIC GROUPS: White 66%, Mulatto 22%, Black 12%
LANGUAGES: *Spanish*
RELIGIONS: Roman Catholic 40%, Protestant 3%
LAND USE: Arable 30%, grass 27%, forest 25%
EMPLOYMENT: Agric. 24%, ind. 29%, services 48%
ANNUAL INCOME: $1,250 per person, –10%
ORIGIN OF INCOME: Agriculture 12%, industry 52%, services 36%
ENERGY: Prod. 0.12 tonnes, consump. 0.99 tonnes
TRADE: $678 per person
CURRENCY: Peso = 100 centavos
ROADS: 424 km per 1,000 sq km of land
RAILWAYS: 44 km per 1,000 sq km of land
POPULATION PER DOCTOR: 300 people
ADULT LITERACY: 75%
EDUCATIONAL EXPENDITURE: 6.6% of GNP
MILITARY EXPENDITURE: 11.3% of GNP
AID RECEIVED: $6 per person

Cyprus
CAPITAL CITY: Nicosia
AREA: 9,250 sq km
POPULATION: 770,000 people
POPULATION DENSITY: 83 people per sq km
POPULATION CHANGE: 1.4% per year
BIRTH RATE: 15 per 1,000 people
DEATH RATE: 8 per 1,000 people
LIFE EXPECTANCY: Males 74, females 79 years
INFANT MORTALITY: 8 per 1,000 live births
URBAN POPULATION: 68% of population
FERTILITY RATE: 2 children per female
AGE GROUPS: 0–14 yrs 26%, 15–59 yrs 60%, 60+ yrs 14%
ETHNIC GROUPS: Greek Cypriot 81%, Turkish Cypriot 19%
LANGUAGES: *Greek, Turkish*
RELIGIONS: Greek Orthodox 81%, Sunni Muslim 19%
LAND USE: Arable 17%, forest 13%
EMPLOYMENT: Agric. 15%, ind. 21%, services 64%
ANNUAL INCOME: $11,500 per person, 4.6%
ORIGIN OF INCOME: Agriculture 7%, industry 27%, services 56%

ENERGY: Consumption 1.21 tonnes per person
TRADE: $5,032 per person
CURRENCY: Cyprus £ = 100 cents
ROADS: 1,095 km per 1,000 sq km of land
POPULATION PER DOCTOR: 1,100 people
ADULT LITERACY: 94%
EDUCATIONAL EXPENDITURE: 3.6% of GNP
MILITARY EXPENDITURE: 1.4% of GNP
AID RECEIVED: $30 per person

Czech Republic
CAPITAL CITY: Prague
AREA: 78,864 sq km (Land area 77,280 sq km)
POPULATION: 10,500,000people
POPULATION DENSITY: 133 people per sq km
POPULATION CHANGE: 0.3% per year
BIRTH RATE: 11 per 1,000 people
DEATH RATE: 11 per 1,000 people
LIFE EXPECTANCY: Males 70, females 78 years
INFANT MORTALITY: 8 per 1,000 live births
URBAN POPULATION: 65% of population
FERTILITY RATE: 2 children per female
ETHNIC GROUPS: Czech 81%, Moravian 13%,
  Slovak 3%, Polish
LANGUAGES: Czech, Moravian
RELIGIONS: Roman Catholic 39%, Protestant
LAND USE: Arable 41%, grass 11%, forest 34%
EMPLOYMENT: Agric. 12%, ind. 45%,
  services 43%
ANNUAL INCOME: $3,870 per person, −1.8%
ORIGIN OF WEALTH: Agriculture. 6%, industry
  50%, services 44%
TRADE: $2,431 per person
CURRENCY: Koruna = 100 halura
ROADS: 723 km per 1,000 sq km of land
RAILWAYS: 122 km per 1,000 sq km of land
POPULATION PER DOCTOR: 325 people
ADULT LITERACY: 99%
EDUCATIONAL EXPENDITURE: 5% of GNP
MILITARY EXPENDITURE: 3% of GNP
AID RECEIVED: $5 per person

Denmark
CAPITAL CITY: Copenhagen
AREA: 43,070 sq km (Land area 42,390 sq km)
POPULATION: 5,350,000 people
POPULATION DENSITY: 126 people per sq km
POPULATION CHANGE: 0.6% per year
BIRTH RATE: 12 per 1,000 people
DEATH RATE: 10 per 1,000 people
LIFE EXPECTANCY: Males 74, females 81 years
INFANT MORTALITY: 5 per 1,000 live births
URBAN POPULATION: 86% of population
FERTILITY RATE: 2 children per female
AGE GROUPS: 0–14 yrs 17%, 15–59 yrs 63%,
  60+ yrs 20%
ETHNIC GROUPS: Danish 97%
LANGUAGES: Danish
RELIGIONS: Lutheran 91%, Roman Catholic 1%
LAND USE: Arable 61%, grass 5%, forest 12%
EMPLOYMENT: Agric. 6%, ind. 28%, services 66%
ANNUAL INCOME: $29,890 per person, 1.5%
ORIGIN OF INCOME: Agriculture 5%, industry 28%,
  services 67%
ENERGY: Prod. 2.52 tonnes, consump. 5.44 tonnes
TRADE: $14,046 per person
CURRENCY: Krone = 100 øre
ROADS: 1,679 km per 1,000 sq km of land
RAILWAYS: 67 km per 1,000 sq km of land
POPULATION PER DOCTOR: 390 people
ADULT LITERACY: 99%
EDUCATIONAL EXPENDITURE: 7.3% of GNP
MILITARY EXPENDITURE: 2.1% of GNP
AID GIVEN: $273 per person

Djibouti
CAPITAL CITY: Djibouti
AREA: 23,200 sq km
POPULATION: 650,000 people
POPULATION DENSITY: 28 people per sq km
POPULATION CHANGE: 5.7% per year
BIRTH RATE: 42 per 1,000 people
DEATH RATE: 15 per 1,000 people
LIFE EXPECTANCY: Males 49, females 53 years
INFANT MORTALITY: 105 per 1,000 live births
URBAN POPULATION: 83% of population
FERTILITY RATE: 7 children per female
AGE GROUPS: 0–14 yrs 46%, 15–59 yrs 50%,
  60+ yrs 4%
ETHNIC GROUPS: Issa 47%, Afar 38%, Arab 6%
LANGUAGES: Arabic, French, Somali, Afar
RELIGIONS: Sunni Muslim 94%, Roman Catholic 4%
LAND USE: Grass 9%
EMPLOYMENT: Agric. 77%, ind. 9%, services 14%
ANNUAL INCOME: $1,000 per person, −1%
ORIGIN OF INCOME: Agriculture 5%, industry 15%,
  services 80%
ENERGY: Consumption 0.3 tonnes per person
TRADE: $550 per person
CURRENCY: Franc = 100 centimes
ROADS: 125 km per 1,000 sq km of land
RAILWAYS: 5 km per 1,000 sq km of land
POPULATION PER DOCTOR: 1,000 people
ADULT LITERACY: 19%
EDUCATIONAL EXPENDITURE: 2.7% of GNP
AID RECEIVED: $293 per person

Dominica
CAPITAL CITY: Roseau
AREA: 751 sq km
POPULATION: 78,000 people
POPULATION DENSITY: 104 people per sq km
POPULATION CHANGE: −0.7% per year
BIRTH RATE: 18 per 1,000 people
DEATH RATE: 5 per 1,000 people
LIFE EXPECTANCY: Males 75, females 81 years
INFANT MORTALITY: 9 per 1,000 live births
URBAN POPULATION: 41% of population
FERTILITY RATE: 3 children per female
AGE GROUPS: 0–14 yrs 31%, 15–59 yrs 57%,
  60+ yrs 12%
ETHNIC GROUPS: Of African descent
LANGUAGES: English, French patois
RELIGIONS: Roman Catholic 75%, Protestant 15%
LAND USE: Arable 23%, grass 3%, forest 41%
EMPLOYMENT: Agric. 31%, ind. 13%, services 56%
ANNUAL INCOME: $2,990 per person, 4%
ORIGIN OF INCOME: Agriculture 27%, industry
  16%, services 57%
ENERGY: Consumption 0.18 tonnes per person
TRADE: $2,163 per person
CURRENCY: East Caribbean $ = 100 cents
ROADS: 1,000 km per 1,000 sq km of land
POPULATION PER DOCTOR: 2,000 people
ADULT LITERACY: 97%
EDUCATIONAL EXPENDITURE: 5.7% of GNP
AID RECEIVED: $185 per person

Dominican Republic
CAPITAL CITY: Santo Domingo
AREA: 48,730 sq km
POPULATION: 8,150,000 people
POPULATION DENSITY: 168 people per sq km
POPULATION CHANGE: 1.8% per year
BIRTH RATE: 23 per 1,000 people
DEATH RATE: 6 per 1,000 people
LIFE EXPECTANCY: Males 67, females 72 years
INFANT MORTALITY: 46 per 1,000 live births
URBAN POPULATION: 62% of population
FERTILITY RATE: 3 children per female
AGE GROUPS: 0–14 yrs 38%, 15–59 yrs 57%,
  60+ yrs 6%
ETHNIC GROUPS: Mulatto 73%, White 16%,
  Black 11%
LANGUAGES: Spanish
RELIGIONS: Roman Catholic 93%
LAND USE: Arable 30%, grass 43%, forest 13%
EMPLOYMENT: Agric. 46%, ind. 15%, services 39%
ANNUAL INCOME: $1,460 per person, 2.1%
ORIGIN OF INCOME: Agriculture 18%, industry
  25%, services 57%
ENERGY: Prod. 0.01 tonnes, consump. 0.32 tonnes
TRADE: $324 per person
CURRENCY: Peso = 100 centavos
ROADS: 248 km per 1,000 sq km of land
RAILWAYS: 36 km per 1,000 sq km of land
POPULATION PER DOCTOR: 1,000 people
ADULT LITERACY: 83%
EDUCATIONAL EXPENDITURE: 1.5% of GNP
MILITARY EXPENDITURE: 0.8% of GNP
AID RECEIVED: $16 per person

Ecuador
CAPITAL CITY: Quito
AREA: 283,560 sq km (Land area 276,840 sq km)
POPULATION: 11,800,000 people
POPULATION DENSITY: 43 people per sq km
POPULATION CHANGE: 1.6% per year
BIRTH RATE: 25 per 1,000 people
DEATH RATE: 5 per 1,000 people
LIFE EXPECTANCY: Males 69, females 74 years
INFANT MORTALITY: 33 per 1,000 live births
URBAN POPULATION: 59% of population
FERTILITY RATE: 4 children per female
AGE GROUPS: 0–14 yrs 40%, 15–59 yrs 55%,
  60+ yrs 6%
ETHNIC GROUPS: Mestizo 40%, Amerindian 40%,
  White 5%, Black 5%
LANGUAGES: Spanish, Quechua
RELIGIONS: Roman Catholic 93%
LAND USE: Arable 6%, grass 18%, forest 37%
EMPLOYMENT: Agric. 33%, ind. 19%, services 48%
ANNUAL INCOME: $1,390 per person, 0.8%
ORIGIN OF INCOME: Agriculture 12%, industry
  38%, services 50%
ENERGY: Prod. 2.29 tonnes, consump. 0.77 tonnes
TRADE: $498 per person
CURRENCY: Sucre = 100 centavos
ROADS: 164 km per 1,000 sq km of land
RAILWAYS: 3 km per 1,000 sq km of land
POPULATION PER DOCTOR: 671 people
ADULT LITERACY: 88%
EDUCATIONAL EXPENDITURE: 2.8% of GNP
MILITARY EXPENDITURE: 2.2% of GNP
AID RECEIVED: $21 per person

Egypt
CAPITAL CITY: Cairo
AREA: 1,001,450 sq km
POPULATION: 63,000,000 people
POPULATION DENSITY: 63 people per sq km
POPULATION CHANGE: 2.6% per year
BIRTH RATE: 28 per 1,000 people

DEATH RATE: 9 per 1,000 people
LIFE EXPECTANCY: Males 60, females 64 years
INFANT MORTALITY: 71 per 1,000 live births
URBAN POPULATION: 45% of population
FERTILITY RATE: 4 children per female
AGE GROUPS: 0–14 yrs 39%, 15–59 yrs 54%,
  60+ yrs 6%
ETHNIC GROUPS: Egyptian 99%
LANGUAGES: Arabic, French, English
RELIGIONS: Sunni Muslim 90%, Coptic Christian
LAND USE: Arable 2%
EMPLOYMENT: Agric. 42%, ind. 21%, services 37%
ANNUAL INCOME: $790 per person, 1.1%
ORIGIN OF INCOME: Agriculture 18%, industry
  30%, services 52%
ENERGY: Prod. 1.42 tonnes, consump. 0.70 tonnes
TRADE: $184 per person
CURRENCY: Egyptian £ = 100 piastres
ROADS: 48 km per 1,000 sq km of land
RAILWAYS: 9 km per 1,000 sq km of land
POPULATION PER DOCTOR: 1,300 people
ADULT LITERACY: 49%
EDUCATIONAL EXPENDITURE: 6.7% of GNP
MILITARY EXPENDITURE: 6.0% of GNP
AID RECEIVED: $35 per person

El Salvador
CAPITAL CITY: San Salvador
AREA: 21,040 sq km (Land area 20,720 sq km)
POPULATION: 5,950,000 people
POPULATION DENSITY: 287 people per sq km
POPULATION CHANGE: 1.8% per year
BIRTH RATE: 27 per 1,000 people
DEATH RATE: 6 per 1,000 people
LIFE EXPECTANCY: Males 66, females 73 years
INFANT MORTALITY: 30 per 1,000 live births
URBAN POPULATION: 52% of population
FERTILITY RATE: 4 children per female
AGE GROUPS: 0–14 yrs 45%, 15–59 yrs 50%,
  60+ yrs 6%
ETHNIC GROUPS: Mestizo 90%, Indian 5%,
  White 5%
LANGUAGES: Spanish
RELIGIONS: Roman Catholic 75%
LAND USE: Arable 27%, grass 29%, forest 5%
EMPLOYMENT: Agric. 11%, ind. 23%, services 66%
ANNUAL INCOME: $1,610 per person, 2.9%
ORIGIN OF INCOME: Agriculture 9%, industry 25%,
  services 66%
ENERGY: Prod. 0.12 tonnes, consump.
  0.40 tonnes
TRADE: $481 per person
CURRENCY: Colón = 100 centavos
ROADS: 751 km per 1,000 sq km of land
RAILWAYS: 27 km per 1,000 sq km of land
POPULATION PER DOCTOR: 1,563 people
ADULT LITERACY: 70%
EDUCATIONAL EXPENDITURE: 1.8% of GNP
MILITARY EXPENDITURE: 1.7% of GNP
AID RECEIVED: $54 per person

Equatorial Guinea
CAPITAL CITY: Malabo
AREA: 28,050 sq km
POPULATION: 420,000 people
POPULATION DENSITY: 15 people per sq km
POPULATION CHANGE: 2.7% per year
BIRTH RATE: 39 per 1,000 people
DEATH RATE: 14 per 1,000 people
LIFE EXPECTANCY: Males 51, females 56 years
INFANT MORTALITY: 96 per 1,000 live births
URBAN POPULATION: 39% of population
FERTILITY RATE: 6 children per female
AGE GROUPS: 0–14 yrs 42%, 15–59 yrs 51%,
  60+ yrs 6%
ETHNIC GROUPS: Fang 83%, Bubi 10%
LANGUAGES: Spanish, Fang, Bubi
RELIGIONS: Roman Catholic 89%
LAND USE: Arable 5%, grass 4%, forest 46%
EMPLOYMENT: Agric. 77%, ind. 2%, services 21%
ANNUAL INCOME: $380 per person, 2.3%
ORIGIN OF INCOME: Agriculture 47%, industry
  26%, services 27%
ENERGY: Consumption 0.15 tonnes per person
TRADE: $355 per person
CURRENCY: CFA franc = 100 centimes
ROADS: 96 km per 1,000 sq km of land
POPULATION PER DOCTOR: 3,550 people
ADULT LITERACY: 75%
EDUCATIONAL EXPENDITURE: 1.7% of GNP
MILITARY EXPENDITURE: 11% of GNP
AID RECEIVED: $135 per person

Eritrea
CAPITAL CITY: Asmara
AREA: 93,700 sq km
POPULATION: 3,500,000 people
POPULATION DENSITY: 35 people per sq km
POPULATION CHANGE: 0.6% per year
BIRTH RATE: 44 per 1,000 people
DEATH RATE: 15 per 1,000 people
URBAN POPULATION: 17% of population
ETHNIC GROUPS: Tigrinya 48%, Tigre 31%
LANGUAGES: Arabic, Tigrinya, Tigre
RELIGIONS: Coptic Christian 50%, Sunni
  Muslim 50%

Estonia
CAPITAL CITY: Tallinn
AREA: 45,100 sq km
POPULATION: 1,460,000 people
POPULATION DENSITY: 34 people per sq km
POPULATION CHANGE: −1.1% per year
BIRTH RATE: 12 per 1,000 people
DEATH RATE: 14 per 1,000 people
LIFE EXPECTANCY: Males 63, females 74 years
INFANT MORTALITY: 17 per 1,000 live births
URBAN POPULATION: 73% of population
FERTILITY RATE: 2 children per female
AGE GROUPS: 0–14 yrs 23%, 15–59 yrs 60%,
  60+ yrs 17%
ETHNIC GROUPS: Estonian 62%, Russian 30%,
  Ukrainian 3%, Belarusian 2%, Finnish 1%
LANGUAGES: Estonian, Russian
RELIGIONS: Lutheran 85%, Russian Orthodox 10%
LAND USE: Arable 22%, grass 21%, forest 43%
EMPLOYMENT: Agric. 9%, ind. 33%, services 58%
ANNUAL INCOME: $2,860 per person, −4.3%
ORIGIN OF INCOME: Agriculture 8%, industry 29%,
  services 63%
ENERGY: Prod. 3.35 tonnes, consump. 5.36 tonnes
TRADE: $3,485 per person
CURRENCY: Kroon = 100 sents
ROADS: 342 km per 1,000 sq km of land
RAILWAYS: 24 km per 1,000 sq km of land
POPULATION PER DOCTOR: 250 people
ADULT LITERACY: 99%
MILITARY EXPENDITURE: 0.6% of GNP
AID RECEIVED: $22 per person

Ethiopia
CAPITAL CITY: Addis Ababa
AREA: 1,221,900 sq km (Land area
  1,101,000 sq km)
POPULATION: 58,500,000 people
POPULATION DENSITY: 53 people per sq km
POPULATION CHANGE: 3.5% per year
BIRTH RATE: 46 per 1,000 people
DEATH RATE: 18 per 1,000 people
LIFE EXPECTANCY: Males 45, females 48 years
INFANT MORTALITY: 122 per 1,000 live births
URBAN POPULATION: 13% of population
FERTILITY RATE: 7 children per female
AGE GROUPS: 0–14 yrs 45%, 15–59 yrs 50%,
  60+ yrs 5%
ETHNIC GROUPS: Amharic 38%, Galla 35%,
  Tigrinya 9%, Guage 3%, 60 others
LANGUAGES: Amharic, Galla, Tigre, 280 others
RELIGIONS: Ethiopian Orthodox 53%, Sunni
  Muslim 31%, traditional animist beliefs 11%
LAND USE: Arable 12%, grass 41%, forest 24%
EMPLOYMENT: Agric. 88%, ind. 2%, services 10%
ANNUAL INCOME: $100 per person, −0.5%
ORIGIN OF INCOME: Agriculture 60%, industry
  10%, services 29%
ENERGY: Consumption 0.03 tonnes per person
TRADE: $16 per person
CURRENCY: Birr = 100 cents
ROADS: 25 km per 1,000 sq km of land
RAILWAYS: 1 km per 1,000 sq km of land
POPULATION PER DOCTOR: 33,000 people
ADULT LITERACY: 33%
EDUCATIONAL EXPENDITURE: 4.8% of GNP
MILITARY EXPENDITURE: 20.1% of GNP
AID RECEIVED: $16 per person

Falkland Islands
BRITISH DEPENDENT TERRITORY
CAPITAL CITY: Stanley
AREA: 12,170 sq km
POPULATION: 2,000 people
POPULATION DENSITY: 0.2 people per sq km
POPULATION CHANGE: 0% per year
BIRTH RATE: 15 per 1,000 people
DEATH RATE: 8 per 1,000 people
ETHNIC GROUPS: British
LANGUAGES: English
RELIGIONS: Christian
LAND USE: Grass 99%
EMPLOYMENT: Agric. 95%, services 5%
TRADE: $14,300 per person
CURRENCY: Falkland £ = 100 pence
ROADS: 3 km per 1,000 sq km of land

Faroe Islands
DANISH SELF-GOVERNING REGION
CAPITAL CITY: Tórshavn
AREA: 1,400 sq km
POPULATION: 45,000 people
POPULATION DENSITY: 32 people per sq km
POPULATION CHANGE: −0.6% per year
BIRTH RATE: 13 per 1,000 people
DEATH RATE: 9 per 1,000 people
LIFE EXPECTANCY: Males 75, females 81 years
INFANT MORTALITY: 7 per 1,000 live births
URBAN POPULATION: 33% of population
FERTILITY RATE: 2 children per female
ETHNIC GROUPS: Of Scandinavian descent
LANGUAGES: Faroese, Danish
RELIGIONS: Lutheran 75%
LAND USE: Arable 2%
EMPLOYMENT: Agric. 30%
ANNUAL INCOME: $16,000 per person

Faroe Islands continued
ORIGIN OF INCOME: Agric. 27%
ENERGY: Consumption 3.28 tonnes per person
TRADE: $14,750 per person
CURRENCY: Danish currency and Faroese króna
ROADS: 327 km per 1,000 sq km of land
ADULT LITERACY: 99%

Fiji
CAPITAL CITY: Suva
AREA: 18,270 sq km
POPULATION: 800,000 people
POPULATION DENSITY: 44 people per sq km
POPULATION CHANGE: 0.7% per year
BIRTH RATE: 23 per 1,000 people
DEATH RATE: 6 per 1,000 people
LIFE EXPECTANCY: Males 64, females 68 years
INFANT MORTALITY: 17 per 1,000 live births
URBAN POPULATION: 40% of population
FERTILITY RATE: 3 children per female
AGE GROUPS: 0–14 yrs 37%, 15–59 yrs 58%, 60+ yrs 5%
ETHNIC GROUPS: Fijian 49%, Indian 46%
LANGUAGES: *English*, Bauan, Hindustani
RELIGIONS: Christian 53%, Hindu 38%, Muslim 8%
LAND USE: Arable 10%, grass 10%, forest 65%
EMPLOYMENT: Agric. 44%, ind. 20%, services 36%
ANNUAL INCOME: $2,440 per person, 2.5%
ORIGIN OF INCOME: Agriculture 18%, industry 20%, services 62%
ENERGY: Prod. 0.06 tonnes, consump. 0.49 tonnes
TRADE: $1,352 per person
CURRENCY: Fiji $ = 100 cents
ROADS: 279 km per 1,000 sq km of land
RAILWAYS: 33 km per 1,000 sq km of land
POPULATION PER DOCTOR: 2,750 people
ADULT LITERACY: 90%
EDUCATIONAL EXPENDITURE: 5% of GNP
MILITARY EXPENDITURE: 2.0% of GNP
AID RECEIVED: $78 per person

Finland
CAPITAL CITY: Helsinki
AREA: 338,130 sq km (Land area 304,610 sq km)
POPULATION: 5,180,000 people
POPULATION DENSITY: 17 people per sq km
POPULATION CHANGE: 0.6% per year
BIRTH RATE: 11 per 1,000 people
DEATH RATE: 11 per 1,000 people
LIFE EXPECTANCY: Males 74, females 77 years
INFANT MORTALITY: 5 per 1,000 live births
URBAN POPULATION: 63% of population
FERTILITY RATE: 2 children per female
AGE GROUPS: 0–14 yrs 19%, 15–59 yrs 62%, 60+ yrs 18%
ETHNIC GROUPS: Finnish 93%, Swedish 6%
LANGUAGES: *Finnish, Swedish*
RELIGIONS: Lutheran 87%, Greek Orthodox 1%
LAND USE: Arable 8%, forest 76%
EMPLOYMENT: Agric. 9%, ind. 29%, services 62%
ANNUAL INCOME: $20,580 per person, –0.2%
ORIGIN OF INCOME: Agriculture 5%, industry 31%, services 64%
ENERGY: Prod. 2.18 tonnes, consump. 6.57 tonnes
TRADE: $8,199 per person
CURRENCY: Markka = 100 penniä
ROADS: 255 km per 1,000 sq km of land
RAILWAYS: 19 km per 1,000 sq km of land
POPULATION PER DOCTOR: 405 people
ADULT LITERACY: 99%
EDUCATIONAL EXPENDITURE: 6.6% of GNP
MILITARY EXPENDITURE: 1.9% of GNP
AID GIVEN: $59 per person

France
CAPITAL CITY: Paris
AREA: 551,500 sq km
POPULATION: 58,800,000 people
POPULATION DENSITY: 107 people per sq km
POPULATION CHANGE: 0.7% per year
BIRTH RATE: 13 per 1,000 people
DEATH RATE: 9 per 1,000 people
LIFE EXPECTANCY: Males 75, females 83 years
INFANT MORTALITY: 6 per 1,000 live births
URBAN POPULATION: 74% of population
FERTILITY RATE: 2 children per female
AGE GROUPS: 0–14 yrs 20%, 15–59 yrs 61%, 60+ yrs 19%
ETHNIC GROUPS: French 93%, Arab 3%, German 2%, Breton 1%, Catalan 1%
LANGUAGES: *French*, Breton, Catalan, Basque, Arabic, Occitan
RELIGIONS: Roman Catholic 76%, Protestant 4%, Muslim 3%
LAND USE: Arable 33%, grass 20%, forest 27%
EMPLOYMENT: Agric. 6%, ind. 29%, services 65%
ANNUAL INCOME: $24,990 per person, 1.5%
ORIGIN OF INCOME: Agriculture 3%, industry 29%, services 69%
ENERGY: Prod. 2.67 tonnes, consump. 5.43 tonnes
TRADE: $7,059 per person
CURRENCY: Franc = 100 centimes
ROADS: 1,477 km per 1,000 sq km of land
RAILWAYS: 62 km per 1,000 sq km of land
POPULATION PER DOCTOR: 333 people
ADULT LITERACY: 99%
EDUCATIONAL EXPENDITURE: 6.0% of GNP
MILITARY EXPENDITURE: 3.4% of GNP
AID GIVEN: $137 per person

French Guiana
DEPARTMENT OF FRANCE
CAPITAL CITY: Cayenne
AREA: 90,000 sq km (Land area 88,150 sq km)
POPULATION: 155,000 people
POPULATION DENSITY: 2 person per sq km
POPULATION CHANGE: 6.8% per year
BIRTH RATE: 24 per 1,000 people
DEATH RATE: 5 per 1,000 people
LIFE EXPECTANCY: Males 73, females 79 years
INFANT MORTALITY: 14 per 1,000 live births
URBAN POPULATION: 77% of population
FERTILITY RATE: 4 children per female
ETHNIC GROUPS: Creole 42%, Chinese 14%, French 10%, Haitian 7%
LANGUAGES: *French*, Creole patois
RELIGIONS: Roman Catholic 80%, Protestant 4%
LAND USE: Forest 83%
EMPLOYMENT: Agric. 9%, ind. 15%, services 76%
ANNUAL INCOME: $6,500 per person
ORIGIN OF INCOME: Agric. 35%
ENERGY: Consumption 2.52 tonnes per person
TRADE: $4,762 per person
CURRENCY: French currency
ROADS: 13 km per 1,000 sq km of land
POPULATION PER DOCTOR: 700 people
ADULT LITERACY: 82%
EDUCATIONAL EXPENDITURE: 17.6 % of GNP

French Polynesia
OVERSEAS DEPARTMENT OF FRANCE
CAPITAL CITY: Papeete
AREA: 4,000 sq km (Land area 3,660 sq km)
POPULATION: 226,000 people
POPULATION DENSITY: 62 people per sq km
POPULATION CHANGE: 1.3% per year
BIRTH RATE: 23 per 1,000 people
DEATH RATE: 5 per 1,000 people
LIFE EXPECTANCY: Males 70, females 75 years
INFANT MORTALITY: 14 per 1,000 live births
URBAN POPULATION: 67% of population
FERTILITY RATE: 3 children per female
ETHNIC GROUPS: Polynesian 78%, Chinese 12%, French
LANGUAGES: *French, Tahitian*
RELIGIONS: Protestant 54%, Roman Catholic 30%
LAND USE: Arable 1%, grass 5%, forest 31%
EMPLOYMENT: Agric. 10%, ind. 14%, services 76%
ANNUAL INCOME: $7,500 per person, 5.3%
ORIGIN OF INCOME: Agric. 5%, ind. 15%, services 80%
ENERGY: Prod. 0.04 tonnes, consump. 1.48 tonnes
TRADE: $4,647 per person
CURRENCY: CFP franc = 100 centimes
ROADS: 257 km per 1,000 sq km of land
POPULATION PER DOCTOR: 750 people
ADULT LITERACY: 95%
EDUCATIONAL EXPENDITURE: % of GNP

Gabon
CAPITAL CITY: Libreville
AREA: 267,670 sq km (Land area 257,670 sq km)
POPULATION: 1,200,000 people
POPULATION DENSITY: 5 people per sq km
POPULATION CHANGE: 0.5% per year
BIRTH RATE: 28 per 1,000 people
DEATH RATE: 13 per 1,000 people
LIFE EXPECTANCY: Males 53, females 59 years
INFANT MORTALITY: 88 per 1,000 live births
URBAN POPULATION: 73% of population
FERTILITY RATE: 5 children per female
AGE GROUPS: 0–14 yrs 32%, 15–59 yrs 59%, 60+ yrs 9%
ETHNIC GROUPS: Fang 36%, Mpongwe 15%, Mbete 14%, Punu 12%
LANGUAGES: *French*, Bantu languages
RELIGIONS: Roman Catholic 65%, traditionalist
LAND USE: Arable 1%, grass 18%, forest 77%
EMPLOYMENT: Agric. 75%, ind. 11%, services 14%
ANNUAL INCOME: $3,490 per person, –1.6%
ORIGIN OF INCOME: Agriculture 8%, industry 45%, services 47%
ENERGY: Prod. 17.22 tonnes, consump. 0.86 tonnes
TRADE: $2,675 per person
CURRENCY: CFA franc = 100 centimes
ROADS: 30 km per 1,000 sq km of land
RAILWAYS: 3 km per 1,000 sq km of land
POPULATION PER DOCTOR: 2,500 people
ADULT LITERACY: 59%
EDUCATIONAL EXPENDITURE: 5.7% of GNP
MILITARY EXPENDITURE: 3.7% of GNP
AID RECEIVED: $138 per person

Gambia, The
CAPITAL CITY: Banjul
AREA: 11,300 sq km (Land area 10,000 sq km)
POPULATION: 1,200,000 people
POPULATION DENSITY: 120 people per sq km
POPULATION CHANGE: 4.9% per year
BIRTH RATE: 44 per 1,000 people
DEATH RATE: 13 per 1,000 people
LIFE EXPECTANCY: Males 51, females 56 years
INFANT MORTALITY: 79 per 1,000 live births
URBAN POPULATION: 26% of population
FERTILITY RATE: 6 children per female
AGE GROUPS: 0–14 yrs 44%, 15–59 yrs 51%, 60+ yrs 5%
ETHNIC GROUPS: Madinka 40%, Fulani 19%, Wolof 15%, Dyolo 10%, Soninke 8%
LANGUAGES: *English*, Madinka, Fula, Wolof
RELIGIONS: Sunni Muslim 95%, Christian 4%
LAND USE: Arable 18%, grass 9%, forest 15%
EMPLOYMENT: Agric. 84%, ind. 7%, services 9%
ANNUAL INCOME: $320 per person, 0.3%
ORIGIN OF INCOME: Agriculture 28%, industry 15%, services 58%
ENERGY: Consumption 0.10 tonnes per person
TRADE: $273 per person
CURRENCY: Dalasi = 100 butut
ROADS: 239 km per 1,000 sq km of land
POPULATION PER DOCTOR: 10,000 people
ADULT LITERACY: 36%
EDUCATIONAL EXPENDITURE: 3.8% of GNP
MILITARY EXPENDITURE: 0.7% of GNP
AID RECEIVED: $43 per person

Georgia
CAPITAL CITY: Tbilisi
AREA: 69,700 sq km
POPULATION: 5,450,000 people
POPULATION DENSITY: 78 people per sq km
POPULATION CHANGE: 0% per year
BIRTH RATE: 14 per 1,000 people
DEATH RATE: 12 per 1,000 people
LIFE EXPECTANCY: Males 64, females 73 years
INFANT MORTALITY: 22 per 1,000 live births
URBAN POPULATION: 58% of population
FERTILITY RATE: 2 children per female
AGE GROUPS: 0–14 yrs 24%, 15–59 yrs 60%, 60+ yrs 16%
ETHNIC GROUPS: Georgian 70%, Armenian 8%, Russian 6%, Azeri 6%, Ossetian 3%, Greek 2%, Abkhazian 2%
LANGUAGES: *Georgian*, Armenian, Russian, Azerbaijani, Ossetian
RELIGIONS: Orthodox (Georgian 65%, Russian 10%, Armenian 8%), Sunni Muslim 11%
LAND USE: Arable 70%, grass 29%
EMPLOYMENT: Agric. 14%, ind. 30%, services 56%
ANNUAL INCOME: $440 per person, –17%
ORIGIN OF INCOME: Agriculture 58%, industry 22%, services 21%
ENERGY: Prod. 0.10 tonnes, consump. 1.29 tonnes
TRADE: $1,410 per person
CURRENCY: Lari
ROADS: 301 km per 1,000 sq km of land
RAILWAYS: 23 km per 1,000 sq km of land
POPULATION PER DOCTOR: 182 people
ADULT LITERACY: 99%
MILITARY EXPENDITURE: 3.2% of GNP
AID RECEIVED: $106 per person

Germany
CAPITAL CITY: Berlin/Bonn
AREA: 356,950 sq km (Land area 349,270 sq km)
POPULATION: 82,300,000 people
POPULATION DENSITY: 236 people per sq km
POPULATION CHANGE: 0.5% per year
BIRTH RATE: 9 per 1,000 people
DEATH RATE: 11 per 1,000 people
LIFE EXPECTANCY: Males 73, females 79 years
INFANT MORTALITY: 6 per 1,000 live births
URBAN POPULATION: 87% of population
FERTILITY RATE: 1 child per female
AGE GROUPS: 0–14 yrs 16%, 15–59 yrs 79%, 60+ yrs 6%
ETHNIC GROUPS: German 93%, Turkish 2%, Yugoslav 1%, Italian 1%
LANGUAGES: *German*, Turkish, Serbo-Croat
RELIGIONS: Protestant 45%, Roman Catholic 37%, Muslim 2%
LAND USE: Arable 33%, grass 15%, forest 30%
EMPLOYMENT: Agric. 3%, ind. 39%, services 58%
ANNUAL INCOME: $27,510 per person, 1.9%
ORIGIN OF INCOME: Agriculture 1%, industry 38%, services 61%
ENERGY: Prod. 2.84 tonnes, consump. 5.89 tonnes
TRADE: $9,815 per person
CURRENCY: Deutschmark = 100 Pfennig
ROADS: 1,863 km per 1,000 sq km of land
RAILWAYS: 253 km per 1,000 sq km of land
POPULATION PER DOCTOR: 370 people
ADULT LITERACY: 99%
EDUCATIONAL EXPENDITURE: 5.4% of GNP
MILITARY EXPENDITURE: 2.4% of GNP
AID GIVEN: $81 per person

Ghana
CAPITAL CITY: Accra
AREA: 238,540 sq km (Land area 227,540 sq km)
POPULATION: 18,100,000 people
POPULATION DENSITY: 80 people per sq km
POPULATION CHANGE: 2.7% per year
BIRTH RATE: 34 per 1,000 people
DEATH RATE: 11 per 1,000 people
LIFE EXPECTANCY: Males 54, females 59 years
INFANT MORTALITY: 79 per 1,000 live births
URBAN POPULATION: 36% of population
FERTILITY RATE: 6 children per female
AGE GROUPS: 0–14 yrs 45%, 15–59 yrs 50%, 60+ yrs 5%
ETHNIC GROUPS: Akan 52%, Mossi 16%, Ewe 12%
LANGUAGES: *English*, Akan, Mossi, Ewe, Ga-Adangme, Gurma, Yoruba, Hausa
RELIGIONS: Protestant 28%, traditional beliefs 21%, Roman Catholic 19%, Muslim 16%
LAND USE: Arable 5%, grass 22%, forest 35%
EMPLOYMENT: Agric. 59%, ind. 11%, services 30%
ANNUAL INCOME: $390 per person, 1.5%
ORIGIN OF INCOME: Agriculture 48%, industry 17%, services 30%
ENERGY: Prod. 0.05 tonnes, consump. 0.14 tonnes
TRADE: $158 per person
CURRENCY: Cedi = 100 pesewas
ROADS: 161 km per 1,000 sq km of land
RAILWAYS: 4 km per 1,000 sq km of land
POPULATION PER DOCTOR: 25,000 people
ADULT LITERACY: 61%
EDUCATIONAL EXPENDITURE: 3.3% of GNP
MILITARY EXPENDITURE: 0.8% of GNP
AID RECEIVED: $38 per person

Gibraltar
BRITISH COLONY
AREA: 6.5 sq km
POPULATION: 28,000 people
POPULATION DENSITY: 2,800 people per sq km
POPULATION CHANGE: –1.0% per year
BIRTH RATE: 13 per 1,000 people
DEATH RATE: 9 per 1,000 people
LIFE EXPECTANCY: Males 75, females 81 years
INFANT MORTALITY: 7 per 1,000 live births
FERTILITY RATE: 3 children per female
ETHNIC GROUPS: English, Italian, Maltese, Spanish, Portuguese
LANGUAGES: English, Spanish
RELIGIONS: Roman Catholic 74%, Protestant 11%
EMPLOYMENT: Industry 27%, services 73%
ANNUAL INCOME: $7,500 per person, 5%
ENERGY: Consumption 0.79 tonnes per person
TRADE: $11,333 per person
CURRENCY: Gibraltar £ = 100 pence
ROADS: 4,300 km per 1,000 sq km of land

Greece
CAPITAL CITY: Athens
AREA: 131,990 sq km (Land area 128,900 sq km)
POPULATION: 10,600,000 people
POPULATION DENSITY: 82 people per sq km
POPULATION CHANGE: 0.8% per year
BIRTH RATE: 10 per 1,000 people
DEATH RATE: 10 per 1,000 people
LIFE EXPECTANCY: Males 76, females 81 years
INFANT MORTALITY: 7 per 1,000 live births
URBAN POPULATION: 65% of population
FERTILITY RATE: 1 child per female
AGE GROUPS: 0–14 yrs 20%, 15–59 yrs 61%, 60+ yrs 20%
ETHNIC GROUPS: Greek 96%, Macedonian 2%, Turkish 1%, Albanian, Slav
LANGUAGES: *Greek*
RELIGIONS: Greek Orthodox 97%, Muslim 2%
LAND USE: Arable 22%, grass 41%, forest 20%
EMPLOYMENT: Agric. 23%, ind. 27%, services 50%
ANNUAL INCOME: $8,210 per person, 1.2%
ORIGIN OF INCOME: Agriculture 18%, industry 32%, services 50%
ENERGY: Prod. 1.1 tonnes, consump. 3.24 tonnes
TRADE: $3,176 per person
CURRENCY: Drachma = 100 lepta
ROADS: 901 km per 1,000 sq km of land
RAILWAYS: 19 km per 1,000 sq km of land
POPULATION PER DOCTOR: 313 people
ADULT LITERACY: 94%
EDUCATIONAL EXPENDITURE: 3.0% of GNP
MILITARY EXPENDITURE: 5.6% of GNP

Greenland
SELF-GOVERNING DIVISION OF DENMARK
CAPITAL CITY: Nuuk (Godthåb)
AREA: 341,700 sq km
POPULATION: 57,000 people
POPULATION DENSITY: 0.2 people per sq km
POPULATION CHANGE: 0.3% per year
BIRTH RATE: 16 per 1,000 people
DEATH RATE: 7 per 1,000 people
LIFE EXPECTANCY: Males 65, females 73 years
INFANT MORTALITY: 23 per 1,000 live births
FERTILITY RATE: 2 children per female
ETHNIC GROUPS: Greenlander 86%, Danish 14%
LANGUAGES: *Inuktitut, Danish*
RELIGIONS: Lutheran 95%
LAND USE: Grass 1%
EMPLOYMENT: Agric. 15%, ind. 30%, services 55%
ANNUAL INCOME: $12,000 per person, 4.1%
ORIGIN OF INCOME: Agric. 30%
ENERGY: Consumption 4.0 tonnes per person
TRADE: $13,167 per person
CURRENCY: Danish currency
ROADS: 0.2 km per 1,000 sq km of land
POPULATION PER DOCTOR: 620 people
ADULT LITERACY: 100%

Grenada
CAPITAL CITY: St George's
AREA: 344 sq km
POPULATION: 99,000 people
POPULATION DENSITY: 291 people per sq km
POPULATION CHANGE: 2.2% per year
BIRTH RATE: 29 per 1,000 people
DEATH RATE: 6 per 1,000 people
LIFE EXPECTANCY: Males 69, females 74 years
INFANT MORTALITY: 12 per 1,000 live births
URBAN POPULATION: 33% of population
FERTILITY RATE: 3 children per female
AGE GROUPS: 0–14 yrs 38%, 15–59 yrs 51%, 60+ yrs 11%
ETHNIC GROUPS: Of African descent
LANGUAGES: *English*, Creole
RELIGIONS: Roman Catholic 53%, Protestant 25%
LAND USE: Arable 15%, grass 3%, forest 9%
EMPLOYMENT: Agric. 14%, ind. 18%, services 68%
ANNUAL INCOME: $2,980 per person, 3.9%
ORIGIN OF INCOME: Agriculture 14%, industry 19%, services 67%
ENERGY: Consumption 0.64 tonnes per person
TRADE: $1,600 per person
CURRENCY: East Caribbean $ = 100 cents
ROADS: 3,076 km per 1,000 sq km of land
POPULATION PER DOCTOR: 1,800 people
ADULT LITERACY: 98%
EDUCATIONAL EXPENDITURE: 4.6% of GNP
AID RECEIVED: $98 per person

Guadeloupe
OVERSEAS DEPARTMENT OF FRANCE
CAPITAL CITY: Basse-Terre
AREA: 1,710 sq km (Land area 1,690 sq km)
POPULATION: 440,000 people
POPULATION DENSITY: 260 people per sq km
POPULATION CHANGE: 3.6% per year
BIRTH RATE: 17 per 1,000 people
DEATH RATE: 6 per 1,000 people
LIFE EXPECTANCY: Males 75, females 81 years
INFANT MORTALITY: 8 per 1,000 live births
URBAN POPULATION: 51% of population
FERTILITY RATE: 2 children per female
AGE GROUPS: 0–14 yrs 27%, 15–59 yrs 61%, 60+ yrs 12%
ETHNIC GROUPS: Mixed (Black and White) 90%
LANGUAGES: *French*, Creole patois
RELIGIONS: Roman Catholic 88%
LAND USE: Arable 18%, grass 14%, forest 39%
EMPLOYMENT: Agric. 7%, ind. 12%, services 79%
ANNUAL INCOME: $9,500 per person
ENERGY: Consumption 1.25 tonnes per person
TRADE: $1,893 per person
CURRENCY: French currency
ROADS: 947 km per 1,000 sq km of land
POPULATION PER DOCTOR: 750 people
ADULT LITERACY: 90%
EDUCATIONAL EXPENDITURE: 14.3% of GNP

Guam
TERRITORY OF THE US
CAPITAL CITY: Agana
AREA: 541 sq km
POPULATION: 161,000 people
POPULATION DENSITY: 293 people per sq km
POPULATION CHANGE: 4.5% per year
BIRTH RATE: 23 per 1,000 people
DEATH RATE: 4 per 1,000 people
LIFE EXPECTANCY: Males 72, females 76 years
INFANT MORTALITY: 15 per 1,000 live births
FERTILITY RATE: 3 children per female
ETHNIC GROUPS: Chamorro 47%, Filipino 25%,
LANGUAGES: *English*, Chamorro
RELIGIONS: Roman Catholic 98%
LAND USE: Arable 11%, grass 15%, forest 18%
ANNUAL INCOME: $714,000 per person
ENERGY: Consumption 5.07 tonnes per person
TRADE: $5,416 per person
CURRENCY: US currency
ROADS: 1,225 km per 1,000 sq km of land
ADULT LITERACY: 96%

Guatemala
CAPITAL CITY: Guatemala City
AREA: 108,890 sq km
POPULATION: 11,250,000 people
POPULATION DENSITY: 104 people per sq km
POPULATION CHANGE: 2.9% per year
BIRTH RATE: 33 per 1,000 people
DEATH RATE: 7 per 1,000 people
LIFE EXPECTANCY: Males 63, females 68 years
INFANT MORTALITY: 49 per 1,000 live births
URBAN POPULATION: 42% of population
FERTILITY RATE: 5 children per female
AGE GROUPS: 0–14 yrs 46%, 15–59 yrs 49%, 60+ yrs 5%
ETHNIC GROUPS: Mayaquiche Indian 55%, Ladino (Mestizo) 42%
LANGUAGES: *Spanish*, Mayan languages
RELIGIONS: Roman Catholic 75%, Protestant 23%
LAND USE: Arable 13%, grass 13%, forest 33%
EMPLOYMENT: Agric. 50%, ind. 18%, services 32%
ANNUAL INCOME: $1,340 per person, 0.3%
ORIGIN OF INCOME: Agric. 25%, ind. 19%, services 55%

ENERGY: Prod. 0.07 tonnes, consump. 0.27 tonnes
TRADE: $399 per person
CURRENCY: Quetzal = 100 centavos
ROADS: 109 km per 1,000 sq km of land
RAILWAYS: 11 km per 1,000 sq km of land
POPULATION PER DOCTOR: 4,000 people
ADULT LITERACY: 54%
EDUCATIONAL EXPENDITURE: 1.4% of GNP
MILITARY EXPENDITURE: 1.1% of GNP
AID RECEIVED: $21 per person

Guinea
CAPITAL CITY: Conakry
AREA: 245,860 sq km
POPULATION: 7,450,000 people
POPULATION DENSITY: 30 people per sq km
POPULATION CHANGE: 3.8% per year
BIRTH RATE: 42 per 1,000 people
DEATH RATE: 18 per 1,000 people
LIFE EXPECTANCY: Males 43, females 48 years
INFANT MORTALITY: 132 per 1,000 live births
URBAN POPULATION: 30% of population
FERTILITY RATE: 7 children per female
AGE GROUPS: 0–14 yrs 47%, 15–59 yrs 49%, 60+ yrs 4%
ETHNIC GROUPS: Fulani 40%, Malinke 26%, Susu 11%
LANGUAGES: *French*, Fulani, Susu, Malinke
RELIGIONS: Muslim 85%, traditional beliefs 5%
LAND USE: Arable 2%, grass 22%, forest 59%
EMPLOYMENT: Agric. 78%, ind. 1%, services 21%
ANNUAL INCOME: $550 per person, 1.4%
ORIGIN OF INCOME: Agriculture 24%, industry 31%, services 45%
ENERGY: Consumption 0.08 tonnes per person
TRADE: $258 per person
CURRENCY: Guinean franc = 100 cauris
ROADS: 65 km per 1,000 sq km of land
RAILWAYS: 3 km per 1,000 sq km of land
POPULATION PER DOCTOR: 7,692 people
ADULT LITERACY: 33%
EDUCATIONAL EXPENDITURE: 2.2% of GNP
MILITARY EXPENDITURE: 1.3% of GNP
AID RECEIVED: $62 per person

Guinea-Bissau
CAPITAL CITY: Bissau
AREA: 36,120 sq km (Land area 28,120 sq km)
POPULATION: 1,150,000 people
POPULATION DENSITY: 41 people per sq km
POPULATION CHANGE: 2.6% per year
BIRTH RATE: 39 per 1,000 people
DEATH RATE: 16 per 1,000 people
LIFE EXPECTANCY: Males 47, females 50 years
INFANT MORTALITY: 114 per 1,000 live births
URBAN POPULATION: 22% of population
FERTILITY RATE: 6 children per female
AGE GROUPS: 0–14 yrs 41%, 15–59 yrs 53%, 60+ yrs 7%
ETHNIC GROUPS: Balante 39%, Fulani 23%, Malinke 12%, Mandyako 11%, Pepel 10%
LANGUAGES: *Portuguese*, Crioulo
RELIGIONS: Traditional beliefs 54%, Muslim 38%
LAND USE: Arable 11%, grass 38%, forest 38%
EMPLOYMENT: Agric. 82%, ind. 4%, services 14%
ANNUAL INCOME: $250 per person, 1.8%
ORIGIN OF INCOME: Agriculture 45%, industry 19%, services 36%
ENERGY: Consumption 0.10 tonnes per person
TRADE: $67 per person
CURRENCY: Peso = 100 centavos
ROADS: 148 km per 1,000 sq km of land
POPULATION PER DOCTOR: 6,000 people
ADULT LITERACY: 52%
EDUCATIONAL EXPENDITURE: 2.8% of GNP
MILITARY EXPENDITURE: 2.4% of GNP
AID RECEIVED: $113 per person

Guyana
CAPITAL CITY: Georgetown
AREA: 214,970 sq km (Land area 196,850 sq km)
POPULATION: 820,000 people
POPULATION DENSITY: 4 people per sq km
POPULATION CHANGE: 0.4% per year
BIRTH RATE: 19 per 1,000 people
DEATH RATE: 10 per 1,000 people
LIFE EXPECTANCY: Males 57, females 62 years
INFANT MORTALITY: 51 per 1,000 live births
URBAN POPULATION: 35% of population
FERTILITY RATE: 3 children per female
AGE GROUPS: 0–14 yrs 33%, 15–59 yrs 61%, 60+ yrs 6%
ETHNIC GROUPS: Asian Indian 49%, Black 36%, Mulatto 7%, Amerindian 7%
LANGUAGES: English, Creole, Amerindian languages
RELIGIONS: Hindu 34%, Protestant 34%, Roman Catholic 18%, Sunni Muslim 9%
LAND USE: Arable 2%, grass 6%, forest 83%
EMPLOYMENT: Agric. 27%, ind. 26%, services 47%
ANNUAL INCOME: $590 per person, 0.8%
ORIGIN OF INCOME: Agriculture 30%, industry 38%, services 32%
ENERGY: Consumption 0.49 tonnes per person
TRADE: $833 per person
CURRENCY: Guyanan $ = 100 cents

ROADS: 37 km per 1,000 sq km of land
RAILWAYS: 1 km per 1,000 sq km of land
POPULATION PER DOCTOR: 6,000 people
ADULT LITERACY: 98%
EDUCATIONAL EXPENDITURE: 4.7% of GNP
MILITARY EXPENDITURE: 1.0% of GNP
AID RECEIVED: $104 per person

Haiti
CAPITAL CITY: Port-au-Prince
AREA: 27,750 sq km
POPULATION: 7,400,000 people
POPULATION DENSITY: 269 people per sq km
POPULATION CHANGE: 1.8% per year
BIRTH RATE: 33 per 1,000 people
DEATH RATE: 15 per 1,000 people
LIFE EXPECTANCY: Males 47, females 52 years
INFANT MORTALITY: 102 per 1,000 live births
URBAN POPULATION: 32% of population
FERTILITY RATE: 5 children per female
AGE GROUPS: 0–14 yrs 40%, 15–59 yrs 54%, 60+ yrs 6%
ETHNIC GROUPS: Black 95%, Mulatto 5%
LANGUAGES: *Haitian Creole, French*
RELIGIONS: Roman Catholic 85%, Voodoo
LAND USE: Arable 20%, grass 18%, forest 1%
EMPLOYMENT: Agric. 68%, ind. 9%, services 23%
ANNUAL INCOME: $250 per person, –5.2%
ORIGIN OF INCOME: Agriculture 39%, industry 16%, services 46%
ENERGY: Consumption 0.05 tonnes
TRADE: $72 per person
CURRENCY: Gourde = 100 centimes
ROADS: 155 km per 1,000 sq km of land
POPULATION PER DOCTOR: 7,143 people
ADULT LITERACY: 43%
EDUCATIONAL EXPENDITURE: 1.8% of GNP
MILITARY EXPENDITURE: 2.1% of GNP
AID RECEIVED: $104 per person

Honduras
CAPITAL CITY: Tegucigalpa
AREA: 112,090 sq km
POPULATION: 6,300,000 people
POPULATION DENSITY: 56 people per sq km
POPULATION CHANGE: 3.0% per year
BIRTH RATE: 33 per 1,000 people
DEATH RATE: 6 per 1,000 people
LIFE EXPECTANCY: Males 66, females 71 years
INFANT MORTALITY: 40 per 1,000 live births
URBAN POPULATION: 48% of population
FERTILITY RATE: 5 children per female
AGE GROUPS: 0–14 yrs 45%, 15–59 yrs 50%, 60+ yrs 5%
ETHNIC GROUPS: Mestizo 90%, Amerinidian 7%, Black 2%, White 1%
LANGUAGES: *Spanish*, Black Carib (Garifuna)
RELIGIONS: Roman Catholic 85%, Protestant 10%
LAND USE: Arable 15%, grass 23%, forest 28%
EMPLOYMENT: Agric. 38%, ind. 15%, services 47%
ANNUAL INCOME: $600 per person, 0.2%
ORIGIN OF INCOME: Agriculture 20%, industry 30%, services 50%
ENERGY: Prod. 0.05 tonnes, consump. 0.27 tonnes
TRADE: $348 per person
CURRENCY: Lempira = 100 centavos
ROADS: 127 km per 1,000 sq km of land
RAILWAYS: 9 km per 1,000 sq km of land
POPULATION PER DOCTOR: 1,266 people
ADULT LITERACY: 71%
EDUCATIONAL EXPENDITURE: 4.6% of GNP
MILITARY EXPENDITURE: 1.5% of GNP
AID RECEIVED: $75 per person

Hungary
CAPITAL CITY: Budapest
AREA: 93,030 sq km
POPULATION: 10,150,000 people
POPULATION DENSITY: 110 people per sq km
POPULATION CHANGE: –0.6% per year
BIRTH RATE: 11 per 1,000 people
DEATH RATE: 15 per 1,000 people
LIFE EXPECTANCY: Males 64, females 74 years
INFANT MORTALITY: 12 per 1,000 live births
URBAN POPULATION: 64% of population
FERTILITY RATE: 2 children per female
AGE GROUPS: 0–14 yrs 20%, 15–59 yrs 61%, 60+ yrs 19%
ETHNIC GROUPS: Magyar 97%, German, Slovak
LANGUAGES: *Hungarian*, Slovak, German
RELIGIONS: Roman Catholic 68%, Protestant 25%
LAND USE: Arable 51%, grass 13%, forest 19%
EMPLOYMENT: Agric. 15%, ind. 31%, services 54%
ANNUAL INCOME: $4,120 per person, –1%
ORIGIN OF INCOME: Agriculture 6%, industry 28%, services 66%
ENERGY: Prod. 1.88 tonnes, consump. 3.34 tonnes
TRADE: $2,053 per person
CURRENCY: Forint = 100 fillér
ROADS: 325 km per 1,000 sq km of land
RAILWAYS: 143 km per 1,000 sq km of land
POPULATION PER DOCTOR: 312 people
ADULT LITERACY: 99%
EDUCATIONAL EXPENDITURE: 3.5% of GNP
MILITARY EXPENDITURE: 6.7% of GNP
AID RECEIVED: $7 per person

Iceland
CAPITAL CITY: Reykjavik
AREA: 103,000 sq km (Land area 100,250 sq km)
POPULATION: 275,000 people
POPULATION DENSITY: 3 people per sq km
POPULATION CHANGE: 1.2% per year
BIRTH RATE: 17 per 1,000 people
DEATH RATE: 6 per 1,000 people
LIFE EXPECTANCY: Males 78, females 83 years
INFANT MORTALITY: 4 per 1,000 live births
URBAN POPULATION: 92% of population
FERTILITY RATE: 2 children per female
AGE GROUPS: 0–14 yrs 25%, 15–59 yrs 61%, 60+ yrs 14%
ETHNIC GROUPS: Icelandic 97%
LANGUAGES: *Icelandic*
RELIGIONS: Lutheran 92%, Roman Catholic 1%
LAND USE: Grass 23%, forest 1%
EMPLOYMENT: Agric. 11%, ind. 26%, services 63%
ANNUAL INCOME: $24,950 per person, 0.3%
ORIGIN OF INCOME: Agriculture 12%, industry 28%, services 60%
ENERGY: Prod. 3.13 tonnes, consump. 6.22 tonnes
TRADE: $10,546 per person
CURRENCY: Króna = 100 aurar
ROADS: 123 km per 1,000 sq km of land
POPULATION PER DOCTOR: 425 people
ADULT LITERACY: 99%
EDUCATIONAL EXPENDITURE: 6.0% of GNP

India
CAPITAL CITY: New Delhi
AREA: 3,287,260 sq km (Land area 2,973,190 sq km)
POPULATION: 980,000,000 people
POPULATION DENSITY: 330 people per sq km
POPULATION CHANGE: 2.5% per year
BIRTH RATE: 25 per 1,000 people
DEATH RATE: 9 per 1,000 people
LIFE EXPECTANCY: Males 60, females 61 years
INFANT MORTALITY: 69 per 1,000 live births
URBAN POPULATION: 27% of population
FERTILITY RATE: 4 children per female
AGE GROUPS: 0–14 yrs 37%, 15–59 yrs 56%, 60+ yrs 7%
ETHNIC GROUPS: Indo-Aryan 72%, Dravidian 25%
LANGUAGES: *Hindi, English*, Telugu, Bengali, Marati, Urdu, Tamil, local languages
RELIGIONS: Hindu 80%, Muslim 11%, Christian 2%, Sikh 2%, Buddhist 1%
LAND USE: Arable 56%, grass 4%, forest 23%
EMPLOYMENT: Agric. 62%, ind. 11%, services 27%
ANNUAL INCOME: $340 per person, 3.1%
ORIGIN OF INCOME: Agriculture 31%, industry 27%, services 41%
ENERGY: Prod. 0.31 tonnes, consump. 0.35 tonnes
TRADE: $50 per person
CURRENCY: Rupee = 100 paisa
ROADS: 647 km per 1,000 sq km of land
RAILWAYS: 21 km per 1,000 sq km of land
POPULATION PER DOCTOR: 2,439 people
ADULT LITERACY: 50%
EDUCATIONAL EXPENDITURE: 3.5% of GNP
MILITARY EXPENDITURE: 2.5% of GNP
AID RECEIVED: $2 per person

Indonesia
CAPITAL CITY: Jakarta
AREA: 1,904,570 sq km (Land area 1,811,570 sq km)
POPULATION: 203,500,000 people
POPULATION DENSITY: 112 people per sq km
POPULATION CHANGE: 1.8% per year
BIRTH RATE: 23 per 1,000 people
DEATH RATE: 8 per 1,000 people
LIFE EXPECTANCY: Males 60, females 64 years
INFANT MORTALITY: 61 per 1,000 live births
URBAN POPULATION: 33% of population
FERTILITY RATE: 3 children per female
AGE GROUPS: 0–14 yrs 36%, 15–59 yrs 58%, 60+ yrs 6%
ETHNIC GROUPS: Javanese 39%, Sundanese 16%, Bahasa Indonesian 12%, Madurese 5%, over 300 others
LANGUAGES: *Bahasa Indonesia*, Javanese, Sundanese, Madurese, Dutch, over 200 others
RELIGIONS: Sunni Muslim 87%, Christian 10% (Protestant 6%), Hindu 2%, Buddhist 1%
LAND USE: Arable 9%, grass 7%, forest 60%
EMPLOYMENT: Agric. 56%, ind. 14%, services 30%
ANNUAL INCOME: $980 per person, 6%
ORIGIN OF INCOME: Agriculture 19%, industry 40%, services 42%
ENERGY: Prod. 1.05 tonnes, consump. 0.38 tonnes
TRADE: $293 per person
CURRENCY: Rupiah = 100 sen
ROADS: 176 km per 1,000 sq km of land
RAILWAYS: 4 km per 1,000 sq km of land
POPULATION PER DOCTOR: 7,143 people
ADULT LITERACY: 83%
EDUCATIONAL EXPENDITURE: 2.2% of GNP
MILITARY EXPENDITURE: 1.4% of GNP
AID RECEIVED: $7 per person

Iran

CAPITAL CITY: Tehran
AREA: 1,648,000 sq km
POPULATION: 69,500,000 people
POPULATION DENSITY: 42 people per sq km
POPULATION CHANGE: 3.5% per year
BIRTH RATE: 33 per 1,000 people
DEATH RATE: 6 per 1,000 people
LIFE EXPECTANCY: Males 66, females 69 years
INFANT MORTALITY: 51 per 1,000 live births
URBAN POPULATION: 58% of population
FERTILITY RATE: 5 children per female
AGE GROUPS: 0–14 yrs 45%, 15–59 yrs 50%, 60+ yrs 6%
ETHNIC GROUPS: Persian 46%, Azerbaijani 17%, Kurdish 9%, Gilaki 5%, Luri, Mazandarani, Baluchi, Arab
LANGUAGES: *Farsi (Persian)*, Kurdish, Baluchi, Luri, Gilaki, Mazandarami, Turkic languages
RELIGIONS: Shiite Muslim 91%, Sunni Muslim 6%
LAND USE: Arable 10%, grass 27%, forest 11%
EMPLOYMENT: Agric. 30%, ind. 26%, services 44%
ANNUAL INCOME: $4,800 per person, 0.5%
ORIGIN OF INCOME: Agriculture 21%, industry 36%, services 43%
ENERGY: Prod. 4.77 tonnes, consump. 1.66 tonnes
TRADE: $376 per person
CURRENCY: Rial = 100 dinars
ROADS: 93 km per 1,000 sq km of land
RAILWAYS: 3 km per 1,000 sq km of land
POPULATION PER DOCTOR: 3,300 people
ADULT LITERACY: 65%
EDUCATIONAL EXPENDITURE: 4.1% of GNP
MILITARY EXPENDITURE: 7.1% of GNP
AID RECEIVED: $3 per person

Iraq

CAPITAL CITY: Baghdad
AREA: 438,320 sq km
POPULATION: 22,500,000 people
POPULATION DENSITY: 51 people per sq km
POPULATION CHANGE: 2.5% per year
BIRTH RATE: 43 per 1,000 people
DEATH RATE: 6 per 1,000 people
LIFE EXPECTANCY: Males 66, females 69 years
INFANT MORTALITY: 58 per 1,000 live births
URBAN POPULATION: 73% of population
FERTILITY RATE: 6 children per female
AGE GROUPS: 0–14 yrs 46%, 15–59 yrs 49%, 60+ yrs 4%
ETHNIC GROUPS: Arab 77%, Kurd 19%, Turkmen 2%, Persian 2%
LANGUAGES: *Arabic*, Kurdish, Azerbaijani
RELIGIONS: Shiite Muslim 62%, Sunni Muslim 34%
LAND USE: Arable 12%, grass 9%, forest 4%
EMPLOYMENT: Agric. 14%, ind. 19%, services 67%
ANNUAL INCOME: $1,800 per person
ORIGIN OF INCOME: Agriculture 20%, industry 42%, services 38%
ENERGY: Prod. 2.11 tonnes, consump. 1.25 tonnes
TRADE: $1,496 per person
CURRENCY: Dinar = 20 dirhams = 1,000 fils
ROADS: 108 km per 1,000 sq km of land
RAILWAYS: 5 km per 1,000 sq km of land
POPULATION PER DOCTOR: 1,667 people
ADULT LITERACY: 55%
EDUCATIONAL EXPENDITURE: 5.1% of GNP
MILITARY EXPENDITURE: 21% of GNP
AID RECEIVED: $16 per person

Ireland

CAPITAL CITY: Dublin
AREA: 70,280 sq km (Land area 68,890 sq km)
POPULATION: 3,625,000 people
POPULATION DENSITY: 53 people per sq km
POPULATION CHANGE: 0.5% per year
BIRTH RATE: 13 per 1,000 people
DEATH RATE: 9 per 1,000 people
LIFE EXPECTANCY: Males 73, females 79 years
INFANT MORTALITY: 6 per 1,000 live births
URBAN POPULATION: 58% of population
FERTILITY RATE: 2 children per female
AGE GROUPS: 0–14 yrs 28%, 15–59 yrs 58%, 60+ yrs 14%
ETHNIC GROUPS: Irish 94%
LANGUAGES: *English, Irish*
RELIGIONS: Roman Catholic 93%, Anglican 3%
LAND USE: Arable 13%, grass 68%, forest 5%
EMPLOYMENT: Agric. 14%, ind. 29%, services 57%
ANNUAL INCOME: $14,710 per person, 5.2%
ORIGIN OF INCOME: Agriculture 8%, industry 10%, services 82%
ENERGY: Prod. 1.35 tonnes, consump. 4.0 tonnes
TRADE: $14,128 per person
CURRENCY: Punt = 100 pence
ROADS: 1,340 km per 1,000 sq km of land
RAILWAYS: 28 km per 1,000 sq km of land
POPULATION PER DOCTOR: 633 people
ADULT LITERACY: 99%
EDUCATIONAL EXPENDITURE: 5.9% of GNP
MILITARY EXPENDITURE: 1.2% of GNP
AID GIVEN: $35 per person

Israel

DATA INCLUDE WEST BANK AND GAZA STRIP
CAPITAL CITY: Jerusalem
AREA: 21,060 sq km (Land area 20,620 sq km)
POPULATION: 5,900,000 people
POPULATION DENSITY: 286 people per sq km
POPULATION CHANGE: 3.6% per year
BIRTH RATE: 20 per 1,000 people
DEATH RATE: 6 per 1,000 people
LIFE EXPECTANCY: Males 76, females 80 years
INFANT MORTALITY: 8 per 1,000 live births
URBAN POPULATION: 91% of population
FERTILITY RATE: 3 children per female
AGE GROUPS: 0–14 yrs 31%, 15–59 yrs 57%, 60+ yrs 12%
ETHNIC GROUPS: Jewish 81%, Arab 19%
LANGUAGES: *Hebrew, Arabic*, English, Yiddish
RELIGIONS: Jewish 81%, Muslim 14%, Christian 3%, Druze 2%
LAND USE: Arable 17%, grass 7%, forest 6%
EMPLOYMENT: Agric. 4%, ind. 22%, services 74%
ANNUAL INCOME: $15,920 per person, 2.5%
ORIGIN OF INCOME: Agriculture 7%, industry 24%, services 69%
ENERGY: Prod. 0.01 tonnes, consump. 3.27 tonnes
TRADE: $7,110 per person
CURRENCY: Shekel = 100 agorat
ROADS: 713 km per 1,000 sq km of land
RAILWAYS: 30 km per 1,000 sq km of land
POPULATION PER DOCTOR: 300 people
ADULT LITERACY: 95%
EDUCATIONAL EXPENDITURE: 6.0% of GNP
MILITARY EXPENDITURE: 11.1% of GNP
AID RECEIVED: $226 per person

Italy

CAPITAL CITY: Rome
AREA: 301,270 sq km (Land area 294,060 sq km)
POPULATION: 57,750,000 people
POPULATION DENSITY: 196 people per sq km
POPULATION CHANGE: 0.2% per year
BIRTH RATE: 10 per 1,000 people
DEATH RATE: 10 per 1,000 people
LIFE EXPECTANCY: Males 75, females 82 years
INFANT MORTALITY: 7 per 1,000 live births
URBAN POPULATION: 67% of population
FERTILITY RATE: 1 child per female
AGE GROUPS: 0–14 yrs 17%, 15–59 yrs 63%, 60+ yrs 20%
ETHNIC GROUPS: Italian 94%, Tirolean German, French, Greek, Albanian, Slovene, Ladino
LANGUAGES: *Italian*, German, French
RELIGIONS: Roman Catholic 83%
LAND USE: Arable 31%, grass 17%, forest 23%
EMPLOYMENT: Agric. 9%, ind. 32%, services 59%
ANNUAL INCOME: $19,020 per person, 1.7%
ORIGIN OF INCOME: Agriculture 3%, industry 32%, services 65%
ENERGY: Prod. 0.70 tonnes, consump. 4.02 tonnes
TRADE: $6,449 per person
CURRENCY: Lira = 100 centesimi
ROADS: 1,032 km per 1,000 sq km of land
RAILWAYS: 54 km per 1,000 sq km of land
POPULATION PER DOCTOR: 211 people
ADULT LITERACY: 97%
EDUCATIONAL EXPENDITURE: 4.1% of GNP
MILITARY EXPENDITURE: 2.0% of GNP
AID GIVEN: $37 per person

Ivory Coast (Côte d'Ivoire)

CAPITAL CITY: Yamoussoukro
AREA: 322,460 sq km (Land area 318,000 sq km)
POPULATION: 15,100,000 people
POPULATION DENSITY: 47 people per sq km
POPULATION CHANGE: 3.4% per year
BIRTH RATE: 42 per 1,000 people
DEATH RATE: 17 per 1,000 people
LIFE EXPECTANCY: Males 44, females 46 years
INFANT MORTALITY: 100 per 1,000 live births
URBAN POPULATION: 46% of population
FERTILITY RATE: 7 children per female
AGE GROUPS: 0–14 yrs 48%, 15–59 yrs 48%, 60+ yrs 4%
ETHNIC GROUPS: Akan 41%, Kru 18%, Voltaic 16%, Malinke 15%, Southern Mande 10%
LANGUAGES: *French*, Akan, Voltaic, Malinke
RELIGIONS: Traditional beliefs 44%, Christian 32%, Muslim 24%
LAND USE: Arable 8%, grass 41%, forest 22%
EMPLOYMENT: Agric. 65%, ind. 8%, services 27%
ANNUAL INCOME: $660 per person, –4.3%
ORIGIN OF INCOME: Agric. 37%, ind. 24%, services 39%
ENERGY: Prod. 0.05 tonnes, consump. 0.21 tonnes
TRADE: $443 per person
CURRENCY: CFA franc = 100 centimes
ROADS: 158 km per 1,000 sq km of land
RAILWAYS: 2 km per 1,000 sq km of land
POPULATION PER DOCTOR: 11,111 people
ADULT LITERACY: 37%
EDUCATIONAL EXPENDITURE: 7.2% of GNP
MILITARY EXPENDITURE: 0.8% of GNP
AID RECEIVED: $87 per person

Jamaica

CAPITAL CITY: Kingston
AREA: 10,990 sq km (Land area 10,830 sq km)
POPULATION: 2,600,000 people
POPULATION DENSITY: 240 people per sq km
POPULATION CHANGE: 0.8% per year
BIRTH RATE: 22 per 1,000 people
DEATH RATE: 6 per 1,000 people
LIFE EXPECTANCY: Males 73, females 78 years
INFANT MORTALITY: 15 per 1,000 live births
URBAN POPULATION: 53% of population
FERTILITY RATE: 2 children per female
AGE GROUPS: 0–14 yrs 33%, 15–59 yrs 58%, 60+ yrs 9%
ETHNIC GROUPS: Black 76%, Afro-European 15%, East Indian and Afro-East Indian 3%, White 5%
LANGUAGES: *English*, English Creole, Hindi
RELIGIONS: Protestant 70%, Roman Catholic 8%
LAND USE: Arable 14%, grass 24%, forest 17%
EMPLOYMENT: Agric. 26%, ind. 24%, services 50%
ANNUAL INCOME: $1,510 per person, 3.7%
ORIGIN OF INCOME: Agriculture 8%, industry 41%, services 57%
ENERGY: Prod. 0.01 tonnes, consump. 1.51 tonnes
TRADE: $1,317 per person
CURRENCY: Jamaican $ = 100 cents
ROADS: 1,518 km per 1,000 sq km of land
RAILWAYS: 19 km per 1,000 sq km of land
POPULATION PER DOCTOR: 7,143 people
ADULT LITERACY: 84%
EDUCATIONAL EXPENDITURE: 6.1% of GNP
MILITARY EXPENDITURE: 0.7% of GNP
AID RECEIVED: $43 per person

Japan

CAPITAL CITY: Tokyo
AREA: 377,800 sq km
POPULATION: 125,900,000 people
POPULATION DENSITY: 334 people per sq km
POPULATION CHANGE: 0.3% per year
BIRTH RATE: 10 per 1,000 people
DEATH RATE: 8 per 1,000 people
LIFE EXPECTANCY: Males 77, females 83 years
INFANT MORTALITY: 4 per 1,000 live births
URBAN POPULATION: 78% of population
FERTILITY RATE: 2 children per female
AGE GROUPS: 0–14 yrs 18%, 15–59 yrs 64%, 60+ yrs 17%
ETHNIC GROUPS: Japanese 99%, Korean, Chinese
LANGUAGES: *Japanese*, Korean, Chinese
RELIGIONS: Shinto 40%, Buddhist 38%, Christian 4%
LAND USE: Arable 11%, grass 2%, forest 67%
EMPLOYMENT: Agric. 7%, ind. 34%, services 59%
ANNUAL INCOME: $39,640 per person, 2.9%
ORIGIN OF INCOME: Agriculture 2%, industry 41%, services 57%
ENERGY: Prod. 0.86 tonnes, consump. 4.74 tonnes
TRADE: $4,849 per person
CURRENCY: Yen = 100 sen
ROADS: 3,018 km per 1,000 sq km of land
RAILWAYS: 54 km per 1,000 sq km of land
POPULATION PER DOCTOR: 600 people
ADULT LITERACY: 99%
EDUCATIONAL EXPENDITURE: 5.0% of GNP
MILITARY EXPENDITURE: 1% of GNP
AID GIVEN: $106 per person

Jordan

CAPITAL CITY: Amman
AREA: 89,210 sq km
POPULATION: 5,600,000 people
POPULATION DENSITY: 63 people per sq km
POPULATION CHANGE: 4.9% per year
BIRTH RATE: 36 per 1,000 people
DEATH RATE: 4 per 1,000 people
LIFE EXPECTANCY: Males 71, females 75 years
INFANT MORTALITY: 31 per 1,000 live births
URBAN POPULATION: 72% of population
FERTILITY RATE: 6 children per female
AGE GROUPS: 0–14 yrs 45%, 15–59 yrs 51%, 60+ yrs 4%
ETHNIC GROUPS: Arab 99%
LANGUAGES: *Arabic*
RELIGIONS: Sunni Muslim 93%, Christian 5%
LAND USE: Arable 4%, grass 9%, forest 1%
EMPLOYMENT: Agric. 10%, ind. 26%, services 64%
ANNUAL INCOME: $1,510 per person, –2.8%
ORIGIN OF INCOME: Agriculture 8%, industry 26%, services 66%
ENERGY: Prod. 0.01 tonnes, consump. 1.13 tonnes
TRADE: $969 per person
CURRENCY: Dinar = 1,000 fils
ROADS: 77 km per 1,000 sq km of land
RAILWAYS: 8 km per 1,000 sq km of land
POPULATION PER DOCTOR: 649 people
ADULT LITERACY: 84%
EDUCATIONAL EXPENDITURE: 5.9% of GNP
MILITARY EXPENDITURE: 11.2% of GNP
AID RECEIVED: $127 per person

Kazakstan

CAPITAL CITY: Aqmola
AREA: 2,717,300 sq km
POPULATION: 17,000,000 people
POPULATION DENSITY: 6 people per sq km
POPULATION CHANGE: 0.2% per year
BIRTH RATE: 19 per 1,000 people
DEATH RATE: 10 per 1,000 people
LIFE EXPECTANCY: Males 59, females 70 years
INFANT MORTALITY: 62 per 1,000 live births
URBAN POPULATION: 58% of population
FERTILITY RATE: 3 children per female
AGE GROUPS: 0–14 yrs 32%, 15–59 yrs 59%, 60+ yrs 9%
ETHNIC GROUPS: Kazak 41%, Russian 37%, Ukrainian 5%, German 5%
LANGUAGES: *Kazak*, Russian, German
RELIGIONS: Sunni Muslim 46%, Russian Orthodox 44%, other Christian 2%
LAND USE: Arable 13%, grass 69%, forest 6%
EMPLOYMENT: Agric. 20%, ind. 22%, services 58%
ANNUAL INCOME: $1,330 per person, –8.6%
ORIGIN OF INCOME: Agric. 29%, ind. 41%, services 30%
TRADE: $500 per person
CURRENCY: Tenge =100 rubles
ROADS: 59 km per 1,000 sq km of land
RAILWAYS: 8 km per 1,000 sq km of land
POPULATION PER DOCTOR: 250 people
ADULT LITERACY: 98%
MILITARY EXPENDITURE: 3.8% of GNP
AID RECEIVED: $2 per person

Kenya

CAPITAL CITY: Nairobi
AREA: 580,370 sq km (Land area 569,690 sq km)
POPULATION: 31,900,000 people
POPULATION DENSITY: 56 people per sq km
POPULATION CHANGE: 4.1% per year
BIRTH RATE: 32 per 1,000 people
DEATH RATE: 11 per 1,000 people
LIFE EXPECTANCY: Males 54, females 55 years
INFANT MORTALITY: 55 per 1,000 live births
URBAN POPULATION: 25% of population
FERTILITY RATE: 6 children per female
AGE GROUPS: 0–14 yrs 50%, 15–59 yrs 46%, 60+ yrs 4%
ETHNIC GROUPS: Kikuyu 18%, Luhya 12%, Luo 11%, Kamba 10%, Kalenjin 10%
LANGUAGES: *Swahili*, English, Kikuyu, over 200 tribal languages
RELIGIONS: Roman Catholic 29%, Protestant 21%, African indigenous 21%, Muslim 6%
LAND USE: Arable 3%, grass 67%, forest 4%
EMPLOYMENT: Agric. 81%, ind. 7%, services 12%
ANNUAL INCOME: $280 per person, 0.1%
ORIGIN OF INCOME: Agriculture 29%, industry 17%, services 54%
ENERGY: Prod. 0.03 tonnes, consump. 0.11 tonnes
TRADE: $110 per person
CURRENCY: Shilling = 100 cents
ROADS: 111 km per 1,000 sq km of land
RAILWAYS: 5 km per 1,000 sq km of land
POPULATION PER DOCTOR: 10,000 people
ADULT LITERACY: 75%
EDUCATIONAL EXPENDITURE: 6.8% of GNP
MILITARY EXPENDITURE: 2.8% of GNP
AID RECEIVED: $42 per person

Kiribati

CAPITAL CITY: Tarawa
AREA: 728 sq km
POPULATION: 85,000 people
POPULATION DENSITY: 116 people per sq km
POPULATION CHANGE: 3.7% per year
BIRTH RATE: 27 per 1,000 people
DEATH RATE: 8 per 1,000 people
LIFE EXPECTANCY: Males 61, females 64 years
INFANT MORTALITY: 51 per 1,000 live births
URBAN POPULATION: 39% of population
FERTILITY RATE: 4 children per female
AGE GROUPS: 0–14 yrs 39%, 15–59 yrs 55%, 60+ yrs 6%
ETHNIC GROUPS: Micronesian
LANGUAGES: *English*, Gilbertese
RELIGIONS: Roman Catholic 53%, Protestant 51%
LAND USE: Forest 3%
EMPLOYMENT: Agric. 71%, ind. 8%, services 21%
ANNUAL INCOME: $710 per person, 1.3%
ORIGIN OF INCOME: Agriculture 25%, industry 8%, services 68%
ENERGY: Consumption 0.14 tonnes
TRADE: $600 per person
CURRENCY: Australian currency
ROADS: 877 km per 1,000 sq km of land
POPULATION PER DOCTOR: 5,000 people
ADULT LITERACY: 90%
EDUCATIONAL EXPENDITURE: 6.5% of GNP
AID RECEIVED: $3,000 per person

Korea, North

CAPITAL CITY: Pyongyang
AREA: 120,540 sq km
POPULATION: 24,500,000 people
POPULATION DENSITY: 203 people per sq km
POPULATION CHANGE: 1.7% per year
BIRTH RATE: 22 per 1,000 people
DEATH RATE: 5 per 1,000 people
LIFE EXPECTANCY: Males 68, females 74 years
INFANT MORTALITY: 25 per 1,000 live births
URBAN POPULATION: 61% of population
FERTILITY RATE: 2 children per female
AGE GROUPS: 0–14 yrs 29%, 15–59 yrs 65%, 60+ yrs 7%
ETHNIC GROUPS: Korean 99%
LANGUAGES: *Korean*

RELIGIONS: Traditional beliefs 16%, Chondogyo 14%, Buddhist 2%, Christian 1%
LAND USE: Arable 14%, forest 74%
EMPLOYMENT: Agric. 43%, ind. 30%, services 27%
ANNUAL INCOME: $1,000 per person, −8%
ENERGY: Prod. 3.86 tonnes, consump. 4.26 tonnes
TRADE: $159 per person
CURRENCY: North Korean won = 100 chon
ROADS: 249 km per 1,000 sq km of land
RAILWAYS: 71 km per 1,000 sq km of land
POPULATION PER DOCTOR: 400 people
ADULT LITERACY: 95%
EDUCATIONAL EXPENDITURE: 3.7% of GNP
MILITARY EXPENDITURE: 25.7% of GNP

Korea, South
CAPITAL CITY: Seoul
AREA: 99,020 sq km
POPULATION: 46,050,000 people
POPULATION DENSITY: 466 people per sq km
POPULATION CHANGE: 1.1% per year
BIRTH RATE: 16 per 1,000 people
DEATH RATE: 6 per 1,000 people
LIFE EXPECTANCY: Males 70, females 78 years
INFANT MORTALITY: 8 per 1,000 live births
URBAN POPULATION: 75% of population
FERTILITY RATE: 2 children per female
AGE GROUPS: 0–14 yrs 26%, 15–59 yrs 67%, 60+ yrs 8%
ETHNIC GROUPS: Korean 99%
LANGUAGES: Korean
RELIGIONS: Buddhist 28%, Protestant 19%, Roman Catholic 6%, Confucian 1%
LAND USE: Arable 19%, grass 1%, forest 65%
EMPLOYMENT: Agric. 17%, ind. 36%, services 47%
ANNUAL INCOME: $9,700 per person, 7.6%
ORIGIN OF INCOME: Agric. 7%, ind. 44%, services 50%
ENERGY: Prod. 0.67 tonnes, consump. 3.19 tonnes
TRADE: $3,767 per person
CURRENCY: South Korean won = 100 chon
ROADS: 798 km per 1,000 sq km of land
RAILWAYS: 66 km per 1,000 sq km of land
POPULATION PER DOCTOR: 1,205 people
ADULT LITERACY: 97%
EDUCATIONAL EXPENDITURE: 3.6% of GNP
MILITARY EXPENDITURE: 3.8% of GNP

Kuwait
CAPITAL CITY: Kuwait City
AREA: 17,820 sq km
POPULATION: 2,050,000 people
POPULATION DENSITY: 115 people per sq km
POPULATION CHANGE: 4.6% per year
BIRTH RATE: 20 per 1,000 people
DEATH RATE: 2 per 1,000 people
LIFE EXPECTANCY: Males 74, females 79 years
INFANT MORTALITY: 11 per 1,000 live births
URBAN POPULATION: 97% of population
FERTILITY RATE: 3 children per female
AGE GROUPS: 0–14 yrs 36%, 15–59 yrs 62%, 60+ yrs 3%
ETHNIC GROUPS: Kuwaiti Arab 44%, non-Kuwaiti Arab 36%, various Asian 20%
LANGUAGES: Arabic, Kurdish, Farsi (Persian)
RELIGIONS: Muslim 90% (Sunni 63%), Christian 8%, Hindu 2%
LAND USE: Grass 8%
EMPLOYMENT: Ind. 26%, services 73%
ANNUAL INCOME: $17,390 per person, 0.9%
ORIGIN OF INCOME: Ind. 55%, services 45%
ENERGY: Prod. 52.38 tonnes, consump. 4.04 tonnes
TRADE: $12,009 per person
CURRENCY: Dinar = 1,000 fils
ROADS: 240 km per 1,000 sq km of land
POPULATION PER DOCTOR: 600 people
ADULT LITERACY: 77%
EDUCATIONAL EXPENDITURE: 5% of GNP
MILITARY EXPENDITURE: 62% of GNP

Kyrgyzstan
CAPITAL CITY: Bishkek
AREA: 198,500 sq km
POPULATION: 4,650,000 people
POPULATION DENSITY: 24 people per sq km
POPULATION CHANGE: 0.8% per year
BIRTH RATE: 26 per 1,000 people
DEATH RATE: 9 per 1,000 people
LIFE EXPECTANCY: Males 59, females 69 years
INFANT MORTALITY: 77 per 1,000 live births
URBAN POPULATION: 40% of population
FERTILITY RATE: 4 children per female
AGE GROUPS: 0–14 yrs 39%, 15–59 yrs 53%, 60+ yrs 8%
ETHNIC GROUPS: Kyrgyz 53%, Russian 22%, Uzbek 13%, Ukrainian 3%, German 2%
LANGUAGES: Kyrgyz, Russian, Uzbek
RELIGIONS: Sunni Muslim 70%, Russian Orthodox
LAND USE: Arable 14%, grass 85%
EMPLOYMENT: Agric. 16%, ind. 24%, services 60%
ANNUAL INCOME: $700 per person, −6.9%
ORIGIN OF INCOME: Agriculture 44%, industry 35%, services 21%
ENERGY: Prod. 0.80 tonnes, consump. 1.77 tonnes
TRADE: $1641 per person
CURRENCY: Som = 100 tyiyn

ROADS: 148 km per 1,000 sq km of land
RAILWAYS: 2 km per 1,000 sq km of land
POPULATION PER DOCTOR: 300 people
ADULT LITERACY: 97%
MILITARY EXPENDITURE: 0.7% of GNP
AID RECEIVED: $19 per person

Laos
CAPITAL CITY: Vientiane (Viangchan)
AREA: 236,800 sq km (Land area 230,800 sq km)
POPULATION: 5,200,000 people
POPULATION DENSITY: 23 people per sq km
POPULATION CHANGE: 3.3% per year
BIRTH RATE: 41 per 1,000 people
DEATH RATE: 13 per 1,000 people
LIFE EXPECTANCY: Males 52, females 55 years
INFANT MORTALITY: 94 per 1,000 live births
URBAN POPULATION: 22% of population
FERTILITY RATE: 7 children per female
AGE GROUPS: 0–14 yrs 44%, 15–59 yrs 52%, 60+ yrs 5%
ETHNIC GROUPS: Lao 67%, Palaung-Wa 12%, Thai 8%, Man 5%
LANGUAGES: Lao, Khmer, Tai, Miao
RELIGIONS: Buddhist 58%, tribal religions 34%, Christian 2%, Muslim 1%
LAND USE: Arable 3%, grass 3%, forest 54%
EMPLOYMENT: Agric. 76%, ind. 7%, services 17%
ANNUAL INCOME: $350 per person, 2.7%
ORIGIN OF INCOME: Agriculture 51%, industry 18%, services 31%
ENERGY: Prod. 0.02 tonnes, consump. 0.04 tonnes
TRADE: $91 per person
CURRENCY: Kip = 100 at
ROADS: 61 km per 1,000 sq km of land
POPULATION PER DOCTOR: 4,545 people
ADULT LITERACY: 54%
EDUCATIONAL EXPENDITURE: 1.1% of GNP
MILITARY EXPENDITURE: 6.1% of GNP
AID RECEIVED: $66 per person

Latvia
CAPITAL CITY: Riga
AREA: 64,500 sq km (Land area 62,050 sq km)
POPULATION: 2,450,000 people
POPULATION DENSITY: 38 people per sq km
POPULATION CHANGE: −1.3% per year
BIRTH RATE: 12 per 1,000 people
DEATH RATE: 15 per 1,000 people
LIFE EXPECTANCY: Males 61, females 73 years
INFANT MORTALITY: 21 per 1,000 live births
URBAN POPULATION: 72% of population
FERTILITY RATE: 2 children per female
AGE GROUPS: 0–14 yrs 22%, 15–59 yrs 60%, 60+ yrs 18%
ETHNIC GROUPS: Latvian 54%, Russian 33%, Belarusian 4%, Ukrainian 3%, Polish 2%
LANGUAGES: Latvian, Russian
RELIGIONS: Roman Catholic 25%, Lutheran 20%, Russian Orthodox, Jewish
LAND USE: Arable 68%, grass 32%
EMPLOYMENT: Agric. 9%, ind. 33%, services 58%
ANNUAL INCOME: $2,270 per person, −6.6%
ORIGIN OF INCOME: Agriculture 15%, industry 32%, services 54%
ENERGY: Prod. 0.17 tonnes, consump. 3.24 tonnes
TRADE: $2,970 per person
CURRENCY: Lats = 100 santimi
ROADS: 1,009 km per 1,000 sq km of land
RAILWAYS: 38 km per 1,000 sq km of land
POPULATION PER DOCTOR: 280 people
ADULT LITERACY: 99%
MILITARY EXPENDITURE: 0.5% of GNP
AID RECEIVED: $14 per person

Lebanon
CAPITAL CITY: Beirut
AREA: 10,400 sq km (Land area 10,230 sq km)
POPULATION: 3,200,000 people
POPULATION DENSITY: 313 people per sq km
POPULATION CHANGE: 2.5% per year
BIRTH RATE: 28 per 1,000 people
DEATH RATE: 6 per 1,000 people
LIFE EXPECTANCY: Males 68, females 73 years
INFANT MORTALITY: 35 per 1,000 live births
URBAN POPULATION: 87% of population
FERTILITY RATE: 3 children per female
AGE GROUPS: 0–14 yrs 36%, 15–59 yrs 56%, 60+ yrs 8%
ETHNIC GROUPS: Lebanese, Palestinian, Armenian
LANGUAGES: Arabic, French, English, Armenian
RELIGIONS: Maronite Christian 35%, Shiite Muslim 34%, Sunni Muslim 23%, Druze 7%
LAND USE: Arable 21%, grass 1%, forest 8%
EMPLOYMENT: Agric. 14%, ind. 27%, services 59%
ANNUAL INCOME: $2,660 per person, 2.7%
ORIGIN OF INCOME: Agriculture 10%, industry 21%, services 69%
ENERGY: Prod. 0.02 tonnes, consump. 1.78 tonnes
TRADE: $1,624 per person
CURRENCY: Lebanese £ = 100 piastres
ROADS: 720 km per 1,000 sq km of land
RAILWAYS: 22 km per 1,000 sq km of land
POPULATION PER DOCTOR: 413 people
ADULT LITERACY: 91%

EDUCATIONAL EXPENDITURE: 2.0% of GNP
MILITARY EXPENDITURE: 5% of GNP
AID RECEIVED: $48 per person

Lesotho
CAPITAL CITY: Maseru
AREA: 30,350 sq km
POPULATION: 2,100,000 people
POPULATION DENSITY: 69 people per sq km
POPULATION CHANGE: 2.7% per year
BIRTH RATE: 32 per 1,000 people
DEATH RATE: 14 per 1,000 people
LIFE EXPECTANCY: Males 49, females 54 years
INFANT MORTALITY: 80 per 1,000 live births
URBAN POPULATION: 23% of population
FERTILITY RATE: 5 children per female
AGE GROUPS: 0–14 yrs 43%, 15–59 yrs 51%, 60+ yrs 6%
ETHNIC GROUPS: Basotho 95%, Zulu
LANGUAGES: Sesotho, English, Zulu
RELIGIONS: Christian 93% (Roman Catholic 44%)
LAND USE: Arable 11%, grass 66%
EMPLOYMENT: Agric. 23%, ind. 33%, services 44%
ANNUAL INCOME: $770 per person, 1.5%
ORIGIN OF INCOME: Agriculture 10%, industry 47%, services 43%
TRADE: $423 per person
CURRENCY: Loti = 100 lisente
ROADS: 175 km per 1,000 sq km of land
POPULATION PER DOCTOR: 25,000 people
ADULT LITERACY: 69%
EDUCATIONAL EXPENDITURE: 3.8% of GNP
MILITARY EXPENDITURE: 5.3% of GNP
AID RECEIVED: $57 per person

Liberia
CAPITAL CITY: Monrovia
AREA: 97,750 sq km (Land area 96,750 sq km)
POPULATION: 2,950,000 people
POPULATION DENSITY: 30 people per sq km
POPULATION CHANGE: 2.9% per year
BIRTH RATE: 42 per 1,000 people
DEATH RATE: 12 per 1,000 people
LIFE EXPECTANCY: Males 56, females 62 years
INFANT MORTALITY: 106 per 1,000 live births
URBAN POPULATION: 45% of population
FERTILITY RATE: 7 children per female
AGE GROUPS: 0–14 yrs 45%, 15–59 yrs 49%, 60+ yrs 5%
ETHNIC GROUPS: Kpelle 19%, Bassa 14%, Grebo 9%, Gio 8%, Kru 7%, Mano 7%
LANGUAGES: English, Mande, Mel, Kwa
RELIGIONS: Christian 68%, Sunni Muslim 14%, traditional beliefs 18%
LAND USE: Arable 1%, grass 59%, forest 18%
EMPLOYMENT: Agric. 75%, ind. 9%, services 16%
ANNUAL INCOME: $850 per person, 1.5%
ORIGIN OF INCOME: Agriculture 37%, industry 28%, services 35%
ENERGY: Prod. 0.01 tonnes, consump. 0.06 tonnes
TRADE: $285 per person
CURRENCY: Liberian $ = 100 cents
ROADS: 45 km per 1,000 sq km of land
RAILWAYS: 5 km per 1,000 sq km of land
POPULATION PER DOCTOR: 9,250 people
ADULT LITERACY: 35%
EDUCATIONAL EXPENDITURE: 5.7% of GNP
MILITARY EXPENDITURE: 4.8% of GNP
AID RECEIVED: $23 per person

Libya
CAPITAL CITY: Tripoli
AREA: 1,759,540 sq km
POPULATION: 5,500,000 people
POPULATION DENSITY: 3 people per sq km
POPULATION CHANGE: 2.8% per year
BIRTH RATE: 44 per 1,000 people
DEATH RATE: 7 per 1,000 people
LIFE EXPECTANCY: Males 63, females 67 years
INFANT MORTALITY: 58 per 1,000 live births
URBAN POPULATION: 86% of population
FERTILITY RATE: 6 children per female
AGE GROUPS: 0–14 yrs 46%, 15–59 yrs 50%, 60+ yrs 4%
ETHNIC GROUPS: Arab-Berber 89%
LANGUAGES: Arabic, Berber
RELIGIONS: Sunni Muslim 97%
LAND USE: Arable 1%, grass 8%
EMPLOYMENT: Agric. 20%, ind. 30%, services 50%
ANNUAL INCOME: $7,000 per person, 1%
ORIGIN OF INCOME: Agriculture 6%, industry 50%, services 44%
ENERGY: Prod. 22.52 tonnes, consump. 3.46 tonnes
TRADE: $3,827 per person
CURRENCY: Dinar = 1,000 dirhams
ROADS: 46 km per 1,000 sq km of land
POPULATION PER DOCTOR: 962 people
ADULT LITERACY: 72%
EDUCATIONAL EXPENDITURE: 9.6% of GNP
MILITARY EXPENDITURE: 6.3% of GNP

Liechtenstein
CAPITAL CITY: Vaduz
AREA: 157 sq km
POPULATION: 32,000 people
POPULATION DENSITY: 200 people per sq km

POPULATION CHANGE: 1.9% per year
BIRTH RATE: 11 per 1,000 people
DEATH RATE: 7 per 1,000 people
LIFE EXPECTANCY: Males 76, females 82 years
INFANT MORTALITY: 5 per 1,000 live births
URBAN POPULATION: 21% of population
FERTILITY RATE: 2 children per female
ETHNIC GROUPS: Alemannic 95%
LANGUAGES: German
RELIGIONS: Roman Catholic 81%, Protestant 7%
LAND USE: Arable 25%, grass 38%, forest 19%
EMPLOYMENT: Agric. 2%, ind. 39%, services 59%
ANNUAL INCOME: $34,000 per person
CURRENCY: Swiss currency
ROADS: 2,019 km per 1,000 sq km of land
RAILWAYS: 119 km per 1,000 sq km of land
POPULATION PER DOCTOR: 950people
ADULT LITERACY: 99%

Lithuania
CAPITAL CITY: Vilnius
AREA: 65,200 sq km
POPULATION: 3,710,000 people
POPULATION DENSITY: 57 people per sq km
POPULATION CHANGE: −0.1% per year
BIRTH RATE: 14 per 1,000 people
DEATH RATE: 13 per 1,000 people
LIFE EXPECTANCY: Males 63, females 74 years
INFANT MORTALITY: 16 per 1,000 live births
URBAN POPULATION: 71% of population
FERTILITY RATE: 2 children per female
AGE GROUPS: 0–14 yrs 23%, 15–59 yrs 62%, 60+ yrs 15%
ETHNIC GROUPS: Lithuanian 81%, Russian 9%, Polish 7%, Belarusian 2%
LANGUAGES: Lithuanian, Russian, Polish
RELIGIONS: Roman Catholic 80%, Lutheran
LAND USE: Arable 35%, grass 17%, forest 28%
EMPLOYMENT: Agric. 10%, ind. 33%, services 57%
ANNUAL INCOME: $1,900 per person, −11.7%
ORIGIN OF INCOME: Agriculture 21%, industry 41%, services 38%
ENERGY: Prod. 1.50 tonnes, consump. 4.16 tonnes
TRADE: $3,219 per person
CURRENCY: Litas = 100 centai
ROADS: 941 km per 1,000 sq km of land
RAILWAYS: 46 km per 1,000 sq km of land
POPULATION PER DOCTOR: 230 people
ADULT LITERACY: 98%
MILITARY EXPENDITURE: 0.7% of GNP

Luxembourg
CAPITAL CITY: Luxembourg
AREA: 2,590 sq km
POPULATION: 425,000 people
POPULATION DENSITY: 164 people per sq km
POPULATION CHANGE: 1.9% per year
BIRTH RATE: 13 per 1,000 people
DEATH RATE: 8 per 1,000 people
LIFE EXPECTANCY: Males 76, females 82 years
INFANT MORTALITY: 5 per 1,000 live births
URBAN POPULATION: 88% of population
FERTILITY RATE: 2 children per female
AGE GROUPS: 0–14 yrs 17%, 15–59 yrs 64%, 60+ yrs 19%
ETHNIC GROUPS: Luxembourger 70%, Portuguese 11%, Italian 5%, French 4%, German 3%
LANGUAGES: Luxembourgian, French, German
RELIGIONS: Roman Catholic 94%
LAND USE: Arable 22%, grass 27%, forest 34%
EMPLOYMENT: Agric. 3%, ind. 31%, services 66%
ANNUAL INCOME: $41,210 per person, 1%
ORIGIN OF INCOME: Agriculture 1%, industry 34%, services 65%
ENERGY: Prod. 0.19 tonnes, consump. 14 tonnes
TRADE: $36,903 per person
CURRENCY: Luxembourg franc = 100 centimes
ROADS: 1,990 km per 1,000 sq km of land
RAILWAYS: 105 km per 1,000 sq km of land
POPULATION PER DOCTOR: 500 people
ADULT LITERACY: 99%
EDUCATIONAL EXPENDITURE: 5.8% of GNP
MILITARY EXPENDITURE: 1.2% of GNP
AID GIVEN: $148 per person

Macau
OVERSEAS TERRITORY OF PORTUGAL
AREA: 16 sq km
POPULATION: 450,000 people
POPULATION DENSITY: 22,500 people per sq km
POPULATION CHANGE: −0.9% per year
BIRTH RATE: 14 per 1,000 people
DEATH RATE: 4 per 1,000 people
LIFE EXPECTANCY: Males 78, females 83 years
INFANT MORTALITY: 5 per 1,000 live births
URBAN POPULATION: 99% of population
FERTILITY RATE: 2 children per female
AGE GROUPS: 0–14 yrs 24%, 15–59 yrs 65%, 60+ yrs 11%
ETHNIC GROUPS: Chinese 95%, Portuguese 3%
LANGUAGES: Cantonese, Portuguese
RELIGIONS: Buddhist 45%, Roman Catholic 7%
EMPLOYMENT: Industry 41%, services 59%
ANNUAL INCOME: $16,000 per person, 12%
ORIGIN OF INCOME: Agriculture 1%, industry 34%, services 65%

Macau continued

ENERGY: Consumption 1.06 tonnes per person
TRADE: $9,177 per person
CURRENCY: Pataca = 100 avos
ROADS: 4,850 km per 1,000 sq km of land
POPULATION PER DOCTOR: 800 people
ADULT LITERACY: 90%

Macedonia

CAPITAL CITY: Skopje
AREA: 25,710 sq km (Land area 25,430 sq km)
POPULATION: 2,150,000 people
POPULATION DENSITY: 86 people per sq km
POPULATION CHANGE: 0.9% per year
BIRTH RATE: 13 per 1,000 people
DEATH RATE: 9 per 1,000 people
LIFE EXPECTANCY: Males 70, females 74 years
INFANT MORTALITY: 29 per 1,000 live births
FERTILITY RATE: 2 children per female
URBAN POPULATION: 60% of population
ETHNIC GROUPS: Macedonian 65%, Albanian 21%
LANGUAGES: *Macedonian*, Albanian, Turkish, Serbo-Croat
RELIGIONS: Orthodox 67%, Sunni Muslim 30%
LAND USE: Arable 16%, grass 26%, forest 37%
EMPLOYMENT: Agric. 5%, ind. 33%, services 62%
ANNUAL INCOME: $860 per person, −15%
ORIGIN OF INCOME: Agriculture 17%, industry 60%, services 23%
ENERGY: Prod. 0.04 tonnes, consump. 0.98 tonnes
TRADE: $833 per person
CURRENCY: Dinar = 100 paras
ROADS: 338 km per 1,000 sq km of land
RAILWAYS: 37 km per 1,000 sq km of land
POPULATION PER DOCTOR: 425 people
ADULT LITERACY: 90%

Madagascar

CAPITAL CITY: Antananarivo
AREA: 587,040 sq km
POPULATION: 15,500,000 people
POPULATION DENSITY: 27 people per sq km
POPULATION CHANGE: 4.8% per year
BIRTH RATE: 42 per 1,000 people
DEATH RATE: 14 per 1,000 people
LIFE EXPECTANCY: Males 51, females 54 years
INFANT MORTALITY: 92 per 1,000 live births
URBAN POPULATION: 27% of population
FERTILITY RATE: 6 children per female
AGE GROUPS: 0–14 yrs 45%, 15–59 yrs 50%, 60+ yrs 5%
ETHNIC GROUPS: Merina 26%, Betsimisaraka 15%, Betsileo 12%
LANGUAGES: *Malagasy, French*, English
RELIGIONS: Traditional beliefs 47%, Protestant 25%, Roman Catholic 25%, Muslim 2%
LAND USE: Arable 4%, grass 58%, forest 27%
EMPLOYMENT: Agric. 81%, ind. 6%, services 13%
ANNUAL INCOME: $230 per person, −2%
ORIGIN OF INCOME: Agriculture 34%, industry 14%, services 52%
ENERGY: Consumption 0.04 tonnes per person
TRADE: $52 per person
CURRENCY: Malagasy franc = 100 centimes
ROADS: 60 km per 1,000 sq km of land
RAILWAYS: 2 km per 1,000 sq km of land
POPULATION PER DOCTOR: 8,333 people
ADULT LITERACY: 81%
EDUCATIONAL EXPENDITURE: 1.5% of GNP
MILITARY EXPENDITURE: 1.1% of GNP
AID RECEIVED: $23 per person

Madeira

PORTUGUESE AUTONOMOUS REGION
CAPITAL CITY: Funchal
AREA: 813 sq km
POPULATION: 300,000 people
POPULATION DENSITY: 369 people per sq km

Malawi

CAPITAL CITY: Lilongwe
AREA: 118,480 sq km (Land area 94,080 sq km)
POPULATION: 10,250,000 people
POPULATION DENSITY: 109 people per sq km
POPULATION CHANGE: 3.1% per year
BIRTH RATE: 41 per 1,000 people
DEATH RATE: 25 per 1,000 people
LIFE EXPECTANCY: Males 35, females 36 years
INFANT MORTALITY: 139 per 1,000 live births
URBAN POPULATION: 13% of population
FERTILITY RATE: 7 children per female
AGE GROUPS: 0–14 yrs 49%, 15–59 yrs 47%, 60+ yrs 4%
ETHNIC GROUPS: Maravi 58%, Lomwe 18%, Yao 13%, Ngoni 7%
LANGUAGES: *English*, Chichewa, Yao
RELIGIONS: Protestant (Presbyterian) 49%, Roman Catholic 19%, Muslim 19%, animist 10%
LAND USE: Arable 18%, grass 20%, forest 36%
EMPLOYMENT: Agric. 87%, ind. 5%, services 18%
ANNUAL INCOME: $170 per person, −0.7%
ORIGIN OF INCOME: Agriculture 39%, industry 18%, services 43%
ENERGY: Prod. 0.01 tonnes, consump. 0.04 tonnes
TRADE: $95 per person
CURRENCY: Kwacha = 100 tambala

ROADS: 290 km per 1,000 sq km of land
RAILWAYS: 8 km per 1,000 sq km of land
POPULATION PER DOCTOR: 50,000 people
ADULT LITERACY: 54%
EDUCATIONAL EXPENDITURE: 3.4% of GNP
MILITARY EXPENDITURE: 1.4% of GNP
AID RECEIVED: $40 per person

Malaysia

CAPITAL CITY: Kuala Lumpur
AREA: 329,750 sq km
POPULATION: 20,900,000 people
POPULATION DENSITY: 64 people per sq km
POPULATION CHANGE: 2.2% per year
BIRTH RATE: 26 per 1,000 people
DEATH RATE: 5 per 1,000 people
LIFE EXPECTANCY: Males 67, females 73 years
INFANT MORTALITY: 23 per 1,000 live births
URBAN POPULATION: 52% of population
FERTILITY RATE: 4 children per female
AGE GROUPS: 0–14 yrs 38%, 15–59 yrs 56%, 60+ yrs 6%
ETHNIC GROUPS: Malay 62%, Chinese 30%, Indian 8%
LANGUAGES: *Malay*, Chinese, Tamil, Iban, Dusan, English
RELIGIONS: Sunni Muslim 53%, Buddhist 17%, Chinese folk religionist 12%, Hindu 7%, Christian 6%
LAND USE: Arable 3%, forest 59%
EMPLOYMENT: Agric. 26%, ind. 28%, services 46%
ANNUAL INCOME: $3,890 per person, 5.7%
ORIGIN OF INCOME: Agriculture 19%, industry 35%, services 46%
ENERGY: Prod. 3.88 tonnes, consump. 1.8 tonnes
TRADE: $4,870 per person
CURRENCY: Ringgit = 100 sen
ROADS: 281 km per 1,000 sq km of land
RAILWAYS: 7 km per 1,000 sq km of land
POPULATION PER DOCTOR: 2,564 people
ADULT LITERACY: 82%
EDUCATIONAL EXPENDITURE: 6.9% of GNP
MILITARY EXPENDITURE: 4.8% of GNP
AID RECEIVED: $6 per person

Maldives

CAPITAL CITY: Malé
AREA: 298 sq km
POPULATION: 275,000 people
POPULATION DENSITY: 917 people per sq km
POPULATION CHANGE: 3.6% per year
BIRTH RATE: 41 per 1,000 people
DEATH RATE: 6 per 1,000 people
LIFE EXPECTANCY: Males 65, females 69 years
INFANT MORTALITY: 44 per 1,000 live births
URBAN POPULATION: 27% of population
FERTILITY RATE: 7 children per female
ETHNIC GROUPS: Mixture of Sinhalese, Indian and Arab
LANGUAGES: *Divehi*
RELIGIONS: Sunni Muslim 99%
LAND USE: Arable 10%, grass 3%, forest 3%
EMPLOYMENT: Agric. 25%, ind. 32%, services 43%
ANNUAL INCOME: $990 per person, 6%
ORIGIN OF INCOME: Agriculture 24%, industry 15%, services 61%
TRADE: $868 per person
CURRENCY: Rufiyaa = 100 laaris
POPULATION PER DOCTOR: 14,500 people
ADULT LITERACY: 93%
EDUCATIONAL EXPENDITURE: 9.2% of GNP
AID RECEIVED: $130 per person

Mali

CAPITAL CITY: Bamako
AREA: 1,240,190 sq km (Land area 1,220,190 sq km)
POPULATION: 11,000,000 people
POPULATION DENSITY: 9 people per sq km
POPULATION CHANGE: 4.4% per year
BIRTH RATE: 51 per 1,000 people
DEATH RATE: 19 per 1,000 people
LIFE EXPECTANCY: Males 46, females 49 years
INFANT MORTALITY: 101 per 1,000 live births
URBAN POPULATION: 27% of population
FERTILITY RATE: 7 children per female
AGE GROUPS: 0–14 yrs 47%, 15–59 yrs 49%, 60+ yrs 4%
ETHNIC GROUPS: Bambara 32%, Fulani 14%, Senufo 12%, Soninke 9%
LANGUAGES: *French*, Mande and Voltaic languages
RELIGIONS: Sunni Muslim 90%, traditional animist beliefs 9%, Christian 1%
LAND USE: Arable 2%, grass 25%, forest 6%
EMPLOYMENT: Agric. 85%, ind. 2%, services 13%
ANNUAL INCOME: $250 per person, 0.6%
ORIGIN OF INCOME: Agriculture 42%, industry 15%, services 42%
ENERGY: Consumption 0.02 tonnes per person
TRADE: $74 per person
CURRENCY: CFA franc = 100 centimes
ROADS: 1 km per 1,000 sq km of land
RAILWAYS: 1 km per 1,000 sq km of land
POPULATION PER DOCTOR: 20,000 people

ADULT LITERACY: 27%
EDUCATIONAL EXPENDITURE: 3.3% of GNP
MILITARY EXPENDITURE: 2.9% of GNP
AID RECEIVED: $57 per person

Malta

CAPITAL CITY: Valletta
AREA: 316 sq km
POPULATION: 375,000 people
POPULATION DENSITY: 1,172 people per sq km
POPULATION CHANGE: 0.9% per year
BIRTH RATE: 15 per 1,000 people
DEATH RATE: 7 per 1,000 people
LIFE EXPECTANCY: Males 76, females 81 years
INFANT MORTALITY: 6 per 1,000 live births
URBAN POPULATION: 88% of population
FERTILITY RATE: 2 children per female
AGE GROUPS: 0–14 yrs 23%, 15–59 yrs 63%, 60+ yrs 14%
ETHNIC GROUPS: Maltese 96%, British 2%
LANGUAGES: *Maltese, English*
RELIGIONS: Roman Catholic 96%
LAND USE: Arable 38%
EMPLOYMENT: Agric. 3%, ind. 28%, services 69%
ANNUAL INCOME: $11,000 per person, 5.1%
ORIGIN OF INCOME: Agriculture 3%, industry 35%, services 62%
ENERGY: Consumption 2.0 tonnes per person
TRADE: $9,764 per person
CURRENCY: Maltese lira = 100 cents
ROADS: 5,013 km per 1,000 sq km of land
POPULATION PER DOCTOR: 750 people
ADULT LITERACY: 87%
EDUCATIONAL EXPENDITURE: 4.4% of GNP
MILITARY EXPENDITURE: 1.1% of GNP

Marshall Islands

TERRITORY IN ASSOCIATION WITH US
CAPITAL CITY: Dalap-Uliga-Darrit (on Majuro atoll)
AREA: 181 sq km
POPULATION: 60,000 people
POPULATION DENSITY: 331 people per sq km
POPULATION CHANGE: 3.9% per year
BIRTH RATE: 46 per 1,000 people
DEATH RATE: 7 per 1,000 people
LIFE EXPECTANCY: Males 63, females 66 years
INFANT MORTALITY: 46 per 1,000 live births
FERTILITY RATE: 7 children per female
ETHNIC GROUPS: Micronesian
LANGUAGES: *English, Marshallese*
RELIGIONS: Protestant 90%, Roman Catholic 9%
LAND USE: Arable 33%, grass 14%, forest 23%
EMPLOYMENT: Agric. 18%, ind. 9%, services 73%
ANNUAL INCOME: $1,600 per person
ORIGIN OF INCOME: Agriculture 1%, industry 8%, services 91%
TRADE: $900 per person
CURRENCY: US currency
POPULATION PER DOCTOR: 2,500 people
ADULT LITERACY: 93%

Martinique

OVERSEAS DEPARTMENT OF FRANCE
CAPITAL CITY: Fort-de-France
AREA: 1,100 sq km (Land area 1,060 sq km)
POPULATION: 405,000 people
POPULATION DENSITY: 382 people per sq km
POPULATION CHANGE: 2.5% per year
BIRTH RATE: 17 per 1,000 people
DEATH RATE: 6 per 1,000 people
LIFE EXPECTANCY: Males 76, females 82 years
INFANT MORTALITY: 7 per 1,000 live births
URBAN POPULATION: 79% of population
FERTILITY RATE: 2 children per female
AGE GROUPS: 0–14 yrs 24%, 15–59 yrs 62%, 60+ yrs 14%
ETHNIC GROUPS: Of African descent, Mixed, White
LANGUAGES: *French*, Creole patois
RELIGIONS: Roman Catholic 85%
LAND USE: Arable 8%, grass 18%, forest 44%
EMPLOYMENT: Agric. 7%, ind. 9%, services 84%
ANNUAL INCOME: $10,000 per person
ORIGIN OF WEALTH: Agriculture 8%, industry 12%, services 80%
ENERGY: Consumption 1.73 tonnes per person
TRADE: $4,722 per person
CURRENCY: French currency
ROADS: 1,952 km per 1,000 sq km of land
POPULATION PER DOCTOR: 650 people
ADULT LITERACY: 93%
EDUCATIONAL EXPENDITURE: 15.3% of GNP

Mauritania

CAPITAL CITY: Nouakchott
AREA: 1,025,220 sq km
POPULATION: 2,400,000 people
POPULATION DENSITY: 2 people per sq km
POPULATION CHANGE: 2.5% per year
BIRTH RATE: 47 per 1,000 people
DEATH RATE: 15 per 1,000 people
LIFE EXPECTANCY: Males 47, females 53 years
INFANT MORTALITY: 80 per 1,000 live births
URBAN POPULATION: 54% of population
FERTILITY RATE: 5 children per female
AGE GROUPS: 0–14 yrs 45%, 15–59 yrs 50%, 60+ yrs 5%

ETHNIC GROUPS: Moor (Arab-Berber) 70%, Wolof 7%, Tukulor 5%
LANGUAGES: *Arabic*, Soninke, Wolof, French
RELIGIONS: Sunni Muslim 99%
LAND USE: Grass 38%, forest 4%
EMPLOYMENT: Agric. 69%, ind. 9%, services 22%
ANNUAL INCOME: $460 per person, 0.5%
ORIGIN OF INCOME: Agriculture 27%, industry 30%, services 42%
ENERGY: Consumption 0.62 tonnes per person
TRADE: $338 per person
CURRENCY: Ouguiya = 5 khoums
ROADS: 7 km per 1,000 sq km of land
RAILWAYS: 1 km per 1,000 sq km of land
POPULATION PER DOCTOR: 16,667 people
ADULT LITERACY: 36%
EDUCATIONAL EXPENDITURE: 4.7% of GNP
MILITARY EXPENDITURE: 3.1% of GNP
AID RECEIVED: $99 per person

Mauritius

CAPITAL CITY: Port Louis
AREA: 2,040 sq km
POPULATION: 1,155,000 people
POPULATION DENSITY: 569 people per sq km
POPULATION CHANGE: 1.1% per year
BIRTH RATE: 19 per 1,000 people
DEATH RATE: 7 per 1,000 people
LIFE EXPECTANCY: Males 67, females 75 years
INFANT MORTALITY: 17 per 1,000 live births
URBAN POPULATION: 44% of population
FERTILITY RATE: 2 children per female
AGE GROUPS: 0–14 yrs 29%, 15–59 yrs 63%, 60+ yrs 8%
ETHNIC GROUPS: Indian 68%, Creole 27%, Chinese 3%, White 2%
LANGUAGES: *English*, Bhojpuri, Creole, French
RELIGIONS: Hindu 51%, Roman Catholic 27%, Muslim 16%
LAND USE: Arable 49%, grass 3%, forest 28%
EMPLOYMENT: Agric. 16%, ind. 30%, services 54%
ANNUAL INCOME: $3,380 per person, 5.7%
ORIGIN OF INCOME: Agriculture 10%, industry 33%, services 57%
ENERGY: Prod. 0.01 tonnes, consump. 0.58 tonnes
TRADE: $3,104 per person
CURRENCY: Rupee = 100 cents
ROADS: 902 km per 1,000 sq km of land
POPULATION PER DOCTOR: 1,176 people
ADULT LITERACY: 81%
EDUCATIONAL EXPENDITURE: 3.7% of GNP
MILITARY EXPENDITURE: 0.4% of GNP
AID RECEIVED: $21 per person

Mayotte

TERRITORIAL COLLECTIVITY OF FRANCE
CAPITAL CITY: Mamoundzou
AREA: 375 sq km
POPULATION: 105,000 people

Mexico

CAPITAL CITY: Mexico City
AREA: 1,958,200 sq km (Land area 1,908,690 sq km)
POPULATION: 97,400,000 people
POPULATION DENSITY: 51 people per sq km
POPULATION CHANGE: 1.8% per year
BIRTH RATE: 26 per 1,000 people
DEATH RATE: 5 per 1,000 people
LIFE EXPECTANCY: Males 70, females 78 years
INFANT MORTALITY: 24 per 1,000 live births
URBAN POPULATION: 75% of population
FERTILITY RATE: 3 children per female
AGE GROUPS: 0–14 yrs 37%, 15–59 yrs 57%, 60+ yrs 6%
ETHNIC GROUPS: Mestizo 60%, Amerindian 30%, European 9%
LANGUAGES: *Spanish*, Amerindian languages
RELIGIONS: Roman Catholic 90%, Protestant 5%
LAND USE: Arable 12%, grass 39%, forest 21%
EMPLOYMENT: Agric. 23%, ind. 29%, services 48%
ANNUAL INCOME: $3,320 per person, 0.1%
ORIGIN OF INCOME: Agriculture 8%, industry 28%, services 63%
ENERGY: Prod. 3.05 tonnes, consump. 1.89 tonnes
TRADE: $1,507 per person
CURRENCY: Peso = 100 centavos
ROADS: 159 km per 1,000 sq km of land
RAILWAYS: 14 km per 1,000 sq km of land
POPULATION PER DOCTOR: 621 people
ADULT LITERACY: 87%
EDUCATIONAL EXPENDITURE: 4.1% of GNP
MILITARY EXPENDITURE: 0.5% of GNP
AID RECEIVED: $4 per person

Micronesia

CAPITAL CITY: Palikir
AREA: 705 sq km
POPULATION: 127,000 people
POPULATION DENSITY: 181 people per sq km
POPULATION CHANGE: 2.6% per year
BIRTH RATE: 28 per 1,000 people
DEATH RATE: 6 per 1,000 people
LIFE EXPECTANCY: Males 66, females 70 years

INFANT MORTALITY: 35 per 1,000 live births
FERTILITY RATE: 4 children per female
AGE GROUPS: 0–14 yrs 41%, 15–59 yrs 52%, 60+ yrs 7%
ETHNIC GROUPS: Micronesian, Polynesian
LANGUAGES: *English*, local languages
RELIGIONS: Roman Catholic 60%, Protestant 40%
LAND USE: Arable 34%, grass 14%, forest 23%
EMPLOYMENT: Agric. 2%, services 80%
ANNUAL INCOME: $1,600 per person
ORIGIN OF INCOME: Agric. 42%, services 58%
TRADE: $700 per person
CURRENCY: US currency
POPULATION PER DOCTOR: 2,500 people
ADULT LITERACY: 78%

Moldova

CAPITAL CITY: Chisinau
AREA: 33,700 sq km (Land area 32,970 sq km)
POPULATION: 4,450,000 people
POPULATION DENSITY: 132 people per sq km
POPULATION CHANGE: 0.3% per year
BIRTH RATE: 17 per 1,000 people
DEATH RATE: 12 per 1,000 people
LIFE EXPECTANCY: Males 61, females 70 years
INFANT MORTALITY: 46 per 1,000 live births
URBAN POPULATION: 50% of population
FERTILITY RATE: 2 children per female
AGE GROUPS: 0–14 yrs 32%, 15–59 yrs 55%, 60+ yrs 13%
ETHNIC GROUPS: Moldovan 65%, Ukrainian 14%, Russian 13%, Gagauz 4%, Jewish 2%, Bulgarian
LANGUAGES: *Moldovan (Romanian)*, Russian, Gagauz, Ukrainian
RELIGIONS: Russian Orthodox 95%, Evangelical
LAND USE: Arable 68%, grass 12%
EMPLOYMENT: Agric. 21%, ind. 26%, services 53%
ANNUAL INCOME: $920 per person, –8.2%
ORIGIN OF INCOME: Agriculture 35%, industry 48%, services 18%
ENERGY: Prod. 0.01 tonnes, consump. 1.69 tonnes
TRADE: 3,421$ per person
CURRENCY: Leu =100 bani
ROADS: 364 km per 1,000 sq km of land
RAILWAYS: 36 km per 1,000 sq km of land
POPULATION PER DOCTOR: 250 people
ADULT LITERACY: 96%
EDUCATIONAL EXPENDITURE: 2.6% of GNP
MILITARY EXPENDITURE: 2.1% of GNP

Monaco

CAPITAL CITY: Monaco
AREA: 1.5 sq km
POPULATION: 33,000 people
POPULATION DENSITY: 16,923 people per sq km
POPULATION CHANGE: 2.4% per year
BIRTH RATE: 11 per 1,000 people
DEATH RATE: 12 per 1,000 people
LIFE EXPECTANCY: Males 75, females 82 years
INFANT MORTALITY: 7 per 1,000 live births
URBAN POPULATION: 100% of population
FERTILITY RATE: 1 child per female
ETHNIC GROUPS: French 47%, Monégasque 16%, Italian 16%
LANGUAGES: *French*, Monégasque
RELIGIONS: Roman Catholic 95%
ANNUAL INCOME: $20,000 per person
CURRENCY: French currency

Mongolia

CAPITAL CITY: Ulan Bator
AREA: 1,566,500 sq km
POPULATION: 2,500,000 people
POPULATION DENSITY: 2 people per sq km
POPULATION CHANGE: 1.9% per year
BIRTH RATE: 25 per 1,000 people
DEATH RATE: 8 per 1,000 people
LIFE EXPECTANCY: Males 59, females 63 years
INFANT MORTALITY: 68 per 1,000 live births
URBAN POPULATION: 60% of population
FERTILITY RATE: 4 children per female
AGE GROUPS: 0–14 yrs 41%, 15–59 yrs 54%, 60+ yrs 5%
ETHNIC GROUPS: Khalkha Mongol 79%, Kazak 6%
LANGUAGES: *Khalkha Mongolian*, Chinese, Russian, Kazak, Dorbed
RELIGIONS: Tibetan Buddhist (Lamaist) 95%, Muslim 3%, Shamanist
LAND USE: Arable 1%, grass 80%, forest 9%
EMPLOYMENT: Agric. 40%, ind. 21%, services 39%
ANNUAL INCOME: $310 per person, –3.8%
ORIGIN OF INCOME: Agriculture 21%, industry 47%, services 33%
ENERGY: Prod. 2.8 tonnes, consump. 1.58 tonnes
TRADE: $652 per person
CURRENCY: Tugrik = 100 möngös
ROADS: 32 km per 1,000 sq km of land
RAILWAYS: 1 km per 1,000 sq km of land
POPULATION PER DOCTOR: 389 people
ADULT LITERACY: 81%
EDUCATIONAL EXPENDITURE: 8.5% of GNP
MILITARY EXPENDITURE: 5.9% of GNP
AID RECEIVED: $88 per person

Montserrat

DEPENDENT TERRITORY OF UK
CAPITAL CITY: Plymouth
AREA: 102 sq km
POPULATION: 12,000 people
POPULATION DENSITY: 120 people per sq km
POPULATION CHANGE: 0% per year
BIRTH RATE: 14 per 1,000 people
DEATH RATE: 10 per 1,000 people
LIFE EXPECTANCY: Males 74, females 77 years
INFANT MORTALITY: 12 per 1,000 live births
URBAN POPULATION: 14% of population
FERTILITY RATE: 2 children per female
ETHNIC GROUPS: Afro-Caribbean, European
LANGUAGES: *English*
RELIGIONS: Protestant 90%, Roman Catholic 10%
LAND USE: Arable 20%, grass 10%, forest 40%
ANNUAL INCOME: $4,500 per person, 4.3%
ORIGIN OF INCOME: Agriculture 4%, industry 6%, services 90%
TRADE: $6,672 per person
CURRENCY: East Caribbean $ = 100 cents
ROADS: 2,000 km per 1,000 sq km of land
ADULT LITERACY: 97%

Morocco

CAPITAL CITY: Rabat
AREA: 446,550 sq km
POPULATION: 28,100,000 people
POPULATION DENSITY: 63 people per sq km
POPULATION CHANGE: 1.6% per year
BIRTH RATE: 27 per 1,000 people
DEATH RATE: 6 per 1,000 people
LIFE EXPECTANCY: Males 68, females 72 years
INFANT MORTALITY: 41 per 1,000 live births
URBAN POPULATION: 52% of population
FERTILITY RATE: 4 children per female
AGE GROUPS: 0–14 yrs 41%, 15–59 yrs 54%, 60+ yrs 6%
ETHNIC GROUPS: Arab 70%, Berber 30%
LANGUAGES: *Arabic*, Berber, French
RELIGIONS: Sunni Muslim 99%
LAND USE: Arable 21%, grass 47%, forest 18%
EMPLOYMENT: Agric. 46%, ind. 25%, services 29%
ANNUAL INCOME: $1,110 per person, 0.8%
ORIGIN OF INCOME: Agriculture 14%, industry 32%, services 53%
ENERGY: Prod. 0.03 tonnes, consump. 0.41 tonnes
TRADE: $406 per person
CURRENCY: Dirham = 100 cents
ROADS: 134 km per 1,000 sq km of land
RAILWAYS: 4 km per 1,000 sq km of land
POPULATION PER DOCTOR: 4,500 people
ADULT LITERACY: 41%
EDUCATIONAL EXPENDITURE: 5.5% of GNP
MILITARY EXPENDITURE: 4.0% of GNP
AID RECEIVED: $19 per person

Mozambique

CAPITAL CITY: Maputo
AREA: 801,590 sq km (Land area 784,090 sq km)
POPULATION: 19,100,000 people
POPULATION DENSITY: 24 people per sq km
POPULATION CHANGE: 4.3% per year
BIRTH RATE: 44 per 1,000 people
DEATH RATE: 18 per 1,000 people
LIFE EXPECTANCY: Males 44, females 46 years
INFANT MORTALITY: 123 per 1,000 live births
URBAN POPULATION: 32% of population
FERTILITY RATE: 7 children per female
AGE GROUPS: 0–14 yrs 44%, 15–59 yrs 51%, 60+ yrs 5%
ETHNIC GROUPS: Makua/Lomwe 47%, Tsonga 23%, Malawi 12%, Shona 11%, Yao 4%, Swahili 1%, Makonde 1%
LANGUAGES: *Portuguese*, Bantu languages
RELIGIONS: Traditional beliefs 48%, Roman Catholic 31%, Muslim 13%
LAND USE: Arable 4%, grass 56%, forest 18%
EMPLOYMENT: Agric. 85%, ind. 7%, services 8%
ANNUAL INCOME: $80 per person, 3.6%
ORIGIN OF INCOME: Agric. 33%, ind. 12%, services 5%
ENERGY: Consumption 0.03 tonnes per person
TRADE: $70 per person
CURRENCY: Metical = 100 centavos
ROADS: 52 km per 1,000 sq km of land
RAILWAYS: 3 km per 1,000 sq km of land
POPULATION PER DOCTOR: 33,333 people
ADULT LITERACY: 37%
EDUCATIONAL EXPENDITURE: 6.3% of GNP
MILITARY EXPENDITURE: 10.2% of GNP
AID RECEIVED: $66 per person

Namibia

CAPITAL CITY: Windhoek
AREA: 824,290 sq km
POPULATION: 1,650,000 people
POPULATION DENSITY: 2 people per sq km
POPULATION CHANGE: 2.0% per year
BIRTH RATE: 37 per 1,000 people
DEATH RATE: 8 per 1,000 people
LIFE EXPECTANCY: Males 63, females 67 years
INFANT MORTALITY: 46 per 1,000 live births
URBAN POPULATION: 34% of population
FERTILITY RATE: 5 children per female
AGE GROUPS: 0–14 yrs 46%, 15–59 yrs 49%, 60+ yrs 5%
ETHNIC GROUPS: Ovambo 47%, Kavango 9%, Herero 7%, Damara 7%, White 6%, Nama 5%
LANGUAGES: *English*, Ovambo, Nama, Herero, Kavango, Afrikaans
RELIGIONS: Lutheran 52%, Roman Catholic 32%, Dutch Reformed 9%, Anglican, animist
LAND USE: Arable 1%, grass 46%, forest 22%
EMPLOYMENT: Agric. 43%, ind. 22%, services 35%
ANNUAL INCOME: $2,000 per person, 2.8%
ORIGIN OF INCOME: Agriculture 10%, industry 27%, services 63%
ENERGY: Prod. 3.38 tonnes, consump. 2.49 tonnes
TRADE: $1,473 per person
CURRENCY: Namibian $ = 100 cents
ROADS: 52 km per 1,000 sq km of land
RAILWAYS: 3 km per 1,000 sq km of land
POPULATION PER DOCTOR: 4,545 people
ADULT LITERACY: 40%
EDUCATIONAL EXPENDITURE: 4.7% of GNP
MILITARY EXPENDITURE: 2.9% of GNP
AID RECEIVED: $125 per person

Nauru

CAPITAL CITY: Yaren district
AREA: 21 sq km
POPULATION: 12,000 people
POPULATION DENSITY: 600 people per sq km
POPULATION CHANGE: 4.2% per year
BIRTH RATE: 18 per 1,000 people
DEATH RATE: 5 per 1,000 people
LIFE EXPECTANCY: Males 64, females 69 years
INFANT MORTALITY: 41 per 1,000 live births
FERTILITY RATE: 2 children per female
ETHNIC GROUPS: Nauruan 58%, other Pacific groups 26%
LANGUAGES: *Nauruan*, English
RELIGIONS: Protestant, Roman Catholic
ANNUAL INCOME: $10,000 per person
ENERGY: Consumption 6.3 tonnes per person
TRADE: $10,467 per person
CURRENCY: Australian currency
ROADS: 1,400 km per 1,000 sq km of land
RAILWAYS: 250 km per 1,000 sq km of land

Nepal

CAPITAL CITY: Katmandu
AREA: 140,800 sq km (Land area 136,800 sq km)
POPULATION: 22,100,000 people
POPULATION DENSITY: 162 people per sq km
POPULATION CHANGE: 2.1% per year
BIRTH RATE: 37 per 1,000 people
DEATH RATE: 12 per 1,000 people
LIFE EXPECTANCY: Males 54, females 55 years
INFANT MORTALITY: 77 per 1,000 live births
URBAN POPULATION: 13% of population
FERTILITY RATE: 5 children per female
AGE GROUPS: 0–14 yrs 42%, 15–59 yrs 53%, 60+ yrs 5%
ETHNIC GROUPS: Nepali 53%, Bihari 18%, Tharu 5%, Tamang 5%, Newar 3%
LANGUAGES: *Nepalese*, local languages
RELIGIONS: Hindu 86%, Buddhist 8%, Muslim 4%
LAND USE: Arable 17%, grass 15%, forest 39%
EMPLOYMENT: Agric. 93%, ind. 1%, services 7%
ANNUAL INCOME: $200 per person, 2.4%
ORIGIN OF INCOME: Agriculture 43%, industry 21%, services 36%
ENERGY: Consumption 0.01 tonnes per person
TRADE: $61 per person
CURRENCY: Nepalese rupee = 100 paisa
ROADS: 70 km per 1,000 sq km of land
POPULATION PER DOCTOR: 16,667 people
ADULT LITERACY: 26%
EDUCATIONAL EXPENDITURE: 2.0% of GNP
MILITARY EXPENDITURE: 1.1% of GNP
AID RECEIVED: $21 per person

Netherlands

CAPITAL CITY: Amsterdam/The Hague
AREA: 37,330 sq km (Land area 33,920 sq km)
POPULATION: 15,900,000 people
POPULATION DENSITY: 469 people per sq km
POPULATION CHANGE: 0.9% per year
BIRTH RATE: 12 per 1,000 people
DEATH RATE: 12 per 1,000 people
LIFE EXPECTANCY: Males 75, females 81 years
INFANT MORTALITY: 5 per 1,000 live births
URBAN POPULATION: 89% of population
FERTILITY RATE: 2 children per female
AGE GROUPS: 0–14 yrs 18%, 15–59 yrs 65%, 60+ yrs 17%
ETHNIC GROUPS: White 95%, Indonesian, Turkish, Moroccan, Surinamese
LANGUAGES: *Dutch*, Frisian
RELIGIONS: Roman Catholic 33%, Dutch Reformed Church 15%, Reformed Churches 8%, Muslim 3%
LAND USE: Arable 26%, grass 31%, forest 10%
EMPLOYMENT: Agric. 5%, ind. 25%, services 70%
ANNUAL INCOME: $24,000 per person, 1.8%
ORIGIN OF INCOME: Agriculture 4%, industry 28%, services 68%
ENERGY: Prod. 6.89 tonnes, consump. 7.12 tonnes
TRADE: $16,529 per person
CURRENCY: Guilder (florin) = 100 cents
ROADS: 3,507 km per 1,000 sq km of land
RAILWAYS: 81 km per 1,000 sq km of land
POPULATION PER DOCTOR: 398 people
ADULT LITERACY: 99%
EDUCATIONAL EXPENDITURE: 5.8% of GNP
MILITARY EXPENDITURE: 2.4% of GNP
AID GIVEN: $172 per person

Netherlands Antilles

SELF-GOVERNING DUTCH TERRITORY
CAPITAL CITY: Willemstad
AREA: 993 sq km
POPULATION: 210,000 people
POPULATION DENSITY: 263 people per sq km
POPULATION CHANGE: 1.6% per year
BIRTH RATE: 16 per 1,000 people
DEATH RATE: 5 per 1,000 people
LIFE EXPECTANCY: Males 75, females 80 years
INFANT MORTALITY: 9 per 1,000 live births
URBAN POPULATION: 60% of population
FERTILITY RATE: 2 children per female
AGE GROUPS: 0–14 yrs 25%, 15–59 yrs 68%, 60+ yrs 7%
ETHNIC GROUPS: African descent 85%, European
LANGUAGES: *Dutch*, Papiamento, English
RELIGIONS: Roman Catholic 75%
LAND USE: Arable 10%
EMPLOYMENT: Agric. 1%, ind. 15%, services 84%
ANNUAL INCOME: $10,500 per person, 2%
ORIGIN OF INCOME: Agriculture 1%, industry 10%, services 89%
ENERGY: Consumption 7.53 tonnes per person
TRADE: $19,858 per person
CURRENCY: Neths Antilles guilder = 100 cents
ROADS: 740 km per 1,000 sq km of land
POPULATION PER DOCTOR: 800 people
ADULT LITERACY: 95%
EDUCATIONAL EXPENDITURE: 2.8% of GNP

New Caledonia

FRENCH OVERSEAS TERRITORY
CAPITAL CITY: Nouméa
AREA: 18,580 sq km (Land area 18,280 sq km)
POPULATION: 192,000 people
POPULATION DENSITY: 11 people per sq km
POPULATION CHANGE: 2.0% per year
BIRTH RATE: 21 per 1,000 people
DEATH RATE: 5 per 1,000 people
LIFE EXPECTANCY: Males 71, females 78 years
INFANT MORTALITY: 13 per 1,000 live births
URBAN POPULATION: 62% of population
FERTILITY RATE: 3 children per female
AGE GROUPS: 0–14 yrs 30%, 15–59 yrs 61%, 60+ yrs 9%
ETHNIC GROUPS: Melanesian 43%, European 37%
LANGUAGES: *French*, Melanesian and Polynesian dialects
RELIGIONS: Roman Catholic 60%, Protestant 30%
LAND USE: Grass 12%, forest 39%
EMPLOYMENT: Agric. 12%, ind. 16%, services 72%
ANNUAL INCOME: $16,000 per person, 2.4%
ORIGIN OF INCOME: Agriculture 25%, industry 7%, services 68%
ENERGY: Prod. 0.24 tonnes, consump. 4.65 tonnes
TRADE: $6,700 per person
CURRENCY: CFP franc = 100 centimes
ROADS: 315 km per 1,000 sq km of land
POPULATION PER DOCTOR: 1,250 people
ADULT LITERACY: 58%
EDUCATIONAL EXPENDITURE: 13.4% of GNP

New Zealand

CAPITAL CITY: Wellington
AREA: 270,990 sq km (Land area 267,990 sq km)
POPULATION: 3,650,000 people
POPULATION DENSITY: 14 people per sq km
POPULATION CHANGE: 1.1% per year
BIRTH RATE: 15 per 1,000 people
DEATH RATE: 8 per 1,000 people
LIFE EXPECTANCY: Males 74, females 81 years
INFANT MORTALITY: 7 per 1,000 live births
URBAN POPULATION: 86% of population
FERTILITY RATE: 2 children per female
AGE GROUPS: 0–14 yrs 23%, 15–59 yrs 62%, 60+ yrs 15%
ETHNIC GROUPS: White 74%, Maori 10%, Polynesian 4%
LANGUAGES: *English, Maori*
RELIGIONS: Anglican 21%, Presbyterian 16%, Roman Catholic 15%, Methodist 4%
LAND USE: Arable 1%, grass 51%, forest 28%
EMPLOYMENT: Agric. 11%, ind. 23%, services 66%
ANNUAL INCOME: $14,340 per person, 0.6%
ORIGIN OF INCOME: Agriculture 7%, industry 26%, services 67%
ENERGY: Prod. 5.03 tonnes, consump. 5.94 tonnes
TRADE: $5,830 per person
CURRENCY: New Zealand $ = 100 cents
ROADS: 343 km per 1,000 sq km of land
RAILWAYS: 15 km per 1,000 sq km of land
POPULATION PER DOCTOR: 521 people

New Zealand continued
ADULT LITERACY: 99%
EDUCATIONAL EXPENDITURE: 5.8% of GNP
MILITARY EXPENDITURE: 1.6% of GNP
AID GIVEN: $31 per person

Nicaragua
CAPITAL CITY: Managua
AREA: 130,000 sq km (Land area 118,750 sq km)
POPULATION: 4,544,000 people
POPULATION DENSITY: 39 people per sq km
POPULATION CHANGE: 2.5% per year
BIRTH RATE: 33 per 1,000 people
DEATH RATE: 6 per 1,000 people
LIFE EXPECTANCY: Males 64, females 69 years
INFANT MORTALITY: 44 per 1,000 live births
URBAN POPULATION: 63% of population
FERTILITY RATE: 5 children per female
AGE GROUPS: 0–14 yrs 46%, 15–59 yrs 50%, 60+ yrs 4%
ETHNIC GROUPS: Mestizo 69%, White 17%, Black 9%
LANGUAGES: *Spanish*, Misumalpan, Creole
RELIGIONS: Roman Catholic 85%, Protestant 10%
LAND USE: Arable 9%, grass 46%, forest 27%
EMPLOYMENT: Agric. 46%, ind. 16%, services 38%
ANNUAL INCOME: $380 per person, –5.8%
ORIGIN OF INCOME: Agriculture 30%, industry 20%, services 50%
ENERGY: Prod. 0.15 tonnes, consump. 0.42 tonnes
TRADE: $269 per person
CURRENCY: Córdoba = 100 centavos
ROADS: 129 km per 1,000 sq km of land
RAILWAYS: 3 km per 1,000 sq km of land
POPULATION PER DOCTOR: 2,000 people
ADULT LITERACY: 65%
EDUCATIONAL EXPENDITURE: 4.1% of GNP
MILITARY EXPENDITURE: 10.9% of GNP
AID RECEIVED: $155 per person

Niger
CAPITAL CITY: Niamey
AREA: 1,267,000 sq km
POPULATION: 9,149,000 people
POPULATION DENSITY: 8 people per sq km
POPULATION CHANGE: 3.3% per year
BIRTH RATE: 54 per 1,000 people
DEATH RATE: 24 per 1,000 people
LIFE EXPECTANCY: Males 41, females 41 years
INFANT MORTALITY: 116 per 1,000 live births
URBAN POPULATION: 16% of population
FERTILITY RATE: 7 children per female
AGE GROUPS: 0–14 yrs 48%, 15–59 yrs 48%, 60+ yrs 4%
ETHNIC GROUPS: Hausa 53%, Djerma 21%, Tuareg 11%, Fulani 10%
LANGUAGES: *French*, Hausa, Songhai, Tuareg
RELIGIONS: Sunni Muslim 99%
LAND USE: Arable 3%, grass 7%, forest 1%
EMPLOYMENT: Agric. 85%, ind. 3%, services 12%
ANNUAL INCOME: $220 per person, –2.1%
ORIGIN OF INCOME: Agriculture 39%, industry 18%, services 44%
ENERGY: Prod. 0.02 tonnes, consump. 0.06 tonnes
TRADE: $81 per person
CURRENCY: CFA franc = 100 centimes
ROADS: 11 km per 1,000 sq km of land
POPULATION PER DOCTOR: 50,000 people
ADULT LITERACY: 12%
EDUCATIONAL EXPENDITURE: 3.1% of GNP
MILITARY EXPENDITURE: 1.0% of GNP
AID RECEIVED: $30 per person

Nigeria
CAPITAL CITY: Abuja (commercial, Lagos)
AREA: 923,770 sq km (Land area 910,770 sq km)
POPULATION: 88,515,000 people
POPULATION DENSITY: 130 people per sq km
POPULATION CHANGE: 1.2% per year
BIRTH RATE: 43 per 1,000 people
DEATH RATE: 12 per 1,000 people
LIFE EXPECTANCY: Males 53, females 56 years
INFANT MORTALITY: 70 per 1,000 live births
URBAN POPULATION: 38% of population
FERTILITY RATE: 6 children per female
AGE GROUPS: 0–14 yrs 47%, 15–59 yrs 49%, 60+ yrs 4%
ETHNIC GROUPS: Hausa 21%, Yoruba 21%, Ibo 18%, Fulani 11%
LANGUAGES: *English*, Hausa, Yoruba, Ibo, Fulani
RELIGIONS: Sunni Muslim 45%, Protestant 26%, Roman Catholic 12%, African indigenous 11%
LAND USE: Arable 33%, grass 44%, forest 12%
EMPLOYMENT: Agric. 48%, ind. 7%, services 45%
ANNUAL INCOME: $260 per person, 1.2%
ORIGIN OF INCOME: Agriculture 33%, industry 43%, services 24%
ENERGY: Prod. 1.27 tonnes, consump. 0.21 tonnes
TRADE: $197 per person
CURRENCY: Naira = 100 kobo
ROADS: 123 km per 1,000 sq km of land
RAILWAYS: 4 km per 1,000 sq km of land
POPULATION PER DOCTOR: 5,882 people
ADULT LITERACY: 53%
EDUCATIONAL EXPENDITURE: 1.7% of GNP
MILITARY EXPENDITURE: 0.7% of GNP
AID RECEIVED: $2 per person

Niue
FREE ASSOCIATION WITH NEW ZEALAND
CAPITAL CITY: Alofi
AREA: 260 sq km
POPULATION: 1,950 people

Norfolk Island
TERRITORY OF AUSTRALIA
CAPITAL CITY: Kingston
AREA: 35 sq km
POPULATION: 2,700 people

Northern Mariana Islands
COMMONWEALTH IN UNION WITH USA
CAPITAL CITY: Saipan
AREA: 477 sq km
POPULATION: 50,000 people
POPULATION DENSITY: 111 people per sq km
POPULATION CHANGE: 2.7% per year
BIRTH RATE: 33 per 1,000 people
DEATH RATE: 5 per 1,000 people
LIFE EXPECTANCY: Males 66, females 69 years
INFANT MORTALITY: 38 per 1,000 live births
FERTILITY RATE: 3 children per female
ETHNIC GROUPS: Chamorro, Micronesian, Spanish
LANGUAGES: *English*, Chamorro
RELIGIONS: Roman Catholic 80%
LAND USE: Arable 1%, grass 19%
ANNUAL INCOME: $3,500 per person
TRADE: $12,000 per person
CURRENCY: US currency
ROADS: 1 km per 1,000 sq km of land
ADULT LITERACY: 96%

Norway
CAPITAL CITY: Oslo
AREA: 323,900 sq km (Land area 306,830 sq km)
POPULATION: 4,361,000 people
POPULATION DENSITY: 14 people per sq km
POPULATION CHANGE: 0.8% per year
BIRTH RATE: 11 per 1,000 people
DEATH RATE: 11 per 1,000 people
LIFE EXPECTANCY: Males 75, females 81 years
INFANT MORTALITY: 5 per 1,000 live births
URBAN POPULATION: 73% of population
FERTILITY RATE: 2 children per female
AGE GROUPS: 0–14 yrs 19%, 15–59 yrs 60%, 60+ yrs 21%
ETHNIC GROUPS: Norwegian 97%
LANGUAGES: *Norwegian*, Lappish
RELIGIONS: Lutheran 88%
LAND USE: Arable 3%, forest 27%
EMPLOYMENT: Agric. 6%, ind. 24%, services 70%
ANNUAL INCOME: $31,250 per person, 1.6%
ORIGIN OF INCOME: Agriculture 3%, industry 35%, services 62%
ENERGY: Prod. 48.28 tonnes, consump. 6.71 tonnes
TRADE: $12,916 per person
CURRENCY: Krone = 100 øre
ROADS: 294 km per 1,000 sq km of land
RAILWAYS: 13 km per 1,000 sq km of land
Population per doctor: 309 people
ADULT LITERACY: 99%
EDUCATIONAL EXPENDITURE: 7.6% of GNP
MILITARY EXPENDITURE: 3.3% of GNP
AID GIVEN: $255 per person

Oman
CAPITAL CITY: Muscat
AREA: 212,460 sq km
POPULATION: 2,252,000 people
POPULATION DENSITY: 11 people per sq km
POPULATION CHANGE: 6.9% per year
BIRTH RATE: 38 per 1,000 people
DEATH RATE: 4 per 1,000 people
LIFE EXPECTANCY: Males 69, females 73 years
INFANT MORTALITY: 26 per 1,000 live births
URBAN POPULATION: 13% of population
FERTILITY RATE: 7 children per female
AGE GROUPS: 0–14 yrs 47%, 15–59 yrs 49%, 60+ yrs 4%
ETHNIC GROUPS: Omani Arab 74%, other Asian 25%
LANGUAGES: *Arabic*, Baluchi, English
RELIGIONS: Ibadiyah Muslim 86%, Hindu
LAND USE: Grass 5%
EMPLOYMENT: Agric. 49%, ind. 22%, services 29%
ANNUAL INCOME: $4,820 per person, 0.3%
ORIGIN OF INCOME: Agriculture 4%, industry 66%, services 30%
ENERGY: Prod. 31.28 tonnes, consump. 2.86 tonnes
TRADE: $4,730 per person
CURRENCY: Rial = 1,000 baiza
ROADS: 124 km per 1,000 sq km of land
POPULATION PER DOCTOR: 1,200 people
ADULT LITERACY: 35%
EDUCATIONAL EXPENDITURE: 3.5% of GNP
MILITARY EXPENDITURE: 17.5% of GNP
AID RECEIVED: $29 per person

Pakistan
CAPITAL CITY: Islamabad
AREA: 796,100 sq km (Land area 770,880 sq km)
POPULATION: 143,595,000 people
POPULATION DENSITY: 176 people per sq km
POPULATION CHANGE: 2.8% per year
BIRTH RATE: 35 per 1,000 people
DEATH RATE: 11 per 1,000 people
LIFE EXPECTANCY: Males 58, females 60 years
INFANT MORTALITY: 95 per 1,000 live births
URBAN POPULATION: 34% of population
FERTILITY RATE: 6 children per female
AGE GROUPS: 0–14 yrs 46%, 15–59 yrs 50%, 60+ yrs 4%
ETHNIC GROUPS: Punjabi 60%, Pushtun 13%, Sindhi 12%, Baluchi, Muhajir
LANGUAGES: *Urdu*, Punjabi, Pashto, Sindhi, Baluchi, Brahvi, English
RELIGIONS: Sunni Muslim 80%, Shiite Muslim 17%, Christian 2%, Hindu 1%
LAND USE: Arable 27%, grass 6%, forest 5%
EMPLOYMENT: Agric. 47%, ind. 20%, services 33%
ANNUAL INCOME: $460 per person, 1.2%
ORIGIN OF INCOME: Agriculture 25%, industry 25%, services 50%
ENERGY: Prod. 0.21 tonnes, consump. 0.30 tonnes
TRADE: $132 per person
CURRENCY: Rupee = 100 paisa
ROADS: 257 km per 1,000 sq km of land
RAILWAYS: 11 km per 1,000 sq km of land
POPULATION PER DOCTOR: 2,000 people
ADULT LITERACY: 36%
EDUCATIONAL EXPENDITURE: 3.4% of GNP
MILITARY EXPENDITURE: 7.7% of GNP
AID RECEIVED: $6 per person

Palau (Belau)
CAPITAL CITY: Koror
AREA: 458 sq km
POPULATION: 18,000 people
POPULATION DENSITY: 35 people per sq km
POPULATION CHANGE: 1.8% per year
BIRTH RATE: 21 per 1,000 people
DEATH RATE: 7 per 1,000 people
LIFE EXPECTANCY: Males 69, females 73 years
INFANT MORTALITY: 25 per 1,000 live births
FERTILITY RATE: 3 children per female
ETHNIC GROUPS: Palauan (mixture of Polynesian, Melanesian and Malay)
LANGUAGES: *Palauan, English*
RELIGIONS: Roman Catholic 45%, Protestant 30%
ANNUAL INCOME: $2,260 per person
TRADE: $2,790 per person
CURRENCY: US currency

Panama
CAPITAL CITY: Panama City
AREA: 77,080 sq km (Land area 75,990 sq km)
POPULATION: 2,629,000 people
POPULATION DENSITY: 37 people per sq km
POPULATION CHANGE: 1.7% per year
BIRTH RATE: 22 per 1,000 people
DEATH RATE: 5 per 1,000 people
LIFE EXPECTANCY: Males 72, females 77 years
INFANT MORTALITY: 25 per 1,000 live births
URBAN POPULATION: 55% of population
FERTILITY RATE: 3 children per female
AGE GROUPS: 0–14 yrs 35%, 15–59 yrs 58%, 60+ yrs 7%
ETHNIC GROUPS: Mestizo 64%, Black and Mulatto 14%, White 10%, Amerindian 8%
LANGUAGES: *Spanish*, Amerindian languages
RELIGIONS: Roman Catholic 80%, Protestant 10%, Muslim 5%
LAND USE: Arable 7%, grass 20%, forest 43%
EMPLOYMENT: Agric. 27%, ind. 14%, services 59%
ANNUAL INCOME: $2,750 per person, –0.4%
ORIGIN OF INCOME: Agriculture 10%, industry 18%, services 72%
ENERGY: Prod. 0.09 tonnes, consump. 0.86 tonnes
TRADE: $1,049 per person
CURRENCY: Balboa = 100 centésimos
ROADS: 138 km per 1,000 sq km of land
RAILWAYS: 5 km per 1,000 sq km of land
POPULATION PER DOCTOR: 562 people
ADULT LITERACY: 90%
EDUCATIONAL EXPENDITURE: 5.5% of GNP
MILITARY EXPENDITURE: 1.2% of GNP
AID RECEIVED: $19 per person

Papua New Guinea
CAPITAL CITY: Port Moresby
AREA: 462,840 sq km (Land area 452,860 sq km)
POPULATION: 4,292,000 people
POPULATION DENSITY: 10 people per sq km
POPULATION CHANGE: 1.8% per year
BIRTH RATE: 33 per 1,000 people
DEATH RATE: 10 per 1,000 people
LIFE EXPECTANCY: Males 57, females 59 years
INFANT MORTALITY: 59 per 1,000 live births
URBAN POPULATION: 16% of population
FERTILITY RATE: 5 children per female
AGE GROUPS: 0–14 yrs 41%, 15–59 yrs 55%, 60+ yrs 5%
ETHNIC GROUPS: Papuan 84%, Melanesian 15%
LANGUAGES: *English*, Tok Pisin, Papuan and Melanesian languages
RELIGIONS: Protestant 60%, Roman Catholic 30%, traditional beliefs
LAND USE: Forest 84%
EMPLOYMENT: Agric. 76%, ind. 10%, services 14%
ANNUAL INCOME: $1,160 per person, 2.1%
ORIGIN OF INCOME: Agriculture 26%, industry 43%, services 31%
ENERGY: Prod. 0.01 tonnes, consump. 0.28 tonnes
TRADE: $947 per person
CURRENCY: Kina = 100 toea
ROADS: 44 km per 1,000 sq km of land
POPULATION PER DOCTOR: 12,500 people
ADULT LITERACY: 70%
EDUCATIONAL EXPENDITURE: 4.7% of GNP
MILITARY EXPENDITURE: 1.8% of GNP
AID RECEIVED: $88 per person

Paraguay
CAPITAL CITY: Asunción
AREA: 406,750 sq km (Land area 397,300 sq km)
POPULATION: 4,979,000 people
POPULATION DENSITY: 13 people per sq km
POPULATION CHANGE: 2.8% per year
BIRTH RATE: 30 per 1,000 people
DEATH RATE: 4 per 1,000 people
LIFE EXPECTANCY: Males 73, females 76 years
INFANT MORTALITY: 22 per 1,000 live births
URBAN POPULATION: 52% of population
FERTILITY RATE: 4 children per female
AGE GROUPS: 0–14 yrs 40%, 15–59 yrs 54%, 60+ yrs 5%
ETHNIC GROUPS: Mestizo 90%, Amerindian 3%
LANGUAGES: *Spanish, Guarani*
RELIGIONS: Roman Catholic 93%
LAND USE: Arable 6%, grass 55%, forest 32%
EMPLOYMENT: Agric. 48%, ind. 21%, services 31%
ANNUAL INCOME: $1,690 per person, 1.1%
ORIGIN OF INCOME: Agriculture 26%, industry 21%, services 53%
ENERGY: Prod. 0.73 tonnes, consump. 0.33 tonnes
TRADE: $461 per person
CURRENCY: Guaraní = 100 céntimos
ROADS: 74 km per 1,000 sq km of land
RAILWAYS: 1 km per 1,000 sq km of land
POPULATION PER DOCTOR: 1,587 people
ADULT LITERACY: 91%
EDUCATIONAL EXPENDITURE: 1.9% of GNP
MILITARY EXPENDITURE: 2.0% of GNP
AID RECEIVED: $30 per person

Peru
CAPITAL CITY: Lima
AREA: 1,285,220 sq km
POPULATION: 25,588,000 people
POPULATION DENSITY: 19 people per sq km
POPULATION CHANGE: 1.3% per year
BIRTH RATE: 24 per 1,000 people
DEATH RATE: 6 per 1,000 people
LIFE EXPECTANCY: Males 67, females 72 years
INFANT MORTALITY: 50 per 1,000 live births
URBAN POPULATION: 72% of population
FERTILITY RATE: 3 children per female
AGE GROUPS: 0–14 yrs 38%, 15–59 yrs 57%, 60+ yrs 6%
ETHNIC GROUPS: Quechua 47%, Mestizo 32%, White 12%
LANGUAGES: *Spanish*, Quechua, Aymara
RELIGIONS: Roman Catholic 93%
LAND USE: Arable 3%, grass 21%, forest 53%
EMPLOYMENT: Agric. 35%, ind. 12%, services 53%
ANNUAL INCOME: $2,310 per person, –1.6%
ORIGIN OF INCOME: Agriculture 11%, industry 43%, services 46%
ENERGY: Prod. 0.47 tonnes, consump. 0.48 tonnes
TRADE: $369 per person
CURRENCY: Nuevo sol = 100 centavos
ROADS: 56 km per 1,000 sq km of land
RAILWAYS: 2 km per 1,000 sq km of land
POPULATION PER DOCTOR: 1,031 people
ADULT LITERACY: 87%
EDUCATIONAL EXPENDITURE: 1.5% of GNP
MILITARY EXPENDITURE: 3.8% of GNP
AID RECEIVED: $18 per person

Philippines
CAPITAL CITY: Manila
AREA: 300,000 sq km
POPULATION: 67,167,000 people
POPULATION DENSITY: 247 people per sq km
POPULATION CHANGE: 2.4% per year
BIRTH RATE: 29 per 1,000 people
DEATH RATE: 7 per 1,000 people
LIFE EXPECTANCY: Males 63, females 69 years
INFANT MORTALITY: 35 per 1,000 live births
URBAN POPULATION: 52% of population
FERTILITY RATE: 4 children per female
AGE GROUPS: 0–14 yrs 40%, 15–59 yrs 55%, 60+ yrs 5%
ETHNIC GROUPS: Tagalog 30%, Cebuano 24%, Ilocano 10%, Hiligayon Ilongu 9%, Bicol 6%, Samar-Leyte 4%
LANGUAGES: *Pilipino (Tagalog), English*, Spanish, Cebuano, Ilocano, Hiligayon, Bicol, Pampango
RELIGIONS: Roman Catholic 84%, Aglipayan 6%, Sunni Muslim 4%, Protestant 4%
LAND USE: Arable 19%, grass 4%, forest 34%
EMPLOYMENT: Agric. 45%, ind. 16%, services 39%

ANNUAL INCOME: $1,050 per person, 1.5%
ORIGIN OF INCOME: Agriculture 22%, industry 33%, services 45%
ENERGY: Prod. 0.14 tonnes, consump. 0.40 tonnes
TRADE: $460 per person
CURRENCY: Peso = 100 centavos
ROADS: 540 km per 1,000 sq km of land
RAILWAYS: 4 km per 1,000 sq km of land
POPULATION PER DOCTOR: 8,333 people
ADULT LITERACY: 94%
EDUCATIONAL EXPENDITURE: 2.9% of GNP
MILITARY EXPENDITURE: 2.2% of GNP
AID RECEIVED: $109 per person

Pitcairn Islands
BRITISH DEPENDENT TERRITORY
CAPITAL CITY: Adamstown
AREA: 48 sq km
POPULATION: 60 people

Poland
CAPITAL CITY: Warsaw
AREA: 312,680 sq km (Land area 304,420 sq km)
POPULATION: 38,587,000 people
POPULATION DENSITY: 127 people per sq km
POPULATION CHANGE: 0.1% per year
BIRTH RATE: 12 per 1,000 people
DEATH RATE: 10 per 1,000 people
LIFE EXPECTANCY: Males 68, females 77 years
INFANT MORTALITY: 12 per 1,000 live births
URBAN POPULATION: 64% of population
FERTILITY RATE: 2 children per female
AGE GROUPS: 0–14 yrs 25%, 15–59 yrs 60%, 60+ yrs 15%
ETHNIC GROUPS: Polish 99%, Ukrainian 1%
LANGUAGES: Polish
RELIGIONS: Roman Catholic 91%, other Christian 4%
LAND USE: Arable 47%, grass 13%, forest 29%
EMPLOYMENT: Agric. 27%, ind. 37%, services 36%
ANNUAL INCOME: $2,790 per person, –0.4%
ORIGIN OF INCOME: Agriculture 6%, industry 39%, services 55%
ENERGY: Prod. 3.35 tonnes, consump. 3.48 tonnes
TRADE: $857 per person
CURRENCY: Zloty = 100 groszy
ROADS: 1,224 km per 1,000 sq km of land
RAILWAYS: 82 km per 1,000 sq km of land
POPULATION PER DOCTOR: 467 people
ADULT LITERACY: 99%
EDUCATIONAL EXPENDITURE: 4.9% of GNP
MILITARY EXPENDITURE: 2.3% of GNP

Portugal
CAPITAL CITY: Lisbon
AREA: 92,390 sq km
POPULATION: 10,600,000 people
POPULATION DENSITY: 110 people per sq km
POPULATION CHANGE: –0.3% per year
BIRTH RATE: 11 per 1,000 people
DEATH RATE: 10 per 1,000 people
LIFE EXPECTANCY: Males 72, females 79 years
INFANT MORTALITY: 8 per 1,000 live births
URBAN POPULATION: 36% of population
FERTILITY RATE: 2 children per female
AGE GROUPS: 0–14 yrs 21%, 15–59 yrs 16%, 60+ yrs 18%
ETHNIC GROUPS: Portuguese 99%, Cape Verdean, Brazilian, Spanish, British
LANGUAGES: Portuguese
RELIGIONS: Roman Catholic 95%
LAND USE: Arable 26%, grass 9%, forest 36%
EMPLOYMENT: Agric. 17%, ind. 34%, services 49%
ANNUAL INCOME: $9,740 per person, 3.7%
ORIGIN OF INCOME: Agriculture 6%, industry 38%, services 56%
ENERGY: Prod. 0.08 tonnes, consump. 2.11 tonnes
TRADE: $4,017 per person
CURRENCY: Escudo = 100 centavos
ROADS: 763 km per 1,000 sq km of land
RAILWAYS: 33 km per 1,000 sq km of land
POPULATION PER DOCTOR: 352 people
ADULT LITERACY: 86%
EDUCATIONAL EXPENDITURE: 5.5% of GNP
MILITARY EXPENDITURE: 2.9% of GNP
AID GIVEN: $27 per person

Puerto Rico
COMMONWEALTH ASSOCIATED WITH US
CAPITAL CITY: San Juan
AREA: 8,900 sq km
POPULATION: 3,689,000 people
POPULATION DENSITY: 432 people per sq km
POPULATION CHANGE: 1.4% per year
BIRTH RATE: 18 per 1,000 people
DEATH RATE: 8 per 1,000 people
LIFE EXPECTANCY: Males 71, females 80 years
INFANT MORTALITY: 11 per 1,000 live births
URBAN POPULATION: 77% of population
FERTILITY RATE: 2 children per female
AGE GROUPS: 0–14 yrs 26%, 15–59 yrs 60%, 60+ yrs 14%
ETHNIC GROUPS: Spanish 99%, Negro, Indian
LANGUAGES: Spanish, English
RELIGIONS: Roman Catholic 80%
LAND USE: Arable 7%, grass 38%, forest 20%
EMPLOYMENT: Agric. 3%, ind. 25%, services 72%

ANNUAL INCOME: $7,500 per person, 2.1%
ORIGIN OF INCOME: Agriculture 1%, industry 41%, services 58%
ENERGY: Prod. 0.01 tonnes, consump. 2.27 tonnes
TRADE: $7,459 per person
CURRENCY: US currency
ROADS: 2,612 km per 1,000 sq km of land
RAILWAYS: 11 km per 1,000 sq km of land
POPULATION PER DOCTOR: 350 people
ADULT LITERACY: 89%
EDUCATIONAL EXPENDITURE: 8.2% of GNP

Qatar
CAPITAL CITY: Doha
AREA: 11,000 sq km
POPULATION: 594,000 people
POPULATION DENSITY: 56 people per sq km
POPULATION CHANGE: 7.7% per year
BIRTH RATE: 20 per 1,000 people
DEATH RATE: 4 per 1,000 people
LIFE EXPECTANCY: Males 71, females 76 years
INFANT MORTALITY: 19 per 1,000 live births
URBAN POPULATION: 91% of population
FERTILITY RATE: 4 children per female
AGE GROUPS: 0–14 yrs 35%, 15–59 yrs 62%, 60+ yrs 4%
ETHNIC GROUPS: Southern Asian 34%, Qatari 20%
LANGUAGES: Arabic
RELIGIONS: Sunni Muslim 92%, Christian, Hindu
LAND USE: Arable 1%, grass 5%, forest 0%
EMPLOYMENT: Agric. 3%, ind. 28%, services 69%
ANNUAL INCOME: $11,600 per person, –2.6%
ORIGIN OF INCOME: Agriculture 1%, industry 49%, services 50%
ENERGY: Prod. 109.6 tonnes, consump. 39.58 tonnes
TRADE: $9,654 per person
CURRENCY: Riyal = 100 dirhams
ROADS: 98 km per 1,000 sq km of land
POPULATION PER DOCTOR: 650 people
ADULT LITERACY: 78%
EDUCATIONAL EXPENDITURE: 3.4% of GNP
MILITARY EXPENDITURE: 9.3% of GNP

Réunion
FRENCH OVERSEAS DEPARTMENT
CAPITAL CITY: Saint-Denis
AREA: 2,510 sq km
POPULATION: 655,000 people
POPULATION DENSITY: 272 people per sq km
POPULATION CHANGE: 1.8% per year
BIRTH RATE: 23 per 1,000 people
DEATH RATE: 5 per 1,000 people
LIFE EXPECTANCY: Males 72, females 78 years
INFANT MORTALITY: 7 per 1,000 live births
URBAN POPULATION: 74% of population
FERTILITY RATE: 2 children per female
AGE GROUPS: 0–14 yrs 32%, 15–59 yrs 61%, 60+ yrs 8%
ETHNIC GROUPS: Mixed 64%, East Indian 28%, Chinese 2%, White 2%, East African 1%
LANGUAGES: French, Creole
RELIGIONS: Roman Catholic 90%, Muslim 2%
LAND USE: Arable 17%, grass 5%, forest 35%
EMPLOYMENT: Agric. 5%, ind. 11%, services 84%
ANNUAL INCOME: $4,500 per person
ORIGIN OF WEALTH: Agric. 6%, ind. 17%, services 77%
ENERGY: Prod. 0.14 tonnes, consump. 1.01 tonnes
TRADE: $3,532 per person
CURRENCY: French currency
ROADS: 1,102 km per 1,000 sq km of land
RAILWAYS: 246 km per 1,000 sq km of land
POPULATION PER DOCTOR: 1,250 people
EDUCATIONAL EXPENDITURE: 15.6% of GNP
ADULT LITERACY: 78%

Romania
CAPITAL CITY: Bucharest
AREA: 237,500 sq km (Land area 230,340 sq km)
POPULATION: 22,863,000 people
POPULATION DENSITY: 98 people per sq km
POPULATION CHANGE: –0.3% per year
BIRTH RATE: 10 per 1,000 people
DEATH RATE: 12 per 1,000 people
LIFE EXPECTANCY: Males 66, females 74 years
INFANT MORTALITY: 23 per 1,000 live births
URBAN POPULATION: 55% of population
FERTILITY RATE: 2 children per female
AGE GROUPS: 0–14 yrs 23%, 15–59 yrs 61%, 60+ yrs 16%
ETHNIC GROUPS: Romanian 89%, Hungarian 8%
LANGUAGES: Romanian, Hungarian, Romany
RELIGIONS: Romanian Orthodox 87%, Roman Catholic 5%, Greek Orthodox 4%
LAND USE: Arable 41%, grass 21%, forest 29%
EMPLOYMENT: Agric. 29%, ind. 43%, services 28%
ANNUAL INCOME: $1,480 per person, –4%
ORIGIN OF INCOME: Agriculture 21%, industry 40%, services 40%
ENERGY: Prod. 2.0 tonnes, consump. 2.70 tonnes
TRADE: $541 per person
CURRENCY: Leu = 100 bani
ROADS: 664 km per 1,000 sq km of land
RAILWAYS: 49 km per 1,000 sq km of land
POPULATION PER DOCTOR: 552 people

ADULT LITERACY: 97%
EDUCATIONAL EXPENDITURE: 3.1% of GNP
MILITARY EXPENDITURE: 2.9% of GNP
AID RECEIVED: $3 per person

Russia
CAPITAL CITY: Moscow
AREA: 17,075,400 sq km
POPULATION: 148,385,000 people
POPULATION DENSITY: 9 people per sq km
POPULATION CHANGE: 0% per year
BIRTH RATE: 11 per 1,000 people
DEATH RATE: 16 per 1,000 people
LIFE EXPECTANCY: Males 57, females 71 years
INFANT MORTALITY: 24 per 1,000 live births
URBAN POPULATION: 75% of population
FERTILITY RATE: 2 children per female
AGE GROUPS: 0–14 yrs 22%, 15–59 yrs 58%, 60+ yrs 20%
ETHNIC GROUPS: Russian 82%, Tatar 4%, Ukrainian 3%, Chuvash 2%
LANGUAGES: Russian, Tatar, Chuvash, Bashkir, Ukrainian, Mordvin, Mari, local languages
RELIGIONS: Russian Orthodox 40%, Muslim, Jewish
LAND USE: Arable 8%, grass 6%, forest 45%
EMPLOYMENT: Agric. 20%, ind. 46%, services 34%
ANNUAL INCOME: $2,240 per person, –5.1%
ORIGIN OF INCOME: Agriculture 12%, industry 48%, services 40%
ENERGY: Prod. 10.81 tonnes, consump. 7.36 tonnes
TRADE: $492 per person
CURRENCY: Rouble = 100 kopeks
ROADS: 56 km per 1,000 sq km of land
RAILWAYS: 9 km per 1,000 sq km of land
POPULATION PER DOCTOR: 222 people
ADULT LITERACY: 99%
EDUCATIONAL EXPENDITURE: 8% of GNP
MILITARY EXPENDITURE: 8% of GNP
AID RECEIVED: $12 per person

Rwanda
CAPITAL CITY: Kigali
AREA: 26,340 sq km (Land area 24,670 sq km)
POPULATION: 7,899,000 people
POPULATION DENSITY: 284 people per sq km
POPULATION CHANGE: –0.4% per year
BIRTH RATE: 39 per 1,000 people
DEATH RATE: 21 per 1,000 people
LIFE EXPECTANCY: Males 39, females 40 years
INFANT MORTALITY: 119 per 1,000 live births
URBAN POPULATION: 6% of population
FERTILITY RATE: 7 children per female
AGE GROUPS: 0–14 yrs 49%, 15–59 yrs 47%, 60+ yrs 4%
ETHNIC GROUPS: Hutu 90%, Tutsi 9%, Twa 1%
LANGUAGES: English, French, Kinyarwanda
RELIGIONS: Roman Catholic 65%, Protestant 12%, Muslim and traditional beliefs
LAND USE: Arable 35%, grass 18%, forest 22%
EMPLOYMENT: Agric. 90%, ind. 2%, services 8%
ANNUAL INCOME: $180 per person, –5%
ORIGIN OF INCOME: Agriculture 41%, industry 22%, services 38%
ENERGY: Consumption 0.03 tonnes per person
TRADE: $48 per person
CURRENCY: Rwandan franc = 100 centimes
ROADS: 590 km per 1,000 sq km of land
POPULATION PER DOCTOR: 25,000 people
ADULT LITERACY: 57%
EDUCATIONAL EXPENDITURE: 4.2% of GNP
MILITARY EXPENDITURE: 6.8% of GNP
AID RECEIVED: $92 per person

St Helena
DEPENDENT TERRITORY OF UK
CAPITAL CITY: Jamestown
AREA: 122 sq km
POPULATION: 8,200 people
POPULATION DENSITY: 20 people per sq km
POPULATION CHANGE: 2.6% per year
BIRTH RATE: 9 per 1,000 people
DEATH RATE: 7 per 1,000 people
LIFE EXPECTANCY: Males 74, females 77 years
INFANT MORTALITY: 34 per 1,000 live births
FERTILITY RATE: 1 child per female
ETHNIC GROUPS: Mixed European (British), Asian and African
LANGUAGES: English
RELIGIONS: Protestant 90%
TRADE: $373 per person
CURRENCY: St Helenian £ = 100 pence
ADULT LITERACY: 98%

St Kitts and Nevis
CAPITAL CITY: Basseterre
AREA: 360 sq km
POPULATION: 45,000 people
POPULATION DENSITY: 117 people per sq km
POPULATION CHANGE: –0.7% per year
BIRTH RATE: 23 per 1,000 people
DEATH RATE: 9 per 1,000 people
LIFE EXPECTANCY: Males 64, females 70 years
INFANT MORTALITY: 18 per 1,000 live births
URBAN POPULATION: 41% of population
FERTILITY RATE: 3 children per female

AGE GROUPS: 0–14 yrs 32%, 15–59 yrs 52%, 60+ yrs 16%
ETHNIC GROUPS: Of African descent
LANGUAGES: English, Creole
RELIGIONS: Protestant 62%, Roman Catholic 7%
LAND USE: Arable 22%, grass 3%, forest 17%
EMPLOYMENT: Agric. 26%, ind. 25%, services 49%
ANNUAL INCOME: $5,170 per person, 4.6%
ORIGIN OF INCOME: Agriculture 6%, industry 26%, services 68%
ENERGY: Consumption 0.83 tonnes
TRADE: $3,475 per person
CURRENCY: East Caribbean $ = 100 cents
ROADS: 861 km per 1,000 sq km of land
POPULATION PER DOCTOR: 2,000 people
ADULT LITERACY: 99%
EDUCATIONAL EXPENDITURE: 2.8% of GNP
AID RECEIVED: $262 per person

St Lucia
CAPITAL CITY: Castries
AREA: 620 sq km (Land area: 610 sq km)
POPULATION: 147,000 people
POPULATION DENSITY: 246 people per sq km
POPULATION CHANGE: 0% per year
BIRTH RATE: 22 per 1,000 people
DEATH RATE: 6 per 1,000 people
LIFE EXPECTANCY: Males 67, females 74 years
INFANT MORTALITY: 20 per 1,000 live births
URBAN POPULATION: 47% of population
FERTILITY RATE: 3 children per female
AGE GROUPS: 0–14 yrs 36%, 15–59 yrs 55%, 60+ yrs 9%
ETHNIC GROUPS: African descent 90%, Mixed 6%, East Indian 3%
LANGUAGES: English, French patois
RELIGIONS: Roman Catholic 79%, Protestant 16%
LAND USE: Arable 8%, grass 5%, forest 13%
EMPLOYMENT: Agric. 26%, ind. 15%, services 59%
ANNUAL INCOME: $3,370 per person, 3.9%
ORIGIN OF INCOME: Agriculture 11%, industry 21%, services 68%
ENERGY: Consumption 3.45 tonnes per person
TRADE: $3,114 per person
CURRENCY: East Caribbean $ = 100 cents
ROADS: 1,320 km per 1,000 sq km of land
POPULATION PER DOCTOR: 2,000 people
ADULT LITERACY: 93%
EDUCATIONAL EXPENDITURE: 5.5% of GNP
AID RECEIVED: $194 per person

St Pierre and Miquelon
CAPITAL CITY: Saint-Pierre
AREA: 242 sq km
POPULATION: 6,750 people
POPULATION DENSITY: 30 people per sq km
POPULATION CHANGE: 2.2% per year
BIRTH RATE: 13 per 1,000 people
DEATH RATE: 6 per 1,000 people
LIFE EXPECTANCY: Males 75, females 79 years
INFANT MORTALITY: 9 per 1,000 live births
FERTILITY RATE: 1 child per female
ETHNIC GROUPS: Basque and Breton descent
LANGUAGES: French
RELIGIONS: Roman Catholic 98%
LAND USE: Arable 13%, forest 4%
ANNUAL INCOME: $10,000 per person
ENERGY: Consumption 7.5 tonnes per person
TRADE: $14,429 per person
CURRENCY: French currency
ADULT LITERACY: 99%
EDUCATIONAL EXPENDITURE: 8% of GNP

St Vincent and the Grenadines
CAPITAL CITY: Kingstown
AREA: 388 sq km
POPULATION: 111,000 people
POPULATION DENSITY: 292 people per sq km
POPULATION CHANGE: 0.3% per year
BIRTH RATE: 19 per 1,000 people
DEATH RATE: 5 per 1,000 people
LIFE EXPECTANCY: Males 72, females 75 years
INFANT MORTALITY: 16 per 1,000 live births
URBAN POPULATION: 43% of population
FERTILITY RATE: 2 children per female
AGE GROUPS: 0–14 yrs 32%, 15–59 yrs 60%, 60+ yrs 8%
ETHNIC GROUPS: Of African descent
LANGUAGES: English, French patois
RELIGIONS: Protestant 63%, Roman Catholic 12%
LAND USE: Arable 10%, grass 5%, forest 36%
EMPLOYMENT: Agric. 26%, ind. 17%, services 57%
ANNUAL INCOME: $2,280 per person, 3.9%
ORIGIN OF INCOME: Agriculture 18%, industry 23%, services 59%
ENERGY: Prod. 0.04 tonnes, consump. 0.41 tonnes
TRADE: $1,991 per person
CURRENCY: East Caribbean $ = 100 cents
ROADS: 2,615 km per 1,000 sq km of land
POPULATION PER DOCTOR: 2,000 people
ADULT LITERACY: 98%
EDUCATIONAL EXPENDITURE: 6.7% of GNP
AID RECEIVED: $127 per person

San Marino

CAPITAL CITY: San Marino
AREA: 61 sq km
POPULATION: 26,000 people
POPULATION DENSITY: 433 people per sq km
POPULATION CHANGE: 1.8% per year
BIRTH RATE: 11 per 1,000 people
DEATH RATE: 8 per 1,000 people
LIFE EXPECTANCY: Males 77, females 85 years
INFANT MORTALITY: 6 per 1,000 live births
FERTILITY RATE: 1 child per female
ETHNIC GROUPS: San Marinese, Italian
LANGUAGES: *Italian*
RELIGIONS: Roman Catholic 99%
LAND USE: Arable 17%
ANNUAL INCOME: $17,000 per person
CURRENCY: Italian currency and San Marino lira = 100 centisimi
ROADS: 3,950 km per 1,000 sq km of land
ADULT LITERACY: 96%

São Tomé and Príncipe

CAPITAL CITY: São Tomé
AREA: 964 sq km
POPULATION: 133,000 people
POPULATION DENSITY: 141 people per sq km
POPULATION CHANGE: 1.8% per year
BIRTH RATE: 34 per 1,000 people
DEATH RATE: 8 per 1,000 people
LIFE EXPECTANCY: Males 62, females 66 years
INFANT MORTALITY: 60 per 1,000 live births
URBAN POPULATION: 45% of population
FERTILITY RATE: 5 children per female
AGE GROUPS: 0–14 yrs 41%, 15–59 yrs 50%, 60+ yrs 9%
ETHNIC GROUPS: Mainly descendants of slaves
LANGUAGES: *Portuguese*, Creole
RELIGIONS: Roman Catholic 81%
LAND USE: Arable 2%, grass 1%
EMPLOYMENT: Agric. 54%, ind. 12%, services 34%
ANNUAL INCOME: $350 per person, –2.1%
ORIGIN OF INCOME: Agriculture 24%, industry 13%, services 63%
ENERGY: Prod. 0.01 tonnes, consump. 0.29 tonnes
TRADE: $303 per person
CURRENCY: Dobra = 100 centimos
ROADS: 250 km per 1,000 sq km of land
POPULATION PER DOCTOR: 1,800 people
ADULT LITERACY: 60%
EDUCATIONAL EXPENDITURE: 4.3% of GNP
MILITARY EXPENDITURE: 1.6% of GNP
AID RECEIVED: $378 per person

Saudi Arabia

CAPITAL CITY: Riyadh
AREA: 2,149,690 sq km
POPULATION: 18,395,000 people
POPULATION DENSITY: 9 people per sq km
POPULATION CHANGE: 4.4% per year
BIRTH RATE: 38 per 1,000 people
DEATH RATE: 5 per 1,000 people
LIFE EXPECTANCY: Males 68, females 71 years
INFANT MORTALITY: 44 per 1,000 live births
URBAN POPULATION: 79% of population
FERTILITY RATE: 6 children per female
AGE GROUPS: 0–14 yrs 45%, 15–59 yrs 51%, 60+ yrs 4%
ETHNIC GROUPS: Arab 92% (Saudi 82% and Yemeni 10%)
LANGUAGES: *Arabic*
RELIGIONS: Sunni Muslim 92%, Shiite Muslim 8%
LAND USE: Arable 2%, grass 56%, forest 1%
EMPLOYMENT: Agric. 48%, ind. 14%, services 38%
ANNUAL INCOME: $7,040 per person, –1.9%
ORIGIN OF INCOME: Agriculture 6%, industry 50%, services 43%
ENERGY: Prod. 42.92 tonnes, consump. 6.10 tonnes
TRADE: $4,636 per person
CURRENCY: Riyal = 100 halalas
ROADS: 73 km per 1,000 sq km of land
POPULATION PER DOCTOR: 704 people
ADULT LITERACY: 61%
EDUCATIONAL EXPENDITURE: 6.2% of GNP
MILITARY EXPENDITURE: 11.8% of GNP

Senegal

CAPITAL CITY: Dakar
AREA: 196,720 sq km (Land area 192,530 sq km)
POPULATION: 8,308,000 people
POPULATION DENSITY: 46 people per sq km
POPULATION CHANGE: 2.8% per year
BIRTH RATE: 45 per 1,000 people
DEATH RATE: 11 per 1,000 people
LIFE EXPECTANCY: Males 54, females 60 years
INFANT MORTALITY: 63 per 1,000 live births
URBAN POPULATION: 42% of population
FERTILITY RATE: 6 children per female
AGE GROUPS: 0–14 yrs 45%, 15–59 yrs 50%, 60+ yrs 5%
ETHNIC GROUPS: Wolof 44%, Fulani 23%, Serer 4%
LANGUAGES: *French*, Wolof, tribal languages
RELIGIONS: Sunni Muslim 94%, Christian 5%, animist
LAND USE: Arable 12%, grass 16%, forest 54%

EMPLOYMENT: Agric. 81%, ind. 6%, services 13%
ANNUAL INCOME: $600 per person, –1.2%
ORIGIN OF INCOME: Agriculture 19%, industry 19%, services 62%
ENERGY: Consumption 0.15 tonnes
TRADE: $271 per person
CURRENCY: CFA franc = 100 centimes
ROADS: 74 km per 1,000 sq km of land
RAILWAYS: 5 km per 1,000 sq km of land
POPULATION PER DOCTOR: 16,667 people
ADULT LITERACY: 31%
EDUCATIONAL EXPENDITURE: 3.7% of GNP
MILITARY EXPENDITURE: 2.1% of GNP
AID RECEIVED: $63 per person

Seychelles

CAPITAL: Victoria
AREA: 455 sq km
POPULATION: 75,000 people
POPULATION DENSITY: 173 people per sq km
POPULATION CHANGE: 2.2% per year
BIRTH RATE: 21 per 1,000 people
DEATH RATE: 7 per 1,000 people
LIFE EXPECTANCY: Males 65, females 74 years
INFANT MORTALITY: 12 per 1,000 live births
URBAN POPULATION: 52% of population
FERTILITY RATE: 3 children per female
AGE GROUPS: 0–14 yrs 34%, 15–59 yrs 55%, 60+ yrs 11%
ETHNIC GROUPS: Mixture of African, Asian and European
LANGUAGES: *Seselwa*, English, French
RELIGIONS: Roman Catholic 89%, Anglican 9%
LAND USE: Arable 2%, forest 11%
EMPLOYMENT: Agric. 9%, ind. 18%, services 73%
ANNUAL INCOME: $6,620 per person, 4.2%
ORIGIN OF INCOME: Agriculture 4%, industry 19%, services 77%
ENERGY: Consumption 0.99 tonnes per person
TRADE: $3,486 per person
CURRENCY: Rupee = 100 cents
ROADS: 736 km per 1,000 sq km of land
POPULATION PER DOCTOR: 2,000 people
ADULT LITERACY: 77%
EDUCATIONAL EXPENDITURE: 8.5% of GNP
MILITARY EXPENDITURE: 4% of GNP
AID RECEIVED: $515 per person

Sierra Leone

CAPITAL CITY: Freetown
AREA: 71,740 sq km
POPULATION: 4,467,000 people
POPULATION DENSITY: 64 people per sq km
POPULATION CHANGE: 1.5% per year
BIRTH RATE: 47 per 1,000 people
DEATH RATE: 18 per 1,000 people
LIFE EXPECTANCY: Males 45, females 51 years
INFANT MORTALITY: 133 per 1,000 live births
URBAN POPULATION: 35% of population
FERTILITY RATE: 7 children per female
AGE GROUPS: 0–14 yrs 45%, 15–59 yrs 50%, 60+ yrs 5%
ETHNIC GROUPS: Mande 34%, Temne 31%, Limba 8%
LANGUAGES: *English*, Creole, Mande, Limba, Temne
RELIGIONS: Sunni Muslim 60%, Traditional beliefs 30%, Christian 10%
LAND USE: Arable 7%, grass 31%, forest 28%
EMPLOYMENT: Agric. 70%, ind. 14%, services 16%
ANNUAL INCOME: $180 per person, –3.4%
ORIGIN OF INCOME: Agriculture 38%, industry 16%, services 46%
ENERGY: Consumption 0.04 tonnes per person
TRADE: $62 per person
CURRENCY: Leone = 100 cents
ROADS: 163 km per 1,000 sq km of land
RAILWAYS: 1 km per 1,000 sq km of land
POPULATION PER DOCTOR: 12,500 people
ADULT LITERACY: 29%
EDUCATIONAL EXPENDITURE: 1.4% of GNP
MILITARY EXPENDITURE: 2.3% of GNP
AID RECEIVED: $45 per person

Singapore

CAPITAL CITY: Singapore
AREA: 618 sq km
POPULATION: 2,990,000 people
POPULATION DENSITY: 5,246 people per sq km
POPULATION CHANGE: 2.5% per year
BIRTH RATE: 16 per 1,000 people
DEATH RATE: 5 per 1,000 people
LIFE EXPECTANCY: Males 75, females 82 years
INFANT MORTALITY: 5 per 1,000 live births
URBAN POPULATION: 100% of population
FERTILITY RATE: 2 children per female
AGE GROUPS: 0–14 yrs 23%, 15–59 yrs 68%, 60+ yrs 9%
ETHNIC GROUPS: Chinese 76%, Malay 14%, Indian 7%
LANGUAGES: *Mandarin, Malay, Tamil, English*
RELIGIONS: Buddhist 38%, Muslim 15%, Christian 13%, Taoist 13%, Hindu 4%
LAND USE: Arable 2%, forest 5%
EMPLOYMENT: Ind. 35%, services 65%
ANNUAL INCOME: $26,730 per person, 6.2%

ORIGIN OF INCOME: Industry 36%, services 64%
ENERGY: Consumption 8.5 tonnes per person
TRADE: $55,483 per person
CURRENCY: Singapore $ = 100 cents
ROADS: 4,900 km per 1,000 sq km of land
RAILWAYS: 110 km per 1,000 sq km of land
POPULATION PER DOCTOR: 725 people
ADULT LITERACY: 90%
EDUCATIONAL EXPENDITURE: 3.4% of GNP
MILITARY EXPENDITURE: 5.4% of GNP
AID RECEIVED: $6 per person

Slovak Republic

CAPITAL CITY: Bratislava
AREA: 49,000 sq km (Land area 48,080 sq km)
POPULATION: 5,400,000 people
POPULATION DENSITY: 110 people per sq km
POPULATION CHANGE: 0.3% per year
BIRTH RATE: 13 per 1,000 people
DEATH RATE: 9 per 1,000 people
LIFE EXPECTANCY: Males 69, females 77 years
INFANT MORTALITY: 11 per 1,000 live births
URBAN POPULATION: 58% of population
FERTILITY RATE: 2 children per female
ETHNIC GROUPS: Slovak 86%, Hungarian 11%
LANGUAGES: *Slovak*, Hungarian
RELIGIONS: Roman Catholic 60%, Protestant 8%
LAND USE: Arable 31%, grass 17%, forest 41%
EMPLOYMENT: Agriculture 14%, industry 42%, services 44%
ANNUAL INCOME: $2,950 per person, –2.6%
ORIGIN OF WEALTH: Agriculture 6%, industry 44%, services 50%
ENERGY: Consumption 4.25 tonnes
TRADE: $1,300 per person
CURRENCY: Koruna = 100 halura
ROADS: 372 km per 1,000 sq km of land
RAILWAYS: 76 km per 1,000 sq km of land
POPULATION PER DOCTOR: 275 people
ADULT LITERACY: 99%
EDUCATIONAL EXPENDITURE: 7% of GNP
AID RECEIVED: $6 per person

Slovenia

CAPITAL CITY: Ljubljana
AREA: 20,251 sq km
POPULATION: 2,000,000 people
POPULATION DENSITY: 99 people per sq km
POPULATION CHANGE: 0.2% per year
BIRTH RATE: 8 per 1,000 people
DEATH RATE: 10 per 1,000 people
LIFE EXPECTANCY: Males 71, females 79 years
INFANT MORTALITY: 7 per 1,000 live births
URBAN POPULATION: 50% of population
FERTILITY RATE: 1 children per female
AGE GROUPS: 0–14 yrs 20%, 15–59 yrs 62%, 60+ yrs 18%
ETHNIC GROUPS: Slovene 90%, Croat 3%, Serb 2%, Muslim 1%
LANGUAGES: *Slovene*, Serbo-Croat
RELIGIONS: Roman Catholic 98%, Orthodox 2%, Muslim 1%
LAND USE: Arable 12%, grass 32%, forest 50%
EMPLOYMENT: Agric. 13%, ind. 39%, services 48%
ANNUAL INCOME: $8,200 per person, –1%
ORIGIN OF INCOME: Agriculture 8%, industry 61%, services 31%
ENERGY: Prod. 1.54 tonnes, consump. 1.88 tonnes
TRADE: $4,000 per person
CURRENCY: Tolar = 100 stotin
ROADS: 726 km per 1,000 sq km of land
RAILWAYS: 59 km per 1,000 sq km of land
POPULATION PER DOCTOR: 500 people
ADULT LITERACY: 99%

Solomon Islands

CAPITAL CITY: Honiara
AREA: 28,900 sq km (Land area 27,990 sq km)
POPULATION: 378,000 people
POPULATION DENSITY: 15 people per sq km
POPULATION CHANGE: 3.6% per year
BIRTH RATE: 37 per 1,000 people
DEATH RATE: 4 per 1,000 people
LIFE EXPECTANCY: Males 69, females 74 years
INFANT MORTALITY: 25 per 1,000 live births
URBAN POPULATION: 20% of population
FERTILITY RATE: 5 children per female
AGE GROUPS: 0–14 yrs 43%, 15–59 yrs 52%, 60+ yrs 5%
ETHNIC GROUPS: Melanesian 94%, Polynesian 4%
LANGUAGES: *English*, Melanesian languages
RELIGIONS: Anglican 34%, Roman Catholic 19%, Evangelical 18%
LAND USE: Arable 1%, grass 1%, forest 91%
EMPLOYMENT: Agric. 24%, ind. 13%, services 63%
ANNUAL INCOME: $910 per person, 2.2%
ORIGIN OF INCOME: Agriculture 35%, industry 7%, services 58%
ENERGY: Consumption 0.22 tonnes per person
TRADE: $563 per person
CURRENCY: Solomon Is $ = 100 cents
ROADS: 48 km per 1,000 sq km of land
POPULATION PER DOCTOR: 6,500 people
ADULT LITERACY: 24%
EDUCATIONAL EXPENDITURE: 4.2% of GNP
AID RECEIVED: $181 per person

Somalia

CAPITAL CITY: Mogadishu
AREA: 637,660 sq km (Land area 627,340 sq km)
POPULATION: 9,180,000 people
POPULATION DENSITY: 16 people per sq km
POPULATION CHANGE: 1.9% per year
BIRTH RATE: 44 per 1,000 people
DEATH RATE: 13 per 1,000 people
LIFE EXPECTANCY: Males 56, females 56 years
INFANT MORTALITY: 119 per 1,000 live births
URBAN POPULATION: 27% of population
FERTILITY RATE: 7 children per female
AGE GROUPS: 0–14 yrs 47%, 15–59 yrs 49%, 60+ yrs 4%
ETHNIC GROUPS: Somali 98%, Arab 1%
LANGUAGES: *Somali, Arabic*, English, Italian
RELIGIONS: Sunni Muslim 99%
LAND USE: Arable 2%, grass 69%, forest 14%
EMPLOYMENT: Agric. 76%, ind. 8%, services 16%
ANNUAL INCOME: $500 per person, –2.3%
ORIGIN OF INCOME: Agriculture 65%, industry 9%, services 26%
ENERGY: Consumption 0.05 tonnes per person
TRADE: $29 per person
CURRENCY: Shilling = 100 cents
ROADS: 36 km per 1,000 sq km of land
POPULATION PER DOCTOR: 14,000 people
ADULT LITERACY: 27%
EDUCATIONAL EXPENDITURE: 0.4% of GNP
MILITARY EXPENDITURE: 3.2% of GNP
AID RECEIVED: $61 per person

South Africa

CAPITAL CITY: Pretoria/Cape Town/Bloemfontein
AREA: 1,221,040 sq km
POPULATION: 44,000,000 people
POPULATION DENSITY: 35 people per sq km
POPULATION CHANGE: 1.6% per year
BIRTH RATE: 27 per 1,000 people
DEATH RATE: 12 per 1,000 people
LIFE EXPECTANCY: Males 54, females 58 years
INFANT MORTALITY: 53 per 1,000 live births
URBAN POPULATION: 57% of population
FERTILITY RATE: 4 children per female
AGE GROUPS: 0–14 yrs 37%, 15–59 yrs 57%, 60+ yrs 6%
ETHNIC GROUPS: Black 76%, White 13%, Coloured 9%, Asian 3%
LANGUAGES: *Afrikaans, English, Ndebele, Pedi, Sotho, Swazi, Tsonga, Tswana, Venda, Xhosa, Zulu*
RELIGIONS: Black Christian churches 19%, Dutch Reform 11%, Roman Catholic 8%, Hindu 2%
LAND USE: Arable 10%, grass 67%, forest 4%
EMPLOYMENT: Agric. 13%, ind. 25%, services 62%
ANNUAL INCOME: $3,160 per person, –1%
ORIGIN OF INCOME: Agriculture 4%, industry 40%, services 56%
ENERGY: Prod. 3.42 tonnes, consump. 2.49 tonnes
TRADE: $1,151 per person
CURRENCY: Rand = 100 cents
ROADS: 149 km per 1,000 sq km of land
RAILWAYS: 17 km per 1,000 sq km of land
POPULATION PER DOCTOR: 1,750 people
ADULT LITERACY: 81%
EDUCATIONAL EXPENDITURE: 3.8% of GNP
MILITARY EXPENDITURE: 3.0% of GNP
AID RECEIVED: $10 per person

Spain

CAPITAL CITY: Madrid
AREA: 504,780 sq km (Land area 499,440 sq km)
POPULATION: 39,664,000 people
POPULATION DENSITY: 79 people per sq km
POPULATION CHANGE: 0% per year
BIRTH RATE: 10 per 1,000 people
DEATH RATE: 9 per 1,000 people
LIFE EXPECTANCY: Males 75, females 82 years
INFANT MORTALITY: 6 per 1,000 live births
URBAN POPULATION: 77% of population
FERTILITY RATE: 1 child per female
AGE GROUPS: 0–14 yrs 20%, 15–59 yrs 62%, 60+ yrs 18%
ETHNIC GROUPS: Castilian Spanish 73%, Catalan 16%, Galician 8%, Basque 2%
LANGUAGES: *Castilian Spanish*, Basque (Euskera), Catalan, Galician
RELIGIONS: Roman Catholic 94%, Muslim 1%
LAND USE: Arable 30%, grass 21%, forest 32%
EMPLOYMENT: Agric. 11%, ind. 33%, services 56%
ANNUAL INCOME: $13,580 per person, 2.6%
ORIGIN OF INCOME: Agriculture 5%, industry 35%, services 61%
ENERGY: Prod. 1.08 tonnes, consump. 3.11 tonnes
TRADE: $3,704 per person
CURRENCY: Peseta = 100 céntimos
ROADS: 683 km per 1,000 sq km of land
RAILWAYS: 25 km per 1,000 sq km of land
POPULATION PER DOCTOR: 262 people
ADULT LITERACY: 98%
EDUCATIONAL EXPENDITURE: 5.6% of GNP
MILITARY EXPENDITURE: 1.7% of GNP
AID GIVEN: $31 per person

Sri Lanka

CAPITAL CITY: Colombo

AREA: 65,610 sq km (Land area 64,630 sq km)
POPULATION: 18,359,000 people
POPULATION DENSITY: 289 people per sq km
POPULATION CHANGE: 1.2% per year
BIRTH RATE: 18 per 1,000 people
DEATH RATE: 6 per 1,000 people
LIFE EXPECTANCY: Males 70, females 75 years
INFANT MORTALITY: 20 per 1,000 live births
URBAN POPULATION: 22% of population
FERTILITY RATE: 3 children per female
AGE GROUPS: 0–14 yrs 33%, 15–59 yrs 59%, 60+ yrs 8%
ETHNIC GROUPS: Sinhalese 83%, Tamil 19%, Sri Lankan Moor 8%
LANGUAGES: *Sinhala, Tamil*, English
RELIGIONS: Buddhist 69%, Hindu 16%, Muslim 8%, Roman Catholic 8%
LAND USE: Arable 14%, grass 7%, forest 32%
EMPLOYMENT: Agric. 49%, ind. 21%, services 30%
ANNUAL INCOME: $700 per person, 2.7%
ORIGIN OF INCOME: Agriculture 25%, industry 26%, services 50%
ENERGY: Prod. 0.02 tonnes, consump. 0.15 tonnes
TRADE: $370 per person
CURRENCY: Rupee = 100 cents
ROADS: 402 km per 1,000 sq km of land
RAILWAYS: 23 km per 1,000 sq km of land
POPULATION PER DOCTOR: 7,143 people
ADULT LITERACY: 89%
EDUCATIONAL EXPENDITURE: 2.7% of GNP
MILITARY EXPENDITURE: 4.9% of GNP
AID RECEIVED: $31 per person

Sudan

CAPITAL CITY: Khartoum
AREA: 2,505,810 sq km (Land area 2,376,000 sq km)
POPULATION: 29,980,000 people
POPULATION DENSITY: 13 people per sq km
POPULATION CHANGE: 3.0% per year
BIRTH RATE: 41 per 1,000 people
DEATH RATE: 11 per 1,000 people
LIFE EXPECTANCY: Males 55, females 57 years
INFANT MORTALITY: 74 per 1,000 live births
URBAN POPULATION: 35% of population
FERTILITY RATE: 6 children per female
AGE GROUPS: 0–14 yrs 45%, 15–59 yrs 50%, 60+ yrs 5%
ETHNIC GROUPS: Sudanese Arab 49%, Dinka 12%, Nuba 8%, Beja 6%, Nuer 5%, Azande 3%
LANGUAGES: *Arabic*, Nubian, Dinka,
RELIGIONS: Sunni Muslim 75%, traditional beliefs, Roman Catholic 6%, Protestant 2%
LAND USE: Arable 5%, grass 46%, forest 19%
EMPLOYMENT: Agric. 72%, ind. 5%, services 23%
ANNUAL INCOME: $750 per person, 0.6%
ORIGIN OF INCOME: Agriculture 34%, industry 17%, services 49%
ENERGY: Consumption 0.06 tonnes per person
TRADE: $65 per person
CURRENCY: Sudanese dinar = 10 Sudanese pounds = 100 piastres
ROADS: 9 km per 1,000 sq km of land
RAILWAYS: 2 km per 1,000 sq km of land
POPULATION PER DOCTOR: 10,000 people
ADULT LITERACY: 43%
EDUCATIONAL EXPENDITURE: 4.8% of GNP
MILITARY EXPENDITURE: 15.8% of GNP
AID RECEIVED: $8 per person

Surinam

CAPITAL CITY: Paramaribo
AREA: 163,270 sq km (Land area 156,000 sq km)
POPULATION: 421,000 people
POPULATION DENSITY: 3 people per sq km
POPULATION CHANGE: 1.5% per year
BIRTH RATE: 24 per 1,000 people
DEATH RATE: 6 per 1,000 people
LIFE EXPECTANCY: Males 68, females 73 years
INFANT MORTALITY: 28 per 1,000 live births
URBAN POPULATION: 52% of population
FERTILITY RATE: 3 children per female
AGE GROUPS: 0–14 yrs 34%, 15–59 yrs 59%, 60+ yrs 7%
ETHNIC GROUPS: Creole 35%, Asian Indian 33%, Indonesian 16%, Black 10%, Amerindian 3%
LANGUAGES: *Dutch*, English, Sranantonga
RELIGIONS: Hindu 26%, Roman Catholic 22%, Sunni Muslim 19%, Protestant 18%
LAND USE: Forest 95%
EMPLOYMENT: Agric. 20%, ind. 20%, services 60%
ANNUAL INCOME: $880 per person, 0.7%
ORIGIN OF INCOME: Agriculture 22%, industry 24%, services 54%
ENERGY: Prod. 1.31 tonnes, consump. 1.79 tonnes
TRADE: $2,360 per person
CURRENCY: Surinam guilder = 100 cents
ROADS: 29 km per 1,000 sq km of and
RAILWAYS: 2 km per 1,000 sq km of land
POPULATION PER DOCTOR: 1,200 people
ADULT LITERACY: 92%
EDUCATIONAL EXPENDITURE: 8.3% of GNP
MILITARY EXPENDITURE: 3.4% of GNP
AID RECEIVED: $183 per person

Svalbard

Territory of Norway
CAPITAL CITY: Longyearbyen
AREA: 62,049 sq km
POPULATION: 2,900 people

Swaziland

CAPITAL CITY: Mbabane
AREA: 17,360 sq km
POPULATION: 849,000 people
POPULATION DENSITY: 55 people per sq km
POPULATION CHANGE: 3.1% per year
BIRTH RATE: 43 per 1,000 people
DEATH RATE: 10 per 1,000 people
LIFE EXPECTANCY: Males 54, females 62 years
INFANT MORTALITY: 86 per 1,000 live births
URBAN POPULATION: 29% of population
FERTILITY RATE: 5 children per female
AGE GROUPS: 0–14 yrs 47%, 15–59 yrs 48%, 60+ yrs 5%
ETHNIC GROUPS: African 97%, European 3%
LANGUAGES: *English, Swazi*
RELIGIONS: Christian 77%, traditional beliefs 21%
LAND USE: Arable 11%, grass 62%, forest 7%
EMPLOYMENT: Agric. 74%, ind. 10%, services 16%
ANNUAL INCOME: $1,170 per person, 0.6%
ORIGIN OF INCOME: Agriculture 12%, industry 39%, services 50%
TRADE: $1,600 per person
CURRENCY: Lilangeni = 100 cents
ROADS: 168 km per 1,000 sq km of land
RAILWAYS: 18 km per 1,000 sq km of land
POPULATION PER DOCTOR: 9,091 people
ADULT LITERACY: 74%
EDUCATIONAL EXPENDITURE: 6.4% of GNP
MILITARY EXPENDITURE: 1.4% of GNP
AID RECEIVED: $59 per person

Sweden

CAPITAL CITY: Stockholm
AREA: 449,960 sq km (Land area 411,620 sq km)
POPULATION: 8,893,000 people
POPULATION DENSITY: 22 people per sq km
POPULATION CHANGE: 0.7% per year
BIRTH RATE: 11 per 1,000 people
DEATH RATE: 11 per 1,000 people
LIFE EXPECTANCY: Males 76, females 81 years
INFANT MORTALITY: 5 per 1,000 live births
URBAN POPULATION: 84% of population
FERTILITY RATE: 2 children per female
AGE GROUPS: 0–14 yrs 17%, 15–59 yrs 60%, 60+ yrs 23%
ETHNIC GROUPS: Swedish 90%, Finnish 2%
LANGUAGES: *Swedish*, Finnish
RELIGIONS: Lutheran 88%, Roman Catholic 2%
LAND USE: Arable 7%, grass 1%, forest 68%
EMPLOYMENT: Agric. 3%, ind. 28%, services 69%
ANNUAL INCOME: $23,750 per person, –0.1%
ORIGIN OF INCOME: Agriculture 2%, industry 31%, services 67%
ENERGY: Prod. 3.81 tonnes, consump. 5.77 tonnes
TRADE: $10,577 per person
CURRENCY: Krona = 100 öre
ROADS: 330 km per 1,000 sq km of land
RAILWAYS: 26 km per 1,000 sq km of land
POPULATION PER DOCTOR: 395 people
ADULT LITERACY: 99%
EDUCATIONAL EXPENDITURE: 6.5% of GNP
MILITARY EXPENDITURE: 2.5% of GNP
AID GIVEN: $189 per person

Switzerland

CAPITAL CITY: Bern
AREA: 41,290 sq km (Land area 39,770 sq km)
POPULATION: 7,268,000 people
POPULATION DENSITY: 180 people per sq km
POPULATION CHANGE: 1.0% per year
BIRTH RATE: 11 per 1,000 people
DEATH RATE: 10 per 1,000 people
LIFE EXPECTANCY: Males 75, females 81 years
INFANT MORTALITY: 5 per 1,000 live births
URBAN POPULATION: 61% of population
FERTILITY RATE: 2 children per female
AGE GROUPS: 0–14 yrs 16%, 15–59 yrs 64%, 60+ yrs 20%
ETHNIC GROUPS: Swiss German 64%, Swiss French 19%, Swiss Italian 18%, Yugoslav 2%, Romansch 1%
LANGUAGES: *French, German, Italian*, Romansch
RELIGIONS: Roman Catholic 46%, Protestant 40%, Muslim 2%
LAND USE: Arable 10%, grass 28%, forest 32%
EMPLOYMENT: Agric. 6%, ind. 34%, services 60%
ANNUAL INCOME: $40,630 per person, 0.2%
ORIGIN OF INCOME: Agriculture 4%, industry 36%, services 61%
ENERGY: Prod. 1.88 tonnes, consump. 4.88 tonnes
TRADE: $16,631 per person
CURRENCY: Swiss franc = 100 centimes (rappen)
ROADS: 1,804 km per 1,000 sq km of land
RAILWAYS: 127 km per 1,000 sq km of land
POPULATION PER DOCTOR: 585 people
ADULT LITERACY: 99%
EDUCATIONAL EXPENDITURE: 5.4% of GNP
MILITARY EXPENDITURE: 1.6% of GNP
AID GIVEN: $135 per person

Syria

CAPITAL CITY: Damascus
AREA: 185,180 sq km
POPULATION: 14,614,000 people
POPULATION DENSITY: 83 people per sq km
POPULATION CHANGE: 2.9% per year
BIRTH RATE: 39 per 1,000 people
DEATH RATE: 6 per 1,000 people
LIFE EXPECTANCY: Males 66, females 69 years
INFANT MORTALITY: 39 per 1,000 live births
URBAN POPULATION: 52% of population
FERTILITY RATE: 6 children per female
AGE GROUPS: 0–14 yrs 48%, 15–59 yrs 48%, 60+ yrs 4%
ETHNIC GROUPS: Arab 89%, Kurdish 6%
LANGUAGES: *Arabic*, Kurdish, Armenian
RELIGIONS: Sunni Muslim 77%, Shiite Muslim 12%, Christian 10%, Druze 1%
LAND USE: Arable 28%, grass 44%, forest 4%
EMPLOYMENT: Agric. 26%, ind. 23%, services 51%
ANNUAL INCOME: $1,120 per person, 1%
ORIGIN OF INCOME: Agriculture 30%, industry 22%, services 48%
ENERGY: Prod. 3.06 tonnes, consump. 1.29 tonnes
TRADE: $540 per person
CURRENCY: Syrian £= 100 piastres
ROADS: 197 km per 1,000 sq km of land
RAILWAYS: 10 km per 1,000 sq km of land
POPULATION PER DOCTOR: 1,220 people
ADULT LITERACY: 68%
EDUCATIONAL EXPENDITURE: 4.1% of GNP
MILITARY EXPENDITURE: 16.6% of GNP
AID RECEIVED: $25 per person

Taiwan

CAPITAL CITY: Taipei
AREA: 36,000 sq km
POPULATION: 21,100,000 people
POPULATION DENSITY: 603 people per sq km
POPULATION CHANGE: 0.9% per year
BIRTH RATE: 15 per 1,000 people
DEATH RATE: 6 per 1,000 people
LIFE EXPECTANCY: Males 74, females 79 years
INFANT MORTALITY: 7 per 1,000 live births
URBAN POPULATION: 75% of population
FERTILITY RATE: 2 children per female
AGE GROUPS: 0–14 yrs 28%, 15–59 yrs 63%, 60+ yrs 9%
ETHNIC GROUPS: Taiwanese (Han Chinese) 84%, mainland Chinese 14%
LANGUAGES: *Mandarin*, Min (Fukien), Hakka, Ami
RELIGIONS: Buddhist 43%, Taoist and Confucian 49%, Christian 7%
LAND USE: Arable 24%, grass 11%, forest 52%
EMPLOYMENT: Agric. 11%, ind. 39%, services 50%
ANNUAL INCOME: $12,000 per person, 7%
ORIGIN OF INCOME: Agriculture 4%, industry 41%, services 56%
TRADE: $7,713 per person
CURRENCY: New Taiwan $ = 100 cents
ROADS: 529 km per 1,000 sq km of land
RAILWAYS: 108 km per 1,000 sq km of land
POPULATION PER DOCTOR: 900 people
ADULT LITERACY: 93%
EDUCATIONAL EXPENDITURE: 3.6% of GNP
MILITARY EXPENDITURE: 5.2% of GNP

Tajikistan

CAPITAL CITY: Dushanbe
AREA: 143,100 sq km (Land area 140,600 sq km)
POPULATION: 6,102,000 people
POPULATION DENSITY: 42 people per sq km
POPULATION CHANGE: 1.8% per year
BIRTH RATE: 34 per 1,000 people
DEATH RATE: 8 per 1,000 people
LIFE EXPECTANCY: Males 61, females 68 years
INFANT MORTALITY: 111 per 1,000 live births
URBAN POPULATION: 32% of population
FERTILITY RATE: 5 children per female
AGE GROUPS: 0–14 yrs 45%, 15–59 yrs 49%, 60+ yrs 6%
ETHNIC GROUPS: Tajik 64%, Uzbek 24%, Russian 7%
LANGUAGES: *Tajik*, Uzbek, Russian
RELIGIONS: Sunni Muslim 83%, Shiite Muslim 5%
LAND USE: Arable 19%, grass 77%
EMPLOYMENT: Agric. 14%, ind. 19%, services 69%
ANNUAL INCOME: $340 per person, –13%
ORIGIN OF INCOME: Agriculture 33%, industry 33%, services 33%
ENERGY: Prod. 0.37 tonnes, consump. 0.001 tonnes
TRADE: $1,762 per person
CURRENCY: Tajik rouble = 100 tanga
ROADS: 91 km per 1,000 sq km of land
RAILWAYS: 4 km per 1,000 sq km of land
POPULATION PER DOCTOR: 430 people
ADULT LITERACY: 97%
MILITARY EXPENDITURE: 3.7% of GNP
AID RECEIVED: $5 per person

Tanzania

CAPITAL CITY: Dodoma (commercial Dar-es-Salaam)
AREA: 945,090 sq km (Land area 883,590 sq km)
POPULATION: 29,710,000 people
POPULATION DENSITY: 35 people per sq km
POPULATION CHANGE: 2.8% per year
BIRTH RATE: 50 per 1,000 people
DEATH RATE: 13 per 1,000 people
LIFE EXPECTANCY: Males 41, females 20 years
INFANT MORTALITY: 105 per 1,000 live births
URBAN POPULATION: 24% of population
FERTILITY RATE: 6 children per female
AGE GROUPS: 0–14 yrs 49%, 15–59 yrs 47%, 60+ yrs 4%
ETHNIC GROUPS: Nyamwezi and Sukama 21%, Swahili 9%, Hehet and Bena 5%, Haya 5%
LANGUAGES: *English, Swahili*, Nyamwezi, Chaga, Gogo, Haya, Hehet, Luguru, Makonde, Ha
RELIGIONS: Christian 34%, Sunni Muslim 33%, Hindu 4%, traditional beliefs
LAND USE: Arable 3%, grass 40%, forest 46%
EMPLOYMENT: Agric. 85%, ind. 5%, services 10%
ANNUAL INCOME: $120 per person, 0.9%
ORIGIN OF INCOME: Agriculture 56%, industry 14%, services 30%
ENERGY: Consumption 0.04 tonnes per person
TRADE: $53 per person
CURRENCY: Shilling = 100 cents
ROADS: 100 km per 1,000 sq km of land
RAILWAYS: 4 km per 1,000 sq km of land
POPULATION PER DOCTOR: 22,000 people
ADULT LITERACY: 64%
EDUCATIONAL EXPENDITURE: 5.8% of GNP
MILITARY EXPENDITURE: 3.6% of GNP
AID RECEIVED: $59 per person

Thailand

CAPITAL CITY: Bangkok
AREA: 513,120 sq km
POPULATION: 58,432,000 people
POPULATION DENSITY: 119 people per sq km
POPULATION CHANGE: 0.9% per year
BIRTH RATE: 17 per 1,000 people
DEATH RATE: 7 per 1,000 people
LIFE EXPECTANCY: Males 65, females 73 years
INFANT MORTALITY: 32 per 1,000 live births
URBAN POPULATION: 19% of population
FERTILITY RATE: 2 children per female
AGE GROUPS: 0–14 yrs 33%, 15–59 yrs 61%, 60+ yrs 6%
ETHNIC GROUPS: Thai 80%, Chinese 12%, Malay 4%, Khmer 3%
LANGUAGES: *Thai*, Chinese, Malay, Khmer, Lao, Kuy, Karen
RELIGIONS: Buddhist 95%, Muslim 4%, Christian 1%
LAND USE: Arable 33%, grass 2%, forest 26%
EMPLOYMENT: Agric. 67%, ind. 11%, services 22%
ANNUAL INCOME: $2,740 per person, 8.4%
ORIGIN OF INCOME: Agriculture 10%, industry 39%, services 51%
ENERGY: Prod. 0.38 tonnes, consump. 0.89 tonnes
TRADE: $1,421 per person
CURRENCY: Baht = 100 satang
ROADS: 114 km per 1,000 sq km of land
RAILWAYS: 8 km per 1,000 sq km of land
POPULATION PER DOCTOR: 4,762 people
ADULT LITERACY: 94%
EDUCATIONAL EXPENDITURE: 3.8% of GNP
MILITARY EXPENDITURE: 2.7% of GNP
AID RECEIVED: $15 per person

Togo

CAPITAL CITY: Lomé
AREA: 56,790 sq km (Land area 54,390 sq km)
POPULATION: 4,140,000 people
POPULATION DENSITY: 82 people per sq km
POPULATION CHANGE: 3.4% per year
BIRTH RATE: 46 per 1,000 people
DEATH RATE: 10 per 1,000 people
LIFE EXPECTANCY: Males 56, females 61 years
INFANT MORTALITY: 82 per 1,000 live births
URBAN POPULATION: 31% of population
FERTILITY RATE: 7 children per female
AGE GROUPS: 0–14 yrs 45%, 15–59 yrs 50%, 60+ yrs 5%
ETHNIC GROUPS: Ewe-Adja 43%, Tem-Kabre 26%, Gurma 16%
LANGUAGES: *French*, Ewe, Kabre, Ana, Kotokoli, Akposo, Namba, Naudemba, Moba, Gurma
RELIGIONS: Traditional beliefs 59%, Christian 28%, Sunni Muslim 12%
LAND USE: Arable 11%, grass 33%, forest 27%
EMPLOYMENT: Agric. 65%, ind. 6%, services 29%
ANNUAL INCOME: $310 per person, –2.8%
ORIGIN OF INCOME: Agriculture 49%, industry 18%, services 34%
ENERGY: Consumption 0.08 tonnes per person
TRADE: $191 per person
CURRENCY: CFA franc = 100 centimes
ROADS: 138 km per 1,000 sq km of land
RAILWAYS: 10 km per 1,000 sq km of land
POPULATION PER DOCTOR: 11,111 people
ADULT LITERACY: 48%

Togo continued
EDUCATIONAL EXPENDITURE: 5.7% of GNP
MILITARY EXPENDITURE: 3.1% of GNP
AID RECEIVED: $47 per person

Tokelau
TERRITORY OF NEW ZEALAND
AREA: 10 sq km
POPULATION: 1,500 people

Tonga
CAPITAL CITY: Nuku'alofa
AREA: 750 sq km (Land area: 720 sq km)
POPULATION: 107,000 people
POPULATION DENSITY: 146 people per sq km
POPULATION CHANGE: 1.4% per year
BIRTH RATE: 27 per 1,000 people
DEATH RATE: 6 per 1,000 people
LIFE EXPECTANCY: Males 67, females 72 years
INFANT MORTALITY: 39 per 1,000 live births
URBAN POPULATION: 41% of population
FERTILITY RATE: 4 children per female
AGE GROUPS: 0–14 yrs 39%, 15–59 yrs 52%,
  60+ yrs 9%
ETHNIC GROUPS: Tongan 96%
LANGUAGES: Tongan, English
RELIGIONS: Wesleyan Methodist 43%, Roman
  Catholic 15%
LAND USE: Arable 24%, grass 6%, forest 11%
EMPLOYMENT: Agric. 37%, ind. 19%,
  services 44%
ANNUAL INCOME: $1,630 per person, 0.2%
ORIGIN OF INCOME: Agriculture 41%, industry
  19%, services 40%
ENERGY: Consumption 0.44 tonnes per person
TRADE: $780 per person
CURRENCY: Pa'anga = 100 seniti
ROADS: 536 km per 1,000 sq km of land
POPULATION PER DOCTOR: 2,000 people
ADULT LITERACY: 93%
EDUCATIONAL EXPENDITURE: 4.2% of GNP

Trinidad and Tobago
CAPITAL CITY: Port of Spain
AREA: 5,130 sq km
POPULATION: 1,295,000 people
POPULATION DENSITY: 253 people per sq km
POPULATION CHANGE: 0.2% per year
BIRTH RATE: 16 per 1,000 people
DEATH RATE: 7 per 1,000 people
LIFE EXPECTANCY: Males 68, females 73 years
INFANT MORTALITY: 18 per 1,000 live births
URBAN POPULATION: 70% of population
FERTILITY RATE: 2 children per female
AGE GROUPS: 0–14 yrs 34%, 15–59 yrs 58%,
  60+ yrs 8%
ETHNIC GROUPS: Black 40%, East Indian 40%,
  Mixed 18%, White 1%, Chinese 1%
LANGUAGES: English, Creole, Hindi
RELIGIONS: Roman Catholic 29%, Hindu 24%,
  Anglican 11%, Muslim 6%
LAND USE: Arable 15%, grass 2%, forest 42%
EMPLOYMENT: Agric. 10%, ind. 33%,
  -services 57%
ANNUAL INCOME: $3,770 per person, –1.6%
ORIGIN OF INCOME: Agriculture 3%, industry 43%,
  services 55%
ENERGY: Prod. 13.92 tonnes, consump.
  8.42 tonnes
TRADE: $2,429 per person
CURRENCY: Trinidad and Tobago $ = 100 cents
ROADS: 1,559 km per 1,000 sq km of land
POPULATION PER DOCTOR: 1,370 people
ADULT LITERACY: 97%
EDUCATIONAL EXPENDITURE: 4.1% of GNP
MILITARY EXPENDITURE: 1.3% of GNP
AID GIVEN: $20 per person

Tristan da Cunha
DEPENDENT TERRITORY OF UK
CAPITAL CITY: Edinburgh
AREA: 104 sq km
POPULATION: 330 people

Tunisia
CAPITAL CITY: Tunis
AREA: 163,610 sq km (Land area 155,360 sq km)
POPULATION: 8,906,000 people
POPULATION DENSITY: 59 people per sq km
POPULATION CHANGE: 1.9% per year
BIRTH RATE: 24 per 1,000 people
DEATH RATE: 5 per 1,000 people
LIFE EXPECTANCY: Males 72, females 74 years
INFANT MORTALITY: 34 per 1,000 live births
URBAN POPULATION: 57% of population
FERTILITY RATE: 3 children per female
AGE GROUPS: 0–14 yrs 38%, 15–59 yrs 56%,
  60+ yrs 6%
ETHNIC GROUPS: Arab 98%, Berber 1%, French
LANGUAGES: Arabic, French
RELIGIONS: Sunni Muslim 99%
LAND USE: Arable 19%, grass 26%, forest 4%
EMPLOYMENT: Agric. 26%, ind. 34%, services 40%
ANNUAL INCOME: $1,820 per person, 1.8%
ORIGIN OF INCOME: Agriculture 18%, industry
  31%, services 51%

ENERGY: Prod. 0.92 tonnes, consump. 0.73 tonnes
TRADE: $1,169 per person
CURRENCY: Dinar = 1,000 millimes
ROADS: 188 km per 1,000 sq km of land
RAILWAYS: 14 km per 1,000 sq km of land
POPULATION PER DOCTOR: 1,852 people
ADULT LITERACY: 63%
EDUCATIONAL EXPENDITURE: 6.1% of GNP
MILITARY EXPENDITURE: 3.3% of GNP
AID RECEIVED: $8 per person

Turkey
CAPITAL CITY: Ankara
AREA: 779,450 sq km (Land area 769,630 sq km)
POPULATION: 61,303,000 people
POPULATION DENSITY: 83 people per sq km
POPULATION CHANGE: 1.1% per year
BIRTH RATE: 22 per 1,000 people
DEATH RATE: 5 per 1,000 people
LIFE EXPECTANCY: Males 70, females 75 years
INFANT MORTALITY: 41 per 1,000 live births
URBAN POPULATION: 65% of population
FERTILITY RATE: 3 children per female
AGE GROUPS: 0–14 yrs 35%, 15–59 yrs 58%,
  60+ yrs 7%
ETHNIC GROUPS: Turkish 92%, Kurdish 6%,
  Arab 1%
LANGUAGES: Turkish, Kurdish, Arabic
RELIGIONS: Sunni Muslim 70%, Shiite Muslim 30%
LAND USE: Arable 32%, grass 16%, forest 26%
EMPLOYMENT: Agric. 47%, ind. 20%, services 33%
ANNUAL INCOME: $2,780 per person, 2.2%
ORIGIN OF INCOME: Agriculture 15%, industry
  30%, services 55%
ENERGY: Prod. 0.42 tonnes, consump. 1.05 tonnes
TRADE: $743 per person
CURRENCY: Lira = 100 kurus
ROADS: 495 km per 1,000 sq km of land
RAILWAYS: 11 km per 1,000 sq km of land
POPULATION PER DOCTOR: 1,176 people
ADULT LITERACY: 81%
EDUCATIONAL EXPENDITURE: 4.0% of GNP
MILITARY EXPENDITURE: 4.7% of GNP
AID RECEIVED: $5 per person

Turkmenistan
CAPITAL CITY: Ashkhabad
AREA: 488,100 sq km
POPULATION: 4,100,000 people
POPULATION DENSITY: 10 people per sq km
POPULATION CHANGE: 3.9% per year
BIRTH RATE: 29 per 1,000 people
DEATH RATE: 9 per 1,000 people
LIFE EXPECTANCY: Males 57, females 67 years
INFANT MORTALITY: 81 per 1,000 live births
URBAN POPULATION: 47% of population
FERTILITY RATE: 4 children per female
AGE GROUPS: 0–14 yrs 41%, 15–59 yrs 53%,
  60+ yrs 6%
ETHNIC GROUPS: Turkmen 73%, Russian 10%,
  Uzbek 9%, Kazak 2%
LANGUAGES: Turkmen, Russian, Uzbek
RELIGIONS: Sunni Muslim 85%, Russian Orthodox
LAND USE: Arable 3%, grass 96%
EMPLOYMENT: Agric. 44%, ind. 20%, services 36%
ANNUAL INCOME: $920 per person, –9.6%
ORIGIN OF INCOME: Agriculture 31%, industry
  31%, services 38%
ENERGY: Prod. 22.85 tonnes, consump.
  4.13 tonnes
TRADE: $2,623 per person
CURRENCY: Manat = 100 tenesi
ROADS: 48 km per 1,000 sq km of land
RAILWAYS: 4 km per 1,000 sq km of land
POPULATION PER DOCTOR: 375 people
ADULT LITERACY: 98%
MILITARY EXPENDITURE: 48% of GNP
AID RECEIVED: $3 per person

Turks and Caicos Islands
BRITISH COLONY
CAPITAL CITY: Cockburn Town (on Grand Turk I.)
AREA: 430 sq km
POPULATION: 15,000 people
POPULATION DENSITY: 35 people per sq km
POPULATION CHANGE: 6.0% per year
BIRTH RATE: 12 per 1,000 people
DEATH RATE: 5 per 1,000 people
LIFE EXPECTANCY: Males 73, females 77 years
INFANT MORTALITY: 13 per 1,000 live births
URBAN POPULATION: 55% of population
FERTILITY RATE: 4 children per female
ETHNIC GROUPS: Of African descent
LANGUAGES: English
RELIGIONS: Protestant 90%
LAND USE: Arable 2%
ANNUAL INCOME: $6,000 per person
TRADE: $3,674 per person
CURRENCY: US currency
ADULT LITERACY: 98%

Tuvalu
CAPITAL CITY: Fongafale
AREA: 24 sq km
POPULATION: 10,000 people
POPULATION DENSITY: 333 people per sq km

POPULATION CHANGE: 1.5% per year
BIRTH RATE: 23 per 1,000 people
DEATH RATE: 9 per 1,000 people
LIFE EXPECTANCY: Males 62, females 65 years
INFANT MORTALITY: 27 per 1,000 live births
FERTILITY RATE: 3 children per female
ETHNIC GROUPS: Polynesian
LANGUAGES: English, Tuvaluan
RELIGIONS: Protestant 90%
ANNUAL INCOME: $1,000 per person
TRADE: $500 per person
CURRENCY: Tuvaluan $ = 100 cents
ROADS: 267 km per 1,000 sq km of land
POPULATION PER DOCTOR: 2,500 people
ADULT LITERACY: 95%

Uganda
CAPITAL CITY: Kampala
AREA: 235,880 sq km (Land area 199,650 sq km)
POPULATION: 21,466,000 people
POPULATION DENSITY: 104 people per sq km
POPULATION CHANGE: 2.4% per year
BIRTH RATE: 45 per 1,000 people
DEATH RATE: 21 per 1,000 people
LIFE EXPECTANCY: Males 39, females 40 years
INFANT MORTALITY: 98 per 1,000 live births
URBAN POPULATION: 12% of population
FERTILITY RATE: 7 children per female
AGE GROUPS: 0–14 yrs 50%, 15–59 yrs 46%,
  60+ yrs 4%
ETHNIC GROUPS: Baganda 18%, Banyoro 14%,
  Teso 9%, Banyan 8%, Basoga 8%, Bagisu 7%,
  Bachiga 7%, Lango 6%, Acholi 5%
LANGUAGES: English, Swahili, Bantu and Nilotic
  languages
RELIGIONS: Roman Catholic 40%, Protestant
  29%, animist 18%, Sunni Muslim 7%
LAND USE: Arable 25%, grass 9%, forest 28%
EMPLOYMENT: Agric. 86%, ind. 4%, services 10%
ANNUAL INCOME: $240 per person, 2.8%
ORIGIN OF INCOME: Agriculture 53%, industry
  12%, services 35%
ENERGY: Prod. 0.04 tonnes, consump.
  0.03 tonnes
TRADE: $27 per person
CURRENCY: Shilling = 100 cents
ROADS: 134 km per 1,000 sq km of land
RAILWAYS: 6 km per 1,000 sq km of land
POPULATION PER DOCTOR: 25,000 people
ADULT LITERACY: 59%
EDUCATIONAL EXPENDITURE: 2.9% of GNP
MILITARY EXPENDITURE: 2.9% of GNP
AID RECEIVED: $43 per person

Ukraine
CAPITAL CITY: Kiev
AREA: 603,700 sq km (Land area 579,350 sq km)
POPULATION: 52,027,000 people
POPULATION DENSITY: 85 people per sq km
POPULATION CHANGE: –0.1% per year
BIRTH RATE: 12 per 1,000 people
DEATH RATE: 15 per 1,000 people
LIFE EXPECTANCY: Males 62, females 72 years
INFANT MORTALITY: 22 per 1,000 live births
URBAN POPULATION: 69% of population
FERTILITY RATE: 2 children per female
AGE GROUPS: 0–14 yrs 21%, 15–59 yrs 60%,
  60+ yrs 19%
ETHNIC GROUPS: Ukrainian 73%, Russian 22%,
  Jewish 1%, Belarusian, Moldovan, Polish
LANGUAGES: Ukrainian, Russian, Romanian
RELIGIONS: Ukrainian Orthodox 60%, Uniate
  (Greek Orthodox-Catholic), Protestant, Jewish
LAND USE: Arable 56%, grass 12%, forest 14%
EMPLOYMENT: Agric. 21%, ind. 39%, services 40%
ANNUAL INCOME: $1,630 per person, –9.2%
ORIGIN OF INCOME: Agriculture 35%, industry
  47%, services 18%
ENERGY: Prod. 3.26 tonnes, consump. 6.0 tonnes
TRADE: $1,257 per person
CURRENCY: Hryvna
ROADS: 285 km per 1,000 sq km of land
RAILWAYS: 39 km per 1,000 sq km of land
POPULATION PER DOCTOR: 259 people
ADULT LITERACY: 95%
MILITARY EXPENDITURE: 3.8 % of GNP
AID RECEIVED: $5 per person

United Arab Emirates
CAPITAL CITY: Abu Dhabi
AREA: 83,600 sq km
POPULATION: 2,800,000 people
POPULATION DENSITY: 29 people per sq km
POPULATION CHANGE: 6.1% per year
BIRTH RATE: 18 per 1,000 people
DEATH RATE: 3 per 1,000 people
LIFE EXPECTANCY: Males 73, females 76 years
INFANT MORTALITY: 16 per 1,000 live births
URBAN POPULATION: 83% of population
FERTILITY RATE: 4 children per female
AGE GROUPS: 0–14 yrs 31%, 15–59 yrs 66%,
  60+ yrs 3%
ETHNIC GROUPS: Arab 87%, Indo-Pakistani 9%,
  Iranian 2%
LANGUAGES: Arabic, English
RELIGIONS: Sunni Muslim 80%, Shiite Muslim 16%

LAND USE: Grass 2%
EMPLOYMENT: Agric. 5%, ind. 38%, services 57%
ANNUAL INCOME: $17,400 per person, –3.5%
ORIGIN OF INCOME: Agriculture 2%, industry 58%,
  services 48%
ENERGY: Prod. 113.32 tonnes, consump.
  26.07 tonnes
TRADE: $16,000 per person
CURRENCY: Dirham = 100 fils
ROADS: 54 km per 1,000 sq km of land
POPULATION PER DOCTOR: 1,042 people
ADULT LITERACY: 78%
EDUCATIONAL EXPENDITURE: 1.9% of GNP
MILITARY EXPENDITURE: 14.6% of GNP

United Kingdom
CAPITAL CITY: London
AREA: 244,880 sq km (Land area 241,600 sq km)
POPULATION: 58,306,000 people
POPULATION DENSITY: 243 people per sq km
POPULATION CHANGE: 0.3% per year
BIRTH RATE: 13 per 1,000 people
DEATH RATE: 11 per 1,000 people
LIFE EXPECTANCY: Males 74, females 79 years
INFANT MORTALITY: 6 per 1,000 live births
URBAN POPULATION: 90% of population
FERTILITY RATE: 2 children per female
AGE GROUPS: 0–14 yrs 19%, 15–59 yrs 61%,
  60+ yrs 21%
ETHNIC GROUPS: White 94%, Asian Indian 1%,
  West Indian 1%, Pakistani 1%
LANGUAGES: English, Welsh, Scots-Gaelic
RELIGIONS: Anglican 57%, Roman Catholic 13%,
  Presbyterian 3%, Muslim 2%, Methodist 1%
LAND USE: Arable 27%, grass 46%, forest 10%
EMPLOYMENT: Agric. 2%, ind. 28%, services 70%
ANNUAL INCOME: $18,700 per person, 1.4%
ORIGIN OF INCOME: Agriculture 2%, industry 33%,
  services 65%
ENERGY: Prod. 5.34 tonnes, consump. 5.40 tonnes
TRADE: $6,697 per person
CURRENCY: £ sterling = 100 pence
ROADS: 1,611 km per 1,000 sq km of land
RAILWAYS: 157 km per 1,000 sq km of land
POPULATION PER DOCTOR: 300 people
ADULT LITERACY: 99%
EDUCATIONAL EXPENDITURE: 5.3% of GNP
MILITARY EXPENDITURE: 4.0% of GNP
AID GIVEN: $53 per person

United States of America
CAPITAL CITY: Washington, DC
AREA: 9,809,431 sq km (Land area 9,159,125
  sq km) — coterminous USA 8,080,979
  sq km (Land area 7,665,222 sq km)
POPULATION: 263,563,000 people
POPULATION DENSITY: 28 people per sq km
POPULATION CHANGE: 1.0% per year
BIRTH RATE: 15 per 1,000 people
DEATH RATE: 9 per 1,000 people
LIFE EXPECTANCY: Males 73, females 79 years
INFANT MORTALITY: 7 per 1,000 live births
URBAN POPULATION: 77% of population
FERTILITY RATE: 2 children per female
AGE GROUPS: 0–14 yrs 21%, 15–59 yrs 62%,
  60+ yrs 17%
ETHNIC GROUPS: White 85%, Black 12%,
  other races 3%
LANGUAGES: English, Spanish
RELIGIONS: Protestant 53%, Roman Catholic
  26%, Jewish 2%, Eastern Orthodox 2%,
  Muslim 2%
LAND USE: Arable 19%, grass 25%, forest 30%
EMPLOYMENT: Agric. 3%, ind. 25%, services 72%
ANNUAL INCOME: $26,980 per person, 1.4%
ORIGIN OF INCOME: Agriculture 2%, industry 29%,
  services 69%
ENERGY: Prod. 8.99 tonnes, consump.
  10.74 tonnes
TRADE: $4,611 per person
CURRENCY: United States $ = 100 cents
ROADS: 657 km per 1,000 sq km of land
RAILWAYS: 23 km per 1,000 sq km of land
POPULATION PER DOCTOR: 420 people
ADULT LITERACY: 99%
EDUCATIONAL EXPENDITURE: 7.0% of GNP
MILITARY EXPENDITURE: 5.3% of GNP
AID GIVEN: $33 per person

Uruguay
CAPITAL CITY: Montevideo
AREA: 177,410 sq km (Land area 174,810 sq km)
POPULATION: 3,186,000 people
POPULATION DENSITY: 19 people per sq km
POPULATION CHANGE: 0.7% per year
BIRTH RATE: 17 per 1,000 people
DEATH RATE: 9 per 1,000 people
LIFE EXPECTANCY: Males 72, females 79 years
INFANT MORTALITY: 15 per 1,000 live births
URBAN POPULATION: 90% of population
FERTILITY RATE: 2 children per female
AGE GROUPS: 0–14 yrs 26%, 15–59 yrs 58%,
  60+ yrs 17%
ETHNIC GROUPS: White 86%, Mestizo 8%,
  Black 6%
LANGUAGES: Spanish

RELIGIONS: Roman Catholic 66%, Protestant 2%, Jewish 1%
LAND USE: Arable 7%, grass 77%, forest 4%
EMPLOYMENT: Agric. 5%, ind. 22%, services 73%
ANNUAL INCOME: $5,170 per person, 3.3%
ORIGIN OF INCOME: Agriculture 9%, industry 27%, services 64%
ENERGY: Prod. 0.31 tonnes, consump. 0.83 tonnes
TRADE: $1,260 per person
CURRENCY: Peso = 100 centésimos
ROADS: 297 km per 1,000 sq km of land
RAILWAYS: 17 km per 1,000 sq km of land
POPULATION PER DOCTOR: 500 people
ADULT LITERACY: 96%
EDUCATIONAL EXPENDITURE: 3.1% of GNP
MILITARY EXPENDITURE: 2.7% of GNP
AID RECEIVED: $26 per person

Uzbekistan

CAPITAL CITY: Tashkent
AREA: 447,400 sq km
POPULATION: 22,833,000 people
POPULATION DENSITY: 56 people per sq km
POPULATION CHANGE: 2.1% per year
BIRTH RATE: 29 per 1,000 people
DEATH RATE: 8 per 1,000 people
LIFE EXPECTANCY: Males 61, females 69 years
INFANT MORTALITY: 79 per 1,000 live births
URBAN POPULATION: 42% of population
FERTILITY RATE: 4 children per female
AGE GROUPS: 0–14 yrs 42%, 15–59 yrs 53%, 60+ yrs 5%
ETHNIC GROUPS: Uzbek 73%, Russian 8%, Tajik 5%
LANGUAGES: *Uzbek*, Russian, Tajik, Kazak, Tatar, Karakalpak, Korean, Kyrgyz, Turkmen, Turkish
RELIGIONS: Sunni Muslim 75%
LAND USE: Arable 10%, grass 53%, forest 4%
EMPLOYMENT: Agric. 17%, ind. 20%, services 63%
ANNUAL INCOME: $970 per person, –3.9%
ORIGIN OF INCOME: Agriculture 23%, industry 36%, services 41%
ENERGY: Prod. 3.14 tonnes, consump. 3.22 tonnes
TRADE: $1,665 per person
CURRENCY: Som = 100 tiyin
ROADS: 102 km per 1,000 sq km of land
RAILWAYS: 8 km per 1,000 sq km of land
POPULATION PER DOCTOR: 280 people
ADULT LITERACY: 97%

Vanuatu

CAPITAL CITY: Port-Vila
AREA: 12,190 sq km
POPULATION: 167,000 people
POPULATION DENSITY: 14 people per sq km
POPULATION CHANGE: 1.5% per year
BIRTH RATE: 30 per 1,000 people
DEATH RATE: 9 per 1,000 people
LIFE EXPECTANCY: Males 59, females 63 years
INFANT MORTALITY: 63 per 1,000 live births
URBAN POPULATION: 19% of population
FERTILITY RATE: 5 children per female
AGE GROUPS: 0–14 yrs 47%, 15–59 yrs 53%, 60+ yrs 5%
ETHNIC GROUPS: Melanesian 98%, French 1%
LANGUAGES: *English, French, Bislama (pidgin)*
RELIGIONS: Presbyterian 40%, Anglican 20%, Roman Catholic 20%
LAND USE: Arable 2%, grass 2%, forest 75%
EMPLOYMENT: Agric. 68%, ind. 8%, services 24%
ANNUAL INCOME: $1,200 per person, –1.1%
ORIGIN OF INCOME: Agriculture 20%, industry 14%, services 66%
ENERGY: Consumption 0.19 tonnes per person
TRADE: $663 per person
CURRENCY: Vatu = 100 centimes
ROADS: 93 km per 1,000 sq km of land
POPULATION PER DOCTOR: 8,000 people
ADULT LITERACY: 65%
EDUCATIONAL EXPENDITURE: 4.5% of GNP
AID RECEIVED: $199 per person

Vatican City

AREA: 0.44 sq km
POPULATION: 1,000 people
POPULATION DENSITY: 2,273 people per sq km
POPULATION CHANGE: 0% per year
ETHNIC GROUPS: Italian, Swiss
LANGUAGES: Latin, Italian
RELIGIONS: Roman Catholic
CURRENCY: Italian currency

Venezuela

CAPITAL CITY: Caracas
AREA: 912,050 sq km (Land area 882,050 sq km)
POPULATION: 21,810,000 people
POPULATION DENSITY: 26 people per sq km
POPULATION CHANGE: 1.9% per year
BIRTH RATE: 24 per 1,000 people
DEATH RATE: 5 per 1,000 people
LIFE EXPECTANCY: Males 69, females 76 years
INFANT MORTALITY: 29 per 1,000 live births
URBAN POPULATION: 92% of population
FERTILITY RATE: 3 children per female
AGE GROUPS: 0–14 yrs 38%, 15–59 yrs 56%, 60+ yrs 6%
ETHNIC GROUPS: Mestizo 67%, White 21%, Black 10%, Amerindian 2%
LANGUAGES: *Spanish*, Goajiro
RELIGIONS: Roman Catholic 92%
LAND USE: Arable 4%, grass 20%, forest 34%
EMPLOYMENT: Agric. 13%, ind. 17%, services 70%
ANNUAL INCOME: $3,020 per person, 0.5%
ORIGIN OF INCOME: Agriculture 5%, industry 42%, services 53%
ENERGY: Prod. 10.88 tonnes, consump. 3.21 tonnes
TRADE: $1,224 per person
CURRENCY: Bolívar = 100 céntimos
ROADS: 106 km per 1,000 sq km of land
RAILWAYS: 0.6 km per 1,000 sq km of land
POPULATION PER DOCTOR: 620 people
ADULT LITERACY: 90%
EDUCATIONAL EXPENDITURE: 4.1% of GNP
MILITARY EXPENDITURE: 3.6% of GNP
AID RECEIVED: $4 per person

Vietnam

CAPITAL CITY: Hanoi
AREA: 331,690 sq km (Land area 325,490 sq km)
POPULATION: 74,580,000 people
POPULATION DENSITY: 237 people per sq km
POPULATION CHANGE: 2.1% per year
BIRTH RATE: 22 per 1,000 people
DEATH RATE: 7 per 1,000 people
LIFE EXPECTANCY: Males 65, females 70 years
INFANT MORTALITY: 37 per 1,000 live births
URBAN POPULATION: 20% of population
FERTILITY RATE: 4 children per female
AGE GROUPS: 0–14 yrs 39%, 15–59 yrs 54%, 60+ yrs 7%
ETHNIC GROUPS: Vietnamese 87%, Tho 2%, Chinese (Hoa) 2%, Meo 2%, Thai 2%, Khmer 1%, Muong 1%, Nung 1%
LANGUAGES: *Vietnamese*, Chinese, Tho, Khmer, Muong, Thai, Nung, Miao, Jarai, Rhadé, Hre, Bahnar, French, San Chay, Sedang, Koho
RELIGIONS: Buddhist 67%, Roman Catholic 8%
LAND USE: Arable 17%, grass 1%, forest 30%
EMPLOYMENT: Agric. 67%, ind. 12%, services 21%
ANNUAL INCOME: $240 per person, 4.2%
ORIGIN OF INCOME: Agriculture 30%, industry 28%, services 42%
ENERGY: Prod. 0.19 tonnes, consump. 0.12 tonnes
TRADE: $601per person
CURRENCY: Dong = 10 hao or 100 xu
ROADS: 326 km per 1,000 sq km of land
RAILWAYS: 8 km per 1,000 sq km of land
POPULATION PER DOCTOR: 247 people
ADULT LITERACY: 92%
EDUCATIONAL EXPENDITURE: 3.0 % of GNP
MILITARY EXPENDITURE: 11% of GNP
AID RECEIVED: $8 per person

Virgin Islands, British

BRITISH DEPENDENT TERRITORY
CAPITAL CITY: Road Town
AREA: 153 sq km
POPULATION: 20,000 people
POPULATION DENSITY: 130 people per sq km
POPULATION CHANGE: 8.5% per year
BIRTH RATE: 20 per 1,000 people
DEATH RATE: 6 per 1,000 people
LIFE EXPECTANCY: Males 72, females 77 years
INFANT MORTALITY: 19 per 1,000 live births
FERTILITY RATE: 2 children per female
ETHNIC GROUPS: Black 90%
LANGUAGES: *English*
RELIGIONS: Protestant 86%
LAND USE: Arable 20%, grass 33%, forest 7%
ANNUAL INCOME: $11,000 per person
TRADE: $1,200 per person
CURRENCY: US currency
ADULT LITERACY: 98%

Virgin Islands, US

US TERRITORY
CAPITAL CITY: Charlotte Amalie
AREA: 340 sq km
POPULATION: 105,000 people
POPULATION DENSITY: 309 people per sq km
POPULATION CHANGE: –0.8% per year
BIRTH RATE: 18 per 1,000 people
DEATH RATE: 5 per 1,000 people
LIFE EXPECTANCY: Males 74, females 77 years
INFANT MORTALITY: 13 per 1,000 live births
FERTILITY RATE: 2 children per female
AGE GROUPS: 0–14 yrs 28%, 15–59 yrs 63%, 60+ yrs 9%
ETHNIC GROUPS: Black 80%, White 15%
LANGUAGES: *English*, Spanish, Creole
RELIGIONS: Baptist 42%, Roman Catholic 34%
LAND USE: Arable 15%, grass 26%, forest 6%
EMPLOYMENT: Agric. %, ind. %, services %
ANNUAL INCOME: $12,000 per person
ENERGY: Consumption 42.42 tonnes per person
TRADE: $59,000 per person
CURRENCY: US currency
ROADS: 2,518 km per 1,000 sq km of land
POPULATION PER DOCTOR: 700 people

Wallis and Futuna Islands

FRENCH OVERSEAS TERRITORY
CAPITAL CITY: Mata-Utu
AREA: 200 sq km
POPULATION: 13,000 people
POPULATION DENSITY: 75 people per sq km
POPULATION CHANGE: –1.8% per year
BIRTH RATE: 24 per 1,000 people
DEATH RATE: 5 per 1,000 people
LIFE EXPECTANCY: Males 73, females 74 years
INFANT MORTALITY: 22 per 1,000 live births
FERTILITY RATE: 4 children per female
ETHNIC GROUPS: Polynesian
LANGUAGES: *French*, Wallisian
RELIGIONS: Roman Catholic
LAND USE: Arable 5%
ANNUAL INCOME: $1,500 per person
TRADE: $800 per person
CURRENCY: CPF franc = 100 centimes
ADULT LITERACY: 50%

Western Sahara

SOVEREIGNTY UNRESOLVED
CAPITAL: El Aaiún
AREA: 266,000 sq km
POPULATION: 220,000 people

Western Samoa

CAPITAL CITY: Apia
AREA: 2,840 sq km
POPULATION: 169,000 people
POPULATION DENSITY: 62 people per sq km
POPULATION CHANGE: 0.6% per year
BIRTH RATE: 31 per 1,000 people
DEATH RATE: 7 per 1,000 people
LIFE EXPECTANCY: Males 67, females 72 years
INFANT MORTALITY: 33 per 1,000 live births
URBAN POPULATION: 22% of population
FERTILITY RATE: 5 children per female
AGE GROUPS: 0–14 yrs 40%, 15–59 yrs 53%, 60+ yrs 7%
ETHNIC GROUPS: Samoan, mixed European and Polynesian
LANGUAGES: *Samoan, English*
RELIGIONS: Christian
LAND USE: Arable 19%, forest 47%
EMPLOYMENT: Agric. 64%, ind. 5%, services 31%
ANNUAL INCOME: $1,120 per person, –0.4%
ORIGIN OF INCOME: Agriculture 40%, industry 20%, services 40%
ENERGY: Prod. 0.01 tonnes, consump. 0.41 tonnes
TRADE: $427 per person
CURRENCY: Tala = 100 sene
ROADS: 737 km per 1,000 sq km of land
POPULATION PER DOCTOR: 2,500 people
ADULT LITERACY: 98%
EDUCATIONAL EXPENDITURE: 5.3% of GNP

Yemen

CAPITAL CITY: Sana
AREA: 527,970 sq km
POPULATION: 14,609,000 people
POPULATION DENSITY: 31 people per sq km
POPULATION CHANGE: 5.6% per year
BIRTH RATE: 51 per 1,000 people
DEATH RATE: 14 per 1,000 people
LIFE EXPECTANCY: Males 59, females 62 years
INFANT MORTALITY: 68 per 1,000 live births
URBAN POPULATION: 34% of population
FERTILITY RATE: 8 children per female
AGE GROUPS: 0–14 yrs 50%, 15–59 yrs 46%, 60+ yrs 4%
ETHNIC GROUPS: Arab 96%, Somali 1%
LANGUAGES: *Arabic*
RELIGIONS: Sunni Muslim 53%, Shiite Muslim 47%
LAND USE: Arable 3%, grass 30%, forest 4%
EMPLOYMENT: Agric. 63%, ind. 11%, services 26%
ANNUAL INCOME: $260 per person, 3.1%
ORIGIN OF INCOME: Agriculture 21%, industry 24%, services 55%
ENERGY: Prod. 0.93 tonnes, consump. 0.18 tonnes
TRADE: $200 per person
CURRENCY: North Yemeni riyal = 100 fils and South Yemeni dinar = 1,000 fils
ROADS: 122 km per 1,000 sq km of land
POPULATION PER DOCTOR: 4,348 people
ADULT LITERACY: 41%
EDUCATIONAL EXPENDITURE: 4.6% of GNP
MILITARY EXPENDITURE: 9.3% of GNP
AID RECEIVED: $13 per person

Yugoslavia (Serbia)

CAPITAL CITY: Belgrade
AREA: 102,170 sq km
POPULATION: 10,881,000 people
POPULATION DENSITY: 103 people per sq km
POPULATION CHANGE: 0.3% per year
BIRTH RATE: 14 per 1,000 people
DEATH RATE: 10 per 1,000 people
LIFE EXPECTANCY: Males 69, females 75 years
INFANT MORTALITY: 23 per 1,000 live births
URBAN POPULATION: 54% of population
FERTILITY RATE: 2 children per female
AGE GROUPS: 0–14 yrs 23%, 15–59 yrs 60%, 60+ yrs 17%
ETHNIC GROUPS: Serb 62%, Albanian 17%, Montenegrin 5%, Hungarian 4%
LANGUAGES: *Serbo-Croat*, Albanian, Hungarian
RELIGIONS: Serbian Orthodox 65%, Sunni Muslim 19%, Roman Catholic 4%, Protestant 1%
LAND USE: Arable 36%, grass 21%, forest 30%
EMPLOYMENT: Agric. 4%, ind. 36%, services 60%
ANNUAL INCOME: $1,400 per person, 1.8%
ORIGIN OF INCOME: Agriculture 18%, industry 52%, services 30%
TRADE: $1,000 per person
ENERGY: Prod. 1.19 tonnes, consump. 1.6 tonnes
CURRENCY: Yugoslav new dinar = 100 paras
ROADS: 188 km per 1,000 sq km of land
RAILWAYS: 16 km per 1,000 sq km of land
POPULATION PER DOCTOR: 500 people
ADULT LITERACY: 89%
EDUCATIONAL EXPENDITURE: 6.1 % of GNP

Zambia

CAPITAL CITY: Lusaka
AREA: 752,610 sq km (Land area 743,390 sq km)
POPULATION: 9,500,000 people
POPULATION DENSITY: 13 people per sq km
POPULATION CHANGE: 2.4% per year
BIRTH RATE: 44 per 1,000 people
DEATH RATE: 24 per 1,000 people
LIFE EXPECTANCY: Males 36, females 36 years
INFANT MORTALITY: 97 per 1,000 live births
URBAN POPULATION: 45% of population
FERTILITY RATE: 6 children per female
AGE GROUPS: 0–14 yrs 49%, 15–59 yrs 47%, 60+ yrs 4%
ETHNIC GROUPS: Bemba 36%, Nyanja 18%, Malawi 14%, Lozi 9%, Tonga 5%
LANGUAGES: *English*, Bemba, Tonga, Nyanja, Lozi, Lunda, Luvale, Kaonde
RELIGIONS: Christian 72%, animist
LAND USE: Arable 7%, grass 40%, forest 39%
EMPLOYMENT: Agric. 38%, ind. 8%, services 54%
ANNUAL INCOME: $400 per person, –1%
ORIGIN OF INCOME: Agriculture 34%, industry 36%, services 30%
ENERGY: Prod. 0.15 tonnes, consump. 0.20 tonnes
TRADE: $224 per person
CURRENCY: Kwacha = 100 ngwee
ROADS: 52 km per 1,000 sq km of land
RAILWAYS: 2 km per 1,000 sq km of land
POPULATION PER DOCTOR: 11,100 people
ADULT LITERACY: 75%
EDUCATIONAL EXPENDITURE: 2.9% of GNP
MILITARY EXPENDITURE: 2.6% of GNP
AID RECEIVED: $221 per person

Zimbabwe

CAPITAL CITY: Harare
AREA: 390,760 sq km (Land area 386,850 sq km)
POPULATION: 11,453,000 people
POPULATION DENSITY: 31 people per sq km
POPULATION CHANGE: 3.7% per year
BIRTH RATE: 32 per 1,000 people
DEATH RATE: 19 per 1,000 people
LIFE EXPECTANCY: Males 41, females 41 years
INFANT MORTALITY: 73 per 1,000 live births
URBAN POPULATION: 32% of population
FERTILITY RATE: 5 children per female
AGE GROUPS: 0–14 yrs 45%, 15–59 yrs 51%, 60+ yrs 4%
ETHNIC GROUPS: Shona 71%, Ndebele 16%, European 2%
LANGUAGES: *English*, Shona, Ndebele, Nyanja
RELIGIONS: Christian 44%, animist 40%
LAND USE: Arable 7%, grass 13%, forest 49%
EMPLOYMENT: Agric. 71%, ind. 8%, services 21%
ANNUAL INCOME: $540 per person, –0.6%
ORIGIN OF INCOME: Agriculture 15%, industry 36%, services 48%
ENERGY: Prod. 0.63 tonnes, consump. 0.72 tonnes
TRADE: $349 per person
CURRENCY: Zimbabwe $ = 100 cents
ROADS: 235 km per 1,000 sq km of land
RAILWAYS: 7 km per 1,000 sq km of land
POPULATION PER DOCTOR: 7,692 people
ADULT LITERACY: 83%
EDUCATIONAL EXPENDITURE: 10.6% of GNP
MILITARY EXPENDITURE: 4.3% of GNP
AID RECEIVED: $45 per person

Population

Population of countries
thousands

	1950	1960	1970	1980	1990	1997
WORLD	2,520,000	3,021,000	3,697,000	4,444,000	5,285,000	5,808,562
Afghanistan	8,958	10,775	13,623	16,063	16,121	23,000
Albania	1,230	1,611	2,138	2,671	3,256	3,600
Algeria	8,753	10,800	13,746	18,740	25,012	29,300
American Samoa	19	21	27	32	47	62
Andorra	5	8	20	32	53	75
Angola	4,131	4,816	5,588	7,723	10,020	11,200
Anguilla	5	6	6	7	7	10
Antigua & Barb.	46	55	66	75	64	66
Argentina	17,150	20,616	23,962	28,237	32,547	35,400
Armenia	1,354	1,867	2,520	3,067	3,545	3,800
Aruba	57	59	61	64	67	70
Australia	8,219	10,315	12,552	14,695	17,065	18,400
Austria	6,935	7,048	7,467	7,549	7,718	8,200
Azerbaijan	2,896	3,895	5,172	6,165	7,153	7,650
Bahamas	79	113	171	210	255	280
Bahrain	116	156	220	347	486	605
Bangladesh	41,783	51,419	66,671	88,219	108,117	124,000
Barbados	211	231	239	249	257	265
Belarus	7,745	8,190	9,040	9,650	10,260	10,500
Belgium	8,639	9,153	9,656	9,852	9,967	10,225
Belize	67	91	120	145	189	228
Benin	2,046	2,237	2,693	3,459	4,739	5,800
Bermuda	39	45	55	56	61	65
Bhutan	734	868	1,045	1,245	1,544	1,790
Bolivia	2,766	3,428	4,325	5,570	6,573	7,650
Bosnia	2,662	3,240	3,703	4,107	4,308	3,600
Botswana	389	481	623	902	1,300	1,510
Brazil	53,444	72,594	95,847	121,286	144,723	159,500
Brit. Indian Oc. Terr.	2	2	2	2	2	2
Brit. Virgin Is.	6	7	10	12	16	13
Brunei	46	90	133	228	253	300
Bulgaria	7,251	7,867	8,490	8,862	8,991	8,560
Burkina Faso	3,654	4,452	5,550	6,957	9,001	10,900
Burma (Myanmar)	18,038	21,780	27,346	34,818	41,813	47,500
Burundi	2,456	2,948	3,522	4,132	5,458	6,250
Cambodia	4,346	5,433	6,938	6,400	8,568	10,500
Cameroon	4,467	5,297	6,610	8,653	11,526	13,800
Canada	13,737	17,909	21,324	24,043	26,584	30,200
Cape Verde Is.	146	196	267	289	341	410
Cayman Is.	6	8	11	18	26	35
Central African Rep.	1,314	1,534	1,849	2,320	2,927	3,400
Chad	2,658	3,064	3,652	4,477	5,687	6,750
Chile	6,082	7,614	9,504	11,145	13,173	14,700
China	554,760	657,492	830,675	996,134	1,155,305	1,210,000
Christmas I.	1	3	3	3	3	2
Cocos Is.	1	1	1	1	0	1
Colombia	11,946	15,939	21,360	26,906	32,300	35,900
Comoros	173	215	245	334	543	630
Congo	808	988	1,263	1,669	2,232	2,730
Congo (Zaïre)	12,184	15,310	19,769	26,225	35,562	47,200
Cook Is.	15	18	21	19	18	20
Costa Rica	862	1,236	1,731	2,284	2,805	3,500
Croatia	3,851	4,140	4,411	4,588	4,778	4,850
Cuba	5,850	6,985	8,520	9,679	10,625	11,250
Cyprus	494	573	615	629	681	770
Czech Rep.	8,925	9,660	9,795	10,289	10,310	10,500
Denmark	4,271	4,581	4,929	5,123	5,140	5,350
Djibouti	60	80	168	304	517	650
Dominica	51	60	71	73	71	78
Dominican Rep.	2,353	3,231	4,423	5,697	7,170	8,150
Ecuador	3,310	4,413	6,051	8,123	10,264	11,800
Egypt	20,330	25,922	33,053	40,875	52,691	63,000
El Salvador	1,940	2,570	3,588	4,525	5,172	5,950
Equat. Guinea	226	252	291	217	348	420
Eritrea	1,403	1,612	2,153	2,555	2,896	3,500
Estonia	1,101	1,216	1,365	1,481	1,571	1,460
Ethiopia	18,323	22,641	28,663	36,270	45,889	58,500
Falkland Is.	2	2	2	2	2	2
Faroe Is.	31	35	39	41	47	45
Fiji	289	394	520	634	731	800
Finland	4,009	4,430	4,606	4,780	4,986	5,180
France	41,829	45,684	50,772	53,880	56,735	58,800
French Guiana	25	31	48	66	117	155
French Polynesia	62	82	109	147	197	226
Gabon	469	486	504	806	1,146	1,200
Gambia, The	294	352	464	641	923	1,200
Gaza Strip	245	308	342	453	635	900
Georgia	3,527	4,160	4,708	5,075	5,464	5,450
Germany	68,376	72,673	77,709	78,303	78,500	82,300
Ghana	4,900	6,774	8,612	10,736	15,020	18,100
Gibraltar	23	24	26	29	31	28
Greece	7,566	8,327	8,793	9,643	10,161	10,600
Greenland	23	33	47	52	56	57
Grenada	76	90	94	107	91	99
Guadeloupe	210	275	320	327	385	440
Guam	59	67	86	108	134	161
Guatemala	2,969	3,964	5,246	6,917	9,198	11,250

	1950	1960	1970	1980	1990	1997
Guinea	2,550	3,136	3,900	4,461	5,755	7,450
Guinea-Bissau	505	542	525	795	964	1,150
Guyana	423	569	709	759	796	820
Haiti	3,261	3,807	4,535	5,370	6,486	7,400
Honduras	1,401	1,935	2,627	3,662	5,105	6,300
Hong Kong	1,974	3,075	3,942	5,039	5,705	6,500
Hungary	9,338	9,984	10,338	10,711	10,261	10,150
Iceland	143	176	204	228	255	275
India	357,561	442,344	554,911	688,856	834,697	980,000
Indonesia	79,538	96,194	120,280	150,958	179,830	203,500
Iran	16,913	21,554	28,429	38,900	54,496	69,500
Iraq	5,158	6,847	9,356	13,291	18,920	22,500
Ireland	2,969	2,834	2,954	3,401	3,503	3,625
Israel	1,258	2,114	2,974	3,878	4,660	5,900
Italy	47,104	50,200	53,822	56,434	57,193	57,750
Ivory Coast	2,775	3,799	5,515	8,194	11,980	15,100
Jamaica	1,403	1,629	1,869	2,133	2,415	2,600
Japan	83,625	94,096	104,331	116,807	123,537	125,900
Jordan	1,237	1,695	2,299	2,923	4,259	5,600
Kazakstan	6,703	9,996	13,110	14,939	16,670	17,000
Kenya	6,265	8,332	11,498	16,632	24,032	31,900
Kiribati	32	41	49	58	72	85
Korea, North	9,726	10,789	14,619	18,260	21,774	24,500
Korea, South	20,357	25,003	31,923	38,124	42,869	46,050
Kuwait	152	278	744	1,375	2,125	2,050
Kyrgyzstan	1,740	2,173	2,965	3,630	4,395	4,650
Laos	1,755	2,177	2,713	3,205	4,202	5,200
Latvia	1,849	2,129	2,374	2,543	2,671	2,450
Lebanon	1,443	1,857	2,469	2,669	2,555	3,200
Lesotho	734	870	1,064	1,339	1,792	2,100
Liberia	824	1,039	1,385	1,876	2,407	2,950
Libya	1,029	1,349	1,986	3,043	4,151	5,500
Liechtenstein	14	16	21	26	29	32
Lithuania	2,567	2,779	3,148	3,439	3,722	3,710
Luxembourg	296	314	339	364	382	425
Macau	188	169	245	287	335	450
Macedonia	1,229	1,392	1,629	1,900	2,028	2,150
Madagascar	4,230	5,309	6,742	8,785	11,197	15,500
Malawi	2,881	3,529	4,518	6,183	8,289	10,250
Malaysia	6,110	8,140	10,853	13,763	17,764	20,900
Maldives	82	92	114	154	216	275
Mali	3,520	4,375	5,484	6,863	8,156	11,000
Malta	312	329	326	364	354	375
Marshall Is.	11	15	22	31	46	60
Martinique	222	282	326	326	362	405
Mauritania	825	991	1,221	1,551	2,003	2,400
Mauritius	493	660	826	966	1,059	1,155
Mayotte	22	28	37	52	80	105
Mexico	28,012	38,020	52,771	70,416	86,154	97,400
Micronesia	31	42	57	77	109	127
Moldova	2,341	3,004	3,595	4,001	4,364	4,450
Monaco	22	23	24	26	30	33
Mongolia	761	959	1,256	1,663	2,177	2,500
Montserrat	13	12	12	14	11	12
Morocco	8,953	11,626	15,310	19,382	24,487	28,100
Mozambique	6,198	7,461	9,395	12,095	14,151	19,100
N. Mariana Is.	6	9	12	17	44	53
Namibia	666	817	1,016	1,306	1,349	1,650
Nauru	3	4	7	8	10	12
Nepal	8,182	9,404	11,488	14,858	18,111	22,100
Netherlands	10,114	11,480	13,032	14,144	14,952	15,900
Neths Antilles	162	192	222	247	190	210
New Caledonia	59	79	110	142	170	192
New Zealand	1,908	2,372	2,820	3,113	3,363	3,650
Nicaragua	1,098	1,493	2,053	2,771	3,871	4,600
Niger	2,400	3,028	4,165	5,586	7,731	9,700
Nigeria	32,935	42,305	56,581	70,000	108,542	118,000
Niue	4	5	3	4	2	2
Norfolk I.	1	1	2	2	2	2
Norway	3,265	3,581	3,877	4,086	4,241	4,440
Oman	413	505	654	984	2,000	2,400
Pacific Is.	57	78	103	136	142	
Pakistan	39,513	49,955	65,706	85,299	112,049	136,000
Palau	7	10	12	13	15	17
Panama	893	1,148	1,531	1,956	2,398	2,720
Papua New Guinea	1,613	1,920	2,422	3,086	3,699	4,400
Paraguay	1,351	1,774	2,351	3,147	4,219	5,200
Peru	7,632	9,931	13,193	17,295	21,550	24,500
Philippines	20,988	27,561	37,540	48,317	61,480	73,500
Pitcairn Is.	0	0	0	0	0	0
Poland	24,824	29,561	32,526	35,574	38,119	38,800
Portugal	8,405	8,826	9,044	9,766	9,896	10,100
Puerto Rico	2,219	2,358	2,718	3,206	3,528	3,825
Qatar	25	45	111	229	486	620
Réunion	257	339	441	508	601	680
Romania	16,311	18,407	20,253	22,201	23,207	22,600
Russia	105,018	119,906	130,392	138,936	148,292	147,800
Rwanda	2,120	2,742	3,728	5,163	7,181	7,000
St Helena	4	5	5	6	5	6
St Kitts & Nevis	50	57	52	52	42	42
St Lucia	79	88	101	120	133	150

	1950	1960	1970	1980	1990	1997
St Pierre & Miq.	5	5	6	6	6	7
St Vincent & G.	67	80	88	99	107	114
San Marino	13	15	18	21	23	26
São Tomé & Príncipe	60	64	74	85	115	135
Saudi Arabia	3,201	4,075	5,745	9,372	14,870	19,100
Senegal	2,500	3,187	4,158	5,538	7,504	8,900
Seychelles	34	42	52	65	70	78
Sierra Leone	1,944	2,241	2,656	3,263	3,999	4,600
Singapore	1,022	1,634	2,075	2,300	2,705	3,200
Slovak Rep.	3,463	3,994	4,524	4,966	5,263	5,400
Slovenia	1,473	1,580	1,718	1,886	1,998	2,000
Solomon Is.	104	123	163	231	320	410
Somalia	2,423	2,935	3,668	5,345	8,677	9,900
South Africa	13,683	17,396	22,458	28,270	37,066	42,300
Spain	28,009	30,455	33,779	37,542	38,959	39,300
Sri Lanka	7,678	9,889	12,514	14,819	16,993	18,700
Sudan	9,190	11,165	13,859	18,681	25,752	31,000
Surinam	215	290	372	352	404	450
Swaziland	264	326	419	563	768	950
Sweden	7,014	7,480	8,043	8,310	8,559	8,850
Switzerland	4,694	5,362	6,187	6,319	6,712	7,100
Syria	3,495	4,561	6,258	8,800	12,116	15,300
Taiwan	7,647	10,792	14,676	17,805	20,353	21,700
Tajikistan	1,532	2,083	2,942	3,967	5,303	6,000
Tanzania	7,886	10,026	13,513	18,867	25,635	31,200
Thailand	20,010	26,392	35,745	46,718	56,082	60,800
Togo	1,329	1,514	2,020	2,615	3,531	4,450
Tokelau	1	2	1	2	2	2
Tonga	50	65	85	96	97	105
Trinidad & Tobago	636	843	971	1,082	1,227	1,300
Tunisia	3,530	4,221	5,127	6,384	8,074	9,200
Turkey	20,809	27,509	35,321	44,438	56,098	63,500
Turkmenistan	1,211	1,594	2,189	2,860	3,670	4,800
Turks & Caicos Is.	6	6	6	6	12	15
Tuvalu	5	5	6	7	9	10
Uganda	4,762	6,562	9,806	13,120	17,949	20,800
Ukraine	36,906	42,783	47,317	50,033	51,839	51,500
United Arab Em.	70	90	223	1,015	1,671	2,400
United Kingdom	50,616	52,372	55,632	56,330	57,237	58,600
United States	152,271	180,671	205,051	227,757	249,911	268,000
US Virgin Is.	27	32	62	106	102	110
Uruguay	2,239	2,538	2,808	2,914	3,094	3,250
Uzbekistan	6,314	8,559	11,973	15,975	20,531	23,750
Vanuatu	52	65	86	118	147	175
Vatican City	1	1	1	1	1	1
Venezuela	5,009	7,502	10,604	15,024	19,325	22,500
Vietnam	29,954	34,743	42,729	53,700	66,233	77,100
Wallis & Futuna	7	8	9	9	14	15
West Bank	771	805	680	833	1,080	1,496
Western Sahara	14	32	76	135	230	280
Western Samoa	82	111	143	157	164	175
Yemen	4,316	5,247	6,332	7,675	11,279	16,500
Yugoslavia (Serbia)	7,131	8,050	8,910	9,866	10,529	10,500
Zambia	2,440	3,141	4,189	5,738	8,073	9,500
Zimbabwe	2,730	3,812	5,260	7,126	9,369	12,100

Population change

average annual change

	1950–60	1960–70	1970–80	1980–90	1990–97
WORLD	**1.8**	**2**	**1.9**	**1.8**	**1.3**
Afghanistan	1.9	2.4	1.7	0.3	4.8
Albania	2.7	2.9	2.3	2	1.5
Algeria	2.1	2.4	3.1	2.9	2.3
American Samoa	1	2.5	1.7	1.7	7.2
Andorra	4.4	9.6	4.8	3.9	6.9
Angola	1.5	1.5	3.3	2.6	1.6
Anguilla	1.8	0	1.6	0	5.2
Antigua & Barb.	1.8	1.8	1.3	0.1	–2
Argentina	1.9	1.5	1.7	1.4	1.3
Armenia	3.3	3	2	0.8	1.9
Aruba	0.3	0.3	0.5	–0.6	2.2
Australia	2.3	2	1.6	1.4	1.2
Austria	0.2	0.6	0.1	0	1.1
Azerbaijan	3	2.9	1.8	1.5	1
Bahamas	3.6	4.2	2.1	1.9	1.5
Bahrain	3	3.5	4.7	4	2.3
Bangladesh	2.1	2.6	2.8	2.7	1
Barbados	0.9	0.3	0.4	0.2	0.6
Belarus	0.6	1	0.7	0.6	0.3
Belgium	0.6	0.5	0.2	0	0.5
Belize	3.1	2.8	1.9	2.6	2.9
Benin	0.9	1.9	2.5	3.2	2.9
Bermuda	1.4	2	0.2	0.4	1.6
Bhutan	1.7	1.9	1.8	2	2.4
Bolivia	2.2	2.4	2.6	2.8	0.6
Bosnia	2	1.3	1	0.6	–2.7
Botswana	2.1	2.6	3.8	3.7	2.2
Brazil	3.1	2.8	2.4	2.2	0.8
Brit.Ind.Oc.Terr.	0	0	0	0	0
Brit. Virgin Is.	2	3	2	0.8	0
Brunei	6.9	4	5.5	1.6	1.7
Bulgaria	0.8	0.8	0.4	0.2	–0.7
Burkina Faso	2	2.2	2.3	2.6	2.8
Burma	1.9	2.3	2.4	1.8	1.9
Burundi	1.8	1.8	1.6	2.8	2
Cambodia	2.3	2.5	–0.8	2.6	3.5
Cameroon	1.7	2.2	2.7	2.9	2.6
Canada	2.7	1.8	1.2	1	1.9
Cape Verde Is.	3	3.1	0.8	2.3	1.8
Cayman Is.	2.4	3.3	5.5	3.3	4.9
Central Afr. Rep.	1.6	1.9	2.3	2.6	1.8
Chad	1.4	1.8	2.1	2.4	2.5
Chile	2.3	2.2	1.6	1.7	1.6
China	1.7	2.4	1.8	1.3	0.9
Christmas I.	10.4	–0.4	1.4	0	–3.1
Cocos Is.	–5.1	0.2	–1.8	7.2	–7.4
Colombia	2.9	3	2.3	2.1	1.2
Comoros	2.2	1.3	3.1	5	2.1
Congo	2	2.5	2.8	2.9	2.9
Congo (Zaïre)	2.3	2.6	2.9	3.1	4.1
Cook Is.	1.8	1.6	–1	–0.5	1.5
Costa Rica	3.7	3.4	2.8	2.8	2.2
Croatia	0.7	0.6	0.4	0.4	0.2
Cuba	1.8	2	1.3	0.9	0.8
Cyprus	1.5	0.7	0.2	1.1	1.4
Czech Rep.	0.7	0.3	0.5	0	0.3
Denmark	0.7	0.7	0.4	0	0.6
Djibouti	2.9	7.7	6.1	3.8	5.7
Dominica	1.6	1.7	0.3	1.2	–0.7
Dominican Rep.	3.2	3.2	2.6	2.3	1.8
Ecuador	2.9	3.2	3	2.7	1.6
Egypt	2.5	2.5	2.1	2.6	2.6
El Salvador	2.9	3.4	2.3	1.5	1.8
Equatorial Guinea	1.1	1.4	–2.9	4.8	2.7
Eritrea	2.2	2.4	2.4	3.1	0.6
Estonia	1	1.2	0.8	0.7	–1.1
Ethiopia	2.1	2.4	2.4	2.4	3.5
Falkland Is.	0	–1.5	1.1	0	0
Faroe Is.	1.2	1.1	0.5	1.4	–0.6
Fiji	3.1	2.8	2	1.9	0.7
Finland	1	0.4	0.4	0.4	0.6
France	0.9	1.1	0.6	0.4	0.7
French Guiana	2.2	4.5	3.2	4	6.8
French Polynesia	2.8	2.9	3	3.4	1.3
Gabon	0.4	0.4	4.8	3.7	0.5
Gambia, The	1.8	2.8	3.3	3	4.9
Gaza Strip	0	0	2.9	3.4	6.5
Georgia	1.7	1.2	0.8	0.7	0
Germany	0.6	0.7	0.1	0.1	0.5
Ghana	3.3	2.4	2.2	3.4	2.7
Gibraltar	0.4	0.8	1.1	0.3	–1
Greece	1	0.5	0.9	0.4	0.8
Greenland	3.7	3.6	1	0.7	0.3
Grenada	1.7	0.4	1.3	–2.3	2.2
Guadeloupe	2.7	1.5	0.2	0.5	3.6
Guam	1.3	2.5	2.3	0.9	4.5
Guatemala	2.9	2.8	2.8	2.9	2.9
Guinea	2.1	2.2	1.4	2.6	3.8
Guinea-Bissau	0.7	–0.3	4.2	1.9	2.6
Guyana	3	2.2	0.7	0.5	0.4
Haiti	1.6	1.8	1.7	1.9	1.8
Honduras	3.3	3.1	3.4	3.4	3
Hong Kong	4.5	2.5	2.5	1.5	1.5
Hungary	0.7	0.3	0.4	–0.1	–0.6
Iceland	2.1	1.5	1.1	1	1.2
India	2.2	2.3	2.2	1.8	2.5
Indonesia	1.9	2.3	2.3	1.7	1.8
Iran	2.5	2.8	3.2	3.4	3.5
Iraq	2.9	3.2	3.6	3.6	2.5
Ireland	–0.5	0.4	1.4	0.3	0.5
Israel	5.3	3.5	2.7	1.7	3.6
Italy	0.6	0.7	0.5	0.1	0.2
Ivory Coast	3.2	3.8	4	3.9	3.4
Jamaica	1.5	1.4	1.3	1.4	0.8
Japan	1.2	1	1.1	0.6	0.3
Jordan	3.2	3.1	2.4	3.2	4.9
Kazakstan	4.1	2.7	1.3	1.1	0.2
Kenya	2.9	3.3	3.8	3.7	4.1
Kiribati	2.5	1.8	1.7	1.3	3.7
Korea, North	1	3.1	2.2	1.8	1.7
Korea, South	2.1	2.5	1.8	1.2	1.1
Kuwait	6.2	10.3	6.3	0.9	4.6
Kyrgyzstan	2.2	3.2	2	1.9	0.8
Laos	2.2	2.2	1.7	2.6	3.3
Latvia	1.4	1.1	0.7	0.5	–1.3
Lebanon	2.6	2.9	0.8	0.1	2.5
Lesotho	1.7	2	2.3	2.7	2.7
Liberia	2.3	2.9	3.1	2.5	2.9
Libya	2.7	3.9	4.4	4.1	2.8
Liechtenstein	1.3	2.8	2.2	0.7	1.9
Lithuania	0.8	1.3	0.9	0.8	–0.1
Luxembourg	0.6	0.8	0.7	0.2	1.9
Macau	–1.1	3.8	1.6	5.3	–0.9
Macedonia	1.3	1.6	1.6	0.6	0.9
Madagascar	2.3	2.4	2.7	2.5	4.8
Malawi	2	2.5	3.2	3	3.1
Malaysia	2.9	2.9	2.4	2.7	2.2
Maldives	1.2	2.2	3.1	3.4	3.6
Mali	2.2	2.3	2.3	1.7	4.4
Malta	0.5	–0.1	1.1	–0.3	0.9
Marshall Is.	4.1	3.9	3.8	3.7	3.9
Martinique	2.4	1.5	0	0.5	2.5
Mauritania	1.9	2.1	2.4	2.7	2.5
Mauritius	3	2.3	1.6	1	1.1
Mexico	3.1	3.3	2.9	2	1.8
Mayotte	2.5	2.8	3.6	4.5	3.9
Micronesia	2.9	3.6	2.5	3.2	2.6
Moldova	2.5	1.8	1.1	0.9	0.3
Monaco	0.4	0.4	0.8	0.7	2.4
Mongolia	2.3	2.7	2.8	2.8	1.9
Montserrat	–0.7	–0.3	1.8	–1.5	0
Morocco	2.6	2.8	2.4	2.6	1.6
Mozambique	1.9	2.3	2.6	1.6	4.3
Namibia	2.1	2.2	2.5	1	2
Nauru	2.5	5.5	1.3	1.2	4.2
Nepal	1.4	2	2.6	2.6	2.1
Netherlands	1.3	1.3	0.8	0.6	0.9
Neths Antilles	1.7	1.5	1.1	–2.7	1.6
New Caledonia	3	3.4	2.6	1.6	2
New Zealand	2.2	1.7	1	0.9	1.1
Nicaragua	3.1	3.2	3	3.4	2.5
Niger	2.4	3.2	3	3.3	3.3
Nigeria	2.5	3	2.2	4.5	1.2
Niue	2.3	–3.8	1.6	–2.8	–3.7
Norfolk I.	0	6.5	2.9	0	0
N. Mariana Is.	3.7	3.4	3.1	10.1	2.7
Norway	0.9	0.8	0.5	0.3	0.8
Oman	2	2.6	4.2	4.3	6.9
Pacific Is.	3.2	2.8	2.8	0.4	–100
Pakistan	2.4	2.8	2.6	2.8	2.8
Palau	2.7	2.4	1	1.3	1.8
Panama	2.5	2.9	2.5	2.1	1.7
Papua N. Guinea	1.8	2.3	2.5	2.3	1.8
Paraguay	2.8	2.9	3	3.1	2.8
Peru	2.7	2.9	2.7	2.6	1.3
Philippines	2.8	3.1	2.6	2.6	2.4
Pitcairn	2.3	–5	–4	0	0
Poland	1.8	1	0.9	0.8	0.1
Portugal	0.5	0.2	0.8	0.5	–0.3
Puerto Rico	0.6	1.4	1.7	0.8	1.4
Qatar	6.1	9.4	7.5	4.9	7.7
Réunion	2.8	2.7	1.4	1.7	1.8
Romania	1.2	1	0.9	0.4	–0.3
Russia	1.3	0.8	0.6	0.7	0
Rwanda	2.6	3.1	3.3	3.4	–0.4
St Helena	1.8	0	1.8	–1.8	2.6
St Kitts & Nevis	1.3	–0.9	0	–1.7	–0.7
St Lucia	1.1	1.4	1.7	2.3	0
St Pierre & Miq.	0.4	1.6	0.7	0	2.2
St Vincent	1.8	1	1.2	1.2	0.3
San Marino	1.4	1.8	1.6	0.9	1.8
São Tomé & P.	0.6	1.5	1.4	3.4	1.8
Saudi Arabia	2.4	3.5	5	4.2	4.4
Senegal	2.5	2.7	2.9	2.8	2.8
Seychelles	2.1	2.2	2.3	0.3	2.2
Sierra Leone	1.4	1.7	2.1	2.4	1.5
Singapore	4.8	2.4	1	1.6	2.5
Slovak Republic	1.5	0.5	1.7	0.6	0.3
Slovenia	0.7	0.8	0.9	0.4	0.2
Solomon Is.	1.7	2.9	3.5	3.3	3.6
Somalia	1.9	2.3	3.8	5	1.9
South Africa	2.4	2.6	2.3	3	1.6
Spain	0.8	1	1.1	0.4	0
Sri Lanka	2.6	2.4	1.7	1.5	1.2
Sudan	2	2.2	3	3	3
Surinam	3	2.5	–0.6	1.4	1.5
Swaziland	2.1	2.5	3	3.2	3.1
Sweden	0.6	0.7	0.3	0.2	0.7
Switzerland	1.3	1.4	0.2	0.4	1
Syria	2.7	3.2	3.5	3.6	2.9
Taiwan	3.5	3.1	2	1.3	0.9
Tajikistan	3.1	3.5	3	2.9	1.8
Tanzania	2.4	3	3.4	3.1	2.8
Thailand	2.8	3.1	2.7	2	0.9
Togo	1.3	2.9	2.6	3	3.4
Tokelau	5.2	–3.5	3.6	0	0
Tonga	2.7	2.7	1.2	–0.1	1.4
Trinidad & Tob.	2.9	1.4	1.1	1.7	0.2
Tunisia	1.8	2	2.2	2.4	1.9
Turkey	2.8	2.5	2.3	2.8	1.1
Turkmenistan	2.8	3.2	2.7	2.5	3.9
Turks & Caicos Is.	–0.5	–0.2	0.7	5.2	6
Tuvalu	0	1.8	2.1	2	1.5
Uganda	3.3	4.1	3	3	2.4
Ukraine	1.5	1	0.6	0.4	–0.1
United Arab Emirates	2.5	9.5	16.4	4.6	6.1
United Kingdom	0.3	0.6	0.1	0.2	0.3
United States	1.7	1.3	1.1	0.9	1
US Virgin Is.	1.7	6.9	5.5	0.9	–0.8
Uruguay	1.3	1	0.4	0.6	0.7
Uzbekistan	3.1	3.4	2.9	2.5	2.1
Vanuatu	2.3	2.8	3.2	3	1.5
Vatican City	1.1	0	0	0	0
Venezuela	4.1	3.5	3.5	2.8	1.9
Vietnam	1.5	2.1	2.3	2.2	2.1
Wallis & Futuna	1.3	0.8	0.3	6.6	–1.8
West Bank	0.4	–1.7	2.1	2.6	4.8
Western Sahara	8.6	9	5.9	5.5	2.8
Western Samoa	3.1	2.6	0.9	0.7	0.6
Yemen	2	1.9	1.9	3.9	5.6
Yugoslavia (Serbia)	1.2	1	1	0.4	0.3
Zambia	2.6	2.9	3.2	3.5	2.4
Zimbabwe	3.4	3.3	3.1	2.8	3.7

Birth and death rates
births/deaths per 1,000 population

	Birth Rate					Death Rate				
	1950–55	1960–65	1970–75	1980–85	1997	1950–55	1960–65	1970–75	1980–85	1997
WORLD	**38**	**35**	**32**	**28**	**26**	**20**	**15**	**12**	**10**	**9**
Afghanistan	48	53	52	49	43	32	30	26	23	18
Albania	38	40	32	27	22	14	10	7	6	8
Algeria	51	50	48	41	28	24	19	15	10	6
American Samoa	...	...	...	...	35	...	...	...	...	4
Andorra	...	18	...	15	10	10	6	5	...	3
Angola	50	49	48	47	44	35	30	25	22	17
Anguilla	...	...	...	...	17	...	...	...	...	5
Antigua & Barb.	35	32	20	15	17	12	9	7	6	5
Argentina	25	23	23	23	20	9	9	9	9	8
Armenia	...	...	...	...	17	...	...	...	...	8
Aruba	...	...	...	...	14	...	...	...	...	6
Australia	23	22	20	16	14	9	9	9	7	7
Austria	15	19	14	12	11	12	13	13	12	10
Azerbaijan	...	...	...	...	22	...	...	...	...	9
Bahamas	35	31	28	23	18	12	8	6	5	6
Bahrain	45	47	36	31	23	16	14	8	5	3
Bangladesh	47	47	49	45	30	24	22	21	18	11
Barbados	33	29	21	17	15	13	9	9	9	8
Belarus	...	...	...	...	11	...	...	...	...	13
Belgium	17	17	14	12	12	12	12	12	11	10
Belize	41	46	40	39	32	12	8	6	5	6
Benin	43	48	49	49	46	37	31	26	21	13
Bermuda	28	26	20	18	15	9	7	7	7	7
Bhutan	44	42	41	39	38	27	24	21	18	15
Bolivia	47	46	45	44	32	24	22	19	16	10
Bosnia	...	...	...	...	6	...	...	...	...	15
Botswana	49	53	52	49	33	23	20	17	14	18
Brazil	45	42	34	31	20	15	12	10	8	9
Brit. Virgin Islands	40	33	26	22	20	11	9	7	6	6
Brunei	54	43	35	32	25	15	8	5	4	5
Bulgaria	21	17	16	14	8	10	8	9	11	14
Burkina Faso	51	51	50	47	46	32	27	24	20	20
Burma (Myanmar)	42	41	38	34	30	24	20	14	11	11
Burundi	49	45	44	47	42	25	22	21	19	15
Cambodia	45	45	40	46	43	24	20	23	20	15
Cameroon	44	45	46	47	42	27	24	20	17	14
Canada	28	25	16	15	13	9	8	7	7	7
Cape Verde Is.	51	49	39	39	35	19	15	12	10	7
Cayman Is.	31	32	28	20	14	7	7	6	6	5
Central African Rep.	44	43	43	46	40	29	25	22	19	18
Chad	45	46	45	44	44	32	29	25	21	17
Chile	37	37	28	24	18	14	12	9	6	6
China	44	38	31	19	17	25	17	9	7	7
Christmas I.	49	26	...	...	...	6	5	5	...	...
Cocos Is.	...	30	21	...	...	...	9	7	...	...
Colombia	47	44	35	29	21	17	12	9	6	5
Comoros	47	52	49	48	45	24	21	18	14	10
Congo	44	45	46	46	39	25	22	19	16	17
Congo (Zaïre)	47	47	47	45	48	26	22	19	16	17
Cook Is.	41	47	32	28	23	19	9	5	5	5
Costa Rica	47	45	32	30	23	13	9	6	4	4
Croatia	...	...	...	...	10	...	...	...	...	11
Cuba	30	35	27	16	13	11	9	7	6	7
Cyprus	27	25	18	20	15	11	11	10	8	8
Czech Rep.	...	...	...	...	11	...	...	...	...	11
Denmark	18	17	15	10	12	9	10	10	11	10
Djibouti	50	50	50	48	42	31	27	23	19	15
Dominica	39	43	...	21	18	17	12	...	6	5
Dominican Rep.	51	49	39	34	23	20	15	10	8	6
Ecuador	47	46	41	35	25	19	14	11	8	5
Egypt	49	45	38	39	28	24	20	16	13	9
El Salvador	48	48	43	38	27	20	15	11	11	6
Equatorial Guinea	42	41	42	43	39	32	28	24	21	14
Eritrea	...	...	...	...	44	...	...	...	...	15
Estonia	...	...	...	...	12	...	...	...	...	14
Ethiopia	52	50	48	45	46	32	27	23	24	18
Falkland Is.	23	22	19	15	15	12	11	12	8	8
Faroe Is.	25	23	20	16	13	8	7	7	7	9
Fiji	44	39	32	31	23	14	11	9	8	6
Finland	23	18	13	14	11	10	9	10	9	11
France	20	18	16	15	13	13	11	11	11	9
French Guiana	28	30	29	28	24	16	13	8	7	5
French Polynesia	43	45	37	30	23	12	10	9	8	5
Gabon	30	31	31	34	28	27	23	20	18	13
Gambia, The	47	51	49	48	44	34	31	27	23	13
Gaza Strip	...	...	...	...	50	...	...	...	...	4
Georgia	...	...	...	...	14	...	...	...	...	12
Germany	16	18	11	11	9	11	12	13	13	11
Ghana	48	48	46	45	34	22	19	16	14	11
Gibraltar	23	25	20	18	13	10	9	8	7	9
Greece	19	18	16	14	10	7	8	9	9	10
Greenland	44	47	43	28	16	19	9	6	7	7
Grenada	40	39	26	25	29	14	10	8	7	6
Guadeloupe	39	37	29	21	17	13	8	7	7	6
Guam	29	26	34	30	23	5	5	4	4	4
Guatemala	51	48	45	43	33	22	18	13	11	7
Guinea	55	52	52	51	42	34	30	27	24	18
Guinea-Bissau	41	40	41	43	39	30	28	27	25	16
Guyana	43	41	35	29	19	18	14	10	9	10
Haiti	44	42	39	37	33	28	22	18	15	15
Honduras	51	51	49	42	33	22	18	14	9	6
Hong Kong	38	33	20	17	10	9	6	5	5	5
Hungary	21	14	16	13	11	11	10	12	14	15
Iceland	28	26	21	18	17	8	7	7	7	6
India	44	42	38	35	25	25	19	16	13	9
Indonesia	43	43	38	32	23	26	22	17	11	8
Iran	48	47	44	42	33	25	20	15	10	6
Iraq	49	49	47	44	43	22	19	15	9	6
Ireland	21	22	22	20	13	13	12	11	9	9
Israel	33	26	27	24	20	7	6	7	7	6
Italy	18	19	16	11	10	10	10	10	10	10
Ivory Coast	53	53	51	50	42	28	24	19	16	17
Jamaica	35	40	33	27	22	12	9	8	6	6
Japan	24	17	19	13	10	9	7	7	6	8
Jordan	47	53	50	38	36	26	22	14	8	4
Kazakstan	...	...	...	...	19	...	...	...	...	10
Kenya	53	53	53	51	32	25	21	17	13	11
Kiribati	...	...	...	...	27	...	...	...	...	8
Korea, North	37	41	36	22	22	32	13	8	6	5
Korea, South	32	13	9	6	16	32	13	9	6	6
Kuwait	45	45	44	35	20	11	9	5	3	2
Kyrgyzstan	...	...	...	...	26	...	...	...	...	9
Laos	46	45	44	45	41	25	23	23	19	13
Latvia	...	...	...	...	12	...	...	...	...	15
Lebanon	41	43	32	29	28	19	13	9	9	6
Lesotho	42	43	42	42	32	27	23	19	14	14
Liberia	48	50	48	47	42	27	24	20	17	12
Libya	48	49	49	46	44	23	18	15	11	7
Liechtenstein	22	22	16	14	11	9	8	7	7	7
Lithuania	...	...	...	...	14	...	...	...	...	13
Luxembourg	15	16	12	12	13	12	12	12	11	8
Macau	...	21	11	...	14	13	8	6	5	4
Macedonia	...	...	...	...	13	...	...	...	...	9
Madagascar	48	48	46	46	42	27	23	19	15	14
Malawi	52	55	57	57	41	31	28	24	22	25
Malaysia	45	43	35	32	26	20	13	9	6	5
Maldives	34	37	40	41	41	29	27	20	10	6
Mali	53	52	51	51	51	32	29	25	22	19
Malta	29	23	18	17	15	10	9	9	9	7
Marshall Islands	...	...	...	...	46	...	...	...	...	7
Martinique	40	36	26	18	17	13	9	7	7	6
Mauritania	48	48	47	47	47	31	28	24	21	15
Mauritius	47	43	26	22	19	16	9	7	6	7
Mayotte	...	...	...	...	47	...	...	...	...	10
Mexico	47	46	43	32	26	16	11	9	6	5
Micronesia	...	...	...	...	28	...	...	...	...	6
Moldova	...	...	...	...	17	...	...	...	...	12
Monaco	14	19	8	...	11	14	16	12	15	12
Mongolia	44	43	42	38	25	22	17	13	10	8
Montserrat	32	27	24	20	14	14	10	10	10	10
Morocco	50	50	46	37	27	26	20	16	11	6
Mozambique	46	47	46	46	44	30	25	22	20	18
Namibia	45	46	45	44	37	25	23	18	14	8
Nauru	27	32	...	...	18	7	7	4	5	5
Nepal	46	46	47	43	37	27	25	21	17	12
Netherlands	22	21	15	12	12	8	8	8	8	9
Neths Antilles	35	32	21	19	16	5	5	5	5	5
New Caledonia	27	33	33	29	21	10	9	9	7	5
New Zealand	26	26	21	16	15	9	9	8	8	8
Nicaragua	54	50	47	44	33	23	17	13	10	6
Niger	54	53	52	52	54	32	28	25	22	24
Nigeria	51	52	49	49	43	27	24	20	17	12
Niue	37	42	29	26	21	15	9	10	7	5
Norfolk I.	15	12	11	11	11	14	16	6	7	8
Northern Mariana Is.	...	...	...	...	33	...	...	...	...	5
Norway	19	17	17	12	11	8	10	10	10	11
Oman	51	50	50	48	38	32	26	20	13	4
Pacific Is.	29	34	35	33	...	6	7	5	5	...
Pakistan	50	48	48	50	35	29	22	18	14	11
Palau	...	...	...	...	21	...	...	...	...	7
Panama	40	41	36	28	22	13	10	7	5	5
Papua New Guinea	44	44	41	35	33	29	21	17	13	10
Paraguay	47	42	37	36	30	9	8	7	7	4
Peru	47	46	41	34	24	22	18	13	11	6
Philippines	49	44	37	36	29	20	13	11	9	7
Pitcairn	45	8	15	...	...	16	10	...	...	...
Poland	30	20	18	19	12	11	8	8	10	10
Portugal	24	24	20	15	11	12	11	11	10	10
Puerto Rico	37	31	24	21	18	9	7	7	7	8
Qatar	46	41	31	35	20	22	17	12	5	4
Réunion	39	40	31	24	23	13	10	7	6	5
Romania	25	17	19	16	10	12	9	9	10	12
Russia	...	...	...	...	11	...	...	...	...	16
Rwanda	47	51	53	52	39	23	21	21	19	21
St Helena	28	28	25	...	9	9	10	10	10	6
St Kitts & Nevis	37	36	18	24	23	14	11	8	10	9
St Lucia	36	42	39	29	22	15	12	8	6	6

	Birth Rate					Death Rate				
	1950–55	1960–65	1970–75	1980–85	1997	1950–55	1960–65	1970–75	1980–85	1997
St Pierre & M.	...	...	...	...	13	...	...	...	...	6
St Vincent & G.	42	46	30	26		19	16	12	9	7
Samoa	37	33	29	30	30	7	5	4	6	6
San Marino	18	18	16	14	11	8	8	8	8	8
Saudi Arabia	49	49	48	43	38	26	21	17	9	5
Senegal	49	50	49	47	45	28	27	24	19	11
Seychelles	31	41	32	28	21	12	12	9	9	7
Sierra Leone	48	48	49	48	47	34	32	29	25	18
Singapore	44	34	21	17	16	11	7	5	5	5
Slovak Rep.	...	...	...	...	13	...	...	...	...	9
Slovenia	...	...	...	...	8	...	...	...	...	10
Solomon Is.	...	...	...	...	37	15	15	14	12	4
Somalia	49	48	48	53	44	31	27	23	22	13
South Africa	43	42	36	33	27	20	17	13	11	12
Spain	20	22	20	13	10	10	9	8	8	9
Sri Lanka	39	35	29	27	18	12	9	8	6	6
Sudan	47	47	47	46	41	27	25	21	17	11
Surinam	44	44	35	29	24	13	10	8	7	6
Swaziland	50	49	48	47	43	28	23	18	14	10
Sweden	16	15	14	11	11	10	10	10	11	11
Switzerland	17	19	14	12	11	10	10	9	9	10
Syria	47	47	47	46	39	21	17	12	9	6
São Tomé & P.	41	50	45	40	34	26	19	11	11	8
Taiwan	45	36	24	21	15	10	6	5	5	6
Tajikistan	...	...	...	...	34	...	...	...	...	8
Tanzania	49	52	51	51	41	27	23	19	15	20
Thailand	47	44	35	28	17	19	13	9	8	7
Togo	47	48	46	45	46	29	24	19	16	10
Tokelau	...	...	...	...	22	14	12	9	8	...
Tonga	37	33	32	31	27	9	4	3	3	6
Trinidad & Tob.	38	38	26	28	16	11	8	7	7	7
Tunisia	46	47	37	34	24	23	18	12	8	5
Turkey	48	43	35	31	22	24	16	12	9	5
Turkmenistan	...	...	...	...	29	...	...	...	...	9
Turks & Caicos Is.	39	39	30	26	12	13	11	8	6	5
Tuvalu	34	28	23	...	23	19	9	7	...	9
Uganda	51	49	50	53	45	25	20	19	17	21
Ukraine	...	...	...	...	12	...	...	...	...	15
United Arab Em.	48	44	33	27	18	23	17	10	4	3
United Kingdom	16	18	15	13	13	12	12	12	12	11
United States	24	22	16	16	15	10	9	9	9	9
US Virgin Islands	...	...	...	...	17	...	...	...	...	5
Uruguay	21	22	21	18	17	11	10	10	10	9
Uzbekistan	...	...	...	...	29	...	...	...	...	8
Vanuatu	...	...	...	...	30	...	...	...	...	9
Venezuela	47	44	36	33	24	12	9	7	6	5
Vietnam	42	41	38	35	22	29	21	14	11	7
Wallis & Futuna	...	...	...	...	24	...	...	...	...	5
West Bank	...	...	...	...	38	...	...	...	...	5
Western Sahara	...	...	...	...	46	...	...	...	...	18
Yemen	53	54	55	54	45	32	27	22	18	9
Yugoslavia (Serbia)	...	...	...	...	14	...	...	...	...	10
Zambia	50	49	49	51	44	26	21	18	15	24
Zimbabwe	52	52	49	43	32	23	19	15	12	19

The figures are yearly averages for the period shown.

Infant mortality

deaths under one year per 1,000 live births

	1950–55	1970–75	1990–95	1997
Afghanistan	227	194	162	147
Albania	145	58	32	47
Algeria	185	132	61	47
American Samoa	...	...	...	19
Andorra	...	...	...	2
Angola	231	173	127	136
Anguilla	...	...	...	22
Antigua & Barb.	...	...	...	17
Argentina	64	49	29	19
Armenia	...	...	20	39
Aruba	...	...	...	8
Australia	24	17	7	5
Austria	53	24	9	6
Azerbaijan	...	...	25	74
Bahamas	82	...	21	22
Bahrain	175	55	12	16
Bangladesh	180	140	108	100
Barbados	132	33	10	18
Belarus	...	...	12	13
Belgium	45	19	8	6
Belize	...	...	...	33
Benin	210	136	85	103
Bermuda	...	...	...	13
Bhutan	197	153	118	114
Bolivia	176	151	93	66
Bosnia	...	...	15	36
Botswana	130	95	58	55
Brazil	135	91	57	53
Brit. Virgin Is.	...	...	...	19
Brunei	112	20	7	24
Bulgaria	92	26	14	15
Burkina Faso	226	173	127	117
Burma (Myanmar)	183	100	59	79
Burundi	166	143	110	101
Cambodia	165	181	116	106
Cameroon	190	119	86	78
Canada	36	16	7	6
Cape Verde Is.	129	82	37	50
Cayman Is.	...	...	...	8
Cen. African Rep.	198	132	95	110
Chad	211	166	122	119
Chile	126	70	19	13
China	195	61	27	38
Colombia	123	73	37	25
Comoros	180	135	89	73
Congo	170	90	65	106
Congo (Zaïre)	182	117	75	106
Cook Is.	...	...	...	25
Costa Rica	94	51	17	13
Croatia	...	...	10	10
Cuba	82	36	13	9
Cyprus	53	29	10	8
Czech Rep.	...	...	9	8
Denmark	28	12	6	5
Djibouti	207	154	112	105
Dominica	130	20	17	9
Dominican Rep.	149	94	57	46
Ecuador	150	95	57	33
Egypt	200	150	57	71
El Salvador	175	110	53	30
Equat. Guinea	204	157	117	96
Eritrea	...	...	...	117
Estonia	...	...	14	17
Ethiopia	190	155	122	122
Faroe Is.	...	...	...	7
Fiji	88	45	24	17
Finland	34	12	5	5
France	45	16	7	6
French Guiana	...	...	...	14
French Polynesia	...	...	...	14
Gabon	194	132	94	88
Gambia, The	231	179	132	79
Gaza Strip	...	...	...	26
Georgia	...	...	19	22
Germany	53	20	8	6
Ghana	149	107	81	79
Gibraltar	...	...	...	7
Greece	60	34	13	7
Greenland	120	...	27	23
Grenada	80	40	15	12
Guadeloupe	68	42	12	8
Guam	...	...	...	15
Guatemala	141	95	48	49
Guinea	222	177	134	132
Guinea-Bissau	211	183	140	114
Guyana	119	79	48	51
Haiti	220	135	86	102
Honduras	169	110	57	40
Hong Kong	79	17	6	5
Hungary	71	34	17	12
Iceland	21	12	5	4
India	190	135	88	69
Indonesia	160	114	65	61
Iran	190	122	40	51
Iraq	165	96	56	58
Ireland	41	18	8	6
Israel	41	23	10	8
Italy	60	26	9	7
Ivory Coast	186	129	87	100
Jamaica	85	42	14	15
Japan	51	12	5	4
Jordan	160	82	36	31
Kazakstan	...	...	25	62
Kenya	150	98	64	55
Kiribati	121	89	59	51
Korea, North	115	47	24	25
Korea, South	115	47	21	8
Kuwait	125	43	15	11
Kyrgyzstan	...	...	31	77
Laos	180	145	97	94
Latvia	...	...	11	21
Lebanon	87	48	40	35
Lesotho	160	130	89	80
Liberia	194	181	126	106
Libya	185	117	68	58
Liechtenstein	...	...	...	5
Lithuania	...	...	10	16
Luxembourg	43	16	9	5
Macau	...	...	...	5
Macedonia	...	...	35	29
Madagascar	245	172	110	92
Malawi	212	191	138	139
Malaysia	99	42	20	23
Maldives	...	...	73	44
Mali	213	203	159	101
Malta	75	22	9	6
Marshall Is.	...	...	...	46
Martinique	65	35	10	7
Mauritania	207	160	117	80
Mauritius	99	55	20	17
Mayotte	...	...	...	73
Mexico	114	71	36	24
Micronesia	...	...	...	35
Moldova	...	...	20	46
Monaco	...	...	...	7
Mongolia	148	98	60	68
Montserrat	...	...	...	12
Morocco	180	122	68	41
Mozambique	205	168	130	123
Namibia	168	134	97	46
Nauru	...	...	...	41
Nepal	197	153	118	77
Netherlands	24	12	7	5
Neths Antilles	...	...	...	9
New Caledonia	40	38	34	13
New Zealand	26	16	9	7
Nicaragua	167	100	50	44
Niger	207	166	124	116
Nigeria	207	135	96	70
N. Mariana Is.	...	...	...	38
Norway	23	12	6	5
Oman	231	145	34	26
Pakistan	190	140	98	95
Palau	...	...	...	25
Panama	93	43	21	25
Papua New Guinea	190	105	53	59
Paraguay	106	53	39	22
Peru	159	110	76	50
Philippines	100	64	40	35
Poland	95	27	17	12
Portugal	91	45	13	8
Puerto Rico	63	25	13	11
Qatar	180	57	26	19
Réunion	141	41	12	7
Romania	101	40	19	23
Russia	...	...	17	24
Rwanda	160	140	112	119
St Helena	...	...	...	34
St Kitts & Nevis	86	...	24	18
St Lucia	116	...	18	20
St Pierre & M.	...	...	...	9
St Vincent & G.	115	...	22	16
São Tomé & P.	...	60	45	60
Saudi Arabia	200	120	58	44
Senegal	184	122	80	63
Seychelles	...	...	18	12
Sierra Leone	231	193	143	133
Singapore	66	19	7	5
Slovak Rep.	...	...	10	11
Slovenia	...	...	9	7
Solomon Is.	...	...	50	25
Somalia	190	155	122	119
South Africa	152	110	62	53
Spain	62	21	9	6
Sri Lanka	91	56	24	20
San Marino	...	...	...	6
Sudan	185	145	99	74
Surinam	89	49	28	28
Swaziland	160	144	107	86
Sweden	20	10	6	5
Switzerland	29	13	7	5
Syria	160	88	39	39
Taiwan	34	...	6	7
Tajikistan	...	...	43	111
Tanzania	160	130	97	105
Thailand	132	65	24	32
Togo	204	129	85	82
Tonga	...	59	23	39
Trinidad & Tob.	79	30	14	18
Tunisia	175	120	44	34
Turkey	233	138	62	41
Turkmenistan	...	...	53	81
Turks & Caicos Is.	125	...	...	13
Tuvalu	123	...	...	27
Uganda	160	116	94	98
Ukraine	...	...	13	22
United Arab Em.	180	57	22	16
United Kingdom	28	17	8	6
United States	28	18	8	7
US Virgin Is.	...	...	...	13
Uruguay	57	46	20	15
Uzbekistan	...	...	36	79
Vanuatu	...	...	85	63
Venezuela	106	49	33	29
Vietnam	180	120	54	37
Western Samoa	41	...	47	33
Wallis and Futuna	...	...	...	22
West Bank	...	...	...	28
Western Sahara	...	...	...	143
Yemen	231	168	107	68
Yugoslavia (Serbia)	...	...	24	23
Zambia	150	100	72	97
Zimbabwe	120	93	55	73

Infant mortality is the number of deaths per year of children under one year, per 1,000 births. The figures are yearly averages for the period shown. The 1997 estimates are those of the US Census Bureau.

Life expectancy
years

	1950–55 male	1950–55 female	1970–75 male	1970–75 female	1990–95 male	1990–95 female	1997 male	1997 female
Afghanistan	31	32	38	38	43	44	47	46
Albania	54	56	66	70	70	75	65	72
Algeria	42	44	54	56	68	70	65	67
American Samoa	...	...	...	...	...	...	71	75
Andorra	...	...	...	...	...	...	86	95
Angola	29	32	37	40	45	48	45	50
Anguilla	...	...	...	...	...	...	74	80
Antigua & Barbuda	...	...	...	...	...	...	72	76
Argentina	60	65	64	71	68	75	71	78
Armenia	...	...	...	...	78	73	65	74
Aruba	...	...	...	...	...	...	73	81
Australia	67	72	68	75	74	80	77	83
Austria	63	68	67	74	72	79	74	80
Azerbaijan	...	...	...	...	67	75	60	70
Bahamas	...	...	...	...	...	...	69	77
Bahrain	50	53	62	65	70	74	72	77
Bangladesh	38	35	46	44	53	53	56	56
Barbados	55	60	67	72	73	78	72	77
Belarus	...	...	...	...	64	75	64	74
Belgium	65	70	68	75	72	79	74	81
Belize	...	...	...	...	...	...	67	71
Benin	31	34	39	42	46	50	51	55
Bermuda	...	...	...	...	...	...	73	77
Bhutan	37	36	43	42	51	49	52	51
Bolivia	39	43	45	49	54	58	57	63
Bosnia	...	...	...	...	68	73	55	65
Botswana	41	44	49	53	58	64	44	46
Brazil	49	53	58	62	64	69	57	66
British Virgin Is.	...	...	...	...	...	...	71	75
Brunei	...	...	...	...	...	...	70	73
Bulgaria	62	66	69	74	70	76	67	75
Burkina Faso	32	35	40	43	48	51	42	42
Burma (Myanmar)	39	41	51	54	61	64	55	58
Burundi	38	41	41	45	48	51	48	50
Cambodia	38	41	39	42	50	52	49	52
Cameroon	35	38	44	47	54	57	51	53
Canada	67	72	70	77	74	81	76	83
Cape Verde Is.	47	50	56	59	67	69	67	73
Cayman Is.	...	...	...	...	...	...	75	79
Central African Rep.	33	38	40	46	48	53	44	46
Chad	31	34	38	41	46	49	45	50
Chile	52	56	61	67	69	76	72	78
China	39	42	63	64	69	73	69	72
Colombia	49	52	60	63	66	72	70	76
Comoros	40	41	47	48	56	57	57	62
Congo	36	41	44	49	52	57	44	47
Congo (Zaïre)	38	41	44	48	...	...	45	49
Cook Is.	...	...	...	...	...	...	69	73
Costa Rica	56	59	66	70	73	78	73	78
Croatia	...	...	...	...	67	74	69	77
Cuba	58	61	69	73	74	78	73	78
Cyprus	65	69	70	73	74	79	74	79
Czech Rep.	64	68	67	74	69	76	70	78
Denmark	70	72	71	76	73	79	74	81
Djibouti	32	35	39	43	47	51	49	53
Dominica	...	...	...	...	...	...	75	81
Dominican Rep.	45	47	58	62	65	70	67	72
Ecuador	47	50	57	61	65	69	69	74
Egypt	41	44	51	53	60	63	60	64
El Salvador	44	47	57	61	64	69	66	73
Equat. Guinea	33	35	39	42	46	50	51	56
Eritrea	...	...	...	...	...	...	49	52
Estonia	...	...	...	...	65	75	63	74
Ethiopia	31	34	39	43	45	49	45	48
Faroe Is.	...	...	...	...	...	...	75	81
Fiji	49	52	56	60	64	68	64	68
Finland	63	70	67	75	72	80	74	77
France	64	70	69	76	73	81	75	83
French Guiana	...	...	...	...	...	...	73	79
French Polynesia	...	...	...	...	...	...	70	75
Gabon	37	40	43	47	52	55	53	59
Gambia, The	29	32	36	39	43	47	51	56
Gaza Strip	...	...	...	...	...	...	71	74
Georgia	...	...	...	...	69	76	64	73
Germany	65	70	68	74	72	78	73	79
Ghana	40	44	48	52	54	58	54	59
Gibraltar	...	...	...	...	...	...	75	81
Greece	64	68	71	74	74	79	76	81
Greenland	...	...	...	...	...	...	65	73
Grenada	...	...	...	...	...	...	69	74
Guadeloupe	55	58	65	71	71	78	75	81
Guam	...	...	...	...	...	...	72	76
Guatemala	42	42	53	56	62	67	63	68
Guinea	31	32	37	38	44	45	43	48
Guinea-Bissau	31	34	35	38	42	45	47	50
Guyana	51	54	58	62	62	68	57	62
Haiti	36	39	47	50	55	58	47	52
Honduras	41	44	52	56	64	68	66	71
Hong Kong	57	65	69	76	75	80	79	86
Hungary	62	66	67	73	68	75	64	74
Iceland	70	74	71	77	75	81	78	83
India	39	38	51	49	60	61	60	61
Indonesia	37	38	48	51	61	65	60	64
Iran	46	46	56	56	67	68	66	69
Iraq	43	45	56	58	65	67	66	69
Ireland	66	68	69	74	73	78	73	79
Israel	64	66	70	73	74	78	76	80
Italy	64	68	69	75	73	80	75	82
Ivory Coast	35	38	44	47	53	56	44	46
Jamaica	56	59	67	71	71	76	73	78
Japan	62	66	71	76	76	82	77	83
Jordan	42	44	55	58	66	70	71	75
Kazakstan	...	...	...	...	64	73	59	70
Kenya	39	43	49	53	59	63	54	55
Kiribati	...	...	...	...	...	...	61	64
Korea, North	46	49	59	64	68	74	68	74
Korea, South	46	49	59	64	68	74	70	78
Kuwait	54	58	65	69	72	77	74	79
Kyrgyzstan	...	...	...	...	65	73	59	69
Laos	37	39	39	42	50	53	52	55
Latvia	...	...	...	...	64	75	61	73
Lebanon	54	58	63	67	65	69	68	73
Lesotho	34	41	44	53	54	63	49	54
Liberia	36	39	46	49	54	57	56	62
Libya	42	44	51	55	62	65	63	67
Liechtenstein	...	...	...	...	...	...	76	82
Lithuania	...	...	...	...	67	76	63	74
Luxembourg	63	69	67	74	72	79	76	82
Macau	...	...	...	...	...	...	78	83
Macedonia	...	...	...	...	68	72	70	74
Madagascar	36	39	45	48	54	57	51	54
Malawi	36	37	40	42	48	50	35	36
Malaysia	47	50	61	65	69	73	67	73
Maldives	...	...	...	...	...	...	65	69
Mali	31	34	37	40	44	48	46	49
Malta	64	68	69	73	72	76	76	81
Marshall Is.	...	...	...	...	...	...	63	66
Martinique	55	58	66	72	73	79	76	82
Mauritania	32	35	39	42	46	50	47	53
Mauritius	50	52	61	65	68	73	67	75
Mayotte	...	...	...	...	...	...	57	62
Mexico	49	52	60	65	67	74	70	78
Micronesia	...	...	...	...	...	...	66	70
Moldova	...	...	...	...	65	72	61	70
Monaco	...	...	...	...	...	...	75	82
Mongolia	41	44	53	55	62	65	59	63
Montserrat	...	...	...	...	...	...	74	77
Morocco	42	44	51	55	62	65	68	72
Mozambique	32	35	41	44	47	50	44	46
Namibia	38	40	48	50	58	60	63	67
Nauru	...	...	...	...	...	...	64	69
Nepal	37	36	44	43	54	53	54	55
Netherlands	71	73	71	77	74	81	75	81
Neths Antilles	...	...	...	...	...	...	75	80
New Caledonia	...	...	...	...	...	...	71	78
New Zealand	68	72	69	75	73	79	74	81
Nicaragua	41	44	54	56	65	68	64	69
Niger	32	35	38	41	45	48	41	41
Nigeria	35	38	43	46	51	54	53	56
Northern Mariana Is.	...	...	...	...	...	...	66	69
Norway	71	75	71	78	74	81	75	81
Oman	36	37	48	50	66	70	69	73
Pakistan	40	38	50	48	59	59	58	60
Palau	...	...	...	...	...	...	69	73
Panama	54	56	65	68	71	75	72	77
Papua New Guinea	36	35	48	48	55	57	57	59
Paraguay	61	65	64	68	65	70	73	76
Peru	43	45	54	57	63	67	67	72
Philippines	46	49	56	59	63	67	63	69
Poland	59	64	67	74	68	76	68	77
Portugal	57	62	65	71	71	78	72	79
Puerto Rico	63	67	69	76	73	79	71	80
Qatar	47	49	61	64	68	73	71	76
Réunion	50	56	60	68	68	76	72	78
Romania	59	63	67	71	69	74	66	74
Russia	...	...	...	...	64	74	57	71
Rwanda	39	42	43	46	49	52	39	40
St Helena	...	...	...	...	...	...	74	77
St Kitts & Nevis	...	...	...	...	...	...	64	70
St Lucia	...	...	...	...	...	...	67	74
St Pierre & Miquelon	...	...	...	...	...	...	75	79
St Vincent & G.	...	...	...	...	...	...	72	75
San Marino	...	...	...	...	...	...	77	85

	1950–55		1970–75		1990–95		1997	
	male	female	male	female	male	female	male	female
São Tomé & Príncipe	…	…	…	…	…	…	62	66
Saudi Arabia	39	41	52	56	64	68	68	71
Senegal	36	38	39	41	48	50	54	60
Seychelles	…	…	…	…	…	…	65	74
Sierra Leone	29	32	34	37	41	45	45	51
Singapore	59	62	67	72	72	77	75	82
Slovak Rep.	64	68	67	74	67	75	69	77
Slovenia	…	…	…	…	70	77	71	79
Solomon Is.	…	…	…	…	…	…	69	74
Somalia	32	35	39	43	45	49	56	56
South Africa	44	46	51	57	60	66	54	58
Spain	62	66	70	76	74	80	75	82
Sri Lanka	58	56	64	66	70	74	70	75
Sudan	36	38	41	44	51	53	55	57
Surinam	54	58	62	67	68	73	68	73
Swaziland	34	37	45	50	56	60	54	62
Sweden	70	73	72	78	75	81	76	81
Switzerland	67	72	71	77	75	81	75	81
Syria	45	47	55	59	65	69	66	69
Taiwan	61	65	68	73	72	77	74	79
Tajikistan	…	…	…	…	67	72	61	68
Tanzania	…	…	…	…	…	…	40	43
Thailand	45	49	58	62	65	69	65	73
Togo	35	38	44	47	53	57	56	61
Tonga	…	…	…	…	…	…	67	72
Trinidad & Tobago	56	59	64	69	70	75	68	73
Tunisia	44	45	55	56	67	69	72	74
Turkey	42	45	56	60	65	68	70	75
Turkmenistan	…	…	…	…	63	70	57	67
Turks & Caicos Is.	…	…	…	…	…	…	73	77
Tuvalu	…	…	…	…	…	…	62	65
Uganda	39	42	45	49	51	55	39	40
Ukraine	…	…	…	…	66	75	62	72
United Arab Em.	47	49	61	64	70	74	73	76
United Kingdom	67	72	69	75	73	79	74	79
United States	66	72	68	75	73	80	73	79
US Virgin Is.	…	…	…	…	…	…	74	77
Uruguay	63	69	66	72	69	76	72	79
Uzbekistan	…	…	…	…	66	73	61	69
Vanuatu	…	…	…	…	…	…	59	63
Venezuela	54	57	64	69	67	74	69	76
Vietnam	39	42	48	53	62	66	65	70
Wallis & Futuna	…	…	…	…	…	…	73	74
West Bank	…	…	…	…	…	…	70	74
Western Sahara	…	…	…	…	…	…	47	49
Western Samoa	…	…	…	…	…	…	67	72
Yemen	33	33	43	43	52	52	59	62
Yugoslavia (Serbia)	…	…	…	…	68	73	69	75
Zambia	36	39	46	49	54	57	36	36
Zimbabwe	40	43	50	53	59	63	41	41

Life expectancy is the age to which a baby can expect to live with the rate of mortality pertaining at the time of birth. The figures for 1950–55, 1970–75 and 1990–95 are averages for the period and for 1997 are estimates of the US Census Bureau.

Population density   *inhabitants per square kilometre*

	area	1950 tot. pop.	1970 tot. pop.	1990 tot. pop.	1997 tot. pop.	1950 density	1970 density	1990 density	1997 density
WORLD	**131,163.21**	**2,520,000**	**3,697,000**	**5,285,000**	**5,808,562**	**19**	**28**	**40**	**44**
Afghanistan	652.09	8,958	13,623	16,121	23,000	14	21	25	35
Albania	27.4	1,230	2,138	3,256	3,600	45	78	119	131
Algeria	2,381.74	8,753	13,746	25,012	29,300	4	6	11	12
Am. Samoa	0.2	19	27	47	62	95	135	235	310
Andorra	0.45	5	20	53	75	12	44	118	166
Angola	1,246.70	4,131	5,588	10,020	11,200	3	4	8	9
Anguilla	0.16	5	6	7	10	32	39	45	65
Antigua & B.	0.44	46	66	64	66	105	150	145	150
Argentina	2,736.69	17,150	23,962	32,547	35,400	6	9	12	13
Armenia	28.4	1,354	2,520	3,545	3,800	48	89	125	134
Aruba	0.19	57	61	67	70	300	321	353	368
Australia	7,644.44	8,219	12,552	17,065	18,400	1	2	2	2
Austria	82.73	6,935	7,467	7,718	8,200	84	90	93'	99
Azerbaijan	86.1	2,896	5,172	7,153	7,650	34	60	83	89
Bahamas	10.01	79	171	255	280	8	17	25	28
Bahrain	0.68	116	220	486	605	171	324	715	890
Bangladesh	130.17	41,783	66,671	108,117	124,000	321	512	831	953
Barbados	0.43	211	239	257	265	491	556	598	616
Belarus	207.6	7,745	9,040	10,260	10,500	37	44	49	51
Belgium	30.53	8,639	9,656	9,967	10,225	283	316	326	335
Belize	22.8	67	120	189	228	3	5	8	10
Benin	110.62	2,046	2,693	4,739	5,800	18	24	43	52
Bermuda	0.05	39	55	61	65	780	1,100	1,220	1,300
Bhutan	47	734	1,045	1,544	1,790	16	22	33	38
Bolivia	1,084.38	2,766	4,325	6,573	7,650	3	4	6	7
Bosnia	51.2	2,662	3,703	4,308	3,600	52	72	84	70
Botswana	566.73	389	623	1,300	1,510	1	1	2	3
Brazil	8,456.51	53,444	95,847	144,723	159,500	6	11	17	19
Br. Ind. Oc. Terr.	0.08	2	2	2	2	25	25	25	25
Brit. Virgin Is.	0.15	6	10	16	13	40	65	107	87
Brunei	5.27	46	133	253	300	9	25	48	57
Bulgaria	110.55	7,251	8,490	8,991	8,560	66	77	81	77
Burkina Faso	273.6	3,654	5,550	9,001	10,900	13	20	33	40
Burma	657.55	18,038	27,346	41,813	47,500	27	42	64	72
Burundi	25.68	2,456	3,522	5,458	6,250	96	137	213	243
Cambodia	176.52	4,346	6,938	8,568	10,500	25	39	49	59
Cameroon	465.4	4,467	6,610	11,526	13,800	10	14	25	30
Canada	9,220.97	13,737	21,324	26,584	30,200	1	2	3	3
Cape Verde Is.	4.03	146	267	341	410	36	66	85	102
Cayman Is.	0.26	6	11	26	35	23	40	100	135
Cen. Afr. Rep.	622.98	1,314	1,849	2,927	3,400	2	3	5	5
Chad	1,259.20	2,658	3,652	5,687	6,750	2	3	5	5
Chile	748.8	6,082	9,504	13,173	14,700	8	13	18	20
China	9,326.41	554,760	830,675	1,155,305	1,210,000	59	89	124	
Christmas I.	0.13	1	3	3	2	8	20	23	18
Cocos Is.	0.01	1	1	0	1	100	60	2	59
Colombia	1,038.70	11,946	21,360	32,300	35,900	12	21	31	35
Comoros	2.23	173	245	543	630	78	110	243	283
Congo	341.5	808	1,263	2,232	2,730	2	4	7	8
Congo (Zaïre)	2,267.05	12,184	19,769	35,562	47,200	5	9	16	21
Cook Is.	0.23	15	21	18	20	65	91	78	87
Costa Rica	51.06	862	1,731	2,805	3,500	17	34	55	69
Croatia	56.4	3,851	4,411	4,778	4,850	68	78	85	86
Cuba	109.82	5,850	8,520	10,625	11,250	53	78	97	102
Cyprus	9.24	494	615	681	770	53	67	74	83
Czech Rep.	78.86	8,925	9,795	10,310	10,500	113	124	131	133
Denmark	42.43	4,271	4,929	5,140	5,350	101	116	121	126
Djibouti	23.18	60	168	517	650	3	7	22	28
Dominica	0.75	51	71	71	78	68	95	95	104
Dominican Rep.	48.38	2,353	4,423	7,170	8,150	49	91	148	168
Ecuador	276.84	3,310	6,051	10,264	11,800	12	22	37	43
Egypt	995.45	20,330	33,053	52,691	63,000	20	33	53	63
El Salvador	20.72	1,940	3,588	5,172	5,950	94	173	250	287
Eq. Guinea	28.05	226	291	348	420	8	10	12	15
Eritrea	101	1,403	2,153	2,896	3,500	14	21	29	35
Estonia	43.2	1,101	1,365	1,571	1,460	25	32	36	34
Ethiopia	1,101.00	18,323	28,663	45,889	58,500	17	26	42	53
Falkland Is.	12.17	2	2	2	2	0	0	0	0
Faroe Islands	1.4	31	39	47	45	22	28	34	32
Fiji	18.27	289	520	731	800	16	28	40	44
Finland	304.61	4,009	4,606	4,986	5,180	13	15	16	17
France	550.1	41,829	50,772	56,735	58,800	76	92	103	107
French Guiana	88.15	25	48	117	155	0	1	1	2
French Polynesia	3.66	62	109	197	226	17	30	54	62
Gabon	257.67	469	504	1,146	1,200	2	2	4	5
Gambia, The	10	294	464	923	1,200	29	46	92	120
Gaza Strip	0.36	245	342	635	900	675	942	1,749	2,479
Georgia	69.7	3,527	4,708	5,464	5,450	51	68	78	78
Germany	349.27	68,376	77,709	78,500	82,300	196	222	225	236
Ghana	227.54	4,900	8,612	15,020	18,100	22	38	66	80
Gibraltar	0.01	23	26	31	28	2,300	2,600	3,100	2,800
Greece	128.9	7,566	8,793	10,161	10,600	59	68	79	82
Greenland	341.7	23	47	56	57	0	0	0	0
Grenada	0.34	76	94	91	99	224	276	268	291
Guadeloupe	1.69	210	320	385	440	124	189	228	260

Population density continued

	area	1950 tot. pop.	1970 tot. pop.	1990 tot. pop.	1997 tot. pop.	1950 density	1970 density	1990 density	1997 density
Guam	0.55	59	86	134	161	107	156	244	293
Guatemala	108.43	2,969	5,246	9,198	11,250	27	48	85	104
Guinea	245.72	2,550	3,900	5,755	7,450	10	16	23	30
Guinea-Bissau	28.12	505	525	964	1,150	18	19	34	41
Guyana	196.85	423	709	796	820	2	4	4	4
Haiti	27.56	3,261	4,535	6,486	7,400	118	165	235	269
Honduras	111.89	1,401	2,627	5,105	6,300	13	23	46	56
Hong Kong	0.99	1,974	3,942	5,705	6,500	1,994	3,982	5,763	6,566
Hungary	92.34	9,338	10,338	10,261	10,150	101	112	111	110
Iceland	100.25	143	204	255	275	1	2	3	3
India	2,973.19	357,561	554,911	834,697	980,000	120	187	281	330
Indonesia	1,811.57	79,538	120,280	179,830	203,500	44	66	99	112
Iran	1,636.00	16,913	28,429	54,496	69,500	10	17	33	42
Iraq	437.37	5,158	9,356	18,920	22,500	12	21	43	51
Ireland	68.89	2,969	2,954	3,503	3,625	43	43	51	53
Israel	20.62	1,258	2,974	4,660	5,900	61	144	226	286
Italy	294.06	47,104	53,822	57,193	57,750	160	183	194	196
Ivory Coast	318	2,775	5,515	11,980	15,100	9	17	38	47
Jamaica	10.83	1,403	1,869	2,415	2,600	130	173	223	240
Japan	376.52	83,625	104,331	123,537	125,900	222	277	328	334
Jordan	88.93	1,237	2,299	4,259	5,600	14	26	48	63
Kazakstan	2,669.80	6,703	13,110	16,670	17,000	3	5	6	6
Kenya	569.69	6,265	11,498	24,032	31,900	11	20	42	56
Kiribati	0.73	32	49	72	85	44	67	99	116
Korea, North	120.41	9,726	14,619	21,774	24,500	81	121	181	203
Korea, South	98.73	20,357	31,923	42,869	46,050	206	323	434	466
Kuwait	17.82	152	744	2,125	2,050	9	42	119	115
Kyrgyzstan	191.3	1,740	2,965	4,395	4,650	9	15	23	24
Laos	230.8	1,755	2,713	4,202	5,200	8	12	18	23
Latvia	64.1	1,849	2,374	2,671	2,450	29	37	42	38
Lebanon	10.23	1,443	2,469	2,555	3,200	141	241	250	313
Lesotho	30.35	734	1,064	1,792	2,100	24	35	59	69
Liberia	96.75	824	1,385	2,407	2,950	9	14	25	30
Libya	1,759.54	1,029	1,986	4,151	5,500	1	1	2	3
Liechtenstein	0.16	14	21	29	32	88	131	181	200
Lithuania	65.2	2,567	3,148	3,722	3,710	39	48	57	57
Luxembourg	2.59	296	339	382	425	114	131	148	164
Macau	0.02	188	245	335	450	9,400	12,250	16,750	22,500
Macedonia	24.9	1,229	1,629	2,028	2,150	49	65	81	86
Madagascar	581.54	4,230	6,742	11,197	15,500	7	12	19	27
Malawi	94.08	2,881	4,518	8,289	10,250	31	48	88	109
Malaysia	328.55	6,110	10,853	17,764	20,900	19	33	54	64
Maldives	0.3	82	114	216	275	273	380	720	917
Mali	1,220.19	3,520	5,484	8,156	11,000	3	4	7	9
Malta	0.32	312	326	354	375	975	1,019	1,106	1,172
Marshall Is.	0.18	11	22	46	60	60	120	255	331
Martinique	1.06	222	326	362	405	209	308	342	382
Mauritania	1,025.22	825	1,221	2,003	2,400	1	1	2	2
Mauritius	2.03	493	826	1,059	1,155	243	407	522	569
Mayotte	0.37	22	37	80	105	58	98	215	282
Mexico	1,908.69	28,012	52,771	86,154	97,400	15	28	45	51
Micronesia	0.7	31	57	109	127	44	81	155	181
Moldova	33.7	2,341	3,595	4,364	4,450	69	107	129	132
Monaco	0	22	24	30	33	11,282	12,308	15,385	16,923
Mongolia	1,566.50	761	1,256	2,177	2,500	0	1	1	2
Montserrat	0.1	13	12	11	12	130	117	110	120
Morocco	446.3	8,953	15,310	24,487	28,100	20	34	55	63
Mozambique	784.09	6,198	9,395	14,151	19,100	8	12	18	24
N. Mariana Is.	0.48	6	12	44	53	13	26	93	111
Namibia	823.29	666	1,016	1,349	1,650	1	1	2	2
Nauru	0.02	3	7	10	12	160	350	500	600
Nepal	136.8	8,182	11,488	18,111	22,100	60	84	132	162
Netherlands	33.92	10,114	13,032	14,952	15,900	298	384	441	469
Neths Antilles	0.8	162	222	190	210	203	278	238	263
New Caledonia	18.28	59	110	170	192	3	6	9	11
New Zealand	267.99	1,908	2,820	3,363	3,650	7	11	13	14
Nicaragua	118.75	1,098	2,053	3,871	4,600	9	17	33	39
Niger	1,266.70	2,400	4,165	7,731	9,700	2	3	6	8
Nigeria	910.77	32,935	56,581	108,542	118,000	36	62	119	130
Niue	0.26	4	3	2	2	15	13	8	9
Norfolk I.	0.04	1	2	2	2	20	38	50	50
Norway	306.83	3,265	3,877	4,241	4,440	11	13	14	14
Oman	212.46	413	654	2,000	2,400	2	3	9	11
Pacific Is.	1.78	57	103	142		32	58	80	0
Pakistan	770.88	39,513	65,706	112,049	136,000	51	85	145	176
Palau	0.49	7	12	15	17	15	25	31	35
Panama	74.43	893	1,531	2,398	2,720	12	21	32	37
Papua N.G.	452.86	1,613	2,422	3,699	4,400	4	5	8	10
Paraguay	397.3	1,351	2,351	4,219	5,200	3	6	11	13
Peru	1,280.00	7,632	13,193	21,550	24,500	6	10	17	19
Philippines	298.17	20,988	37,540	61,480	73,500	70	126	206	247
Pitcairn Is.	0	0	0	0	0	26	20	13	13
Poland	304.42	24,824	32,526	38,119	38,800	82	107	125	127
Portugal	91.95	8,405	9,044	9,896	10,100	91	98	108	110
Puerto Rico	8.86	2,219	2,718	3,528	3,825	250	307	398	432
Qatar	11	25	111	486	620	2	10	44	56
Réunion	2.5	257	441	601	680	103	176	240	272
Romania	230.34	16,311	20,253	23,207	22,600	71	88	101	98
Russia	16,995.80	105,018	130,392	148,292	147,800	6	8	9	9
Rwanda	24.67	2,120	3,728	7,181	7,000	86	151	291	284

	area	1950 tot. pop.	1970 tot. pop.	1990 tot. pop.	1997 tot. pop.	1950 density	1970 density	1990 density	1997 density
San Marino	0.06	13	18	23	26	217	300	383	433
São Tomé & P.	0.96	60	74	115	135	63	77	120	141
Saudi Arabia	2,149.69	3,201	5,745	14,870	19,100	1	3	7	9
Senegal	192.53	2,500	4,158	7,504	8,900	13	22	39	46
Seychelles	0.45	34	52	70	78	76	116	156	173
Sierra Leone	71.62	1,944	2,656	3,999	4,600	27	37	56	64
Singapore	0.61	1,022	2,075	2,705	3,200	1,675	3,402	4,434	5,246
Slovak Rep.	49.04	3,463	4,524	5,263	5,400	71	92	107	110
Slovenia	20.3	1,473	1,718	1,998	2,000	73	85	98	99
Solomon Is.	27.99	104	163	320	410	4	6	11	15
Somalia	627.34	2,423	3,668	8,677	9,900	4	6	14	16
South Africa	1,221.04	13,683	22,458	37,066	42,300	11	18	30	35
Spain	499.44	28,009	33,779	38,959	39,300	56	68	78	79
Sri Lanka	64.63	7,678	12,514	16,993	18,700	119	194	263	289
St Helena	0.3	4	5	5	6	14	17	17	20
St Kitts & Nevis	0.36	50	52	42	42	139	144	117	117
St Lucia	0.61	79	101	133	150	130	166	218	246
St Pierre & Miq.	0.23	5	6	6	7	20	24	26	30
St Vincent & G.	0.39	67	88	107	114	172	226	274	292
Sudan	2,376.00	9,190	13,859	25,752	31,000	4	6	11	13
Surinam	156	215	372	404	450	1	2	3	3
Swaziland	17.2	264	419	768	950	15	24	45	55
Sweden	411.62	7,014	8,043	8,559	8,850	17	20	21	22
Switzerland	39.55	4,694	6,187	6,712	7,100	119	156	170	180
Syria	183.78	3,495	6,258	12,116	15,300	19	34	66	83
Taiwan	36	7,647	14,676	20,353	21,700	212	408	565	603
Tajikistan	142.7	1,532	2,942	5,303	6,000	11	21	37	42
Tanzania	883.59	7,886	13,513	25,635	31,200	9	15	29	35
Thailand	510.89	20,010	35,745	56,082	60,800	39	70	110	119
Togo	54.39	1,329	2,020	3,531	4,450	24	37	65	82
Tokelau	0.01	1	1	2	2	120	140	200	200
Tonga	0.72	50	85	97	105	69	118	135	146
Trinidad & Tob.	5.13	636	971	1,227	1,300	124	189	239	253
Tunisia	155.36	3,530	5,127	8,074	9,200	23	33	52	59
Turkey	769.63	20,809	35,321	56,098	63,500	27	46	73	83
Turkmenistan	488.1	1,211	2,189	3,670	4,800	2	4	8	10
Turks & Caicos Is.	0.43	6	6	12	15	14	13	28	35
Tuvalu	0.03	5	6	9	10	167	200	300	333
Uganda	199.65	4,762	9,806	17,949	20,800	24	49	90	104
Ukraine	603.7	36,906	47,317	51,839	51,500	61	78	86	85
UAE	83.6	70	223	1,671	2,400	1	3	20	29
UK	241.6	50,616	55,632	57,237	58,600	210	230	237	243
USA	9,573.11	152,271	205,051	249,911	268,000	16	21	26	28
US Virgin Is.	0.34	27	62	102	110	79	182	300	324
Uruguay	174.81	2,239	2,808	3,094	3,250	13	16	18	19
Uzbekistan	425.4	6,314	11,973	20,531	23,750	15	28	48	56
Vanuatu	12.19	52	86	147	175	4	7	12	14
Vatican City	0	1	1	1	1	2,045	2,273	2,273	2,273
Venezuela	882.05	5,009	10,604	19,325	22,500	6	12	22	26
Vietnam	325.49	29,954	42,729	66,233	77,100	92	131	203	237
Wallis & Futuna	0.2	7	9	14	15	35	44	70	75
West Bank	5.9	771	680	1,080	1,496	131	115	183	254
Western Sahara	267	14	76	230	280	0	0	1	1
Western Samoa	2.83	82	143	164	175	29	51	58	62
Yemen	527.97	4,316	6,332	11,279	16,500	8	12	21	31
Yugoslavia (Serbia)	102.1	7,131	8,910	10,529	10,500	70	87	103	103
Zambia	743.39	2,440	4,189	8,073	9,500	3	6	11	13
Zimbabwe	386.85	2,730	5,260	9,369	12,100	7	14	24	31

The figures use the total area of the country for the calculations; this includes water areas in some cases.

Urban population *percentage of average total population*

	annual change 1990–95	1950	1970	1990	1995	2000
Afghanistan	–1.6	6	11	22	20	22
Albania	0.9	20	34	35	37	40
Algeria	1.5	22	40	52	56	60
Angola	2.5	8	15	28	32	36
Antigua & Barb.	2.9	46	34	32	37	37
Argentina	0.4	65	78	86	88	89
Armenia	0.3	...	...	68	69	70
Australia	0.1	75	85	86	86	85
Austria	2.4	49	52	58	65	56
Azerbaijan	0.7	...	...	54	56	58
Bahamas	5.8	62	58	64	85	89
Bahrain	1.4	64	78	83	89	92
Bangladesh	5.8	4	8	14	18	21
Barbados	0.6	34	37	45	46	50
Belarus	3.5	...	...	58	69	75
Belgium	0	92	94	97	97	97
Belize	1.2	57	51	50	53	55
Benin	–1.1	4	18	38	36	34
Bermuda	0	100	100	100	100	100
Bhutan	2.5	2	3	5	6	8
Bolivia	3.8	38	41	51	62	65
Bosnia	1.5	...	...	38	41	
Botswana	4.4	0	8	25	31	33
Brazil	0.3	36	56	77	78	81

	annual change 1990–95	1950	1970	1990	1995	2000
Brunei	3.3	27	62	58	68	59
Bulgaria	0.2	26	52	70	71	73
Burkina Faso	12.5	4	6	15	27	37
Burma	1.9	16	23	25	27	28
Burundi	7	2	2	5	7	9
Cambodia	12.6	10	12	12	21	24
Cameroon	2.4	10	20	40	45	49
Canada	0.2	61	76	76	77	77
Cape Verde Is.	8.7	8	20	29	44	63
Cayman Is.	0	100	100	100	100	100
Cen. Afr. Rep.	–3.5	16	30	47	39	42
Chad	–7.2	4	12	32	22	23
Chile	–0.1	58	75	86	85	85
China	6.3	11	20	21	29	35
Colombia	0.8	37	57	70	73	75
Comoros	1	3	20	28	29	34
Congo	13.7	31	33	31	59	63
Congo (Zaïre)	0.7	19	30	28	29	31
Cook Is.	–5.7	32	30	35	26	28
Costa Rica	–1.4	34	40	54	50	53
Croatia	1.9	...	...	50	55	
Cuba	0	49	60	75	75	78
Cyprus	5.2	30	41	53	68	57
Czech Rep.	0.9	...	...	62	65	66
Czechoslovakia	–100	37	55	69		74
Denmark	–0.1	68	80	86	86	86
Djibouti	0.6	41	62	81	83	84
Dominican Rep.	0.5	24	40	60	62	68
Ecuador	0.7	28	40	57	59	62
Egypt	0.5	32	42	44	45	46
El Salvador	3.2	37	39	44	52	47
Equat. Guinea	6.1	16	27	29	39	48
Eritrea	...	...	...	...		17
Estonia	0.6	...	...	71	73	75
Ethiopia	1.6	5	9	12	13	15
Faroe Is.	1.6	18	28	31	33	36
Fiji	–1.9	24	35	44	40	43
Finland	–1.5	32	50	68	63	65
France	0	56	71	74	74	73
French Guiana	0.6	54	67	75	77	78
French Poly.	0.8	28	56	65	67	70
Gabon	9.8	11	26	46	73	54
Gambia, The	2.9	11	15	23	26	29
Georgia	1.4	...	...	54	58	61
Germany	0.7	72	78	84	87	88
Ghana	1.1	15	29	34	36	39
Greece	0.8	37	53	63	65	68
Guadeloupe	1	42	41	49	51	54
Guatemala	0	31	36	42	42	44
Guinea	2.9	6	14	26	30	34
Guinea-Bissau	1.9	10	15	20	22	25
Guyana	0.5	28	29	34	35	40
Haiti	1.1	12	20	30	32	35
Honduras	1.9	18	29	44	48	47
Hong Kong	0.4	89	90	93	95	96
Hungary	1.2	37	46	60	64	67
Iceland	0.3	74	83	91	92	93
India	–0.7	17	20	28	27	29
Indonesia	2.8	12	17	29	33	40
Iran	1.1	28	41	55	58	62
Iraq	–0.3	35	56	74	73	73
Ireland	–0.4	41	52	59	58	57
Israel	–0.1	65	84	92	91	91
Italy	–0.5	54	64	69	67	67
Ivory Coast	2.8	13	27	40	46	42
Jamaica	0.3	27	42	52	53	52
Japan	0.3	50	71	77	78	77
Jordan	1.1	35	51	68	72	70
Kazakstan	1.1	...	...	55	58	58
Kenya	1.2	6	10	24	25	25
Kiribati	1.6	10	26	36	39	39
Korea, North	–2	31	50	67	61	63
Korea, South	0.8	21	41	72	75	86
Kuwait	0.3	59	72	96	97	95
Kyrgyzstan	1	...	...	38	40	39
Laos	3.4	7	10	19	22	20
Latvia	0.9	...	...	69	72	72
Lebanon	0.8	23	59	84	87	86
Lesotho	3.9	1	9	19	23	21
Liberia	0	13	26	45	45	44
Libya	1	19	45	82	86	84
Liechtenstein	–5.4	20	21	28	21	23
Lithuania	2.4	...	...	63	71	70
Luxembourg	0.9	59	62	84	88	91
Macau	0.1	97	97	99	99	99
Macedonia	2.1	...	...	54	60	59
Madagascar	2.4	8	14	24	27	25
Malawi	1.6	4	6	12	13	12
Malaysia	4.2	20	27	42	52	51
Maldives	5.6	11	14	21	27	26

	annual change 1990–95	1950	1970	1990	1995	2000
Mali	2.4	9	14	24	27	25
Malta	0.2	61	78	87	88	88
Martinique	1.1	28	54	75	79	78
Mauritania	2.8	2	14	47	54	50
Mauritius	1.4	29	42	41	44	41
Mexico	0.7	43	59	73	75	74
Moldova	3.5	...	...	42	50	49
Monaco	0	100	100	100	100	100
Mongolia	3.2	19	45	51	60	59
Montserrat	...	22	11	12	...	14
Morocco	2.5	26	35	46	52	47
Mozambique	3.6	2	6	27	32	41
Namibia	4	9	19	28	34	34
Nepal	6.3	2	4	10	13	12
Netherlands	0.1	83	86	89	89	89
Neths Antilles	1.7	49	50	55	60	61
New Caledonia	–5.1	40	49	81	62	65
New Zealand	0.4	73	81	84	86	87
Nicaragua	1	35	47	60	63	62
Niger	–3.9	5	9	20	16	16
Nigeria	1.5	10	20	35	38	37
Niue	2.2	24	21	23	26	26
Norway	–0.4	32	65	74	73	73
Oman	4.2	2	5	11	13	12
Pakistan	1.2	18	25	32	34	33
Panama	0.1	36	48	55	55	52
Papua N. Guinea	0.3	1	10	16	16	15
Paraguay	1.8	35	37	48	52	51
Peru	0.5	36	57	70	72	71
Philippines	4.2	27	33	42	52	51
Poland	0.3	39	52	63	64	63
Portugal	1.6	19	26	33	36	34
Puerto Rico	0.8	41	58	74	77	77
Qatar	0.3	63	80	90	91	90
Réunion	3	24	44	64	74	68
Romania	1.8	28	42	50	55	54
Russia	0.8	...	...	72	75	75
Rwanda	0	2	3	6	6	6
São Tomé & P.	1.2	13	23	42	45	44
Saudi Arabia	0.4	16	49	77	79	82
Senegal	1	31	33	40	42	41
Seychelles	–2.6	27	26	59	52	52
Sierra Leone	1.7	9	18	32	35	40
Singapore	0	100	100	100	100	100
Slovak Rep.	1.4	...	...	54	58	57
Slovenia	0.8	...	...	48	50	50
Solomon Is.	13.5	8	9	11	20	16
Somalia	2.4	13	20	24	27	25
South Africa	3.1	43	48	49	57	53
Spain	–0.4	52	66	78	77	76
Sri Lanka	0.6	14	22	21	22	22
St Kitts & Nevis	–1.6	22	34	49	45	41
St Lucia	0.3	38	40	46	47	47
St Vincent	15.9	13	15	21	43	43
Sudan	9.7	6	16	22	35	23
Surinam	1.8	47	46	48	52	49
Swaziland	2.2	1	10	26	29	29
Sweden	0	66	81	84	84	83
Switzerland	0.5	44	55	60	61	60
Syria	0.1	31	43	52	52	51
Tajikistan	0.6	...	...	31	32	32
Tanzania	2.7	4	7	21	24	22
Thailand	–3.4	11	13	23	19	19
Togo	1.3	7	13	29	31	30
Tonga	14.9	13	21	21	41	41
Trinidad & Tob.	0.3	23	39	69	70	70
Tunisia	0.4	31	44	56	57	56
Turkey	6.1	21	38	48	65	64
Turkmenistan	0.4	...	...	46	47	46
Turks & Caicos	1.4	40	41	51	55	58
Uganda	1.8	3	8	11	12	12
Ukraine	1.5	...	...	64	69	69
UAE	1.3	25	42	78	83	82
UK	–0.5	84	89	93	90	89
USA	0.8	64	74	74	77	78
Uruguay	1	78	82	86	90	90
USSR	–100	39	57	68		
Uzbekistan	0.5	...	...	41	42	41
Vanuatu	–2.7	5	14	22	19	19
Venezuela	0.3	53	72	91	92	91
Vietnam	–1.8	12	18	22	20	20
Western Sahara	7.2	68	43	57	80	60
Western Samoa	–0.8	13	20	23	22	21
Yemen	1.2	5	10	32	34	31
Yugoslavia	–100	22	35	50		
Yugoslavia (Serbia)	2.4	...	...	48	54	52
Zambia	1.4	9	30	42	45	42
Zimbabwe	2	11	17	29	32	30

Population of cities

The population of all cities with over 100,000 inhabitants is given. As far as possible, figures for the urban agglomeration, as opposed to the city proper, have been used.

Any list such as this will, inevitably, be affected by the different methods that governments have of defining the boundaries of an urban area. If London, for example, is considered in its widest sense as a metropolitan region, it has a population of 12.53 million, making it one of the world's largest cities. The official population of Greater London (a purely administrative definition) is, however, 6.96 million. In contrast, Shanghai's population of 15.08 million includes large agricultural areas.

As a result of these problems, the suburbs of large cities may be shown elsewhere in the list. An attempt has been made to make the list as consistent and meaningful as possible, which is why figures for urban agglomerations have always been used if available. The capital city is denoted by * and is included regardless of population size. Certain countries have more than one capital, with each serving a different function. In these cases, all are shown.

Figures are based on census results, or more recent estimates where available, and are given in thousands. Where figures differ from the date of the main census (the date in brackets after the country name) this is marked with the symbol † after the city population figure. The local spelling or an accepted transcription of the local name form is used.

The figures for the United Kingdom were made using 1991 census data and updated in the light of later estimates. Populations for the UK administrative districts can be found on page 113.

Afghanistan (1990)

Herat	187
Kabul*	1,565
Mazar-e-Sharif	128
Qandahar	238

Albania (1991)

Tiranë*	251

Algeria (1989)

Algiers*	1,722
Annaba	348
Batna	122
Bejaia	124
Blida	191
Constantine	449
Ech Cheliff	119
Oran	664
Sétif	187
Sidi-Bel-Abbès	186
Skikda	141
Tizi-Ouzou	101
Tlemcen	146

American Samoa (1992)

Pago Pago*	4

Andorra (1994)

Andorra La Vella*	23

Angola (1995)

Huambo	1,544
Luanda*	2,250
Lubango	105

Anguilla (1992)

The Valley*	2

Antigua and Barbuda (1992)

St John's*	38

Argentina (1991)

Bahia Blanca	271
Buenos Aires*	10,990
Catamarca	110
Comodoro Rivadavia	124
Córdoba	1,198
Corrientes	268
Formosa	166
La Plata	640
La Rioja	104
Mar del Plata	520
Mendoza	775
Nequén	183
Paraná	277
Posadas	220
Resistencia	291
Rio Cuarto	139
Rosario	1,096
Salta	370
San Juan	353
San Luis	110
San Miguel de Tucumán	622
San Nicolas	115
San Salvador de Jujuy	183
Santa Fé	395
Santiago del Estero	264

Armenia (1994)

Gyumri	206
Karaklis	170
Kirovakan	159
Kumairi	120
Yerevan*	1,226

Aruba (1991)

Orangestad*	20

Australia (1993)

Adelaide	1,071
Brisbane	1,422
Canberra*	325
Geelong	152
Gold Coast	300
Hobart	193
Melbourne	3,189
Newcastle	455
Perth	1,221
Sydney	3,713
Townsville	122
Wollongong	249

Austria (1991)

Graz	238
Innsbruck	118
Linz	203
Salzburg	144
Vienna*	1,560

Azerbaijan (1991)

Baku*	1,081
Gyandzha	282
Sumgait	236

Bahamas (1992)

Nassau*	190

Bahrain (1992)

Al Manamah*	143

Bangladesh (1991)

Barisal	173
Chittagong	2,041
Comilla	184
Dhaka*	6,105
Dingipur	126
Jamalpur	101
Jessore	160
Khulna	877
Mymensingh	186
Narayanganj	406
Nawabganj	121
Pabna	109
Rajshahi	517
Rangpur	204
Saidpur	102
Tangail	104
Tongi	154

Barbados (1992)

Bridgetown*	8

Belarus (1996)

Baranavichy	172
Babruysk	227
Barysaw	153
Brest	293
Homyel	512
Hrodna	301
Lida	101
Minsk*	1,700
Mahilyow	367
Mazyr	108
Pinsk	130
Salihorsk	101
Vitsyebsk	365

Belgium (1995)

Antwerp	459
Bruges	116
Brussels*	952
Charleroi	206
Ghent	227
Liège	192
Namur	105
Schaerbeek	103

Belize (1994)

Belmopan*	44

Benin (1994)

Cotonou	537
Parakou	104
Porto-Novo*	179

Bermuda (1994)

Hamilton*	1

Bhutan (1993)

Thimphu*	30

Bolivia (1993)

Cochabamba	449
El Alto	446
La Paz*	1,126
Oruro	202
Potosí	123
Santa Cruz	767
Sucre*	145

Bosnia-Herzegovina (1991)

Banja Luka	195
Doboj	103
Mostar	126
Prijedor	112
Sarajevo*	526
Tuzla	132
Zenica	146

Botswana (1991)

Gaborone*	133
Mahalapye	104

Brazil (1991)

Abaeteluba	100
Alagoinhas	116
Altamira	121
Alvoraba	140
Americana	143
Anápolis	239
Aracaju	402
Araçatuba	159
Araguaina	103
Araguari	108
Arapiraca	165
Araraquara	166
Bacabal	103
Bagé	118
Barbacena	100
Barra do Corda	108
Barra Mansa	167
Barueri	130
Baurú	260
Belém	1,246
Belo Horizonte	2,049
Betim	171
Blumenau	212
Boa Vista	143
Bragança	115
Bragança Paulista	108
Brasília*	1,596
Cabo	125
Cáceres	102
Cachoeiro de Itapemirim	144
Camaçari	109
Camaragibe	100
Cameta	103
Campina Grande	326
Campinas	846
Campo Grande	526
Campos dos Goytacazes	389
Canoas	279
Carapicuíba	283
Caratinga	126
Cariacica	274
Caruaru	214
Cascavel	193
Castanhal	102
Caucaia	164
Caxias	146
Caxias do Sul	291
Chapecó	123
Codó	112
Colatina	107
Contagem	449
Coronel Fabriciano	105
Criciúma	146
Cuiabá	401
Curitiba	1,290
Diadema	304
Divinópolis	151
Dourados	136
Duque de Caxias	665
Embu	139
Feira de Santana	406
Florianópolis	255
Fortaleza	1,758
Foz de Iguaçu	188
Franca	233
Garanhuns	103
Goiânia	921
Governador Valadares	230
Gravatá	181
Guarapuava	160
Guaratinguetá	103
Guarujá	203
Guarulhos	781
Ilhéus	223
Imperatriz	276
Ipatinga	180
Itaberaí	161
Itabuna	185
Itaguaí	113
Itaituba	118
Itajaí	120
Itapetininga	105
Itaquaquecetuba	165
Itu	107
Jaboatão	482
Jacareí	163
Jaú	106
Jequié	135
João Pessoa	497
Joinvile	346
Juàzeiro	128
Juàzeiro do Norte	173
Juiz de Fora	386
Jundiaí	313
Lajes	151
Limeira	207
Linhares	120
Londrina	388
Luziânia	207
Macapá	180
Maceió	628
Magé	191
Manaus	1,011
Marabá	122
Maracanau	157
Marília	152
Maringá	240
Mauá	293
Mogi das Cruzes	273
Mogi-Guaçu	107
Montes Claros	247
Mossoró	192
Natal	607
Nilópolis	158
Niterói	416
Nova Friburgo	167
Nôva Hamburgo	167
Nova Iguaçu	1,286
Olinda	341
Osasco	563
Paranaguá	108
Parnaíba	128
Passo Fundo	147
Patos de Minas	103
Paulista	211
Pelotas	289
Petrolina	175
Petrópolis	255
Pindamonhangaba	102
Piracicaba	284
Poços de Caldas	110
Ponta Grossa	234
Pôrto Alegre	1,263
Pôrto Velho	286
Praia Grande	122
Presidente Prudente	165
Recife	1,290
Ribeirao das Neves	144
Ribeirão Prêto	431
Rio Branco	197
Rio Claro	138
Rio de Janeiro	9,888
Rio Grande	172
Rondonópolis	125
Salvador	2,056
Santa Bárbara d'Oeste	121
Santa Cruz do Sol	118
Santa Luzia	138
Santa Maria	218
Santarém	265
Santo André	614
Santos	429
São Bernardo de Campo	565
São Caetano do Sul	149
São Carlos	158
São Francisco do Sul	296
São Gonçalo	748
São João de Meriti	425
São José	139
São José do Rio Prêto	283
São José dos Campos	443
São José dos Pinhais	127
São Leopoldo	168
São Luís	696
São Paulo	16,417
São Vicente	255
Sapucaia	105
Serra	222
Sete Lagôas	144
Sobral	127
Sorocaba	377
Sumaré	226
Susano	156
Taboao da Serra	160
Taubaté	205
Teófilo Otoni	141

Teresina	598
Teresopolis	121
Timon	107
Uberaba	211
Uberlândia	367
Umuarama	100
Uruguaiana	117
Várzea Grande	162
Viamão	168
Vila Velha	265
Vitória	258
Vitória da Conquista	225
Vitória de São Antão	107
Volta Redonda	220

Brunei (1992)

Bandar Seri Begawan*	55

Bulgaria (1996)

Burgas	199
Dobrich	104
Pleven	125
Plovdiv	344
Ruse	168
Sliven	107
Sofia*	1,117
Stara Zagora	150
Sumen	126
Tolbukhin	116
Varna	301

Burkina Faso (1993)

Bobo-Dioulasso	300
Koudougou	105
Ouagadougou*	690

Burma (Myanmar) (1983)

Bassein (Pathein)	144
Insein	144
Kanbe	254
Mandalay	533
Monywa	107
Moulmein (Mawlamyine)	220
Pegu (Bego)	150
Rangoon (Yangon)*	2,513
Sittwe	108
Taunggye	108
Thingangyun	141

Burundi (1994)

Bujumbura*	300
Gitega	102

Cambodia (1994)

Phnom Penh*	920

Cameroon (1991)

Bamenda	138
Douala	884
Maroua	143
Nkongsamba	112
Yaoundé*	750

Canada (1996)

Calgary	822
Chicoutimi-Jonquière	160
Edmonton	863
Halifax	333
Hamilton	624
Kitchener	383
London	399
Montréal	3,327
Oshawa	269
Ottawa–Hull*	1,010
Québec	672
Regina	194
St Catharines-Niagara	372
Saint John	126
St John's	174
Saskatoon	219
Sherbrooke	147
Sudbury	160
Thunder Bay	126
Toronto	4,264

Trois-Rivières	140
Vancouver	1,832
Victoria	304
Windsor	279
Winnipeg	667

Cape Verde Islands (1992)

Praia*	69

Cayman Islands (1992)

George Town*	13

Central African Republic (1990)

Bangui*	706

Chad (1993)

Abéché	188
Bongor	195
Doba	185
Moundou	281
Ndjaména*	530
Sarh	198

Chile (1995)

Antofagasta	237
Arica	173
Calama	121
Chillán	157
Concepción	350
Coquimbo	123
Curicó	104
Iquique	153
La Serena	118
Los Angeles	142
Osorno	123
Puente Alto	319
Puerto Montt	122
Punta Arenas	117
Quilpué	110
Rancagua	194
San Bernardo	206
Santiago*	5,077
Talca	169
Talcahuano	261
Temuco	239
Valdivia	119
Valparaíso	282
Viña del Mar	322

China (1994)

Acheng	219
Aksu	194
Altay	169
Anda	173
Ankang	159
Anqing	318
Anqiu	148
Anshan	1,252
Anshun	206
Anyang	458
Baicheng	251
Baishan	424
Baiyin	235
Baoding	519
Baoji	379
Baotou	1,033
Beihai	135
Beijing*	12,362
Beiliu	120
Beipiao	201
Bei'an	205
Bengbu	471
Benxi	805
Binzhou	163
Bole	141
Bose	104
Bozhou	142
Cangzhou	275
Changchun	1,810
Changde	337
Changge	108
Changji	135
Changsha	1,198
Changshu	214
Changyi	135
Changzhi	347

Changzhou, Jiangsu	683
Chao'an	313
Chaohu	155
Chaoyang	262
Chaozhou	232
Chengde	264
Chengdu	1,933
Chenghai	157
Chenzhou	203
Chifeng	392
Chongqing	3,870
Chuzhou	155
Cixi	112
Conghua	111
Da'an	147
Dachuan	181
Dali	158
Dalian	1,855
Dandong	551
Danjiang	101
Danjiangkou	172
Danyang	200
Danzhou	160
Daqing	753
Dashiqiao	158
Datong	845
Daxian	188
Daye	117
Dehui	139
Dengzhou	100
Deyang	231
Dezhou	244
Dongguang	345
Dongtai	219
Dongying	394
Dujiangyan	140
Dukou	415
Dunhua	244
Duyun	141
Emeishan	113
Enping	153
Enshi	108
Ezhou	263
Fangchenggang	112
Feicheng	304
Fengcheng	165
Foshan	369
Fujin	111
Fuling	203
Fuqing	103
Fushun	1,246
Fuxin	665
Fuyang	269
Fuzhou, Fujian	952
Fuzhou, Jiangxi	122
Gaizhou	172
Ganzhou	239
Gao'an	115
Gaomi	194
Gaoming	107
Gaoyou	123
Gaozhou	167
Gejiu	216
Gongzhuling	258
Guanghan	100
Guangshui	117
Guangyuan	224
Guangzhou	3,114
Guigang	269
Guilin	399
Guiping	136
Guiyang	1,131
Haicheng	236
Haikou	365
Hailar	192
Hailin	239
Hailun	149
Haimen	340
Haining	110
Hami	179
Handan	894
Hangzhou	1,185
Hanzhong	197
Harbin	2,505
Hebi	237
Hechuan	183
Hefei	867
Hegang	569
Helong	137
Hengshui	138
Hengyang	543
Heshan	102
Heyuan	126
Heze	237

Hohhot	683
Honghu	202
Hong Kong/ Xianggang (SAR)	6,205
Huadian	188
Huadu	168
Huai'an	144
Huaibei	506
Huaihua	169
Huainan	769
Huaiyin	261
Huangshan	118
Huangshi	538
Huangzhou	265
Huazhou	166
Huiyang	147
Huizhou	238
Hulodao	402
Hunchun	123
Hunjiang	482
Huzhou	218
Ji'an	164
Jiamusi	549
Jiangdu	154
Jiangmen	293
Jiangyan	145
Jiangyin	210
Jiaohe	169
Jiaonan	167
Jiaoxian	153
Jiaozhou	189
Jiaozuo	477
Jiaxing	228
Jieyang	180
Jilin	1,118
Jimo	166
Jinan	1,660
Jinchang	126
Jincheng	162
Jingdezhen	294
Jingjiang	112
Jingmen	268
Jingsha	683
Jinhua	164
Jining, Inner Mongolia	180
Jining, Shandong	387
Jinjiang	103
Jinxi	357
Jinzhou	610
Jiujiang	322
Jiutai	192
Jixi	736
Jiyuan	207
Kaifeng	535
Kaili	128
Kaiping	172
Kaiyuan	130
Karamay	213
Kashi (Kashgar)	190
Korla	178
Kunming	1,242
Kunshan	129
Kuytun	131
Laiwu	370
Laixi	103
Laiyang	162
Langfang	186
Lanzhou	1,296
Laohekou	148
Lechang	166
Leiyang	148
Leizhou	189
Lengshuijiang	161
Lengshuitan	140
Leping	119
Leshan	384
Lhasa	118
Lianyungang	401
Liaocheng	235
Liaoyang	541
Liaoyuan	377
Liling	122
Linchuan	136
Linfen	206
Lingyuan	130
Linhai	108
Linhe	151
Linjiang	107
Linqing	139
Linyi	521
Lishui	199
Liupanshui	408
Liuzhou	609
Liyang	277

Longhai	101
Longjing	142
Longkou	235
Longyan	218
Loudi	192
Lu'an	261
Luoding	275
Luohe	227
Luoyang	863
Luzhou	263
Ma'anshan	369
Macheng	127
Manzhouli	129
Maoming	247
Meihekou	252
Meixian	132
Meizhou	172
Mianyang	336
Mingguang	104
Mishan	147
Mudanjiang	603
Nanchang	1,169
Nanchong	333
Nanhai	357
Nanjing	2,211
Nanning	829
Nanping	212
Nantong	422
Nanyang	380
Nehe	121
Neijiang	296
Ning'an	150
Ningbo	612
Panjin	416
Panshan	363
Panyu	309
Panzhihua	439
Penglai	135
Pengzhou	106
Pingdingshan	518
Pingdu	175
Pingliang	105
Pingxiang	452
Pizhou	119
Pulandian	153
Puning	284
Puqi	146
Putian	113
Puyang	233
Qianjiang	290
Qidong	212
Qingdao	1,584
Qingyuan	173
Qingzhou	157
Qinhuangdao	413
Qinzhou	140
Qiongshan	111
Qiqihar	1,104
Qitaihe	262
Quanzhou	208
Qufu	118
Qujing	220
Quzhou	132
Renqiu	140
Rizhao	301
Rongcheng	185
Rugao	255
Rui'an	158
Rushan	113
Sanmenxia	164
Sanming	182
Sanshui	214
Sanya	132
Shanghai	15,082
Shangqui	196
Shangrao	154
Shangzhi	217
Shantou	719
Shanwei	142
Shaoguan	404
Shaoxing	205
Shaoyang	278
Shashi	281
Shenyang	3,762
Shenzhen	696
Shihezi	312
Shijiazhuang	1,159
Shishou	120
Shiyan	323
Shizuishan	298
Shougang	177
Shuangcheng	159
Shuangyashan	413
Shulan	208

Shunde	300
Shuozhou	110
Sihui	111
Siping	355
Songyuan	334
Suihua	247
Suining	185
Suizhou	276
Suzhou, Anhui	281
Suzhou, Jiangsu	766
Tai'an	429
Taishan	318
Taixing	178
Taiyuan	1,642
Taizhou	168
Tangshan	1,110
Taonan	151
Teng Xian	315
Tengzhou	368
Tianchang	209
Tianjin	10,687
Tianmen	309
Tianshui	275
Tiefa	150
Tieli	269
Tieling	288
Tongchuan	288
Tonghua	349
Tongliao	273
Tongling	272
Tumen	102
Ürümqi	1,130
Ulanhot	172
Wafangdian	283
Wanxian	258
Weifang	565
Weihai	184
Weinan	171
Wendeng	137
Wenling	102
Wenzhou	450
Wuchuan	162
Wuhai	288
Wuhan	3,520
Wuhu	458
Wujiang	145
Wuwei	151
Wuxi	863
Wuxue	116
Wuzhou	236
Xiamen	459
Xi'an	2,115
Xiangfan	498
Xiangtan	490
Xianning	165
Xiantao	381
Xianyang	403
Xiaogan	174
Xiaoshan	195
Xiaoyi	103
Xichang	154
Xingcheng	116
Xinghua	182
Xingning	167
Xingtai	342
Xinhui	255
Xining	570
Xinmin	115
Xintai	362
Xinxiang	530
Xinyang	218
Xinyu	226
Xinzheng	114
Xinzhou	127
Xuanwei	103
Xuanzhou	128
Xuchang	232
Xuzhou	937
Ya'an	113
Yakeshi	384
Yan'an	127
Yancheng	380
Yangchun	197
Yangjiang	259
Yangquan	402
Yangzhou	355
Yanji	289
Yantai	791
Yanzhou	187
Yibin	261
Yichang	428
Yicheng	109
Yichun, Heilongjiang	800
Yichun, Jiangxi	177

Yima	102
Yinchuan	413
Yingcheng	111
Yingde	200
Yingkou	466
Yining	198
Yixing	319
Yiyang	215
Yizheng	133
Yong'an	121
Yongehuan	162
Yongzhou	104
Yuanjiang	127
Yuci	213
Yueyang	371
Yuhang	165
Yulin	191
Yumen	127
Yuncheng	135
Yunfu	218
Yushu	157
Yuyao	114
Yuzhou	111
Zalantun	141
Zaozhuang	566
Zengcheng	171
Zhangjiagang	127
Zhangjiakou	615
Zhangqiu	230
Zhangshu	104
Zhangzhou	200
Zhanjiang	492
Zhaodong	215
Zhaoqing	274
Zhaotong	100
Zhaoyuan	162
Zhaozhuang	566
Zhengzhou	1,324
Zhenjiang	406
Zhongshan	341
Zhongxiang	168
Zhoukou	160
Zhoushan	169
Zhuanghe	145
Zhucheng	166
Zhuhai	309
Zhumadian	157
Zhuozhou	105
Zhuzhou	474
Zibo	1,346
Zigong	431
Ziyang	130
Zixing	116
Zoucheng	325
Zunyi	195

Colombia (1995)

Armenia	220
Barrancabermeja	181
Barranquilla	1,064
Bello	305
Bogotá*	5,026
Bucaramanga	352
Buenaventura	267
Cali	1,719
Cartagena	746
Cartago	117
Cienaga	144
Cúcuta	479
Dosquebradas	164
Envigado	109
Florencia	118
Floridablanca	247
Ibagué	347
Itagui	169
Manizales	333
Medellin	1,621
Montería	276
Neiva	248
Palmira	257
Pasto	326
Pereira	353
Popayán	223
Quibdó	131
Ríohacha	142
Santa Marta	309
Sincelejo	180
Soacha	267
Soledad	265
Tulua	138
Tumaco	115
Tunja	120
Turbo	127

Valledupar	266
Villavicencio	253

Comoros (1992)

Moroni*	22

Congo (1992)

Brazzaville*	938
Pointe-Noire	576

Congo (Zaïre) (1991)

Boma	246
Bukavu	210
Ilebo	142
Kalemie	172
Kamina	160
Kananga	372
Kikwit	183
Kinshasa*	3,804
Kisangani	373
Kolwezi	544
Likasi	280
Lubumbashi	739
Matadi	173
Mbandaka	166
Mbuji-Mayi	613

Costa Rica (1994)

Alajuela	170
Cartago	117
San José*	1,186

Croatia (1991)

Osijek	165
Rijeka	206
Split	207
Zagreb*	931

Cuba (1994)

Bayamo	138
Camagüey	294
Cíenfuegos	132
Guantánamo	208
Havana*	2,241
Holguín	242
Las Tunas	127
Manzanillo	108
Matanzas	124
Pinar del Río	129
Santa Clara	205
Santiago de Cuba	440

Cyprus (1994)

Limassol	146
Nicosia*	189

Czech Republic (1995)

Brno	390
Hrádec Králové	101
Liberec	101
Olomouc	106
Ostrava	326
Plzen	172
Prague*	1,213

Denmark (1995)

Ålborg	159
Århus	277
Copenhagen*	1,353
Odense	183

Djibouti (1995)

Djibouti*	383

Dominica (1991)

Roseau*	21

Dominican Republic (1993)

Azua	194
Bahoruco	102
Barahona	158

Duarte	272
Espaillat	198
La Altagracia	112
La Romana	158
La Vega	335
Maria Trinidad Sanchez	122
Monte Plata	163
Monsenor Nouel	144
Peravia	200
Puerto Plata	255
San Cristobal	409
San Juan	247
San Pedro de Macoris	213
Santiago de los Cabelleros	691
Santo Domingo*	2,135
Valverde	146

Ecuador (1996)

Ambato	156
Cuenca	247
Duran	128
Esmeraldas	115
Guayaquil	1,925
Ibarra	114
Loja	114
Machala	191
Manta	149
Portovíejo	164
Quevedo	116
Quito*	1,444
Riobamba	114
Santo Domingo	165

Egypt (1992)

Alexandria	3,380
Aswân	220
Asyût	321
Benha	136
Beni-Suef	179
Cairo*	9,656
Damanhûr	222
Damietta	113
El Faiyûm	250
El Gîza	2,144
El Mahalla el Kubra	408
El Mansûra	371
El Minyâ	208
Helwân	328
Ismâ'ilîya	255
Kafr el Dauwâr	226
Kafr el Sheikh	103
Luxor	146
Port Said	460
Qena	141
Shibîn el Kôm	158
Shubra el Kheima	834
Sohâg	156
Suez	388
Tanta	380
Zagazig	287

El Salvador (1992)

Apopa	101
Delgado	105
Mejicanos	145
Nueva San Salvador	117
San Miguel	192
San Salvador*	1,522
Santa Ana	202
Soya Pango	252

Equatorial Guinea (1992)

Malabo*	35

Eritrea (1991)

Asmara*	367

Estonia (1995)

Tallinn*	435
Tartu	105

Ethiopia (1994)

Addis Ababa*	2,316
Bahir Dar	116
Debrezit	106
Dessie	117

Diredawa	195
Gondar	167
Harrar	123
Jimma	120
Mekele	120
Nazerit	147

Falkland Islands (1991)

Stanley*	2

Faroe Islands (1994)

Tórshavn*	16

Fiji (1992)

Suva*	75

Finland (1996)

Espoo	191
Helsinki*	525
Oulu	109
Tampere	183
Turku	165
Vantaa	166

France (1990)

Aix-en-Provence	127
Amiens	156
Angers	208
Angoulême	103
Annecy	127
Avignon	181
Bayonne	162
Besançon	123
Bordeaux	696
Boulogne	102
Brest	202
Caen	192
Calais	102
Clermont-Ferrand	254
Dijon	231
Douai	200
Dunkerque	191
Grasse-Cannes	336
Grenoble	405
Hagondange-Briey	112
La Rochelle	100
Le Havre	254
Le Mans	189
Lens	323
Lille	959
Limoges	170
Lorient	116
Lyons	1,262
Marseilles	1,087
Metz	193
Montbéliard	118
Montpellier	248
Mulhouse	224
Nancy	329
Nantes	496
Nice	516
Nîmes	139
Orléans	243
Paris*	9,469
Pau	145
Perpignan	158
Reims	206
Rennes	245
Rouen	380
St-Étienne	313
St-Nazaire	132
Strasbourg	388
Thionville	132
Toulon	438
Toulouse	650
Tours	282
Troyes	123
Valence	108
Valenciennes	338
Villeurbanne	120

French Guiana (1990)

Cayenne*	42

French Polynesia (1992)

Papeete*	26

Gabon (1993)

Libreville*	418
Port-Gentil	164

Gambia (1990)

Banjul*	171
Serekunda	124

Georgia (1991)

Batumi	138
Kutaisi	238
Rustavi	162
Sukhumi	122
Tbilisi*	1,279

Germany (1995)

Aachen	247
Augsburg	262
Bergisch Gladbach	105
Berlin*	3,472
Bielefeld	324
Bochum	401
Bonn*	293
Bottrop	120
Braunschweig	254
Bremen	549
Bremerhaven	131
Chemnitz	274
Cologne	964
Cottbus	126
Darmstadt	139
Dortmund	601
Dresden	474
Duisburg	536
Düsseldorf	573
Erfurt	213
Erlangen	101
Essen	618
Frankfurt	652
Freiburg im Breisgau	198
Fürth	108
Gelsenkirchen	294
Gera	126
Göttingen	128
Hagen	214
Halle	290
Hamburg	1,706
Hamm	184
Hanover	526
Heidelberg	139
Heilbronn	122
Herne	180
Hildesheim	106
Ingolstadt	111
Jena	102
Kaiserslautern	102
Karlsruhe	277
Kassel	202
Kiel	247
Koblenz	110
Krefeld	250
Leipzig	481
Leverkusen	162
Lübeck	217
Ludwigshafen am Rhein	168
Magdeburg	265
Mainz	185
Mannheim	316
Moers	107
Mönchengladbach	266
Mülheim an der Ruhr	177
Munich	1,245
Münster	265
Neuss	149
Nürnberg	496
Oberhausen	225
Offenbach am Main	116
Oldenburg	150
Osnabrück	168
Paderborn	132
Pforzheim	118
Potsdam	138
Recklinghausen	127
Regensburg	126
Remscheid	123
Reutlingen	108
Rostock	233
Saarbrücken	189
Salzgitter	118
Schwerin	118
Siegen	112
Solingen	166
Stuttgart	588
Ulm	115
Wiesbaden	266
Witten	105
Wolfsburg	127
Wuppertal	384
Würzburg	128
Zwickau	105

Ghana (1988)

Accra*	1,781
Kumasi	385
Sekondi-Takoradi	104
Tamale	151
Tema	110

Gibraltar (1996)

Gibraltar Town*	27

Greece (1991)

Athens*	3,097
Iráklion	117
Kallithea	111
Lárissa	113
Peristerion	146
Pátrai	155
Piraieus	170
Thessaloníki	378

Greenland (1995)

Nuuk (Godthåb)*	13

Grenada (1992)

St George's*	7

Guadeloupe (1990)

Basse-Terre*	14

Guam (1992)

Agana*	4

Guatemala (1994)

Guatemala*	1,814
Mixco	305
Quetzaltenango	109
Villa Nueva	192

Guinea (1995)

Conakry*	1,508

Guinea-Bissau (1992)

Bissau*	145

Guyana (1992)

Georgetown*	200

Haiti (1991)

Cap-Haïtien	157
Carrefour	217
Delmas	179
Gonaïves	175
Hinche	141
Jacmel	238
Jérémie	180
Les Cayes	251
Port-au-Prince*	1,402
Port-de-Paix	161

Honduras (1993)

San Pedro Sula	359
Tegucigalpa*	739

Hungary (1996)

Budapest*	1,909
Debrecen	211
Györ	127
Kecskemét	105
Miskolc	180
Nyíreguháza	113
Pécs	163
Szeged	167
Székesfehérvár	107

Iceland (1994)

Reykjavík*	103

India (1991)

Adoni	136
Agartala	158
Agra	956
Ahmadabad	3,298
Ahmadnagar	222
Ajmer	402
Akola	328
Aligarh	480
Allahabad	858
Alleppey	175
Alwar	211
Amravati	434
Ambala	140
Amritsar	709
Amroha	137
Anantapur	175
Arrah	157
Asansol	764
Aurangabad	592
Baharampur	126
Bahraich	135
Balurghat	126
Bangalore	4,087
Barddhaman	245
Bareilly	608
Batala	106
Belgaum	402
Bellary	246
Bhadravati	149
Bhagalpur	262
Bharatpur	157
Bharuch	138
Bhatinda	159
Bhavnagar	404
Bhilwara	184
Bhimavaram	125
Bhiwandi	392
Bhiwani	121
Bhopal	1,064
Bhubaneshwar	412
Bhusawal	159
Bihar	201
Bijapur	193
Bikaner	415
Bilaspur	234
Bokaro Steel City	416
Brahmapur	211
Bulandshahr	127
Burhanpur	173
Calcutta	11,673
Calicut (Kozhikode)	420
Chandigarh	575
Chandrapur	226
Chapra	137
Chennai (Madras)	5,361
Cochin (Kochi)	564
Coimbatore	1,136
Cuddalore	145
Cuddapah	216
Cuttack	439
Darbhanga	218
Davangere	287
Dehra Dun	367
Delhi	9,882
Dhanbad	818
Dharwad	527
Dhule	278
Dindigul	182
Durgapur	416
Durg-Bhilai	689
Elluru	213
Erode	357
Etawah	124
Faizabad	178
Faridabad	614
Farrukhabad	208
Firozabad	271
Gadag-Betgeri	134
Ganganagar	161
Gaya	294
Ghaziabad	520
Gondia	109
Gorakhpur	490
Gulbarga	310
Guntur	471
Gurgaon	135
Gwalior	720
Habra	196
Hapur	147
Haridwar	189
Hisar	181
Hospet	135
Hyderabad	4,280
Ichalkaranji	236
Imphal	201
Indore	1,104
Jabalpur	887
Jaipur	1,514
Jalgaon	242
Jalna	175
Jammu	206
Jamnagar	365
Jamshedpur	834
Jaunpur	136
Jhansi	369
Jodhpur	649
Jullundur	520
Junagadh	167
Kakinada	327
Kanchipuram	170
Kanpur	2,111
Karaikkudi	110
Karnal	176
Katihar	154
Khandwa	145
Kharagpur	280
Kolar Gold Fields	156
Kolhapur	417
Kota	536
Kumbakonam	151
Kurnool	275
Latur	197
Lucknow	1,642
Ludhiana	1,012
Machilipatnam	159
Madurai	1,094
Malegaon	342
Mandya	120
Mangalore	426
Mathura	233
Meerut	847
Mirzapur	169
Moradabad	434
Mumbai (Bombay)	15,093
Munger	150
Murwara	163
Muzaffarnagar	248
Muzaffarpur	240
Mysore	652
Nadiad	170
Nagercoil	189
Nagpur	1,661
Nanded	309
Nasik	722
Navadwip	125
Navsari	190
Nellore	316
New Delhi*	301
Nizamabad	241
Ondal	180
Palghat	180
Panipat	191
Parbhani	190
Patan	120
Pathankot	147
Patiala	269
Patna	1,099
Pollachi	127
Pondicherry	401
Porbandar	160
Proddatur	134
Pune	2,485
Puri	125
Purnia	136
Quilon	140
Raichur	171
Raipur	462
Rajahmundry	404
Rajapalayam	114
Rajkot	651
Rampur	243
Ranchi	614
Raniganj	160
Ratlam	196
Raurkela	399
Rewa	129
Rohtak	216
Sagar	257
Saharanpur	374
Salem	574
Sambalpur	193
Sambhal	150
Sangli	364
Shahjahanpur	260
Shiliguri	227
Shillong	222
Shimoga	193
Sikar	148
Solapur	621
Sonipat	142
Srinagar	595
Surat	1,517
Tenali	149
Thane	797
Thanjavur	200
Tiruchchirappalli	711
Tirunelveli	366
Tirupati	189
Tiruppur	306
Trichur	275
Trivandrum	826
Tumkur	179
Tuticorin	284
Udaipur	308
Ujjain	367
Ulhasnagar	369
Vadodara	1,115
Varanasi	1,026
Vazianagaram	176
Vellore	305
Vijayawada	845
Vishakhapatnam	1,052
Wadhawan	166
Warangal	467
Yamunanagar	220

Indonesia (1995)

Ambon	313
Balikpapan	416
Banda Aceh	291
Bandar Lampung	832
Bandjarmasin	535
Bandung	2,368
Batam	168
Bengkulu	262
Binjai	207
Bitung	107
Blitar	123
Bogor	285
Cirebon	262
Denpasar	435
Gorontalo	133
Jakarta*	11,500
Jambi	410
Jayapura	180
Kediri	261
Madiun	107
Magelang	123
Malang	763
Manado	399
Medan	1,910
Mojokerto	171
Padang	721
Pakanbaru	558
Palembang	1,352
Pangkal Pinang	124
Pare Pare	110
Pasuruan	163
Pekalongan	341
Pematangsiantar	231
Pontianak	449
Probolinggo	190
Salatiga	103
Samarinda	536
Semarang	1,366
Sukabumi	125
Surabaya	2,701
Surakarta	516
Tangerang	1,198
Tanjung Balai	115
Tanjung Karang	284
Tebing Tinggi	129
Tegal	313
Ujung Pandang	1,092
Yogyakarta	419

Iran (1994)

Ahvaz	828
Amol	155

Arak	379
Ardabil	330
Babol	153
Bakhtaran (Kermanshah)	666
Bandar 'Abbas	384
Borujerd	212
Bushehr	141
Dezful	202
Esfahan	1,221
Gorgan	178
Hamadan	406
Ilam	137
Islam Shahr (Qasemabad)	240
Karaj	588
Kashan	166
Kerman	350
Khomeini Shahr	127
Khoramabad	277
Khoy	153
Malayer	150
Mashhad	1,964
Masjed Soleyman	109
Najafabad	182
Neyshabur	155
Orumiyeh	396
Qaem Shahr	133
Qazvin	299
Qom	780
Rajai Shahr	193
Rasht	374
Sabzevar	161
Sanandaj	271
Sari	186
Shiraz	1,043
Tabriz	1,166
Tehran*	6,750
Yazd	306
Zahedan	420
Zanjan	281

Iraq (1987)

Adhamiyah	464
Al Amarah	209
Al Hillah	269
Al Mawsil	664
An Najaf	309
An Nasiriyah	265
Ar Ramadi	193
Arbil	770
As Sulaymaniyah	952
Baghdad*	3,841
Ba'qubah	115
Basra	406
Diwaniya	197
Diyala	961
Irbil	486
Kadhimain	521
Karbala	297
Karradah Sharqiyah	236
Kirkuk	419
Kut	183
Mamoon	245
Sulamaniya	364

Ireland (1991)

Cork	174
Dublin*	1,024

Israel (1996)

Ashdod	128
Bat-Yam	142
Be'er Sheva	153
Bene Beraq	129
Haifa	449
Holon	164
Jerusalem*	591
Netanya	148
Petah Tiqwa	153
Ramat Gan	122
Rishon Leziyyon	165
Tel Aviv-Yafo	1,880

Italy (1994)

Ancona	101
Bari	339
Bérgamo	116
Bologna	395
Bréscia	192
Cágliari	178
Catánia	327
Ferrara	137
Florence	393
Fóggia	156
Forlí	109
Genoa	660
Latina	109
Lecce	100
Livorno	166
Messina	234
Milan	1,334
Módena	177
Monza	121
Naples	1,062
Novara	103
Padua	213
Palermo	695
Parma	169
Perugia	147
Pescara	121
Piacenza	102
Prato	166
Ravenna	134
Réggio di Calábria	179
Réggio nell'Emilia	134
Rímini*	130
Rome*	2,688
Salerno	147
Sássari	122
Siracusa	127
Táranto	214
Terni	108
Trento	103
Trieste	227
Turin	946
Venice	306
Verona	257
Vicenza	108

Ivory Coast (1990)

Abidjan	2,500
Bouaké	220
Daloa	† 128
Korhogo	† 113
Man	450
Yamoussoukro*	120

† = 1987

Jamaica (1993)

Kingston*	644

Japan (1993)

Abiko	123
Ageo	203
Aizuwakamatsu	120
Akashi	281
Akishima	108
Akita	308
Amagasaki	496
Anjo	148
Aomori	288
Asahikawa	362
Asaka	108
Ashikaga	167
Atsugi	206
Beppu	129
Chiba	851
Chigasaki	210
Chofu	199
Daito	127
Ebetsu	107
Ebina	111
Fuchu	215
Fuji	228
Fujieda	124
Fujinomiya	119
Fujisawa	362
Fukui	255
Fukuoka	1,269
Fukushima	283
Fukuyama	371
Funabashi	540
Gifu	410
Habikino	117
Hachinohe	241
Hachioji	488
Hadano	162
Hakodate	304
Hamamatsu	561
Handa	105
Higashikurume	113
Higashimurayama	136
Higashiosaka	515
Himeji	463
Hino	167
Hikone	102
Hirakata	397
Hiratsuka	252
Hirosaki	175
Hiroshima	1,102
Hitachi	202
Hofu	119
Ibaraki	255
Ichihara	270
Ichikawa	447
Ichinomiya	267
Ikeda	104
Ikoma	104
Imabari	121
Iruma	142
Ise	103
Isesaki	119
Ishinomaki	122
Itami	188
Iwaki	359
Iwakuni	109
Iwatsuki	109
Izumi	150
Joetsu	131
Kadoma	142
Kagoshima	540
Kakamigahara	132
Kakogawa	249
Kamakura	173
Kanazawa	446
Kariya	125
Kashihara	119
Kashiwa	317
Kasugai	273
Kasukabe	197
Katsuta	114
Kawachinagano	114
Kawagoe	316
Kawaguchi	451
Kawanishi	143
Kawasaki	1,200
Kiryu	123
Kisarazu	126
Kishiwada	190
Kitakyushu	1,020
Kitami	109
Kobe	1,509
Kochi	319
Kodaira	170
Kofu	200
Koganei	107
Kokubunji	104
Komaki	134
Komatsu	107
Koriyama	322
Koshigaya	295
Kumagaya	155
Kumamoto	640
Kurashiki	418
Kure	212
Kurume	233
Kushiro	202
Kyoto	1,452
Machida	359
Maebashi	288
Matsubara	135
Matsudo	464
Matsue	145
Matsumoto	204
Matsusaka	120
Matsuyama	454
Minoo	125
Misato	133
Mishima	107
Mitaka	166
Mito	247
Miyakonojo	131
Miyazaki	294
Moriguchi	156
Morioka	283
Muroran	114
Musashino	137
Nagano	352
Nagaoka	189
Nagareyama	146
Nagasaki	441
Nagoya	2,159
Naha	302
Nara	356
Narashino	155
Neyagawa	257
Niigata	490
Niihama	129
Niiza	142
Nishinomiya	425
Nobeoka	128
Noda	118
Numazu	213
Obihiro	170
Odawara	197
Ogaki	150
Oita	420
Okayama	605
Okazaki	319
Okinawa	110
Ome	134
Omiya	422
Omuta	147
Onomichi	101
Osaka	10,601
Ota	143
Otaru	161
Otsu	269
Oyama	148
Saga	170
Sagamihara	560
Sakai	806
Sakata	101
Sakura	157
Sapporo	1,732
Sasebo	245
Sayama	162
Sendai	951
Seto	129
Shimizu	241
Shimonoseki	260
Shizuoka	474
Soka	214
Suita	340
Suzuka	179
Tachikawa	155
Takamatsu	331
Takaoka	175
Takarazuka	205
Takasaki	238
Takatsuki	361
Tama	149
Tokorozawa	316
Tokushima	265
Tokuyama	110
Tokyo*	26,836
Tomokomai	167
Tondabayashi	118
Tottori	145
Toyama	324
Toyohashi	350
Toyokawa	114
Toyonaka	403
Toyota	341
Tsu	162
Tsuchiura	131
Tsukuba	152
Ube	175
Ueda	121
Uji	182
Urawa	442
Urayasu	122
Utsunomiya	434
Wakayama	395
Yachiyo	154
Yaizu	115
Yamagata	251
Yamaguchi	133
Yamato	202
Yao	276
Yatsushiro	108
Yokkaichi	282
Yokohama	3,288
Yokosuka	435
Yonago	133
Zama	117

Jordan (1994)

Amman*	1,300
Az-Zarqa	609
Irbid	380

Kazakstan (1995)

Alma-Ata (Almaty)	1,151
Aqmola*	280
Aqtau	151
Aqtöbe	259
Atyrau	147
Ekibastuz	141
Kökshetau	141
Oral	219
Öskemen	326
Pavlodar	341
Petropavl	239
Qaraghandy	574
Qostanay	232
Qyzylorda	162
Rudnyy	126
Semey	320
Shymkent	398
Taldyqorghan	116
Temirtau	206
Zhambyl	311
Zhezqazghan	109

Kenya (1991)

Kisumu	201
Mombasa	600
Nairobi*	2,000
Nakuru	124

Kiribati (1990)

Tarawa*	20

Korea, North (1984)

Chinnampo	691
Chongjin	754
Haeju	131
Hamhung	775
Kaesong	346
Kimchaek	281
Pyongyang*	2,639
Sinuiju	500
Wonsan	350

Korea, South (1995)

Andong	188
Ansan	510
Anyang	590
Chechon	137
Cheju	258
Cheonan	330
Chinhae	125
Chinju	330
Chongju	531
Chonju	563
Chunchon	235
Ch'angwon	482
Ch'ungju	205
Hanam	116
Inchon	2,308
Iri	203
Kangnung	220
Kimhai	256
Kumi	311
Kunsan	267
Kuri	142
Kwangju	1,258
Kwangmyong	351
Kyongju	274
Masan	441
Mokpo	248
Puch'on	779
Pusan	3,814
P'ohang	509
Seoul*	11,641
Shihung	133
Songnam	869
Sunch'on	249
Suwon	756
Taegu	2,449
Taejon	1,272
Uijongbu	276
Ulsan	967
Wonju	237
Yosu	184

Kuwait (1993)

Al Jahra	139
Kuwait*	418
Salimiya	116

Kyrgyzstan (1995)

Bishkek*	584
Osh	218

Laos (1992)

| Vientiane (Viangchan)* | 449 |

Latvia (1995)

Daugavpils	120
Liepaja	100
Riga*	840

Lebanon (1991)

Beirut*	1,500
Tripoli	500
Zahlah	200

Lesotho (1992)

| Maseru* | 130 |

Liberia (1992)

| Monrovia* | 490 |

Libya (1988)

Banghazi	472
Misratah	160
Tripoli*	960

Liechtenstein (1995)

| Vaduz* | 5 |

Lithuania (1995)

Kaunas	415
Klaipeda	203
Panevezys	132
Siauliai	147
Vilnius*	576

Luxembourg (1995)

| Luxembourg* | 76 |

Macau (1993)

| Macau* | 381 |

Macedonia (1994)

Bitola	106
Giostivar	108
Kumanovo	127
Skopje*	541
Tetovo	175

Madagascar (1993)

Antananarivo*	1,053
Fianarantsoa	120
Mahajanga	101
Toamasina	127

Malawi (1994)

| Blantyre | 447 |
| Lilongwe* | 395 |

Malaysia (1991)

Alor Setar	125
Ipoh	383
Johor Baharu	329
Kelang	244
Kota Baharu	220
Kota Kinabalu	208
Kuala Lumpur*	1,145
Kuala Terengganu	229
Kuantan	198
Kuching	148
Petaling Jaya	255
Pinang (Georgetown)	219
Sandakan	223
Seremban	183
Taiping	183
Tawau	245

Maldives (1995)

| Malé* | 63 |

Mali (1992)

| Bamako* | 746 |

Malta (1994)

| Valletta* | 102 |

Marshall Islands (1990)

| Dalap Uliga Darrit* | 20 |

Martinique (1990)

| Fort-de-France* | 102 |

Mauritania (1992)

| Nouakchott* | 600 |

Mauritius (1994)

| Port Louis* | 145 |

Mayotte (1991)

| Mamoundzou* | 20 |

Mexico (1990)

Acapulco de Juárez	592
Aguascalientés	506
Atizapàn de Zaragoza	315
Campeche	172
Celaya	316
Chihuahua	530
Ciudad Juárez	798
Ciudad Madero	160
Ciudad Obregón	311
Ciudad Victoria	208
Coatzacoalcos	232
Córdoba	150
Cuernavaca	282
Culiacán Rosales	602
Durango	348
Ensenada	261
Gómez Palacio	233
Guadalajara	2,847
Guasave	258
Hermosillo	449
Irapuato	362
Jalapa	288
León	872
Los Mochis	306
Matamoros	303
Mazatlán	314
Mérida	557
Mexicali	602
Mexico City*	15,643
Minatitlán	200
Monclova	178
Monterrey	2,522
Morelia	490
Nuevo Laredo	218
Oaxaca	213
Orizaba	114
Pachuca	179
Poza Rica de Hidalgo	151
Puebla	1,055
Querétaro	454
Reynosa	281
Salamanca	206
Saltillo	441
San Luis Potosí	526
Tampico	272
Tapachula	222
Tepic	238
Tijuana	743
Toluca	488
Torreón	460
Tuxtla Gutiérrez	296
Uruapan	217
Veracruz	328
Victoria de Durango	414
Villahermosa	390

Moldova (1994)

Balti	159
Chisinau*	700
Tighina	130
Tiraspol	182

Monaco (1995)

| Monaco* | 30 |

Mongolia (1993)

| Ulan Bator* | 619 |

Montserrat (1991)

| Plymouth* (evacuated 1997) | 4 |

Morocco (1993)

Agadir	137
Beni Mellal	139
Casablanca	2,943
El Jadida	125
Fès	564
Kenitra	234
Khouribga	190
Marrakesh	602
Meknès	401
Mohammedia	156
Oujda	331
Rabat-Salé*	1,220
Safi	278
Tangier	307
Tétouan	272

Mozambique (1993)

Beira	299
Maputo*	2,000
Nacala	104
Nampula	203

Namibia (1992)

| Windhoek* | 126 |

Nauru (1990)

| Yaren District* | .1 |

Nepal (1993)

Bhaktapur	130
Biratnagar	132
Katmandu*	535
Lalitapur	190

Netherlands (1994)

Amersfoort	110
Amsterdam*	1,100
Apeldoorn	149
Arnhem	312
Breda	166
Dordrecht-Zwijndrecht	213
Eindhoven	393
Enschede-Hengelo	254
Geleen-Sittard	185
Groningen	210
Haarlem	214
Haarlemmermeer	104
Heerlen-Kerkrade	270
Hilversum	102
Leiden	194
Maastricht	164
Nijmegen	248
Rotterdam	1,074
's-Hertogenbosch	198
The Hague*	695
Tilburg	237
Utrecht	546
Velsen-Beverwijk	134
Zaanstad	133
Zaanstreek	147
Zoetermeer	103

Netherlands Antilles (1993)

| Willemstad* | 197 |

New Caledonia (1989)

| Nouméa* | 98 |

New Zealand (1994)

Auckland-Manukau	929
Christchurch	318
Dunedin	112
Hamilton	154
Northshore	164
Waitakere	148
Wellington*	329

Nicaragua (1992)

| León | 172 |
| Managua* | 974 |

Niger (1988)

Maradi	113
Niamey*	398
Zinder	121

Nigeria (1995)

Aba	292
Abeokuta	417
Abuja*	339
Ado-Ekiti	351
Akure	158
Awka	108
Benin City	224
Bida	123
Calabar	170
Deba Habe	135
Ede	300
Effon-Alaiye	149
Ejigbo	103
Enugu	308
Gombe	105
Gusau	154
Ibadan	1,365
Ife	290
Igboho	104
Ijebu-Ode	153
Ikare	137
Ikerre	239
Ikire	120
Ikirun	177
Ikorodu	180
Ila	257
Ilawe-Ekiti	180
Ilesha	369
Ilobu	194
Ilorin	464
Inisa	117
Ise-Ekiti	127
Iseyin	212
Iwo	353
Jos	201
Kaduna	334
Kano	657
Katsina	202
Kumo	144
Lafia	120
Lagos	10,287
Maiduguri	312
Makurdi	120
Minna	134
Mushin	325
Offa	192
Ogbomosho	712
Oka	140
Ondo	165
Onitsha	363
Oshogbo	465
Owo	179
Oyo	250
Port Harcourt	400
Sapele	136
Shagamu	114
Shaki	170
Shomolu	144
Sokoto	200
Ugep	100
Warri	123
Zaria	370

Northern Mariana Is. (1990)

| Saipan* | 39 |

Norway (1994)

Bergen	195
Oslo*	714
Stavanger	104
Trondheim	134

Oman (1992)

| Muscat* | 350 |

Pakistan (1981/1995)

Chiniot	106
Dera Ghazi Khan	103
Faisalabad	† 1,875
Gujranwala	† 1,663
Gujrat	154
Hyderabad	† 1,107
Islamabad*	204
Jhang	195
Karachi	† 9,863
Kasur	155
Lahore	† 5,085
Mardan	148
Multan	† 1,257
Okara	128
Peshawar	† 1,676
Quetta	286
Rahimyar-Khan	119
Rawalpindi	† 1,290
Sahiwal	106
Sargodha	291
Shekhupura	141
Sialkot	302
Sukkur	159
Wah-Cantt	108
† = 1995	

Palau (1990)

| Koror* | 10 |

Panama (1995)

| Panama* | 452 |
| San Miguelito | 291 |

Papua New Guinea (1990)

| Port Moresby* | 174 |

Paraguay (1992)

Asunción*	945
Ciudad del Este	134
San Lorenzo	133

Peru (1993)

Arequipa	620
Callao	638
Chiclayo	410
Chimbote	297
Cuzco	258
Huancayo	257
Icá	163
Iquitos	266
Juliaca	135
Lima (Lima-Callao)*	6,601
Piura	286
Pucallpa	153
Sullana	155
Tacna	172
Trujillo	509

Philippines (1994)

Angeles	277
Bacolod	343
Bago	140
Baguio	170
Batangas	191
Butuan	245
Cabanatuan	186
Cadiz	143
Cagayan de Oro	414
Calbayog	130
Caloocan	643
Cavite	103
Cebu	688
Cotabato	113
Dagupan	117
Davao	961
General Santos	279
Gingoon	111
Iligan	210
Iloilo	302
Lapu-Lapu	141
Las Pinas	380

Legaspi	125
Lipa	160
Lucena City	161
Makati	453
Malabon	280
Mandaluyong	248
Mandaue	213
Manila*	9,280
Marikina	310
Muntinlupa	275
Naga	103
Navotas	187
Olongapo	209
Ormoc	142
Pagadjan	114
Paranaque	308
Pasay	388
Pasig	398
Quezon City	1,677
Roxas	112
San Carlos (Negros Occ.)	106
San Carlos (Pangasinan)	123
San Juan	127
San Pablo	163
Silay	140
Tacloban	153
Taguig	267
Tarlac	209
Toledo	126
Valenzuela	340
Zamboanga	464

Pitcairn Islands (1994)

Adamstown*	0.06

Poland (1995)

Bialystok	278
Bielsko-Biala	181
Bydgoszcz	386
Bytom	228
Chorzów	127
Czestochowa	260
Dabrowa Górnicza	131
Elblag	129
Gdansk	463
Gdynia	251
Gliwice	214
Gorzów Wielkopolski	125
Grudziadz	103
Jastrzebie Zdrój	103
Kalisz	107
Katowice	354
Kielce	214
Koszalin	112
Kraków	745
Legnica	108
Lódz	826
Lublin	353
Olsztyn	167
Opole	131
Plock	127
Poznan	582
Radom	232
Ruda Slaska	166
Rybnik	144
Rzeszów	160
Slupsk	103
Sosnowiec	249
Szczecin	419
Tarnów	122
Torun	204
Tychy	134
Walbrzych	140
Warsaw*	1,638
Wloclawek	123
Wodzislaw Slaski	112
Wroclaw	643
Zabrze	202
Zielona Góra	116

Portugal (1991)

Amadora	124
Funchal	110
Lisbon*	2,561
Oporto	1,174

Puerto Rico (1993)

Bayamón	225
Caguas	139
Carolina	186
Mayagüez	102
Ponce	190
San Juan*	443

Qatar (1992)

Doha*	243

Réunion (1990)

Saint-Denis*	123

Romania (1994)

Arad	188
Bacau	208
Baia Mare	150
Botosani	128
Braila	236
Brasov	324
Bucharest*	2,061
Buzau	150
Cluj-Napoca	326
Constanta	349
Craiova	307
Drobeta-Turnu Severin	118
Focsani	101
Galati	327
Iasi	340
Oradea	222
Piatra Neamt	126
Pitesti	184
Ploiesti	254
Rimnicu Vilcea	114
Satu Mare	131
Sibiu	171
Suceava	117
Timisoara	328
Tirgu Mures	166

Russia (1994)

Abakan	159
Achinsk	122
Almetyevsk	138
Angarsk	267
Anzhero-Sudzhensk	106
Arkhangelsk	407
Armavir	163
Arzamas	112
Astrakhan	512
Balakovo	206
Balashikha	136
Barnaul	596
Belgorod	318
Berezniki	196
Biysk	233
Blagoveshchensk	214
Bratsk	258
Bryansk	460
Cheboksary	446
Chelyabinsk	1,125
Cherepovets	319
Cherkessk	119
Chita	367
Dimitrovgrad	133
Dzerzhinsk	286
Elektrostal	151
Engels	184
Glazov	107
Grozny	364
Irkutsk	632
Ivanovo	476
Izhevsk	653
Kaliningrad	415
Kaliningrad (Moskovskaya oblast)	135
Kaluga	345
Kamensk-Uralsky	207
Kamyshin	127
Kansk	110
Kazan	1,092
Kemerovo	513
Khabarovsk	609
Khimki	135
Kineshma	103
Kirov	491
Kirovo-Chepetsk	100
Kiselevsk	125
Kislovodsk	119
Kolomna	162
Kolpino	143
Komsomolsk-na-Amure	311
Kostroma	283
Kovrov	161
Krasnodar	638
Krasnoyarsk	914
Kurgan	362
Kursk	439
Kuznetsk	101
Leninsk-Kuznetskiy	131
Lipetsk	470
Lyubertsy	165
Magadan	135
Magnitogorsk	439
Makhachkala	327
Maykop	164
Mezhdurechensk	107
Miass	171
Michurinsk	108
Moscow*	9,233
Murmansk	444
Murom	127
Mytishchi	152
Naberezhnyye-Chelny	524
Nakhodka	164
Nalchik	239
Neftekamsk	116
Nevinnomyssk	129
Nizhnekamsk	207
Nizhne-Vartovsk	241
Nizhniy Novgorod	1,425
Nizhniy Tagil	429
Noginsk	120
Norilsk	163
Novgorod	233
Novocheboksarsk	122
Novocherkassk	189
Novokuybyshevsk	114
Novokuznetsk	593
Novomoskovsk	144
Novorossiysk	194
Novoshakhtinsk	107
Novosibirsk	1,418
Novotroitsk	109
Obninsk	107
Odintsovo	130
Oktyabrskiy	109
Omsk	1,161
Orekhovo-Zuyevo	134
Orel	347
Orenburg	558
Orsk	274
Penza	551
Perm	1,086
Pervouralsk	143
Petropavlovsk-Kamchatskiy	256
Petrozavodsk	279
Podolsk	204
Prokopyevsk	266
Pskov	207
Pyatigorsk	132
Rostov	1,023
Rubtsovsk	171
Ryazan	526
Rybinsk	249
St Petersburg	4,883
Salavat	155
Samara	1,223
Saransk	320
Sarapul	110
Saratov	899
Sergiyev Posad	114
Serov	102
Serpukhov	139
Severodvinsk	243
Shakhty	229
Shchelkovo	108
Simbirsk	670
Smolensk	353
Sochi	353
Solikamsk	109
Starsy Oskol	193
Stavropol	337
Sterlitamak	256
Surgut	259
Syktyvkar	227
Syzran	176
Taganrog	291
Togliatti	689
Tambov	313
Tomsk	496
Tula	535
Tver	454
Tyumen	491
Ufa	1,092
Ukhta	109
Ulan-Ude	365
Usolye Sibirskoye	106
Ussuriisk	162
Ust Ilimsk	111
Velikiye Luky	116
Vladikavkaz	311
Vladimir	339
Vladivostok	637
Volgodonsk	182
Volgograd	1,000
Vologda	296
Volzhskiy	286
Vorkuta	109
Voronezh	905
Votkinsk	104
Yakutsk	194
Yaroslav	631
Yekaterinburg	1,347
Yelets	119
Yoshkar-Ola	248
Yuzhno-Sakhalinsk	162
Zelenograd	183
Zhukovskiy	100
Zlatoust	206

Rwanda (1993)

Kigali*	235

St Helena (1992)

Jamestown*	2

St Kitts and Nevis (1992)

Basseterre*	15

St Lucia (1992)

Castries*	54

St Pierre and Miquelon (1990)

St Pierre*	5

St Vincent and the Grenadines (1992)

Kingstown*	27

San Marino (1994)

San Marino*	4

São Tomé and Príncipe (1992)

São Tomé*	36

Saudi Arabia (1986)

Abha	155
Ad Dammam	128
Al Hufuf	101
At Ta'if	205
Buraidah	184
Haradh	100
Jedda	1,400
Mecca	618
Medina	500
Riyadh*	2,000

Senegal (1994)

Dakar*	1,729
Kaolack	193
Mboure	106
Rufisque	139
St.Louis	132
Thiès	216
Ziguinchor	162

Seychelles (1992)

Victoria*	30

Sierra Leone (1992)

Freetown*	505

Singapore (1993)

Singapore*	2,874

Slovak Republic (1995)

Bratislava*	451
Kosice	240

Slovenia (1994)

Ljubljana*	280
Maribor	130

Solomon Islands (1992)

Honiara*	37

Somalia (1986)

Baidoa	300
Burao	300
Hargeisa	400
Kismayu	200
Merca	100
Mogadishu*	1,000

South Africa (1991)

Alexandra		125
Benoni		114
Bloemfontein*		300
Boksburg		120
Cape Town (metro)*		2,350
Carletonville	†	123
Dlepmeadow		241
Durban (metro)		1,137
East London / King Williams Town		270
East Rand		1,379
Evaton		201
Free State Goldfields		428
Germiston		134
Johannesburg (metro)		1,196
Kathlehong		202
Kayamnandi	†	221
Kempton Park		107
Kimberley		167
Klerksdorp	†	134
Krugersdorp	†	122
Lekoa		218
Mamelodi		155
Mangaung		126
Mdantsane		243
Ntuzuma		102
Nyanga	†	149
Pietermaritzburg		229
Port Elizabeth		853
Pretoria* (metro)		1,080
Roodepoort		163
Sandton		101
Sasolburg		540
Soweto		597
Springs		170
Tembisa		209
Uitenhage	†	125
Umlazi		299
Vanderbijlpark-Vereeniging		774
West Rand		870

† = 1985

Spain (1994)

Albacete	141
Alcalá de Henares	166
Alcorcón	142
Algeciras	104
Alicante	275
Almeria	167
Badajoz	130
Badalona	219
Baracaldo	104
Barcelona	1,631
Bilbao	372
Burgos	166
Cádiz	155
Cartagena	180
Castellón	139
Córdoba	316
Elche	191
Fuenlabrada	158
Getafe	144
Gijón	270

Granada	271
Hospitalet	266
Huelva	145
Jaén	113
Jérez de la Frontera	190
La Coruña	255
La Laguna	125
Las Palmas	372
Leganés	178
León	147
Lérida	114
Logroño	125
Madrid*	3,041
Málaga	531
Mataró	102
Móstoles	199
Murcia	342
Orense	109
Oviedo	202
Palma de Mallorca	322
Pamplona	182
Sabadell	189
Salamanca	167
San Sebastián	178
Santa Coloma de Gramanet	132
Santa Cruz de Tenerife	204
Santander	195
Sevilla	714
Tarragona	115
Tarrasa	161
Valencia	764
Valladolid	337
Vigo	289
Vitoria	214
Zaragoza	607

Sri Lanka (1990)

Colombo*	1,863
Dehiwala	196
Jaffna	129
Kandy	104
Kotte	109
Moratuwa	170

Sudan (1993)

El Obeid	228
Gedaref	189
Juba	115
Kassala	234
Khartoum*	925
Medani	219
Nyala	1,267
Omdurman	229
Port Sudan	305
Sharg el Nil	879

Surinam (1993)

Paramaribo*	201

Swaziland (1992)

Mbabane*	42

Sweden (1996)

Göteborg	788
Helsingborg	114
Jönköping	115
Linköping	131
Malmö	494
Norrköping	124
Örebro	120
Stockholm*	1,553
Uppsala	183
Västerås	124

Switzerland (1992)

Basle	402
Bern*	324
Geneva	429
Lausanne	282
Luzern	177
St Gallen	127
Winterthur	115
Zürich	915

Syria (1994)

Al Kamishli	151
Al Rakka	219
Aleppo	1,640
Damascus*	2,230
Dar'a	180
Deir El-Zor	174
Hamah	222
Homs	644
Idlib	113
Lattakia	307
Tartus	137

Taiwan (1993)

Changhua	221
Chiai	259
Chilung	363
Chungho	387
Chunli	289
Fengshan	298
Fengyüan	157
Hsinchu	335
Hsintien	246
Hualien	108
Kaohsiung	1,405
Luchou	126
Panch'iao	544
Pate	143
Pingchen	159
P'ingtung	214
Sanchung	304
Shulin	125
T'aichung	817
T'ainan	700
T'aipei*	2,653
Taip'ing	135
T'aitung	109
Tali	152
T'aoyüan	257
Tuch'eng	156
Yüanlin	123
Yungho	246
Yungk'ang	156

Tajikistan (1994)

Dushanbe*	524
Khodzent	165

Tanzania (1988)

Dar-es-Salaam	1,361
Dodoma*	204
Mbeya	194
Mwanza	223
Tabora	214
Tanga	188
Zanzibar	158

Thailand (1990)

Bangkok*	5,876
Chiang Mai	167
Chon Buri	187
Khon Kaen	206
Nakhon Ratchasima	278
Nakhon Sawan	152
Nakhon Si Thammarat	112
Nonthaburi	233
Saraburi	107
Songkhla	243
Ubon Ratchathani	137

Togo (1992)

Lomé*	590

Tonga (1992)

Nuku'alofa*	29

Trinidad and Tobago (1994)

Port-of-Spain*	46

Tunisia (1994)

Aryanah	153
Ettadhamen	149
Sfax	231
Susah	125
Tunis*	1,827

Turkey (1993)

Adana	1,472
Adapazari	298
Ankara*	3,028
Antalya	734
Balikesir	501
Batman	225
Bursa	1,317
Denizli	368
Diyarbakir	677
Elazig	287
Erzurum	419
Eskisehir	508
Gaziantep	930
Hatay	561
Icel	908
Iskenderun	156
Isparta	252
Istanbul	7,490
Izmir	2,333
Izmit	271
Kahramanmaras	433
Kayseri	648
Kirikkale	236
Kocaeli	661
Konya	1,040
Kütahya	257
Malatya	412
Manisa	641
Mersin	494
Osmaniye	134
Sakarya	321
Samsun	557
Sivas	414
Tarsus	214
Trabzon	321
Urfa	649
Van	297
Zonguldak	426

Turkmenistan (1990)

Ashkhabad (Ashgabat)*	407
Chärjew	164
Dashhowuz	114

Turks and Caicos (1990)

Grand Turk*	4

Tuvalu (1992)

Fongafale*	3

Uganda (1991)

Kampala*	773

Ukraine (1996)

Alchevsk	124
Berdyansk	135
Bila Tserkva	216
Cherkasy	312
Chernihiv	312
Chernivtsi	261
Dniprodzerzhynsk	281
Dnipropetrovsk	1,147
Donetsk	1,088
Horlivka	322
Ivano-Frankivsk	237
Kamyanets-Podilskyy	108
Kerch	175
Kharkiv	1,555
Kherson	363
Khmelnytskyy	259
Kirovohrad	276
Kiev (Kyyiv)*	2,630
Kostyantynivka	102
Kramatorsk	197
Krasnyy Luch	109
Kremenchuk	246
Kryvyy Rih	720
Luhansk	487
Lutsk	219
Lviv	802
Lysychansk	123
Makiyivka	409
Mariupol	510
Melitopol	174
Mykolayiv	508
Nikopol	157
Odesa	1,046
Oleksandriya	103
Pavlohrad	134
Poltava	321
Rivne	246
Sevastopol	365
Simferopol	348
Slovyansk	133
Stakhanov	109
Sumy	304
Ternopil	235
Uzhhorod	126
Vinnytsya	388
Yenakiyev	114
Yevpatoriya	115
Zaporizhzhya	887
Zhytomyr	301

United Arab Emirates (1995)

Abu Dhabi*	928
Ajman	119
Dubai	674
Ra's al Khaymah	144
Sharjah	400

United Kingdom (1996)

Aberdeen	192
Aldershot/Camberley/ Farnham	239
Barnsley (Dearne Valley)	217
Basildon	104
Belfast	297
Birkenhead	269
Blackburn/Darwen	139
Blackpool/Lytham/ Fleetwood	266
Bournemouth/Poole	378
Brighton/Hove/Worthing	470
Bristol	552
Burnley/Nelson	149
Cambridge	143
Cardiff	343
Chatham/Gillingham	221
Cheltenham	107
Chesterfield	108
Colchester	104
Coventry	345
Crawley	123
Derby	245
Doncaster	130
Dundee	153
Eastbourne	104
Edinburgh	411
Exeter	104
Glasgow	832
Gloucester	132
Grimsby/Cleethorpes	135
Hastings/Bexhill	127
High Wycombe	121
Hull	327
Ipswich	129
Leicester	447
Lincoln	100
Liverpool	852
London*	8,089
Luton/Dunstable	230
Manchester	2,353
Mansfield/Sutton/Ashfield	156
Margate/Ramsgate	119
Milton Keynes	174
Morecambe/Lancaster	101
Newport	119
Northampton	195
Norwich	193
Nottingham	649
Oxford	148
Peterborough	140
Plymouth	258
Portsmouth/Gosport/ Fareham	426
Preston	267
Reading/Wokingham/ Bracknell	230
Sheffield/Rotherham	661
Slough	139
Southampton/Eastleigh	299
Southend	280
Southport/Formby	116
St Albans/Hatfield	119
Sunderland	192
Swansea/Neath/ Port Talbot	282
Swindon	148
Teeside	375
Telford	123
Torbay	106
Tyneside	916
Warrington	157
West Midlands	2,373
West Yorkshire	1,515
Wigan/Skelmersdale	176
York	132

United States (1994)

Abilene	110
Akron	222
Albany	105
Albuquerque	412
Alexandria (Va.)	113
Allentown	105
Amarillo	165
Anaheim	282
Anchorage	254
Ann Arbor	109
Arlington	287
Atlanta	3,331
Aurora (Co.)	251
Aurora (Il.)	112
Austin	514
Bakersfield	191
Baltimore	2,458
Baton Rouge	227
Beaumont	115
Berkeley	265
Birmingham	265
Boise City	146
Boston	3,240
Bridgeport	133
Buffalo	1,189
Burbank	100
Cambridge	100
Cedar Rapids	113
Chandler	119
Charlotte	1,260
Chattanooga	152
Chesapeake	181
Chicago	7,668
Chula Vista	149
Cincinnati	1,581
Clearwater	100
Cleveland	2,222
Colorado Springs	316
Columbia	104
Columbus (Ga.)	186
Columbus (Oh.)	1,423
Concord	112
Corpus Christi	275
Dallas	2,898
Dayton	179
Denver	1,796
Des Moines	194
Detroit	4,307
Durham	143
El Monte	105
El Paso	579
Elizabeth	106
Erie	108
Escondido	116
Eugene	118
Evansville	129
Flint	138
Fort Lauderdale	163
Fort Wayne	183
Fort Worth	452
Fremont	184
Fresno	387
Fullerton	117
Garden Grove	148
Garland	194
Gary	114
Glendale (Az.)	168
Glendale (Ca.)	178
Grand Prairie	109
Grand Rapids	190
Green Bay	103
Greensboro	196
Hampton	140
Hartford	1,151
Hayward	116
Henderson	102
Hialeah	194
Hollywood	125
Honolulu	386
Houston	3,653
Huntington Beach	189

Huntsville	160	Phoenix	2,473
Independence	112	Pittsburgh	2,402
Indianapolis	1,462	Plano	157
Inglewood	110	Pomona	144
Irvine	126	Portland (Or.)	1,676
Irving	165	Portsmouth (Va.)	103
Jackson (Ms.)	193	Providence	151
Jacksonville (Fl.)	665	Pueblo	100
Jersey City	226	Raleigh	237
Kansas City	1,647	Rancho Cucamonga	115
Knoxville	169	Reno	145
Lakewood	126	Richmond	201
Lansing	120	Riverside	242
Laredo	150	Rochester	231
Las Vegas	328	Rockford	143
Lexington-Fayette	238	Sacramento	1,441
Lincoln	203	St Louis	2,536
Little Rock	178	St Petersburg	239
Livonia	100	Salem	116
Long Beach	434	Salinas	120
Los Angeles	12,410	Salt Lake City	1,178
Louisville	270	San Antonio	1,437
Lubbock	194	San Bernardino	182
Macon	109	San Diego	2,632
Madison	195	San Francisco	2,182
Memphis	614	San Jose	1,557
Mesa	314	Santa Ana	291
Mesquite	114	Santa Clarita	124
Miami	2,025	Santa Rosa	117
Milwaukee	1,456	Savannah	141
Minneapolis-St Paul	2,688	Scottsdale	152
Mobile	204	Seattle	2,180
Modesto	176	Shreveport	197
Montgomery	195	Simi Valley	107
Moreno Valley	139	Sioux Falls	109
Naperville	101	South Bend	105
Nashville-Davidson	505	Spokane	193
New Haven	120	Springfield (Il.)	106
New Orleans	1,309	Springfield (Ma.)	149
New York	16,329	Springfield (Mo.)	150
Newark (Nj.)	1,934	Stamford	107
Newport News	179	Sterling Heights	120
Norfolk	1,529	Stockton	223
Oakland	2,182	Sunnyvale	120
Oceanside	146	Syracuse	160
Oklahoma	1,007	Tacoma	183
Omaha	663	Tallahassee	134
Ontario	135	Tampa	2,157
Orange	117	Tempe	144
Orlando	177	Thousand Oaks	111
Overland Park	125	Toledo	323
Oxnard	146	Topeka	121
Pasadena (Ca.)	134	Torrance	138
Pasadena (Tx.)	129	Tucson	435
Paterson	138	Tulsa	375
Peoria	113	Vallejo	111
Philadelphia	4,949	Virginia Beach	430

Waco	106
Warren	143
Washington, DC*	4,466
Waterbury	104
West Covina	103
Wichita	310
Winston-Salem	155
Worcester	165
Yonkers	183

Uruguay (1995)

Montevideo*	1,326

Uzbekistan (1993)

Andijon	303
Angren	132
Bukhoro	236
Chirchiq	156
Farghona	191
Jizzakh	116
Marghilon	129
Namangan	341
Nawoiy	115
Nukus	185
Olmaliq	116
Qarshi	177
Quqon	184
Samarqand	368
Tashkent (Toshkent)*	2,106
Urganch	135

Vanuatu (1992)

Port-Vila*	20

Vatican City State (1994)

Vatican*	1

Venezuela (1990)

Acarigua-Araure	195
Barcelona-Puerto La Cruz	426
Barinas	174
Barquisimento	745
Baruta	165
Cabimas	183
Caracas*	2,784
Catia la Mar	112
Ciudad Bolívar	253
Ciudad Guayana	524
Coro	144
Cumaná	232
Guarenas	153

Los Teques	162
Maracaibo	1,364
Maracay	800
Maturín	258
Mérida	238
Petare	379
Puerto Cabello	144
San Cristóbal	336
Tumero	196
Valencia	1,032
Valera	107

Vietnam (1992)

Ban Me Thuot	282
Bien Hoa	274
Cam Pha	209
Cam-Ranh	114
Can-Tho	216
Da-Nang	383
Dalat	106
Haiphong	783
Hanoi*	3,056
Ho Chi Minh City	4,322
Hon Gai	127
Hue	219
Long Xuyen	133
My Tho	108
Nam Dinh	172
Nguyen	128
Nha-Trang	221
Qui-Nhon	163
Rach-Gia	141
Thanh-Hoa	127
Viettri	116
Vinh	112
Vungtau	145

Virgin Islands, British (1991)

Road Town*	6

Virgin Islands, US (1990)

Charlotte Amalie*	12

Wallis and Futuna (1990)

Mata'utu*	1

Western Sahara (1994)

Al Aaiún*	150

Western Samoa (1992)

Apia*	37

Yemen (1993)

Aden	401
Hodeida	246
Sana'*	972
Ta'izz	290

Yugoslavia (Serbia and Montenegro) (1991)

Belgrade*	1,137
Kragujevac	147
Nis	176
Novi Sad	179
Podgorica	118
Pristina	105
Subotica	100

Zambia (1990)

Chingola	163
Kabwe	167
Kitwe	338
Luanshya	146
Lusaka*	982
Mufulira	153
Ndola	376

Zimbabwe (1992)

Bulawayo	622
Chitungwiza	275
Gweru	128
Harare*	1,189
Mutare	131

Census details

Canada

Census 14 August 1996
Total population: 28,846,761

The ten provinces and two territories are underlined.
Populations of urban agglomerations are listed below, with provincial capitals given in bold.

	Population 1996	% change 1991–96
CANADA	28,846,761	5.7
Alberta	2,696,826	5.9
Calgary	821,628	9.0
Camrose	13,728	2.3
Edmonton	**862,597**	**2.6**
Grand Centre	35,161	2.5
Grande Prairie	31,140	10.1
Lethbridge	63,053	3.4
Medicine Hat	56,570	7.4
Red Deer	60,075	3.3
Wetaskiwin	10,959	2.8
Wood Buffalo	36,124	–3.4
British Columbia	3,724,500	13.5
Abbotsford	136,480	20.2
Campbell River	35,183	14.0
Chilliwack	66,254	20.5
Courtenay	54,912	23.3
Cranbrook	18,131	10.2
Dawson Creek	11,125	1.3
Duncan	35,803	15.8
Fort St John	15,021	6.1
Kamloops	84,914	14.2
Kelowna	136,541	22.1
Kitimat	11,136	–1.5
Nanaimo	85,585	16.4
Penticton	41,276	15.2
Port Alberni	26,893	1.1
Powell River	19,936	7.9
Prince George	75,150	7.9
Prince Rupert	17,414	0.3
Quesnal	25,279	8.5
Terrace	20,941	10.8
Vancouver	1,831,665	14.3
Vernon	55,359	15.0
Victoria	**304,287**	**5.7**
Williams Lake	38,552	11.1
Manitoba	1,113,898	399,692
Brandon	40,581	1.7
Portage la Prairie	20,385	–2.9
Thompson	14,385	–4.0
Winnipeg	**667,209**	**1.0**
New Brunswick	738,795	2.0
Bathurst	25,415	–1.2
Campbellton	16,867	–1.8
Edmundston	22,624	1.9
Fredericton	**78,950**	**5.7**
Moncton	113,491	5.6
Saint John	125,705	–0.1
Newfoundland	551,792	–2.9
Corner Brook	27,945	–2.1
Gander	12,021	–0.1
Grand Falls-Windsor	20,378	–3.2
Labrador City	10,473	–8.1
St John's	**174,051**	**1.3**
Northwest Territories	64,402	11.7
Yellowknife	**17,275**	**13.8**
Nova Scotia	909,282	1.0
Cape Breton	117,849	–1.9
Halifax	**332,518**	**3.7**
Kentville	25,090	4.2
New Glasgow	38,055	–1.6
Quebec	7,138,795	144,654
Alma	30,383	0.6
Baie-Comeau	31,795	–0.9
Chicoutimi-Jonquiere	160,454	–0.3
Cowansville	12,051	0.5
Dolbeau	15,214	1.3
Drummondville	65,119	6.3
Granby	58,872	3.6
Hawkesbury	11,605	4.8
Joliette	34,391	2.6
La Tuque	13,165	–2.8
Lachute	11,493	–2.0
Magog	21,334	4.4
Matane	17,118	–2.6
Montreal	3,326,510	3.7
Ottawa–Hull	1,010,498	7.3
Pembroke	23,745	3.7
Quebec	**671,889**	**4.1**
Rimouski	48,104	3.0
Riviere-du-Loup	22,378	3.4
Rouyn-Noranda	39,096	1.3
Saint-Georges	26,584	5.4
Saint-Hyacinthe	50,027	1.4
Saint-Jean-sur-Richelieu	76,461	4.1
Salaberry-de-Valleyfield	39,563	–1.2
Sept-Iles	28,005	3.0
Shawinigan	59,851	–1.0
Sherbrooke	147,384	4.7
Sorel	43,009	–3.4
Thetford Mines	27,760	–2.6
Trois-Rivieres	139,956	2.7
Val-d'Or	32,648	3.6
Victoriaville	40,438	5.0
Ontario	10,753,573	6.6
Barrie	118,695	22.2
Belleville	93,442	0.6
Brantford	100,238	3.2
Brockville	42,709	3.2
Chatham	67,068	–1.1
Cobourg	16,027	6.3
Collingwood	15,596	8.4
Cornwall	62,183	1.6
Elliot Lake	13,588	–3.6
Guelph	105,420	7.9
Haileybury	13,712	–3.3
Hamilton	624,360	4.1
Kenora	16,365	2.9
Kingston	143,416	5.1
Kitchener	382,940	7.4
Leamington	40,687	8.9
Lindsay	21,949	5.9
London	398,616	4.5
Midland	33,291	4.8
North Bay	64,785	–0.7
Orillia	38,103	10.7
Oshawa	268,773	11.9
Owen Sound	30,319	0.1
Peterborough	100,193	2.2
Port Hope	11,698	1.7
St Catherines-Niagara	372,406	2.2
Sarnia	86,480	–1.6
Sault Ste Maria	83,619	–1.6
Simcoe	15,380	–1.0
Smiths Falls	16,507	2.4
Stratford	28,987	4.8
Strathroy	11,852	12.2
Sudbury	160,488	1.8
Thunder Bay	125,562	0.5
Tillsonburg	13,211	9.9
Timmins	47,499	0.1
Toronto	**4,263,757**	**9.4**
Windsor	278,685	6.3
Woodstock	32,086	6.7
Prince Edward Island	134,557	3.7
Charlottetown	**57,224**	**4.4**
Summerside	16,001	6.1
Saskatchewan	990,237	0.1
Estevan	12,656	3.9
Lloydminster	18,953	9.7
Moose Jaw	34,829	–2.0
North Battleford	17,987	–2.5
Prince Albert	41,706	1.1
Regina	**193,652**	**1.0**
Saskatoon	219,056	3.8
Swift Current	16,437	0.0
Yorkton	17,713	–1.7
Yukon Territory	30,766	10.7
Whitehorse	**21,808**	**8.6**

Finland

Official population estimate 31 December 1995
Total population: 5,116,826
The provinces are underlined. Figures for all urban municipalities are given below, with an overall figure included for rural municipalities.

	Population 1995	Area km	Density per km	Swedish-speaking %
FINLAND	**5,116,826**	**304,593**	**17**	**5.8**
Hämeen	730,472	19,226	38	0.3
Forssa	19,542	249	78	0.3
Hämeenlinna	44,891	167	269	0.3
Ikaalinen	8,074	752	11	0.1
Lahti	95,119	135	705	0.3
Mantta	7,311	64	114	0.3
Nokia	26,287	289	91	0.3
Orivesi	9,012	545	16	0.2
Parkano	8,226	855	10	0.0
Riihimäki	25,838	121	214	0.3
Tampere	182,742	523	350	0.6
Toijala	8,135	51	160	0.1
Valkeaskoski	21,168	273	77	0.3
Virrat	8,879	1,163	8	0.0
Rural municipalities	265,248	14,039	19	0.3
Keski – Suomen	258,078	16,249	16	0.1
Äänekoski	13,750	600	23	0.1
Jämsä	13,085	670	19	0.1
Jämsänkoski	7,951	401	20	0.1
Jyväskylä	74,072	106	699	0.2
Keuruu	12,405	1,261	10	0.1
Saarijärvi	10,753	887	12	0.0
Suolahti	5,999	58	103	0.1
Viitasaari	8,347	1,250	7	0.1
Rural municipalities	111,716	11,017	10	0.1
Kuopion	258,315	16,510	16	0.1
Kiuruvesi	11,179	1,331	8	0.0
Kuopio	84,733	779	109	0.1
Lisalmi	24,042	763	31	0.0
Suonenjoki	8,560	720	12	0.0
Varkaus	24,160	87	278	0.3
Rural municipalities	105,641	12,829	8	0.1
Kymen	331,892	10,780	31	0.6
Anjalankoski	18,396	726	25	0.3
Hamina	10,035	19	537	0.4
Imatra	32,057	155	207	0.1
Kotka	55,903	268	208	1.1
Kouvola	32,078	44	732	0.4
Kuusankoski	21,494	114	189	0.5
Lappeenranta	56,664	760	75	0.2
Rural municipalities	105,265	8,694	12	0.8
Mikkelin	205,630	16,326	13	0.1
Heinola	15,929	49	328	0.3
Mikkeli	32,812	89	370	0.1
Pieksämäki	13,483	36	374	0.1
Savonlinna	28,867	822	35	0.1
Rural municipalities	114,539	15,331	7	0.1
Pohjois – Karjalan	177,271	17,782	10	0.1
Joensuu	50,431	82	616	0.1
Kitee	11,058	861	13	0.0
Lieksa	16,752	3,425	5	0.1
Nurmes	10,718	1,605	7	0.0
Outokumpu	8,887	445	20	0.1
Rural municipalities	79,425	11,364	7	0.1
Turun ja Porin	702,179	19,954	35	3.9
Harjavalta	124	8,374	67	0.2
Huittinen	389	9,388	24	0.0
Kaarina	60	19,088	320	3.8
Kankaanpää	690	13,466	19	0.1
Kokemäki	482	9,145	19	0.1
Laitila	531	9,128	17	0.2
Loimaa	47	7,124	150	0.1
Naantali	12,412	51	243	1.6
Parainen	12,079	272	44	56.2
Pori	76,627	503	152	0.5
Raisio	22,268	49	452	1.2
Rauma	38,162	247	155	0.4
Salo	22,802	143	159	0.7
Turku (Åbo)	164,744	243	677	5.1
Somero	9,894	669	15	0.2
Uusikaupunki	17,590	493	36	0.5
Vammala	15,707	599	26	0.1

Finland continued

	Population 1995	Area km	Density per km	Swedish-speaking %
Rural municipalities	234,181	14,361	16	4.2
Uudenmaan	1,326,589	9,898	134	10.4
Espoo	191,247	312	613	10.1
Hanko	10,825	114	94	46.2
Helsinki	525,031	184	2,846	7.0
Hyvinkää	41,203	323	127	0.6
Järvenpää	34,436	37	918	0.9
Karjaa	8,859	197	45	62.6
Karkkila	8,609	243	35	0.6
Kauniainen	8,298	6	1,406	41.8
Kerava	29,385	31	954	1.3
Lohja	15,265	16	948	3.1
Loviisa	7,758	44	174	40.7
Orimattila	14,211	609	23	0.4
Porvoo	21,155	19	1,108	34.9
Tammisaari	14,687	721	20	82.4
Vantaa	166,480	241	691	3.7
Rural municipalities	229,140	6,799	34	16.3
Vaasan	447,939	26,418	17	22.3
Alajarvi	9,642	739	13	0.1
Alavus	10,307	790	13	0.0
Kannus	6,308	408	15	0.5
Kaskinen	1,596	10	158	29.5
Kauhava	8,527	483	18	0.2
Kokkola	35,552	327	109	19.2
Kristiinankaupunki	8,685	679	13	57.5
Kurikka	11,121	463	24	0.1
Vaasa	55,502	183	303	26.2
Lapua	14,488	737	20	0.1

Indonesia

Official population estimate 31 December 1995
Total population: 194,754,808
The provinces are given in bold and underlined. The name of the provincial capital is given in the last column.

	Population 1995	Area km	Density per km	Net migration	Province capital
INDONESIA	**194,754,808**	**1,919,443**	**101**		
Java and Madura	114,733,486	132,186	868		
DKI Jakarta	9,112,652	590	13,786	1,782,099	Jakarta
Jawa Barat	39,206,787	46,300	848	1,723,484	Bandung
Jawa Tengah	29,653,266	34,206	867	−4,341,844	Semarang
Jawa Timur	33,844,002	47,921	706	−2,070,394	Surabaya
Yogyakarta	2,916,779	3,169	920	−514,434	Yogyakarta
Kalimantan	10,470,843	539,460	19		
Kalimantan Barat	3,635,730	146,760	25	123,783	Ponianak
Kalimantan Selatan	2,893,477	37,660	77	76,360	Banjarmasin
Kalimantan Tengah	1,627,453	152,600	11	267,580	Palangkaraya
Kalimantan Timur	2,314,183	202,440	11	652,463	Samarinda
Pulau – Pulau Lain	14,987,696	584,974	26		
Bali	2,895,649	5,561	521	−72,247	Denpasar
Irian Jaya	1,942,627	421,981	5	226,920	Jayapura
Maluku	2,086,516	74,505	28	24,750	Ambon
Nusa Tenggara Barat	3,645,713	20,177	181	−32,034	Mataram
Nusa Tenggara Timur	3,577,472	47,876	75	−60,710	Kupang
Timor Timur*	839,719	14,874	56	49,164	Dili
Sulawesi	13,732,449	189,216	73		
Sulawesi Selatan	7,558,368	72,781	104	−488,046	Ujung Pandang
Sulawesi Tengah	1,938,071	69,726	28	303,816	Palu
Sulawesi Tenggara	1,586,917	27,686	57	134,738	Kendari
Sulawesi Utara	2,649,093	19,023	139	−142,156	Menado
Sumatra	40,830,334	473,481	86		
Aceh	3,847,583	55,392	69	47,067	Banda Aceh
Bebgkikk	1,409,117	21,168	66	265,318	Bengkulu
Jambi	2,369,959	44,800	53	370,591	Jambi
Lampung	6,657,759	33,307	200	1,650,867	Tanjung Karang
Riau	3,900,534	94,561	41	714,828	Pakanbaru
Suamar	7,207,545	103,688	70	458,821	Ujung Pandang
Sumatera Barat	4,323,170	49,778	87	−576,648	Padang
Sumatera Utara	11,114,667	70,787	157	−473,001	Medan

* The legality of Indonesia's administration of this province is disputed by the United Nations.

Guatemala

Census 17 April 1994.
Total population: 8,331,874
The departments are given in bold and are followed by figures for municipalities with a population of more than 20,000.

	Population 1994	Urban pop. %
GUATEMALA	**8,331,874**	**35.0**
Alta Verapaz	**543,777**	**15.7**
Cahabon	31,425	10.3
Chisec	48,850	10.8
Coban	93,633	36.3
Panzos	53,511	5.6
San Juan Chamelco	27,023	18.0
San Pedro Carcha	102,557	8.4
Senahu	44,405	4.5
Tucuru	20,029	5.1
Baja Verapaz	**155,480**	**20.4**
Cubulco	28,423	15.6
Purulha	20,512	14.3
Rabinal	24,132	25.6
Salamá	35,808	29.1
Chimaltenango	**314,813**	**41.5**
Chimaltenango	44,696	59.3
Comalapa	27,827	58.6
Patzun	32,563	42.3
San Martin Jilotepeque	43,880	14.2
Chiouimula	**230,767**	**25.2**
Camotan	24,473	4.7
Chiquimula	62,894	44.0
Esquipulas	29,609	42.8
Jocotan	28,011	12.6
Quezaltepéque	21,251	14.8
El Progreso	**108,400**	**26.5**
San Agustin Acasaguastlan	26,315	17.6
Sanarate	25,414	36.6
Escuintla	**386,534**	**37.1**
Escuintla	89,914	54.5
La Gomera	36,588	15.0
Masagua	21,818	9.2
Nueva Concepcion	52,756	17.7
San Jose	32,295	44.0
Santa Lucia Cotzumalguapa	52,211	46.0
Tiquisate	33,667	37.8
Guatemala	**1,813,825**	**70.9**
Amatitlan	54,930	67.3
Chinautla	63,463	28.1
Guatemala	823,301	100.0
Mixco	305,297	32.5
Palencia	34,239	8.8
Petapa	41,506	31.2
San Jose Pinula	24,471	18.7
San Juan Sacatepéquez	88,766	9.4
San Pedro Ayampuc	20,260	13.8
San Pedro Sacatepéquez	21,009	20.2
Santa Catarina Pinula	38,628	21.2
Villa Canales	62,334	8.8
Villa Nueva	192,069	52.7
Huehuetenango	**634,374**	**14.5**
Aguacatan	32,803	11.4
Barillas	44,212	13.4
Chiantla	52,124	11.3
Cuilco	36,870	3.5
Huehuetenango	60,808	32.7
Ixtahuacan	21,898	11.6
Jacaltenango	26,951	26.0
La Democracia	29,864	4.3
La Libertad	21,771	10.0
San Mateo Ixtatan	23,055	13.2
San Pedro Necta	20,386	9.4
Santa Eulalia	20,148	6.1
Soloma	26,102	16.2
Izabal	**253,153**	**19.8**
El Estor	27,058	36.3
Livingston	39,051	10.1
Los Amates	52,528	4.1
Morales	67,668	7.6
Puerto Barrios	66,848	43.5

	Population 1994	Urban pop. %
Jalapa	**196,940**	**27.2**
Jalapa	82,922	28.8
San Pedro Pinula	33,699	7.9
Jutiapa	**307,491**	**20.3**
Asuncion Mita	36,992	30.2
Jutiapa	72,611	20.1
Moyuta	28,732	8.2
Santa Catarina Mita	21,207	28.1
Petén	**224,884**	**26.7**
Dolores	23,336	14.6
La Libertad	42,539	9.4
Poptun	21,641	9.8
San Luis	34,225	13.3
Sayaxche	28,394	37.3
Quetzaltenango	**108,605**	**39.8**
Cantel	23,180	15.3
Coatepeque	69,744	43.6
Colomba	37,547	18.3
Genova	23,492	11.3
Ostuncalco	33,002	27.9
Quetzaltenango	108,605	83.6
San Carlos Sija	23,142	6.6
Quiché	**437,669**	**15.1**
Chichicastenango	75,797	4.8
Ixcen	38,535	6.7
Joyabaj	34,583	10.8
Nebaj	33,855	27.0
Sacapulas	26,264	8.7
Santa Cruz del Quiché	38,249	37.5
Uspantan	26,370	10.5
Retalhuleu	**188,764**	**27.7**
Nuevo San Carlos	23,125	3.1
Retalhuleu	57,123	48.2
Sacatepéquez	**180,647**	**70.5**
Antigua Guatemala	34,168	47.9
San Marcos	**645,418**	**12.9**
Ayutla	21,037	41.0
Comitancillo	36,478	4.3
Concepcion Tutuapa	43,458	1.8
El Tumbador	31,727	11.7
Malacatan	51,198	15.8
Ocos	21,236	6.1
San Marcos	27,088	32.7
San Miguel Ixtahuacan	25,278	3.1
San Pablo	26,965	11.8
San Pedro Sacatepéquez	51,043	29.3
Tacana	53,568	3.8
Tajumulco	31,911	1.2
Tejutla	24,242	9.6
Santa Rosa	**246,698**	**24.0**
Barberena	31,573	32.6
Chiquimulilla	37,679	25.7
Cuilapa	22,438	37.9
Nueva Santa Rosa	24,402	16.8
Taxisco	20,779	23.5
Solola	**222,094**	**33.2**
Nahuala	41,310	6.8
Santa Catarina Ixtahuacan	34,198	6.6
Santiago Atitlan	23,303	75.4
Sololá	37,127	20.4
Suchitepéquez	**307,187**	**30.2**
Chicacao	34,906	21.6
Cuyotenango	31,465	16.9
Mazatenango	45,471	66.8
Patulul	21,274	24.8
San Antonio Suchitepéquez	28,182	14.6
Totonicapan	**272,094**	**10.7**
Momostenango	68,391	10.9
San Cristobal Totonicapan	28,120	15.5
San Francisco El Alto	35,969	8.1
Santa Maria Chiquimula	29,200	7.3
Totonicapán	79,372	9.0
Zacapa	**157,008**	**28.5**
Gualan	34,102	18.6
Zacapa	44,145	37.1

Japan

Census 1 October 1995
Total population: 125,568,504
The prefectures are underlined. Also included is information on the cities within each prefecture.

	Population 1995	% Change 1990–95
JAPAN	**125,568,504**	**1.6**
Aichi	**6,868,000**	**2.7**
Anjo	149,459	5.1
Bisai	57,126	2.2
Chiryu	58,570	8.3
Chita	78,203	3.7
Gamagori	83,734	−1.3
Handa	106,451	6.9
Hekinan	66,845	1.4
Ichinomiya	267,359	1.9
Inazawa	98,744	2.6
Inuyama	71,343	2.2
Iwakura	46,158	5.4
Kariya	125,307	4.3
Kasugai	277,579	4.1
Komaki	137,163	10.2
Konan	95,428	1.7
Nagoya	2,152,258	−0.1
Nishio	98,765	3.7
Nisshin	60,311	19.8
Obu	73,091	4.8
Okazaki	322,615	5.1
Owariasahi	70,072	6.7
Seto	129,396	2.4
Shinshiro	36,144	1.4
Takahama	36,028	7.6
Tokai	99,737	2.4
Tokoname	50,851	−1.8
Toyohashi	352,913	4.4
Toyokawa	114,379	2.4
Toyota	341,038	2.6
Tsushima	63,722	7.4
Yoyoake	64,886	4.4
Akita	**1,214,000**	**−1.1**
Akita	312,035	3.2
Honjo	45,107	1.5
Kazuno	41,182	−2.9
Noshiro	55,009	−1.6
Odate	67,214	−1.4
Oga	32,484	−5.3
Omagari	39,938	−1.2
Yokote	41,469	−2.0
Yuzawa	36,223	−0.9
Aomori	**1,482,000**	**−0.1**
Aomori	294,165	2.2
Goshogawara	48,549	1.2
Hachinohe	242,657	0.7
Hirosaki	177,971	1.9
Kuroishi	39,004	−0.5
Misawa	41,606	0.6
Mutsu	48,883	0.9
Towada	62,355	2.4
Chiba	**5,798,000**	**4.4**
Abiko	124,255	3.0
Asahi	40,485	4.1
Chiba	856,882	3.3
Choshi	82,180	−3.5
Funabashi	540,814	1.4
Futtsu	54,273	−1.1
Ichihara	277,080	7.5
Ichikawa	440,527	0.9
Kamagaya	99,700	4.9
Kamogawa	31,110	−0.4
Kashiwa	317,752	4.2
Katsuura	24,329	−4.0
Kimitsu	93,215	4.5
Kisarazu	123,499	0.1
Matsudo	461,489	1.2
Mobara	91,670	9.9
Nagareyama	146,250	4.4
Narashino	152,884	0.9
Narita	91,472	5.5
Noda	119,791	4.6
Sakura	162,624	12.4
Sawara	49,916	0.8
Sodegaura	57,575	9.0

	Population 1995	% Change 1990–95
Tateyama	52,879	−3.1
Togane	54,522	20.7
Urayasu	123,660	6.9
Yachimata	65,219	30.3
Yachiyo	154,507	4.0
Yokaichiba	33,255	2.9
Yotsukaido	79,486	10.2
Ehime	**1,507,000**	**−0.6**
Hojo	29,041	−1.3
Imabari	120,215	−2.4
Iyo	30,270	1.6
Iyomishima	37,588	−2.0
Kawanoe	38,560	−1.1
Matsuyama	460,870	4.0
Niihama	127,916	−1.0
Ozu	38,933	−2.3
Saijo	57,110	0.5
Toyo	33,469	−0.8
Uwajima	65,458	−3.8
Yawatahama	35,906	−6.9
Fukui	**827,000**	**0.4**
Fukui	255,601	1.1
Katsuyama	29,163	−2.2
Obama	33,496	−0.8
Ono	40,247	−1.8
Sabae	62,892	1.0
Takefu	71,110	1.3
Tsuruga	67,210	−1.2
Fukuoka	**4,933,000**	**2.5**
Amagi	42,703	−0.8
Buzen	29,718	−4.4
Chikugo	45,288	3.3
Chikushino	81,988	16.6
Dazaifu	64,914	4.0
Fukuoka	1,284,741	3.9
Iizuka	83,412	0.3
Kasuga	99,207	11.8
Kitakyushu	1,019,562	−0.7
Kurume	234,433	2.7
Maebaru	57,946	15.3
Munakata	76,936	12.7
Nakama	49,354	0.3
Nogata	61,623	−1.5
Ogori	50,612	7.4
Okawa	43,341	−5.2
Omuta	145,085	−3.6
Onojo	82,900	10.2
Tagawa	56,546	−2.0
Yamada	12,679	−4.4
Yame	39,817	0.0
Yanagawa	43,244	−1.2
Yukuhashi	67,834	3.2
Fukushima	**2,133,000**	**1.4**
Aizuwakamatsu	119,632	0.5
Fukushima	285,745	3.0
Haramachi	50,087	2.1
Iwaki	360,497	1.3
Kitakata	37,532	0.7
Koriyama	326,831	3.9
Nihommatsu	35,966	3.0
Shirakawa	46,543	2.0
Soma	39,447	0.8
Sukagawa	64,303	5.9
Gifu	**2,100,000**	**1.6**
Ena	35,687	1.9
Gifu	407,145	−0.8
Hashima	63,963	4.1
Kakamigahara	131,955	1.8
Kani	86,368	7.9
Mino	25,969	−0.2
Minokamo	46,062	7.1
Mizunami	42,003	2.4
Nakatsugawa	54,819	2.0
Ogaki	149,758	1.0
Seki	71,916	5.2
Tajimi	101,274	7.7
Takayama	66,139	1.4
Toki	65,632	1.1
Gumma	**2,004,000**	**1.9**
Annaka	47,079	3.4

Japan continued

	Population 1995	% Change 1990–95
Fujioka	62,665	2.8
Isesaki	120,235	3.7
Kiryu	120,375	–4.8
Maebashi	284,780	–0.5
Numata	47,207	0.8
Ota	143,067	2.3
Shibukawa	49,165	0.2
Takasaki	238,132	0.7
Tatebayashi	76,853	0.8
Tomioka	49,271	0.5
Hiroshima	**2,882,000**	**1.1**
Fuchu	43,687	–4.5
Fukuyama	374,510	2.4
Hatsukaichi	71,228	12.3
Higashihiroshima	113,935	20.9
Hiroshima	1,108,868	2.1
Innoshima	30,300	–7.2
Kure	209,477	–3.3
Mihara	83,769	–2.0
Miyoshi	39,843	1.0
Onomichi	93,757	–3.4
Otake	32,848	–1.2
Shobara	22,377	–1.3
Takehara	33,450	–3.8
Hokkaido	**5,692,000**	**0.9**
Abashiri	44,177	–0.5
Akabira	17,350	–10.6
Asahikawa	360,569	0.4
Ashibetsu	22,931	–8.6
Bibai	33,434	–5.0
Chitose	84,860	7.5
Date	34,429	–0.2
Ebetsu	115,491	18.8
Eniwa	62,349	12.1
Fukagawa	28,770	–6.2
Furano	26,046	–2.3
Hakodate	298,868	–2.7
Iwamizawa	85,125	5.9
Kitami	110,449	3.0
Kushiro	199,325	–3.1
Mikasa	15,115	–11.3
Mombetsu	30,137	–3.0
Muroran	109,767	–6.9
Nayoro	28,750	–6.6
Nemuro	34,934	–5.4
Noboribetsu	56,892	2.4
Obihiro	171,714	2.6
Otaru	157,024	–3.8
Rumoi	30,062	–7.3
Sapporo	1,756,968	5.1
Shibetsu	24,291	–5.7
Sunagawa	21,722	–6.2
Takikawa	48,418	–2.4
Tomakomai	169,324	5.7
Utashinai	6,867	–17.1
Wakkanai	45,754	–5.1
Yubari	17,110	–18.4
Hyogo	**5,402,000**	**–0.1**
Aioi	36,103	–2.1
Akashi	287,613	6.2
Ako	51,426	0.6
Amagasaki	488,574	–2.1
Ashiya	75,027	–14.3
Himeji	470,986	3.7
Itami	188,436	1.2
Kakogawa	260,558	8.7
Kasai	51,708	–0.1
Kawanishi	144,539	2.3
Kobe	1,423,830	–3.6
Miki	78,654	2.8
Nishinomiya	390,388	–8.6
Nishiwaki	38,257	0.1
Ono	48,214	4.8
Sanda	96,278	49.1
Sumoto	42,373	–3.3
Takarazuka	202,547	0.3
Takasago	97,632	4.7
Tatsuno	40,607	–0.6
Toyooka	47,742	1.1
Ibaraki	**2,956,000**	**3.9**
Hitachi	199,241	–1.4

	Population 1995	% Change 1990–95
Hitachinaka	146,753	3.1
Hitachiota	39,545	5.1
Ishioka	52,712	4.1
Iwai	44,325	2.8
Kasama	30,336	–1.5
Kashima	60,671	2.7
Kitaibaraki	52,074	1.9
Koga	59,086	1.5
Mito	246,350	0.3
Mitsukaido	42,689	0.8
Ryugasaki	69,161	20.8
Shimodate	66,062	0.1
Shimotsuma	36,113	7.1
Takahagi	35,604	0.8
Toride	84,475	3.4
Tsuchiura	132,246	3.7
Tsukuba	156,009	8.8
Ushiku	66,340	9.3
Yuki	53,776	0.9
Ishikawa	**1,180,000**	**1.3**
Hakui	26,502	–3.7
Kaga	69,394	0.3
Kanazawa	453,977	2.5
Komatsu	107,964	1.8
Matto	62,990	8.3
Nanao	49,720	–0.8
Suzu	21,580	–8.1
Wajima	28,232	–6.4
Iwate	**1,420,000**	**0.2**
Esashi	34,117	–0.9
Hanamaki	71,949	2.0
Ichinoseki	63,476	2.4
Kamaishi	49,447	–5.8
Kitakami	87,970	6.1
Kuji	37,524	–3.1
Miyako	56,389	–3.6
Mizusawa	60,026	3,2
Morioka	286,478	2.9
Ninohe	28,018	–2.9
Ofunato	37,264	–1.6
Rikuzentakata	26,129	–4.1
Tono	28,173	–2.7
Kagawa	**1,027,000**	**0.4**
Kanonji	45,108	–0.9
Marugame	78,088	3.3
Sakaide	61,352	–4.0
Takamatsu	330,997	0.4
Zentsuji	37,361	–2.8
Kagoshima	**1,794,000**	**–0.2**
Akune	27,501	–1.3
Ibusuki	31,473	–1.7
Izumi	40,107	1.0
Kagoshima	546,294	1.8
Kanoya	79,502	2.4
Kaseda	24,478	–2.4
Kokubu	50,048	7.5
Kushikino	28,341	–3.6
Makurazaki	27,639	–4.0
Naze	44,343	–4.2
Nishinoomote	19,821	–5.4
Okuchi	24,753	–3.7
Sendai	73,132	1.9
Tarumizu	20,931	–6.0
Kanagawa	**8,246,000**	**3.3**
Atsugi	208,622	5.7
Ayase	80,679	3.5
Chigasaki	212,944	5.6
Ebina	113,416	7.2
Fujisawa	368,636	5.2
Hadano	164,703	5.8
Hiratsuka	253,818	3.2
Isehara	98,119	9.5
Kamakura	170,319	–2.3
Kawasaki	1,202,811	2.5
Minamiashigara	43,597	2.3
Miura	54,155	3.3
Odawara	200,092	3.5
Sagamihara	570,594	7.3
Yamato	203,920	4.6

	Population 1995	% Change 1990–95
Yokohama	3,307,408	2.7
Yokosuka	432,202	–0.3
Zama	118,146	5.4
Zushi	56,577	–0.2
Kochi	**817,000**	**–1.0**
Aki	22,378	–5.7
Kochi	322,077	1.6
Muroto	21,430	–8.1
Nakamura	34,927	–2.5
Nankoku	48,189	2.9
Sukumo	25,919	0.4
Susaki	28,743	–5.1
Tosa	30,723	–2.7
Tosashimizu	19,582	–7.6
Kumamoto	**1,860,000**	**1.1**
Arao	57,387	–3.6
Hitoyoshi	39,372	–2.0
Hondo	41,153	–0.2
Kikuchi	27,987	–0.6
Kumamoto	650,322	3.8
Minamata	32,842	–5.1
Tamana	45,339	0.1
Ushibuka	20,098	–6.3
Uto	35,011	4.9
Yamaga	33,558	0.3
Yatsushiro	107,708	–0.4
Kyoto	**2,629,000**	**1.0**
Ayabe	39,981	–1.5
Fukuchiyama	66,758	0.4
Joyo	85,398	0.7
Kameoka	92,399	8.3
Kyoto	1,463,601	0.2
Maizuru	94,797	–1.6
Miyazu	24,937	–5.7
Muko	53,289	0.7
Nagaokakyo	78,700	2.0
Uji	184,829	4.4
Yawata	75,775	0.0
Mie	**1,842,000**	**2.7**
Hisai	40,148	1.2
Ise	102,631	–1.5
Kameyama	38,630	2.7
Kumano	22,257	–6.2
Kuwana	103,049	5.2
Matsusaka	122,449	3.1
Nabari	79,914	15.9
Owase	25,258	–6.8
Suzuka	179,795	3.3
Toba	26,806	–1.9
Tsu	163,309	3.9
Ueno	60,987	1.2
Yokkaichi	285,777	4.2
Miyagi	**2,329,000**	**3.6**
Furukawa	69,183	7.7
Ishinomaki	121,209	–0.6
Iwanuma	40,075	5.2
Kakuda	35,317	–0.3
Kesennuma	63,001	–3.9
Natori	61,993	15.4
Sendai	971,263	5.8
Shiogama	63,567	2.5
Shiroishi	41,852	–0.4
Tagajo	60,625	3.7
Miyazaki	**1,176,000**	**0.6**
Ebino	25,874	–3.5
Hyuga	58,801	0.6
Kobayashi	40,841	–0.5
Kushima	25,243	–5.6
Miyakonojo	132,712	2.0
Miyazaki	300,054	4.4
Nichinan	47,596	–3.2
Nobeoka	126,628	–3.1
Saito	36,331	–2.4
Nagano	**2,194,000**	**1.7**
Chino	52,810	5.5

	Population 1995	% Change 1990–95
Iida	106,774	0.3
Iiyama	27,423	–2.5
Ina	62,245	3.6
Komagane	33,601	2.5
Komoro	45,710	1.8
Koshoku	38,294	3.7
Matsumoto	205,532	2.4
Nagano	358,512	3.3
Nakano	42,292	3.2
Okaya	58,056	–3.0
Omachi	31,020	–1.8
Saku	64,207	3.6
Shiojiri	60,481	5.5
Suwa	52,103	–0.7
Suzuka	53,842	0.3
Ueda	123,282	3.2
Nagasaki	**1,545,000**	**–1.1**
Fukue	28,772	–3.2
Hirado	25,241	–6.0
Isahaya	93,106	2.7
Matsuura	23,707	–2.0
Nagasaki	438,724	–1.3
Omura	79,284	8.0
Sasebo	244,879	0.1
Shimabara	40,780	–9.0
Nara	**1,431,000**	**4.0**
Gojo	35,735	3.4
Gose	36,120	–1.4
Ikoma	106,727	7.2
Kashibashi	56,740	7.4
Kashihara	121,987	5.6
Nara	359,234	2.8
Sakurai	63,210	4.9
Tenri	74,188	7.8
Yamatokoriyama	95,152	2.4
Yamatotakada	73,803	8.2
Niigata	**2,488,000**	**0.6**
Arai	28,118	–0.7
Gosen	39,116	–0.7
Itoigawa	32,932	–3.3
Joetsu	132,202	1.6
Kamo	33,801	–3.0
Kashiwazaki	91,231	3.3
Mitsuke	43,760	1.5
Murakami	31,943	–0.7
Nagaoka	190,470	2.4
Niigata	494,785	1.8
Niitsu	65,572	2.5
Ojiya	42,494	–2.2
Ryotsu	18,430	–5.2
Sanjo	85,691	–0.2
Shibata	80,500	3.0
Shirone	38,653	8.0
Tochio	26,390	–5.1
Tokamachi	44,729	–3.3
Toyosaka	48,066	4.6
Tsubame	43,592	–0.7
Oita	**1,231,000**	**–0.5**
Beppu	128,251	–1.6
Bungotakada	19,130	–4.8
Hita	63,849	–1.3
Kitsuki	22,112	0.8
Nakatsu	67,117	1.1
Oita	426,981	4.5
Saiki	51,377	–1.8
Taketa	18,746	–7.0
Tsukumi	24,848	–7.3
Usa	50,031	–1.6
Usuki	36,614	–3.3
Okayama	**1,951,000**	**1.3**
Bizen	30,391	–2.4
Ibara	35,079	–2.8
Kasaoka	60,479	1.4
Kurashiki	422,824	2.0
Niimi	25,513	–6.5
Okayama	616,056	3.8
Soja	56,101	6.4

	Population 1995	% Change 1990–95
Takahashi	26,071	0.3
Tamano	71,381	-2.5
Tsuyama	91,168	2.0
Okinawa	**1,274,000**	**4.2**
Ginowan	82,891	9.2
Gushikawa	57,129	5.8
Hirara	33,092	1.5
Ishigaki	41,780	1.3
Ishikawa	21,824	5.3
Itoman	53,498	7.8
Nago	53,960	5.5
Naha	301,928	-1.0
Okinawa	115,342	9.0
Urasoe	96,007	6.7
Osaka	**8,797,000**	**0.7**
Daito	128,840	1.9
Fujidera	66,985	1.6
Habikino	117,728	2.3
Hannan	55,624	2.9
Higashiosaka	517,228	-0.2
Hirakata	400,130	2.4
Ibaraki	258,237	1.6
Ikeda	104,292	0.1
Izumi	157,301	7.6
zumiotsu	68,839	2.7
Izumisano	92,595	4.2
Kadoma	140,507	-1.3
Kaizuka	84,653	6.8
Kashiwara	80,302	4.5
Katano	72,398	10.9
Kawachinagano	117,082	7.6
Kishiwada	194,820	3.3
Matsubara	134,457	-1.1
Minoo	127,540	4.4
Moriguchi	157,290	-0.1
Neyagawa	258,440	0.7
Osaka	2,602,352	-0.8
Osakasayama	57,647	6.1
Sakai	802,965	-0.6
Sennan	61,686	2.7
Settsu	87,329	-0.1
Shijonawate	53,764	7.5
Suita	342,794	-0.7
Takaishi	64,290	-1.2
Takatsuki	362,259	0.7
Tondabayashi	121,690	10.2
Toyonaka	398,912	-2.7
Yao	276,658	-0.3
Saga	**884,000**	**0.7**
Imari	60,350	-0.9
Karatsu	79,581	0.5
Kashima	34,085	-0.7
Saga	171,219	0.7
Takeo	35,059	1.6
Taku	24,507	-2.6
Tosu	57,413	2.7
Saitama	**6,759,000**	**5.5**
Ageo	206,099	5.7
Asaka	110,793	6.9
Chichibu	60,798	-0.2
Fujimi	96,957	2.2
Fukaya	100,271	6.7
Gyoda	86,171	3.6
Hanno	80,535	10.0
Hanyu	56,037	4.2
Hasuda	63,917	7.1
Hatogaya	55,766	-1.2
Hidaka	54,886	3.2
Higashimatsuyama	93,347	10.6
Honjo	60,807	2.9
Iruma	144,401	5.0
Iwatsuki	109,551	2.9
Kamifukuoka	56,782	-3.4
Kasukabe	200,130	6.0
Kawagoe	323,345	6.1
Kawaguchi	448,801	2.3
Kazo	66,822	18.5
Kitamoto	69,931	9.4
Konosu	80,354	10.9
Koshigaya	298,285	4.6
Kuki	72,633	8.6

	Population 1995	% Change 1990–95
Kumagaya	156,395	2.8
Misato	133,601	4.1
Niiza	144,735	4.2
Okegawa	73,085	5.9
Omiya	433,768	7.4
Sakado	98,209	2.6
Satte	58,174	7.1
Sayama	162,232	3.1
Shiki	64,430	1.5
Soka	217,912	5.7
Toda	97,569	11.4
Tokorozawa	320,448	5.7
Tsurugashima	66,185	4.9
Urawa	453,300	8.4
Wako	62,590	10.0
Warabi	72,012	-2.2
Yashio	75,315	3.9
Yono	81,923	3.6
Shiga	**1,287,000**	**5.3**
Hikone	103,508	4.0
Kusatu	101,827	7.4
Moriyama	61,859	5.6
Nagahama	57,083	2.9
Omihachiman	67,187	1.7
Otsu	276,331	6.3
Yokaichi	42,909	5.2
Shimane	**771,000**	**-1.2**
Gotsu	26,959	-2.8
Hamada	48,516	-1.3
Hirata	29,708	-3.0
Izumo	84,866	2.6
Masuda	51,560	-1.6
Matsue	147,414	3.1
Oda	35,335	-4.3
Yasugi	31,638	-2.5
Shizuoka	**3,738,000**	**1.8**
Atami	45,610	-3.6
Fuji	229,189	3.0
Fujieda	124,822	4.2
Fujinomiya	119,536	2.1
Fukuroi	57,092	7.4
Gotemba	81,803	2.8
Hamakita	83,810	3.3
Hamamatsu	561,568	2.5
Ito	72,285	1.5
Iwata	85,120	1.9
Kakegawa	76,839	5.6
Kosai	43,762	1.6
Mishima	107,890	2.3
Numazu	212,245	0.2
Shimada	75,018	1.6
Shimizu	240,172	-0.6
Shimoda	29,103	-3.3
Shizuoka	474,089	0.4
Susono	49,729	1.4
Tenryu	24,113	-1.7
Yaizu	115,932	3.3
Tochigi	**1,985,000**	**2.5**
Ashikaga	165,830	-1.1
Imaichi	60,813	8.6
Kanuma	93,053	3.3
Kuroiso	56,275	7.5
Mooka	63,342	2.6
Nikko	18,874	-6.2
Otawara	53,683	2.2
Oyama	150,114	5.5
Sano	84,069	0.7
Tochigi	85,135	-1.3
Utsunomiya	435,446	2.0
Yaita	36,650	2.9
Tokushima	**832,000**	**0.1**
Anan	57,666	-2.3
Komatsushima	43,353	0.4
Naruto	64,923	0.5
Tokushima	268,712	2.0
Tokyo	**11,772,000**	**-0.7**
Akiruno	75,334	4.7

	Population 1995	% Change 1990–95
Akishima	107,289	1.8
Chofu	198,524	0.4
Fuchu	216,202	3.3
Fussa	61,469	5.9
Hachioji	503,320	7.9
Hamura	55,099	5.8
Higashikurume	111,076	-2.4
Higashimurayama	135,115	0.8
Higashiyamato	76,355	1.6
Hino	166,429	0.3
Hoya	100,259	5.4
Inagi	62,801	7.1
Kiyose	67,384	-0.2
Kodaira	173,032	5.5
Koganei	109,275	3.2
Kokubunji	105,781	4.8
Komae	74,649	0.6
Kunitachi	66,717	1.3
Machida	360,418	3.3
Mitaka	165,739	0.1
Musashimurayama	67,000	2.2
Musashino	135,026	-2.9
Ome	137,208	8.9
Tachikawa	157,892	3.3
Tama	148,127	2.5
Tanashi	74,812	-0.4
Tokyo	7,966,195	-2.4
Tottori	**615,000**	**-0.1**
Kurayoshi	51,108	-1.4
Sakaiminato	37,361	0.2
Tottori	146,336	2.7
Yonago	134,769	2.5
Toyama	**1,123,000**	**0.3**
Himi	58,786	-3.3
Kurobe	36,413	-0.2
Namerikawa	31,837	3.0
Oyabe	35,785	-1.6
Shimminato	38,490	-2.4
Takaoka	173,612	-1.1
Tonami	38,525	3.9
Toyama	325,303	1.3
Uozu	48,315	-2.4
Wakayama	**1,080,000**	**0.6**
Arida	34,283	-1.5
Gobo	28,510	-2.1
Hashimoto	53,472	14.8
Kainan	47,191	-2.9
Shingu	34,134	-5.0
Tanabe	70,238	0.5
Wakayama	393,951	-0.7
Yamagata	**1,257,000**	**-0.1**
Higashine	43,208	1.1
Kaminoyama	38,049	-0.5
Murayama	30,506	-3.4
Nagai	32,726	-1.6
Nanyo	36,810	-0.5
Obanazawa	23,129	-3.3
Sagae	42,805	1.7
Sakata	101,224	0.4
Shinjo	42,897	-0.5
Tendo	60,627	5.7
Tsuruoka	100,538	0.6
Yamagata	254,485	2.0
Yonezawa	95,590	0.9
Yamaguchi	**1,556,000**	**-1.1**
Hagi	48,312	-4.6
Hikari	46,830	-1.6
Hofu	118,802	1.0
Iwakuni	107,386	-2.0
Kudamatsu	53,472	0.8
Mine	19,001	-3.3
Nagato	25,118	-3.8
Onoda	45,946	-1.2
Shimonoseki	259,791	-1.1
Shinnanyo	32,336	-2.0
Tokuyama	108,675	-2.0
Ube	175,113	0.0
Yamaguchi	135,581	4.7
Yanai	35,071	-3.5

	Population 1995	% Change 1990–95
Yamanashi	**882,000**	**3.4**
Enzan	27,117	2.1
Fujiyoshida	54,691	-0.2
Kofu	201,123	0.2
Nirasaki	32,098	7.8
Otsuki	35,201	0.7
Tsuru	35,399	4.4
Yamanashi	31,825	2.3

Morocco

Census 2 September 1994. Total population: 26,073,717
Regions are given in bold and are followed by figures for the provinces.

	Population 1994	Area km	Density per km
MOROCCO	**26,073,717**	**710,850**	**36.7**
Centre	**6,931,418**	**41,500**	**167.0**
Azilal	454,914	10,050	45.3
Beni-Mellal	869,748	7,075	122.9
Ben Slimane	213,398	2,760	77.3
Ain Chock-Hay Hassani	516,261		
Ain Sebaa-Hay Mohammedi	520,993		
Ben M'sick-Sidi Othmane	704,365		
Casablanca-Anfa	523,279	} 1,615	1,915.9
Al Fida-Derb-Sultan	386,700		
Sidi Bernoussi-Zenata	268,586		
Mechouar de Casablanca	3,956		
Mohammedia	170,063		
El Jadida	970,894	6,000	161.8
Khouribga	480,839	4,250	113.1
Settat	847,422	9,750	86.9
Centre North	**3,042,310**	**43,950**	**69.2**
Al Hoceima	382,972	3,550	107.9
Boulemane	161,622	14,395	11.2
Fes El Jadid-Dar Dbibagh	256,340		
Fes-Medina	284,822	} 5,400	215.0
Zouagha-Moulay Yacoub	382,594		
Sefrou	237,095		
Taounate	628,840	5,585	112.6
Taza	708,025	15,020	47.1
Centre South	**1,903,790**	**79,210**	**24.0**
Errachidia	522,117	59,585	8.8
Ifrane	127,677	3,310	38.6
Khenifra	465,061	12,320	37.7
Meknes-El Menzeh	293,525		
Al Ismailia	314,916	} 3,995	197.5
El Hajeb	180,494		
Eastern	**1,768,691**	**82,820**	**21.4**
Figuig	117,011	55,990	2.1
Nador	683,914	6,130	111.6
Oujda-Angad	419,063		
Berkane-Taourirt	399,017	} 20,700	46.8
Jerada	149,686		
North West	**5,646,716**	**29,955**	**188.5**
Chefchaouen	439,303	4,350	101.0
Kenitra	979,210	4,745	206.4
Khemisset	485,541	8,305	58.5
Rabat	623,457		
Sale	631,803	} 1,275	1,176.5
Skhirate-Temara	244,801		
Sidi Kacem	645,872	4,060	159.1
Tanger	627,963	1,195	525.5
Tetouan	537,290	} 6,025	160.8
Larache	431,476		
South	**3,234,024**	**394,970**	**8.2**
Agadir-Ida-Tanane	365,965		
Chtouka-Ait Baha	240,092	} 5,910	152.1
Inezgane-Ait Melloul	292,799		
Assa-Zag	21,848		
Guelmim	147,124	28,750	5.9
Boujdour*	21,691	100,120	0.2
Es-Semara*	39,726	61,760	0.6
Laayoune*	153,978	39,360	3.9
Ouarzazate	694,884	41,550	16.7
Oued-Ed-Dahab*	36,751	50,880	0.7
Tan-Tan	58,079	17,295	3.4
Taroudannt	693,968	16,460	42.2
Tata	119,298	25,925	4.6
Tiznit	347,821	6,960	50.0
Tensift	**3,546,768**	**38,445**	**92.3**
El Kalaa des Sraghna	682,428	10,070	67.8
Essaouira	433,681	6,335	68.5
Marrakech-Menara	432,547		
Marrakech-Medina	189,367		
Sidi-Youssef-Ben-Ali	239,291	} 14,755	109.0
Chichaoua	311,800		
Al Haouz	435,090		
Safi	822,564	7,285	112.9

* Western Sahara. Morocco's administration is disputed by the United Nations.

New Zealand

Census 5 March 1996
Total population: 3,681,546
Figures for cities and districts are listed below. The bottom table gives urban area figures.

	Population 1996	% change 1991–96	% change 1986–91
NEW ZEALAND	**3,681,546**	**7.2**	**3.9**
Auckland	354,532	12.3	4.7
Carterton	6,791	−1.8	9.1
Central Hawke's Bay	13,001	3.2	−3.7
Christchurch	315,118	7.6	2.2
Dunedin	119,612	2.6	2.1
Far North	57,079	10.7	7.9
Franklin	48,285	14.4	13.2
Gisborne	45,962	3.6	−3.1
Hamilton	109,043	7.5	6.4
Hastings	66,682	3.1	0.5
Hauraki	17,263	2.0	6.4
Horowhenua	29,770	1.0	2.1
Invercargill	53,243	−5.2	−1.6
Kaipara	17,584	1.5	0.7
Kapiti Coast	38,687	9.6	18.7
Kawerau	7,754	−4.7	−2.1
Lower Hutt	95,390	0.9	−0.8
Manawatu	27,970	2.9	5.3
Manukau	254,603	12.6	9.4
Masterton	23,044	0.4	2.0
Matamata-Piako	29,655	0.8	0.1
Napier	54,224	5.0	−1.7
Nelson	42,034	10.8	5.2
New Plymouth	68,169	0.3	1.5
North Shore	171,494	12.7	5.5
Opotiki	9,607	10.7	6.7
Otorohanga	9,822	6.4	−0.5
Palmerston North	73,080	3.9	5.2
Papakura	39,298	7.5	11.4
Porirua	46,393	−0.4	2.0
Rangitikei	16,531	−0.9	−5.8
Rodney	67,261	20.6	21.6
Rotorua	68,990	6.0	3.5
Ruapehu	18,329	1.2	−7.0
South Taranaki	28,801	−2.4	−4.1
South Waikato	24,671	−5.8	−7.5
South Wairarapa	8,839	−2.2	3.3
Stratford	9,729	−1.2	−2.4
Tararua	18,742	−3.8	−1.9
Taupo	33,778	10.0	5.8
Tauranga	78,318	16.3	12.1
Thames-Coromandel	27,715	10.7	15.3
Upper Hutt	36,738	−1.0	−0.5
Waikato	39,105	4.1	2.8
Waipa	39,621	7.0	4.3
Wairoa	10,084	−2.8	−2.9
Waitakere	154,386	12.9	11.5
Waitomo	9,991	−0.8	−4.2
Wanganui	45,319	0.5	2.4
Wellington	159,845	6.3	0.3
Western Bay of Plenty	35,292	17.1	12.0
Whakatane	33,454	4.2	2.9
Whangerei	67,202	7.3	0.2

Urban Areas

Ashburton	15,598	2.8	−0.4
Auckland	997,940	11.3	7.8
Blenheim	25,875	9.5	4.2
Christchurch	331,443	7.9	2.4
Dunedin	112,279	2.5	1.8
Feilding	13,715	2.6	4.4
Gisborne	32,653	3.7	−2.3
Gore	10,296	−6.4	−2.2
Greymouth	10,633	0.4	−6.0
Hamilton	159,315	6.7	6.1
Hawera	11,317	1.5	−2.0
Invercargill	49,306	−5.2	−1.1
Kapiti	30,004	9.6	18.0
Levin	19,046	0.4	0.0
Masterton	19,954	−0.3	0.4
Napier-Hastings	113,719	3.1	−0.5
Nelson	52,348	10.5	6.3
New Plymouth	49,079	1.2	2.2
Oamaru	13,695	−1.0	−3.0
Palmerston North	73,862	4.1	5.3
Pukekohe	16,604	10.6	7.8
Rotorua	56,928	6.0	3.3
Taupo	21,044	14.6	4.4
Tauranga	82,832	17.0	12.2
Timaru	27,521	−0.4	−3.6
Tokoroa	15,226	−8.5	−8.6
Wanganui	41,320	0.3	1.1
Wellington	335,468	2.9	0.0
Whakatane	17,713	5.4	5.3
Whangerei	45,785	3.6	−0.3

Poland

Official population estimate 30 November 1995. Total population: 38,587,596

The provinces (voivodships) are given in bold, with their capitals in italics. All other cities with a population of more than 20,000 are listed alphabetically.

	Population 1995
POLAND	**38,587,596**
Bialskopodlaskie	**309,394**
Biala Podlaska	*56,271*
Bialostockie	**700,088**
Bialystok	*277,768*
Bielsk Podlaski	27,501
Hajnowka	24,299
Bielskie	**916,560**
Andrychow	23,078
Bielsko-Biala	*180,657*
Cieszyn	37,264
Oswiecim	44,385
Zywiec	32,331
Bydgoskie	**1,130,880**
Bydgoszcz	*385,764*
Chojnice	39,752
Inowroclaw	79,363
Naklo nad Notecia	20,123
Swiecie	26,952
Chelmskie	**249,890**
Chelm	*69,070*
Krasnystaw	20,610
Chiechanówskie	**436,525**
Chiechanów	*46,582*
Dzialdowo	20,748
Mlawa	29,839
Plonsk	22,704
Czestochowskie	**782,061**
Czestochowa	*259,538*
Lubliniec	26,886
Myszkow	33,969
Elblaskie	**491,079**
Elblag	*128,706*
Kwidzyn	39,257
Malbork	40,256
Gdanskie	**1,452,227**
Gdansk	*462,830*
Gdynia	251,400
Koscierzyna	23,111
Pruszcz Gdanski	21,232
Rumia	39,981
Sopot	43,699
Starogard Gdanski	50,572
Tczew	60,628
Wejherowo	47,302
Gorzówskie	**509,868**
Gorzów Wielkopolski	*124,932*
Miedzyrzecz	20,321
Jeleniogorskie	**524,171**
Boleslawiec	44,437
Jelenia Góra	*93,513*
Kamienna Góra	23,645
Luban	24,403
Zgorzelec	36,794
Kaliskie	**721,540**
Jarocin	25,745
Kalisz	*106,842*
Krotoszyn	28,871
Ostrów Wielkopolski	74,712
Katowickie	**3,933,006**
Bedzin	63,110
Bierun	22,120
Bytom	227,606

	Population 1995
Chorzów	125,826
Chrzanów	42,127
Czechowice-Dziedzice	35,620
Czeladz	36,558
Czerwionka-Leszczyny	30,050
Dabrowa Górnicza	130,913
Gliwice	214,012
Jastrzebie-Zdrój	103,452
Jaworzno	98,467
Katowice	354,218
Knurów	44,236
Laziska Gorne	23,039
Mikolów	38,905
Myslowice	79,960
Olkusz	40,489
Piekary Slaskie	67,153
Pszczyna	34,568
Pyskowice	21,933
Racibórz	65,116
Ruda Slaska	166,337
Rybnik	144,311
Rydultowy	24,098
Siemianowice Slaskie	78,099
Sosnowiec	248,986
Swietochlowice	59,632
Tarnowskie Góry	67,227
Trzebinia	20,042
Tychy	133,880
Wodzislaw Slaski	68,612
Zabrze	201,581
Zawiercie	56,297
Zory	66,332
Kieleckie	**1,136,046**
Kielce	*213,701*
Konskie	22,332
Ostrowiec Swietokrzyski	79,179
Skarzysko-Kamienna	51,445
Starachowice	57,487
Koninskie	**479,090**
Kolo	23,858
Konin	*82,655*
Turek	30,701
Koszalinskie	**520,914**
Bialograd	25,093
Kolobrzeg	46,993
Koszalin	*111,667*
Szczecinek	*42,299*
Krakówskie	**1,239,755**
Kraków	*745,435*
Skawina	24,116
Krosnienskie	**506,025**
Jaslo	38,864
Krosno	*49,416*
Sanok	41,434
Legnickie	**523,125**
Glogów	74,154
Jawor	25,569
Legnica	*107,968*
Lubin	83,484
Polkowice	21,596
Leszczynskie	**396,627**
Gostyn	20,614
Koscian	24,562
Leszno	*61,295*
Rawicz	21,535
Lubelskie	**1,025,800**
Krasnik	37,501
Leczna	21,879
Lubartow	23,473
Lublin	*353,300*
Pulawy	54,347
Swidnik	40,340
Lomzynskie	**353,721**
Grajewo	22,385
Lomza	*62,974*
Zambrow	23,580
Lódzkie	**1,118,248**
Aleksandrow Lodzki	20,429
Lódz	*825,615*

	Population 1995
Ozorkow	21,905
Pabianice	75,720
Zgierz	59,083
Nowosadeckie	**730,265**
Nowy Sacz	*82,070*
Nowy Targ	33,987
Zakopane	29,956
Olsztynskie	**770,444**
Bartoszyce	26,078
Ilawa	32,640
Ketrzyn	30,347
Mragowo	22,540
Ostróda	35,010
Olsztyn	*167,403*
Szczytno	27,482
Opolskie	**1,026,580**
Brzeg	39,942
Kedzierzyn-Kozle	70,749
Kluczbork	26,944
Krapkowice	20,115
Nysa	49,027
Opole	*130,570*
Prudnik	24,337
Strzelce Opolskie	21,913
Ostroleckie	**407,863**
Ostroleka	*53,685*
Ostrow Mazowiecka	21,998
Wyszkow	25,269
Pilskie	**492,826**
Chodziez	20,395
Pila	*75,737*
Wagrowiec	24,113
Walcz	27,041
Piotrkówskie	**644,105**
Belchatów	59,869
Opoczno	21,883
Piotrków Trybunalski	*81,131*
Radomskow	50,996
Tomaszów Mazowiecki	69,950
Plockie	**521,704**
Gostynin	20,197
Kutno	50,956
Plock	*126,931*
Poznanskie	**1,352,057**
Gniezno	70,977
Lubon	20,693
Poznan	*581,772*
Swarzedz	26,106
Srem	29,847
Sroda Wielkopolska	21,363
Wrzesnia	28,640
Przemyskie	**414,072**
Jaroslaw	41,834
Przemysl	*68,866*
Radomskie	**763,027**
Kozienice	21,534
Pionki	22,079
Radom	*232,261*
Rzeszówskie	**744,969**
Rzeszów	*160,342*
Mielec	64,386
Siedleckie	**661,590**
Luków	31,980
Minsk Mazowiecki	34,965
Siedlce	*74,136*
Sieradzkie	**412,326**
Lask	20,167
Sieradz	*44,724*
Wielun	25,486
Zdunska Wola	45,887

	Population 1995
Skierniewickie	**423,616**
Lowicz	31,522
Skierniewice	*47,910*
Sochaczew	39,662
Zyrardow	43,481
Slupskie	**425,403**
Lebork	36,339
Slupsk	*102,727*
Suwalskie	**485,175**
Augustow	29,570
Elk	55,064
Gizycko	30,554
Suwalki	*66,198*
Szczecinskie	**989,674**
Goleniów	22,184
Gryfino	22,058
Police	34,544
Stargard Szczecinski	72,998
Swinoujscie	43,175
Szczecin	*419,272*
Tarnobrzeskie	**609,097**
Sandomierz	27,010
Stalowa Wola	71,905
Tarnobrzeg	*50,656*
Tarnówskie	**691,648**
Bochnia	29,612
Debica	48,655
Tarnów	*121,521*
Torunskie	**670,310**
Brodnica	27,423
Chelmno	22,018
Grudziadz	102,948
Torun	*204,348*
Walbrzyskie	**740,072**
Bielawa	34,576
Dzierzoniów	38,289
Klodzko	30,918
Nowa Ruda	27,233
Swidnica	64,790
Swiebodzice	24,687
Walbrzych	*139,622*
Warszawskie	**2,415,514**
Grodzisk Mazowiecki	24,913
Legionowo	50,589
Nowy Dwor Mazowiecki	27,225
Otwock	44,042
Piaseczno	25,215
Piastow	23,689
Pruszkow	53,027
Warszawa (Warsaw)	*1,638,277*
Wolomin	36,505
Wloclawskie	**434,743**
Wloclawek	*123,143*
Wroclawskie	**1,137,260**
Olawa	31,834
Olesnica	38,921
Wroclaw	*642,671*
Zamojskie	**493,506**
Bilgoraj	26,360
Hrubieszow	20,167
Tomaszow Lubelski	21,198
Zamosc	*66,253*
Zielonogórskie	**673,110**
Nowa Sól	43,227
Swiebodzin	22,686
Zagan	28,258
Zary	40,853
Zielona Góra	*116,073*

Agriculture

Land use

	Land area '000 sq km	Arable land %	Permanent crops %	Permanent grassland %	Forest %	Other land %	Irrigated land '000 sq km
Afghanistan	652	12.1	0.22	46.0	2.91	38.7	28.0
Albania	27.4	21.1	4.56	15.5	38.2	20.7	3.50
Algeria	2,382	3.14	0.24	13.3	1.66	81.7	5.55
Amer. Samoa	0.20	5.00	10.0	0	70.0	15.0	0
Andorra	0.45	2.22	0	55.6	22.2	20.0	0
Angola	1,247	2.41	0.40	43.3	18.4	35.4	0.75
Antigua & Barb.	0.44	18.2	0	9.09	11.4	61.4	0
Argentina	2,737	9.14	0.80	51.9	18.6	19.6	17.0
Armenia	28.4	17.1	3.19	24.4	14.9	40.4	2.87
Aruba	0.19	10.5	0	0	0	89.5	0
Australia	7,644	6.15	0.03	54.2	19.0	20.6	21.4
Austria	82.7	17.2	1.12	24.4	39.2	18.2	0.04
Azerbaijan	86.1	18.5	4.62	25.4	11.0	40.5	10.0
Bahamas	10.0	0.60	0.40	0.20	32.4	66.4	0
Bahrain	0.68	1.45	1.45	5.80	0	91.3	0.03
Bangladesh	130	72.6	1.87	4.61	14.6	6.32	32.9
Barbados	0.43	37.2	0	4.65	11.6	46.5	0.01
Belarus	208	29.8	0.67	14.1	33.7	21.7	1.00
Belgium–Lux.	32.8	23.7	0.52	21.0	21.3	33.5	0.01
Belize	22.8	1.97	0.53	2.11	92.1	3.29	0.02
Benin	111	12.9	4.07	4.00	30.7	48.3	0.10
Bermuda	0.05	0	0	0	20.0	80.0	0
Bhutan	47.0	2.45	0.40	5.81	66.0	25.4	0.39
Bolivia	1,084	1.96	0.24	24.4	53.5	19.9	1.00
Bosnia	51.2	11.8	3.92	23.5	39.2	21.6	0.02
Botswana	567	0.74	0	45.2	46.8	7.33	0.01
Brazil	8,457	5.11	0.89	21.9	57.7	14.4	30.0
Brit. Indian Oc. Terr.	0.08	0	0	0	0	100	0
Brit. Virgin Is.	0.15	20.0	6.67	33.3	6.67	33.3	0
Brunei	5.27	0.57	0.76	1.14	85.4	12.1	0.01
Bulgaria	111	36.2	1.97	16.3	35.1	10.5	8.00
Burkina Faso	274	13.0	0.05	21.9	50.4	14.6	0.24
Burma (Myanmar)	658	14.5	0.82	0.52	49.3	34.9	13.4
Burundi	25.7	38.9	7.01	38.6	12.7	2.84	0.14
Cambodia	177	21.6	0.11	8.50	69.1	0.65	1.73
Cameroon	465	12.8	2.32	4.30	77.1	3.44	0.21
Canada	9,221	4.93	0.01	3.03	53.6	38.5	7.10
Cape Verde Is.	4.03	10.7	0.50	6.20	0.25	82.4	0.03
Cayman Is.	0.26	0	0	7.69	23.1	69.2	0
Cen. African Rep.	623	3.10	0.14	4.82	75.0	17.0	0
Chad	1,259	2.58	0	35.7	25.7	35.9	0.14
Chile	749	5.32	0.36	18.2	22.0	54.1	12.7
China	9,326	9.92	0.35	42.9	14.0	32.8	493.7
Christmas I.	0.13	0	0	0	0	100	0
Cocos Is.	0.01	0	0	0	0	100	0
Colombia	1,039	3.77	1.48	39.1	48.1	7.52	7.50
Comoros	2.23	35.0	9.87	6.73	17.9	30.5	0
Congo	342	0.42	0.07	29.3	58.3	11.9	0.01
Congo (Zaïre)	2,267	3.21	0.27	6.62	76.7	13.2	0.11
Cook Is.	0.23	8.70	13.0	0	0	78.3	0
Costa Rica	51.1	5.58	4.80	45.8	30.7	13.0	1.26
Croatia	56.4	19.7	2.09	19.5	37.6	21.1	0.03
Cuba	110	24.0	6.65	27.0	23.7	18.5	9.10
Cyprus	9.24	10.9	4.55	0.43	13.3	70.8	0.40
Czech Rep.		40.8	3.05	11.5	34.0	10.6	0.24
Czechoslovakia	125	38.4	1.66	13.6	36.8	9.48	1.35
Denmark	42.4	55.9	0.05	7.47	10.5	26.1	4.55
Djibouti	23.2	0	0	56.1	0.95	43.0	0.01
Dominica	0.75	9.33	13.3	2.67	66.7	8.00	0
Dominican Rep.	48.4	21.0	9.61	43.4	12.4	13.6	2.50
Ecuador	277	5.86	5.11	18.4	56.4	14.3	5.60
Egypt	995	3.12	0.39	0	0.03	96.5	35.0
El Salvador	20.7	27.3	7.96	29.4	5.02	30.3	1.20
Equatorial Guinea	28.1	4.63	3.57	3.71	65.2	22.9	0
Eritrea	101	4.35	0.79	69.0	7.29	18.6	0.28
Estonia	43.2	26.7	0.35	7.33	47.7	17.9	0
Ethiopia	1,101	10.5	0.54	20.0	13.3	55.7	1.90
Falkland Is.	12.2	0	0	99.4	0	0.58	0
Faroe Is.	1.40	2.14	0	0	0	97.9	0
Fiji	18.3	9.85	4.38	9.47	64.9	11.4	0.03
Finland	305	8.51	0	0.36	76.1	15.0	0.64
France	550	33.3	2.13	19.3	27.3	18.0	14.8
French Guiana	88.2	0.11	0.02	0.11	82.8	16.9	0.02
French Polynesia	3.66	1.37	6.01	5.46	31.4	55.7	0
Gabon	258	1.14	0.64	18.2	77.2	2.74	0.04
Gambia, The	10.0	17.2	0	19.0	10.0	53.8	0.02
Georgia	69.7	11.4	4.76	24.2	33.3	26.3	4.69
Germany	349	33.8	0.60	15.1	30.6	19.9	4.75
Ghana	228	12.3	6.68	36.9	42.2	1.91	0.06
Gibraltar	0.01	0	0	0	0	100	0
Greece	129	18.8	8.39	40.7	20.3	11.8	13.3
Greenland	342	0	0	0.69	0.03	99.3	0
Grenada	0.34	14.7	17.6	2.94	8.82	55.9	0
Guadeloupe	1.69	12.4	3.55	14.2	39.1	30.8	0.03
Guam	0.55	10.9	10.9	14.5	18.2	45.5	0
Guatemala	108	12.5	5.16	24.0	53.6	4.80	1.25
Guinea	246	2.48	0.49	43.5	27.3	26.2	0.93
Guinea-Bissau	28.1	10.7	1.42	38.4	38.1	11.5	0.17
Guyana	197	2.44	0.08	6.25	83.8	7.41	1.30
Haiti	27.6	20.3	12.7	18.0	5.08	43.9	0.75
Honduras	112	15.1	3.04	13.8	53.6	14.5	0.74
Hong Kong	0.99	6.06	1.01	1.01	22.2	69.7	0.02
Hungary	92.3	51.4	2.44	12.4	19.1	14.6	2.10
Iceland	100	0.06	0	22.7	1.20	76.1	0
India	2,973	55.9	1.19	3.83	23.0	16.1	480.0
Indonesia	1,812	9.45	7.20	6.51	61.7	15.1	45.8
Iran	1,636	10.1	0.99	26.9	6.97	55.1	72.6
Iraq	437	12.0	0.46	9.15	4.28	74.1	25.5
Ireland	68.9	19.1	0.04	44.6	4.65	31.6	0
Israel	20.6	17.0	4.12	7.03	6.11	65.8	1.93
Italy	294	28.3	9.57	15.4	23.0	23.7	27.1
Ivory Coast	318	7.67	3.99	40.9	34.3	13.2	0.73
Jamaica	10.8	14.3	5.91	23.7	17.1	39.0	0.35
Japan	377	10.6	1.12	1.76	66.4	20.1	27.8
Jordan	88.9	3.54	1.01	8.89	0.79	85.8	0.64
Kazakstan	2,670	13.0	0.06	70.0	3.59	13.4	21.5
Kenya	570	7.03	0.91	37.4	29.5	25.1	0.67
Kiribati	0.73	0	50.7	0	2.74	46.6	0
Korea, North	120	14.1	2.49	0.42	61.2	21.8	14.6
Korea, South	98.7	19.0	1.80	0.91	65.4	12.8	13.4
Kuwait	17.8	0.20	0	7.69	0.11	92.0	0.05
Kyrgyzstan	191	7.30	0.10	44.3	3.65	44.6	10.0
Laos	231	3.79	0.11	3.47	54.4	38.3	1.55
Latvia	64.1	27.6	0.48	12.9	46.3	12.8	0
Lebanon	10.2	21.1	8.80	0.98	7.82	61.3	0.88
Lesotho	30.4	10.5	0	65.9	0	23.6	0.03
Liberia	96.8	1.35	2.54	20.8	47.8	27.6	0.02
Libya	1,760	1.03	0.20	7.56	0.48	90.7	4.70
Liechtenstein	0.16	25.0	0	37.5	18.8	18.8	0
Lithuania	65.2	35.4	11.6	7.31	30.9	14.8	0
Macau	0.02	0	0	0	0	100	0
Macedonia	24.9	23.9	2.04	25.0	39.3	9.71	0.70
Madagascar	582	4.44	0.90	41.3	39.9	13.5	10.9
Malawi	94.1	17.8	0.32	19.6	39.3	23.0	0.28
Malaysia	329	5.55	17.6	0.86	67.9	8.11	3.40
Maldives	0.30	10.0	0	3.33	3.33	83.3	0
Mali	1,220	2.05	0	24.6	9.83	63.5	0.79
Malta	0.32	37.5	3.13	0	0	59.4	0.01
Martinique	1.06	7.55	9.43	13.2	45.3	24.5	0.04
Mauritania	1,025	0.20	0	38.3	4.30	57.2	0.49
Mauritius	2.03	49.3	2.96	3.45	21.7	22.7	0.18
Mexico	1,909	12.1	0.83	39.0	25.5	22.5	61.0
Moldova	33.7	52.9	13.2	13.2	12.8	7.95	3.11
Mongolia	1,567	0.84	0	74.8	8.78	15.6	0.80
Montserrat	0.10	20.0	0	10.0	40.0	30.0	0
Morocco	446	19.3	1.49	47.1	20.1	12.0	12.6
Mozambique	784	3.76	0.29	56.1	22.1	17.8	1.07
Namibia	823	0.80	0	46.2	15.2	37.9	0.06
Nauru	0.02	0	0	0	0	100	0
Nepal	137	17.0	0.21	14.6	42.0	26.1	8.50
Netherlands	33.9	27.1	0.83	31.0	10.3	30.7	5.65
Neths Antilles	0.80	10.0	0	0	0	90.0	0
New Caledonia	18.3	0.38	0.33	11.8	38.7	48.7	0
New Zealand	268	9.14	5.04	50.4	27.9	7.57	2.85
Nicaragua	119	9.06	1.40	45.3	26.4	17.9	0.88
Niger	1,267	2.85	0	8.24	1.97	86.9	0.66
Nigeria	911	33.1	2.78	43.9	12.0	8.22	2.33
Niue	0.26	19.2	7.69	3.85	19.2	50.0	0
Norfolk I.	0.04	0	0	25.0	0	75.0	0
Norway	307	2.94	0	0.42	27.1	69.5	0.97
Oman	212	0.08	0.22	4.71	0	95.0	0.58
Pacific Is.	1.78	14.0	19.1	13.5	22.5	30.9	0
Pakistan	771	27.0	0.71	6.49	4.51	61.3	171.5
Panama	74.4	6.72	2.22	19.8	43.8	27.5	0.32
Papua New Guinea	453	0.09	0.83	0.20	92.7	6.14	0
Paraguay	397	5.51	0.20	54.6	32.3	7.32	0.67
Peru	1,280	2.93	0.30	21.2	66.3	9.33	17.0
Philippines	298	18.5	12.3	4.29	45.6	19.3	15.8
Poland	304	47.0	1.12	13.3	28.9	9.73	1.00
Portugal	92.0	23.9	7.61	10.9	35.9	21.7	6.30
Puerto Rico	8.86	3.72	4.97	26.2	16.5	48.6	0.39

	Land area '000 sq km	Arable land %	Permanent crops %	Permanent grassland %	Forest %	Other land %	Irrigated land '000 sq km
Qatar	11.0	0.73	0	4.55	0	94.7	0.08
Réunion	2.50	18.0	1.60	4.80	35.2	40.4	0.12
Romania	230	40.5	2.55	21.2	29.0	6.76	31.0
Russia	16,996	7.72	0.12	5.17	45.4	41.6	53.7
Rwanda	24.7	34.7	12.8	28.4	10.1	14.1	0.04
San Marino	0.06	16.7	0	0	0	83.3	0
São Tomé & P.	0.96	2.63	51.3	1.32	0	44.7	0.10
Saudi Arabia	2,150	1.72	0.05	55.8	0.84	41.6	4.35
Senegal	193	12.1	0.10	29.6	39.5	18.7	0.71
Seychelles	0.45	2.22	13.3	0	11.1	73.3	0
Sierra Leone	71.6	6.79	0.75	30.7	28.5	33.3	0.29
Singapore	0.61	1.64	0	0	4.92	93.4	0
Slovak Rep.		30.9	2.72	17.3	41.4	7.65	0.80
Slovenia	20.3	11.6	2.58	25.0	54.4	6.46	0.02
Solomon Is.	28.0	1.43	0.61	1.39	87.5	9.04	0
Somalia	627	1.59	0.03	68.5	25.5	4.33	2.00
South Africa	1,221	10.1	0.67	66.6	6.72	15.8	12.7
Spain	499	31.3	9.05	21.4	32.3	5.99	36.6
Sri Lanka	64.6	14.0	15.1	6.81	32.5	31.6	5.50
St Helena	0.30	0	0	0	0	100	0
St Kitts & Nevis	0.36	22.2	16.7	2.78	16.7	41.7	0
St Lucia	0.61	8.20	21.3	4.92	13.1	52.5	0.01
St Pierre & Miq.	0.23	13.0	0	0	4.35	82.6	0
St Vincent & G.	0.39	10.3	17.9	5.13	35.9	30.8	0.01
Sudan	2,376	5.43	0.03	46.3	18.1	30.1	19.5
Surinam	156	0.37	0.07	0.13	96.2	3.28	0.60
Swaziland	17.2	10.9	0.23	62.2	6.98	19.7	0.67
Sweden	412	6.75	0	1.40	68.0	23.8	1.15
Switzerland	39.6	10.4	0.61	29.0	31.7	28.4	0.25
Syria	184	26.4	3.67	45.2	2.65	22.1	10.8
Taiwan	36.0	24.3	1.67	11.4	51.8	10.8	0
Tajikistan	143	5.83	0.28	25.2	3.82	64.8	7.18
Tanzania	884	3.40	0.57	39.6	38.1	18.3	1.50
Thailand	511	34.4	6.26	1.57	26.4	31.3	48.0
Togo	54.4	38.1	6.62	3.68	16.5	35.1	0.07
Tokelau	0.01	0	0	0	0	100	0
Tonga	0.72	23.6	43.1	5.56	11.1	16.7	0
Trinidad & Tob.	5.13	14.6	9.16	2.14	45.8	28.3	0.22
Tunisia	155	19.2	12.6	20.0	4.35	43.8	3.85
Turkey	770	32.1	3.98	16.1	26.2	21.6	41.9
Turkmenistan	488	2.98	0.17	63.8	8.51	24.5	13.0
Turks & Caicos	0.43	2.33	0	0	0	97.7	0
Tuvalu	0.03	0	0	0	0	100	0
Uganda	200	25.3	8.72	9.02	31.6	25.4	0.09
Ukraine	604	57.5	1.84	13.0	17.9	9.88	25.9
United Arab Em.	83.6	0.35	0.12	2.39	0.04	97.1	0.67
United Kingdom	242	24.6	0.19	45.9	10.3	18.9	1.08
United States	9,573	19.4	0.21	25.0	29.9	25.5	214.0
US Virgin Is.	0.34	14.7	5.88	26.5	5.88	47.1	0
Uruguay	175	7.21	0.25	77.3	5.32	9.88	1.40
USSR	22,273	10.1	0.20	16.6	42.5	30.6	0
Uzbekistan	425	9.90	0.97	50.2	3.14	35.8	40.0
Vanuatu	12.2	1.64	10.2	2.05	75.0	11.2	0
Venezuela	882	3.64	0.79	20.2	34.0	41.4	1.90
Vietnam	325	18.1	3.33	1.01	29.6	47.9	18.6
Wallis & Futuna	0.20	5.00	20.0	0	0	75.0	0
Western Sahara	267	0	0	19.0	0	81.0	0
Western Samoa	2.83	19.4	23.7	0.35	47.3	9.19	0
World	131,163	10.3	0.81	26.0	31.7	31.1	2,495.5
Yemen	528	2.73	0.20	30.4	3.79	62.9	4.81
Yugoslavia	255	27.5	2.81	24.8	36.7	8.13	0
Yugoslavia (Serbia)	102	36.6	3.49	20.8	26.5	12.7	0.75
Zambia	743	7.08	0.01	40.4	43.0	9.51	0.46
Zimbabwe	387	7.11	0.33	44.3	23.0	25.2	1.17

The statistics are for 1994. The land area is the total area of the country less that covered by lakes and major rivers. Arable land is land under temporary crops, including temporary grassland for mowing or pasture. It includes market gardens and fallow land. Land under permanent crops is land that is under the same crop for a long period. Rubber or coffee is an example. Permanent pasture includes both cultivated and natural grassland that has been so for five or more years. Forest and woodland includes both planted and natural forests. Other land includes built-up areas, wasteland and desert. Irrigated land also includes land which is occasionally flooded by rivers for crop production or pasture improvement.

Agricultural population
percentage of the economically active population employed in agriculture

	1945 –64	1970	1980	1990	1995
WORLD	...	**55**	**51**	**49**	**48**
Afghanistan	...	66	61	70	69
Albania	...	66	60	55	54
Algeria	75	47	31	26	24
Angola	...	78	74	74	74
Argentina	19	16	13	12	11
Armenia	...	...	...	17	15
Australia	11	8	7	6	5
Austria	23	15	9	8	7
Azerbaijan	...	...	...	31	30
Bahamas	16	13	9	5	5
Bahrain	...	...	3	2	2
Bangladesh	...	81	75	65	62
Barbados	24	18	10	7	6
Belarus	...	...	...	19	18
Belgium	6.0	5	3	3	3
Belize	35	...	...	34	31
Benin	...	81	70	64	60
Bermuda	6	...	...	2	2
Bhutan	...	94	92	94	94
Bolivia	63	52	46	47	45
Bosnia	...	...	...	10	10
Botswana	...	86	70	46	39
Brazil	54	45	31	23	19
Brunei	34	...	...	4	2
Bulgaria	64	35	18	14	11
Burkina Faso	...	88	87	92	92
Burma	...	59	53	73	72
Burundi	...	94	93	92	91
Cambodia	81	78	74	74	73
Cameroon	...	83	70	70	68
Canada	11	8	5	3	3
Cape Verde Is.	40	64	52	31	27
Cen. Afr. Rep.	...	83	72	80	79
Chad	...	90	83	83	81
Chile	28	23	17	19	17
China	...	78	74	72	71
Colombia	54	39	34	27	24
Comoros	...	87	83	77	75
Congo	...	65	62	49	45
Congo (Zaïre)	86	79	72	68	66
Costa Rica	49	43	31	26	22
Croatia	...	...	...	15	15
Cuba	42	30	24	18	16
Cyprus	40	39	26	14	10
Czech Rep.	38	17	13	11	11
Denmark	17	11	7	6	4
Dominica	50	...	...	25	28
Dom. Rep.	56	55	46	25	21
Ecuador	56	51	39	33	29
Egypt	57	52	46	39	33
El Salvador	60	56	43	36	32
Eq. Guinea	...	75	66	75	73
Eritrea	...	...	...	...	80
Estonia	...	...	...	14	14
Ethiopia	...	85	80	86	86
Fiji	57	52	46	46	44
Finland	35	20	12	8	7
France	20	14	9	6	4
Fr. Guiana	...	...	...	...	9
Fr. Polynesia	41	...	...	10	10
Gabon	84	80	75	52	45
Gambia, The	...	87	84	82	80
Georgia	...	...	...	26	25
Germany	15	12	8	4	3
Ghana	58	58	56	59	56
Greece	54	42	31	23	20
Greenland	34	...	...	14	14
Grenada	40	...	...	14	13
Guadeloupe	...	29	15	7	5
Guam	2	...	...	1	1
Guatemala	68	61	57	52	51
Guinea	...	85	81	87	85
Guinea-Bissau	...	84	82	85	84
Guyana	34	32	27	22	20
Haiti	83	74	70	68	66
Honduras	67	65	61	41	33
Hong Kong	7	4	2	1	1

	1945 –64	1970	1980	1990	1995
Hungary	38	25	18	15	14
Iceland	38	17	10	11	10
India	73	72	70	64	62
Indonesia	68	66	57	55	53
Iran	55	44	36	39	36
Iraq	48	47	30	16	12
Ireland	35	26	19	14	13
Israel	12	10	6	4	3
Italy	25	19	12	9	7
Ivory Coast	86	77	65	60	57
Jamaica	39	33	31	25	24
Japan	27	20	11	7	6
Jordan	35	28	10	15	15
Kazakstan	...	...	...	22	21
Kenya	...	85	81	80	78
Korea, N.	57	53	43	38	34
Korea, S.	...	49	36	18	14
Kuwait	...	2	2	1	1
Kyrgyzstan	...	...	...	32	31
Laos	...	79	76	78	77
Latvia	...	...	...	16	14
Lebanon	...	20	14	7	4
Lesotho	...	90	86	40	39
Liberia	81	78	74	72	70
Libya	...	29	18	11	6
Lithuania	...	...	...	18	18
Macau	5	...	...	0.2	0.2
Macedonia	...	...	...	20	17
Madagascar	...	84	81	78	76
Malawi	...	91	83	87	86
Malaysia	58	54	42	27	23
Maldives	...	...	...	...	30
Mali	...	89	86	86	84
Malta	10	7	5	3	2
Martinique	39	24	13	8	6
Mauritania	...	85	69	55	49
Mauritius	40	34	28	17	12
Mexico	54	44	37	28	24
Moldova	...	...	...	33	31
Mongolia	...	48	40	32	29
Morocco	56	58	46	45	41
Mozambique	75	86	85	83	81
Namibia	59	51	43	49	45
Nepal	93	94	93	94	93
Netherlands	11	7	6	5	4
Neths Antilles	2	...	...	1	1
N. Caledonia	55	...	...	12	11
N. Zealand	14	12	11	10	10
Nicaragua	60	52	47	28	23
Niger	97	94	91	90	89
Nigeria	...	71	68	43	38
Norway	19	12	8	6	5
Oman	...	...	50	45	42
Pakistan	75	59	55	52	48
Panama	46	42	32	26	22
Papua N.G.	...	84	76	79	78
Paraguay	52	53	49	39	35
Peru	50	47	40	36	33
Philippines	57	55	52	46	42
Poland	48	39	29	28	26
Portugal	42	32	26	18	14
Puerto Rico	24	14	4	4	3
Qatar	...	...	...	3	3
Réunion	45	38	18	7	5
Romania	70	49	31	24	19
Russia	...	...	...	14	12
Rwanda	...	94	93	92	91
St Kitts & N.	...	...	...	...	26
St Lucia	...	...	...	...	22
St Vincent & G.	40	...	...	26	20
São Tomé & P.	...	...	...	...	38
Saudi Arabia	...	64	48	19	14
Senegal	...	83	81	77	74
Seychelles	...	...	...	...	8
Sierra Leone	...	76	70	67	67
Singapore	8	3	2	1	1
Slovak Rep.	...	...	...	12	12
Slovenia	...	...	...	5	5
Solomon Is.	...	...	...	77	76
Somalia	...	79	76	75	74
South Africa	30	33	17	14	11
Spain	35	26	17	12	9

Agricultural population continued

	1945 –64	1970	1980	1990	1995
Sri Lanka	52	55	53	49	47
Sudan	86	77	71	70	68
Surinam	25	25	20	21	20
Swaziland	...	81	74	40	34
Sweden	14	8	6	4	4
Switzerland	11	8	6	6	5
Syria	50	50	32	33	33
Taiwan	50	48	28	21	19
Tajikistan	...	...	...	40	38
Tanzania	...	90	86	84	83
Thailand	82	80	71	64	60
Togo	...	77	73	66	62
Trinidad & T.	20	19	10	11	9
Tunisia	58	42	35	28	24
Turkey	75	71	58	53	51
Turkmenistan	...	...	...	37	36
Uganda	...	89	86	85	83

	1945 –64	1970	1980	1990	1995
Ukraine	...	...	...	20	18
UAE	...	...	5	8	9
UK	5	3	3	2	2
United States	7	4	4	3	3
Uruguay	18	19	16	14	14
Uzbekistan	...	...	...	35	34
Venezuela	32	26	16	12	11
Vietnam	...	77	68	71	69
Yemen	...	73	62	61	57
Yugoslavia	...	...	...	21	20
Zambia	...	77	73	75	74
Zimbabwe	...	77	73	68	67

The figures also include people engaged in forestry, hunting and fishing. The economically active population includes people in work and seeking employment. The people working in agriculture does not include dependents unless the latter are working in the enterprises.

Food supply and production   *calories per person per day*

	1960	1970	1980	1992	Index of food production 1996
WORLD	...	**2,464**	**2,559**	**2718**	**1989–91=100**
Afghanistan	2,040	2,294	1,796	1523	...
Albania	2,376	2,533	2,787	2605	...
Algeria	2,180	1,826	2,607	2897	131
Angola	2,038	1,856	2,040	1839	134
Antigua & Barb.	2,196	2,291	2,106	2458	...
Argentina	2,810	3,351	3,239	2880	122
Armenia	...	...	...	...	87
Australia	3,140	3,226	3,287	3179	114
Austria	2,970	3,477	3,370	3497	99
Azerbaijan	...	...	...	...	56
Bahamas	2,467	2,623	2,512	2624	...
Bangladesh	1,984	2,033	1,848	2019	108
Barbados	2,587	2,894	3,122	3207	109
Belarus	...	...	...	...	99
Belgium	3,060	3,482	3,628	3681	114
Belize	2,329	2,644	2,707	2662	...
Benin	2,120	2,056	2,099	2532	128
Bermuda	2,747	2,933	2,525	2679	...
Bolivia	1,990	1,972	2,097	2094	122
Botswana	1,982	2,176	2,148	2266	108
Brazil	2,720	2,485	2,621	2824	122
Brunei	2,175	2,305	2,810	2745	...
Bulgaria	3,440	3,494	3,639	2831	55
Burkina Faso	2,020	1,987	2,032	2387	124
Burma (Myanmar)	1,917	2,031	2,333	2598	151
Burundi	2,383	2,363	2,344	1941	97
Cambodia	...	2,715	2,206	2021	128
Cameroon	2,130	2,151	2,145	1981	118
Canada	3,020	3,369	3,310	3094	114
Cape Verde Is.	1,723	1,992	2,553	2805	...
Central Afr. Rep.	2,120	2,158	2,119	1690	109
Chad	2,180	2,135	1,639	1989	127
Chile	2,480	2,697	2,637	2582	129
China	1,870	2,092	2,328	2727	152
Colombia	2,370	2,133	2,499	2677	113
Comoros	2,289	2,223	2,071	1897	...
Congo	2,120	2,181	2,441	2296	116
Congo (Zaïre)	1,920	2,218	2,126	2060	102
Costa Rica	2,420	2,406	2,615	2883	125
Croatia	...	...	...	...	62
Cuba	2,373	2,576	2,839	2833	63
Cyprus	...	3,173	2,879	3779	111
Czech Rep.	...	...	...	...	89
former Czech	3,396	3,429	3,414	3156	...
Denmark	3,260	3,385	3,524	3664	105
Djibouti	...	1,684	1,782	2338	...
Dominica	2,107	2,237	2,385	2778	...
Dominican Rep.	1,930	1,971	2,323	2286	107
Ecuador	1,990	1,986	2,059	2583	132
Egypt	2,690	2,510	3,031	3335	120
El Salvador	1,890	1,840	2,316	2663	107
Eritrea	...	...	...	...	111
Estonia	...	...	...	...	74
Ethiopia	2,110	1,533	1,858	1610	127
Fiji	2,715	2,439	2,764	3089	108
Finland	3,110	3,128	3,083	3018	91
France	3,090	3,391	3,232	3633	104
Fr. Guiana	2,272	2,509	2,553	2900	...

	1960	1970	1980	1992	Index of food production 1996
French Polynesia	2,619	2,841	2,845	2834	...
Gabon	1,910	2,224	2,378	2500	106
Gambia	2,300	2,348	2,176	2360	71
Georgia	...	...	...	...	67
Germany	2,990	3,300	3,450	3344	92
Ghana	2,160	2,230	1,753	2199	146
Greece	2,940	3,190	3,543	3815	99
Grenada	2,246	2,342	2,294	2402	...
Guadeloupe	2,144	2,329	2,502	2682	93
Guatemala	2,050	2,062	2,194	2255	113
Guinea	2,006	2,041	1,833	2389	126
Guinea-Bissau	1,805	2,107	2,230	2556	109
Guyana	2,276	2,293	2,409	2384	181
Haiti	2,045	1,918	1,887	1706	92
Honduras	2,160	2,151	2,176	2305	111
Hong Kong	2,537	2,690	2,727	3129	...
Hungary	3,030	3,336	3,493	3503	72
Iceland	3,186	2,963	3,005	3058	97
India	2,020	1,992	2,117	2395	115
Indonesia	1,796	1,872	2,441	2752	119
Iran	2,050	2,199	2,656	2860	138
Iraq	1,920	2,349	2,745	2121	94
Ireland	3,480	3,591	3,707	3847	110
Israel	2,810	3,019	2,976	3050	110
Italy	2,690	3,459	3,606	3561	101
Ivory Coast	2,290	2,484	2,541	2491	133
Jamaica	2,230	2,473	2,570	2607	115
Japan	2,330	2,758	2,833	2903	96
Jordan	2,220	2,374	2,661	3022	159
Kazakstan	...	...	...	...	61
Kenya	2,120	2,259	2,206	2075	101
Kiribati	2,114	2,207	2,912	2651	...
Korea, North	2,298	2,501	3,059	2833	...
Korea, South	2,090	2,456	2,828	3285	113
Kuwait	2,796	2,780	3,094	2523	137
Kyrgyzstan	...	...	...	...	77
Laos	2,133	2,061	2,443	2259	109
Latvia	...	...	...	...	73
Lebanon	2,160	2,503	2,743	3317	122
Lesotho	2,024	2,032	2,346	2201	114
Liberia	2,110	2,167	2,380	1640	...
Libya	1,770	2,366	3,664	3308	94
Lithuania	...	...	...	...	86
Macau	2,138	2,181	2,185	2278	...
Macedonia	...	...	...	...	96
Madagascar	2,300	2,469	2,485	2135	107
Malawi	2,196	2,281	2,421	1825	110
Malaysia	2,307	2,417	2,595	2888	125
Maldives	...	1,672	2,130	2580	...
Mali	2,120	2,067	1,702	2278	114
Malta	2,924	3,085	2,961	3486	130
Martinique	2,223	2,363	2,646	2829	92
Mauritania	1,796	1,975	2,052	2685	107
Mauritius	2,330	2,343	2,723	2690	107
Mexico	2,500	2,641	3,051	3146	124
Moldova	...	...	...	...	60
Mongolia	2,333	2,434	2,716	1899	79
Morocco	2,080	2,453	2,763	2984	117
Mozambique	1,704	2,089	1,801	1680	120
Namibia	1,882	1,909	2,215	2134	106
Nepal	1,887	2,020	2,000	1957	113
Netherlands	3,160	3,431	3,306	3222	104
Neths Antilles	...	2,448	2,765	2587	...
New Caledonia	2,824	3,309	2,936	2829	...
New Zealand	3,490	3,475	3,352	3669	122
Nicaragua	2,398	2,374	2,293	2293	123
Niger	1,930	2,074	2,370	2257	122
Nigeria	2,180	2,232	2,246	2124	136
Norway	2,930	3,101	3,327	3244	100
Pakistan	2,090	2,018	2,244	2315	129
Panama	2,350	2,443	2,338	2242	103
Papua N. Guinea	...	...	...	2613	108
Paraguay	2,520	2,753	2,770	2670	117
Peru	2,260	2,251	2,166	1882	126
Philippines	1,880	2,206	2,343	2257	120
Poland	3,292	3,331	3,431	3301	83
Portugal	2,530	3,069	3,034	3634	93
Réunion	2,272	2,497	2,847	3245	109
Romania	3,040	3,065	3,339	3051	96
Russia	...	...	...	...	64
Rwanda	1,660	1,967	2,055	1821	78

	1960	1970	1980	1992	Index of food production 1996
St Kitts & Nevis	2,243	2,145	2,308	2419	...
St Lucia	1,936	2,132	2,319	2588	...
St Vincent & G.	2,003	2,247	2,491	2347	...
São Tomé & P.	2,144	2,167	2,262	2129	...
Saudi Arabia	1,842	1,906	2,819	2735	85
Senegal	2,280	2,300	2,397	2262	116
Seychelles	1,680	2,408	2,302	2287	
Sierra Leone	1,976	2,071	2,052	1694	95
Singapore	1,700	2,682	2,691	...	
Slovak Rep.	...	...	...	...	78
Slovenia	...	...	...	...	94
Solomon Is.	2,164	2,114	2,146	2173	107
Somalia	1,410	2,163	2,080	1499	...
South Africa	2,820	2,767	2,932	2695	103
Spain	2,820	2,867	3,332	3708	98
Sri Lanka	2,080	2,308	2,225	2273	108
Sudan	1,853	2,100	2,379	2202	133
Surinam	1,920	2,337	2,588	2547	93
Swaziland	2,128	2,203	2,504	2706	98
Sweden	2,990	3,038	3,013	2972	98
Switzerland	3,210	3,479	3,501	3379	99
Syria	2,350	2,363	2,945	3175	141
Taiwan	2,390	2,661	2,812	3048	...
Tajikistan	...	...	...	...	61
Tanzania	2,080	1,948	2,279	2018	99
Thailand	2,134	2,160	2,312	2432	108
Togo	2,345	2,191	2,173	2242	115
Tonga	2,491	2,589	2,922	2946	76
Trinidad & Tob.	2,497	2,385	2,882	2585	102
Tunisia	1,730	2,264	2,759	3330	124
Turkey	3,110	2,829	3,113	3429	106
Turkmenistan	...	...	...	...	84
United Arab Em.	2,690	3,130	3,595	3384	...
Uganda	2,090	2,260	2,135	2159	115
Ukraine	...	...	...	...	73
United Kingdom	3,270	3,356	3,257	3317	103
United States	3,120	3,497	3,529	3732	115
Uruguay	3,200	2,982	2,793	2750	126
(former) USSR	3,205	3,348	3,362	3304	...
Uzbekistan	...	...	...	...	81
Vanuatu	2,487	2,408	2,417	2739	114
Venezuela	2,300	2,335	2,662	2618	115
Vietnam	2,172	2,000	2,053	2250	130
Western Samoa	...	2,088	2,403	2828	
Yemen	2,002	1,900	2,210	2203	110
(former) Yugoslavia	2,970	3,340	3,598	...	...
Yugoslavia (Serbia)	...	...	...	...	90
Zambia	2,042	2,194	2,204	1931	105
Zimbabwe	2,044	2,055	2,152	1985	106

Tractors in use   thousands

	1970	1980	1990	1994
WORLD	**15,483**	**21,742**	**26,266**	**25,946**
Afghanistan	0.6	0.8	0.9	0.8
Albania	6.2	11	11	9
Algeria	47	44	91	99
Am. Samoa	0.02	0.01	0.01	0.01
Angola	7.2	10	10	10
Antigua & Barb.	0.1	0.2	0.24	0.24
Argentina	172	167	273	280
Armenia	...	...	...	16
Australia	329	332	317	315
Austria	249	320	351	343
Azerbaijan	...	...	...	32
Bahamas	0.03	0.07	0.78	0.80
Bangladesh	1.9	4.2	5.2	5.3
Barbados	0.4	0.6	0.59	0.61
Belarus	...	...	...	123
Belgium	98	116	117	112
Belize	0.2	1.3	1.1	1.2
Benin	0.07	0.1	0.13	0.14
Bermuda	0.05	0.04	0.05	0.05
Bolivia	0.4	4.5	5.2	5.4
Bosnia	...	...	...	29
Botswana	1.6	2.1	5.6	6.0
Brazil	168	330	720	735
Brunei	0.01	0.03	0.07	0.07
Bulgaria	54	62	52	37
Burkina Faso	0.04	0.07	0.13	0.14
Burma (Myanmar)	5.1	9.3	12	12
Burundi	0.004	0.05	0.16	0.17
Cambodia	1.3	1.4	1.4	1.4
Cameroon	0.2	0.5	0.51	0.50
Canada	596	657	752	740
Cape Verde Is.	0.02	0.03	0.02	0.02
Central Afr. Rep.	0.07	0.2	0.20	0.21
Chad	0.09	0.2	0.17	0.17
Chile	26	35	37	41
China	135	745	829	709
Colombia	23	28	36	37
Congo	0.6	0.7	0.70	0.71
Congo (Zaïre)	1.0	1.9	2.4	2.4
Cook Is.	0.09	0.1	0.18	0.19
Costa Rica	5.1	6.0	6.5	7.0
Croatia	...	...	...	4.0
Cuba	48	68	78	78
Cyprus	6.8	11	14	14
Czech Rep.	...	...	...	60
Denmark	174	189	170	147
Dominica	0.07	0.09	0.09	0.09
Dominican Rep.	2.5	3.2	2.3	2.4
Ecuador	3.1	6.2	8.7	8.9
Egypt	17	36	57	78
El Salvador	2.5	3.3	3.4	3.4
Equat. Guinea	0.07	0.1	0.10	0.10
Eritrea	0.5	1	0.85	0.85
Estonia	...	...	...	15
Ethiopia	2.4	3	3.0	3.0
Falkland Is.	0.09	0.1	0.13	0.14
Fiji	1.2	1.6	6.7	7.0
Finland	156	212	241	230
France	1,239	1,504	1,446	1,440
French Guiana	0.04	0.1	0.30	0.35
French Polynesia	0.1	0.1	0.15	0.16
Gabon	0.8	1.3	1.5	1.5
Gambia	0.06	0.04	0.04	0.04
Georgia	...	...	...	18
Germany	1,516	1,598	1,554	1,300
Ghana	2.7	3.5	4.0	4.1
Greece	62	140	217	227
Greenland	0.2	0.08	0.09	0.09
Grenada	0.02	0.03	0.03	0.03
Guadeloupe	0.5	0.9	0.89	0.81
Guam	0.07	0.08	0.08	0.08
Guatemala	3.2	4.0	4.2	4.3
Guinea	0.05	0.1	0.27	0.29
Guinea-Bissau	0.02	0.03	0.02	0.02
Guyana	3.3	3.5	3.6	3.6
Haiti	0.4	0.5	0.22	0.23
Honduras	0.6	3.3	3.5	4.9
Hungary	67	55	48	36
Iceland	9.9	13	11	10
India	111	418	992	1,258
Indonesia	8.5	13	29	56
Iran	20	75	115	118
Iraq	14	23	36	32
Ireland	84	140	166	168
Israel	16	27	27	26
Italy	619	1,072	1,428	1,470
Ivory Coast	1.4	3.1	3.6	3.7
Jamaica	1.7	2.8	3.1	3.1
Japan	278	1,471	2,052	2,050
Jordan	2.8	4.5	6.2	7.6
Kazakstan	...	...	...	210
Kenya	6.4	6.5	14	14
Kiribati	0.01	0.02	0.02	0.02
Korea, North	20	30	73	75
Korea, South	0.1	2.6	42	80
Kuwait	0.01	0.02	0.12	0.10
Kyrgyzstan	...	...	...	23
Laos	0.3	0.5	0.87	0.89
Latvia	...	...	...	56
Lebanon	2.5	3.0	3.0	3.0
Lesotho	0.4	1.4	1.9	1.9
Liberia	0.2	0.3	0.33	0.34
Libya	3.9	14	32	34
Liechtenstein	0.5	0.4	0.45	0.45
Lithuania	...	...	...	66
Macedonia	...	...	...	47
Madagascar	2.4	2.7	2.9	2.9
Malawi	0.8	1.2	1.4	1.4
Malaysia	4.6	8.1	26	39
Mali	0.4	0.8	0.83	0.84
Malta	0.1	0.4	0.45	0.45
Martinique	0.4	0.9	0.91	0.93
Mauritania	0.3	0.3	0.34	0.33
Mauritius	0.3	0.3	0.36	0.37
Mexico	91	115	170	172
Moldova	...	...	...	53
Mongolia	5.4	9.7	12	12
Montserrat	0.02	0.01	0.01	0.01
Morocco	12	25	39	42
Mozambique	4.2	5.8	5.8	5.8
Namibia	2.1	2.6	3.1	3.2
Nepal	0.4	0.5	4.4	4.6
Netherlands	134	178	182	182
Neths Antilles	0.1	0.1	0.02	0.02
New Caledonia	0.5	1.0	1.4	1.4
New Zealand	96	92	76	76
Nicaragua	0.5	2.2	2.6	2.7
Niger	0.04	0.2	0.18	0.18
Nigeria	2.9	8.6	12	12
Niue	0.007	0.01	0.01	0.01
Norfolk I.	0.01	0.01	0.01	0.01
Norway	91	131	153	148
Oman	0.03	0.1	0.15	0.15
Pacific Is.	0.04	0.05	0.05	0.05
Pakistan	21	71	261	283
Panama	2.4	4.0	5.1	5.0
Papua N. Guinea	1.4	1.4	1.1	1.1
Paraguay	2.2	3.2	15	17
Peru	11	14	13	13
Philippines	7.8	17	10	12
Poland	222	620	1,172	1,311
Portugal	29	72	132	150
Puerto Rico	5.4	3.7	3.9	4.2
Qatar	...	...	0.08	0.07
Réunion	0.3	1.2	1.5	1.8
Romania	108	147	139	161
Russia	...	...	...	1,148
Rwanda	0.06	0.08	0.09	0.09
St Kitts & Nevis	0.2	0.2	0.22	0.22
St Lucia	0.04	0.04	0.09	0.09
St Vincent & G.	0.06	0.08	0.08	0.08
São Tomé & P.	0.1	0.1	0.12	0.13
Saudi Arabia	0.6	1.2	2.0	2.1
Senegal	0.3	0.5	0.49	0.55
Seychelles	0.02	0.03	0.04	0.04
Sierra Leone	0.1	0.3	0.53	0.55
Singapore	0.02	0.04	0.06	0.07
Slovak Rep.	...	...	...	33
Slovenia	...	...	...	50
Somalia	0.9	1.7	2.1	1.8
South Africa	155	180	145	126
Spain	261	524	739	789
Sri Lanka	13	24	31	33
Sudan	5.0	11	9.7	11
Surinam	0.9	1.4	1.3	1.3
Swaziland	1.2	2.9	3.9	4.0
Sweden	179	181	171	165
Switzerland	73	95	112	114
Syria	9.1	28	62	78
Tajikistan	...	...	...	30
Tanzania	5.0	19	6.8	6.6
Thailand	8.0	73	58	121
Togo	0.06	0.2	0.37	0.37
Tonga	0.06	0.06	0.12	0.12
Trinidad & Tob.	1.9	2.4	2.6	2.7
Tunisia	21	34	25	28
Turkey	106	436	687	763
Turkmenistan	...	...	...	50
Tuvalu	...	...	0.01	0.01
Uganda	1.3	2.2	4.5	4.7
Ukraine	...	...	...	437
United Arab Em.	0.1	0.2	0.18	0.16
United Kingdom	456	512	505	500
United States	4,617	4,740	4,800	4,800
US Virgin Is.	0.4	0.3	0.08	0.08
Uruguay	27	33	33	33
Uzbekistan	...	...	...	170
Vanuatu	0.03	0.06	0.07	0.07
Venezuela	19	38	48	49
Vietnam	3.6	37	29	37
Western Sahara	0.01	0.01	...	...
Western Samoa	0.02	0.03	0.08	0.08
Yemen	1.6	3.3	5.4	5.5
Yugoslavia (Serbia)	...	...	...	415
Zambia	3.1	4.6	5.9	6.0
Zimbabwe	17	20	17	20

The figures refer to all tractors, except garden tractors, used in agriculture.

Fertilizer consumption
kg per hectare of agricultural land

	1970	1980	1990	1994
WORLD	**15**	**25**	**28**	**25.4**
Afghanistan	1.4	1.3	1.2	1.3
Albania	38	69	92	16
Algeria	2.5	5.4	3.3	3.1
Angola	0.4	0.5	0.3	0.2
Argentina	0.5	0.6	1.0	2.4
Armenia	...	...	...	5.6
Australia	2	2.5	2.5	3.6
Austria	105	111	86	72
Azerbaijan	...	...	...	9.3
Bahamas	...	109	...	...
Bahrain	...	...	167	167
Bangladesh	15	43	96	102
Barbados	154	157	81	167
Belarus	...	...	...	68
Belgium	298	292	270	215
Belize	51	20	48	57
Benin	1.7	0.4	3.0	7.3
Bhutan	...	0.3	...	...
Bolivia	0.1	0.1	0.4	0.4
Bosnia	...	...	...	2.0
Brazil	5.1	18	13	20
Brunei	...	...	308	308

52 Geographical Digest 1998–99

Fertilizer consumption continued

	1970	1980	1990	1994
Bulgaria	106	134	117	32
Burkina Faso	0	0.3	1.0	2.4
Burma (Myanmar)	2.1	9.6	6.8	17
Burundi	0.3	0.5	0.9	1.4
Cambodia	1	2.2	2.2	2.4
Cameroon	1.3	2.3	1.4	3.3
Canada	12	28	28	30
Central Afr. Rep.	0.4	0.3	0.2	0.2
Chad	...	...	0.1	0.1
Chile	9.1	7.6	16	23
China	13	40	55	60
Colombia	6.5	8.8	13	13
Congo	0.5	...	0.2	0.2
Congo (Zaïre)	0.1	0.5	0.3	0.2
Costa Rica	27	28	39	48
Croatia	...	...	...	78
Cuba	79	93	92	20
Cyprus	52	28	144	177
Czech Rep.	...	...	...	70
Denmark	201	216	227	174
Dominica	...	158	158	263
Dominican Rep.	16	15	25	27
Ecuador	5.7	12	8.0	20
Egypt	131	271	372	243
El Salvador	52	45	56	72
Equat. Guinea	5.8	0.3	...	...
Estonia	...	...	...	28
Ethiopia	0.1	0.7	1.9	1.5
Fiji	21	55	77	42
Finland	172	191	173	142
France	143	178	186	156
French Guiana	...	14	48	45
French Polynesia	...	7.5	21	21
Gabon	...	...	0.2	0.2
Gambia, The	0.5	8.2	3.7	2.8
Georgia	...	...	...	11
Germany	250	280	181	168
Ghana	0.2	1.9	1.7	0.8
Greece	37	57	75	61
Guadeloupe	124	125	111	137
Guatemala	19	28	40	41
Guinea	0.3	0.1	0.1	0.1
Guinea-Bissau	...	0.2	0.7	0.7
Guyana	7.3	3.5	7.0	8.7
Haiti	0.2	0.3	0.7	3.6
Honduras	8.5	5.5	11	16
Hungary	122	211	104	51
Iceland	10	13	9.6	9.6
India	12	29	69	75
Indonesia	8.4	37	74	61
Iran	3.5	9.9	20	16
Iraq	1.9	9.8	22	40
Ireland	87	104	123	171
Israel	47	64	175	179
Italy	66	120	105	121
Ivory Coast	1.3	7.7	2.2	3.8
Jamaica	45	37	41	55
Japan	355	333	351	351
Jordan	1.9	29	16	12
Kazakstan	...	...	...	0.6
Kenya	8.9	10	2.9	5.3
Korea, North	151	318	406	367
Korea, South	240	358	443	448
Kuwait	...	3.3	7.2	7.0
Kyrgyzstan	...	...	...	2.8
Laos	1	2.4	1.2	1.2
Latvia	...	...	...	37
Lebanon	131	74	80	89
Lesotho	0.1	2	2.2	2.6
Liberia	3.8	5.1	...	...
Libya	1.3	5.2	5.0	4.3
Lithuania	...	...	...	11
Macedonia	...	...	...	12
Madagascar	0.4	0.2	0.2	0.4
Malawi	2.8	8.0	11	10
Malaysia	53	105	194	153
Mali	0.1	0.4	0.5	0.6
Malta	46	115	77	77

	1970	1980	1990	1994
Martinique	271	247	641	438
Mauritius	196	233	248	257
Mexico	6.1	13	16	15
Moldova	...	...	...	44
Mongolia	...	0.1	0.1	0.1
Morocco	4.4	13	10	9.6
Mozambique	0.1	0.6	0.1	0.1
Nepal	1.3	5.2	16	21
Netherlands	296	336	277	259
New Caledonia	...	5.2	6.6	8.7
New Zealand	33	32	26	35
Nicaragua	9.7	8.8	6.0	4.6
Niger	...	0.2	0.1	0.1
Nigeria	0.2	3.4	5.5	5.4
Norway	209	277	209	201
Oman	...	1	8.5	9.4
Pakistan	11	43	74	83
Panama	13	18	17	15
Papua N. Guinea	4.6	11	25	26
Paraguay	0.6	0.4	0.6	1.0
Peru	2.8	3.9	4.1	6.7
Philippines	26	26	64	57
Poland	132	185	82	76
Portugal	30	64	69	65
Qatar	...	15	18	103
Réunion	180	71	188	295
Romania	40	82	75	26
Russia	...	...	...	7.0
Rwanda	0.1	0.1	1.9	0.5
Saudi Arabia	0.1	0.5	5.6	2.9
St Kitts & Nevis	140	140	67	67
St Lucia	142	43	286	333
St Vincent & G.	137	205	154	231
Senegal	1.0	1.8	2.2	2.5
Sierra Leone	0.4	0.5	0.4	1.1
Singapore	250	550	6,000	5,000
Slovak Rep.	...	...	...	45
Slovenia	...	...	...	104
Somalia	0.1	...	0.1	0.1
South Africa	5.6	11	8.3	8.8
Spain	38	53	65	60
Sri Lanka	39	64	73	92
Sudan	1.1	1.2	0.7	0.6
Surinam	46	22	11	45
Swaziland	4.2	12	5.8	10
Sweden	146	131	97	95
Switzerland	68	90	83	92
Syria	2.9	9	22	25
Taiwan	0.7	1.5	...	...
Tajikistan	...	...	...	16
Tanzania	0.3	0.9	1.3	1.0
Thailand	5.7	16	46	59
Togo	0.2	1.6	4.9	4.2
Trinidad & Tob.	61	47	61	45
Tunisia	4.5	8.2	10	11
Turkey	7.8	38	52	38
Turkmenistan	...	...	...	4.0
Uganda	0.7	0.1	0.0	0.2
Ukraine	...	...	...	29
United Arab Em.	...	14	54	146
United Kingdom	100	111	137	134
United States	36	50	43	45
US Virgin Is.	60	69	63	63
Uruguay	3.3	5.4	4.9	7.3
Uzbekistan	...	...	...	19
Venezuela	2.8	12	21	11
Vietnam	31	20	78	167
Yemen	...	1	1.0	0.7
Yugoslavia (Serbia)	...	...	...	15
Zambia	1	2	1.7	1.7
Zimbabwe	15	24	22	8.5

Total consumption of fertilizers *thousand tonnes*

	1970	1980	1990	1993	1994	Rank	%
WORLD	**69,245**	**116,473**	**138,049**	**120,815**	**123,252**		
Algeria	112	236	139	131	123		
Argentina	87	116	166	297	401		
Australia	964	1,162	1,164	1,511	1,660		
Austria	408	407	303	261	255		
Bangladesh	143	417	933	948	1,048		
Belarus	...	...	...	752	630		
Belgium	517	447	384	320	319		
Brazil	1,002	4,201	3,164	4,150	4,732	4	4
Bulgaria	639	830	680	229	190		
Burma (Myanmar)	22	100	71	148	173		
Canada	802	1,906	2,074	2,359	2,228	9	2
Chile	153	132	295	376	416		
China	4,220	15,335	27,027	25,317	29,574	1	24
Colombia	144	312	603	526	588		
Costa Rica	...	...	109	108	137		
Croatia	...	...	...	169	181		
Cuba	396	530	580	172	124		
Czech Rep.	...	...	...	256	301		
Denmark	598	627	633	485	468		
Ecuador	...	...	67	96	166		
Egypt	373	664	965	973	852		
Ethiopia	...	...	...	140	46		
Finland	486	489	443	346	385		
France	4,651	5,609	5,683	4,611	4,712	5	4
Germany	4,763	5,169	3,272	2,672	2,906	6	2
Greece	337	527	685	526	535		
Guatemala	...	...	132	160	183		
Hungary	837	1,399	671	209	314		
India	2,177	5,231	12,584	12,366	13,520	3	11
Indonesia	240	1,173	2,387	2,589	2,558	7	2
Iran	95	572	1,161	907	1,017		
Iraq	...	...	209	282	376		
Ireland	423	601	692	710	753		
Italy	1,338	2,111	1,984	1,902	1,891		
Japan	2,139	1,816	1,839	1,817	1,783		
Kazakhstan	...	...	...	324	122		
Kenya	...	...	116	103	138		
Korea, North	309	729	832	781	753		
Korea, South	563	803	916	974	960		
Malaysia	193	453	952	958	1,206		
Mexico	538	1,238	1,799	1,592	1,534		
Morocco	88	259	326	336	290		
Netherlands	650	679	559	522	517		
New Zealand	448	464	362	616	611		
Nigeria	7	174	400	506	394		
Norway	119	259	200	204	207		
Pakistan	283	1,080	1,893	2,147	2,185	10	2
Peru	84	118	125	152	209		
Philippines	201	334	588	566	602		
Poland	2,572	3,499	1,752	1,282	1,429		
Portugal	129	259	278	249	254		
Romania	594	1,223	1,103	604	386		
Russia	...	...	...	3,851	1,540		
Saudi Arabia	5	41	489	455	360		
South Africa	558	1,064	792	844	832		
Spain	1,216	1,662	1,976	1,914	1,844		
Sweden	503	484	328	333	319		
Switzerland	148	181	168	150	146		
Syria	40	126	303	374	351		
Taiwan	679	1,360	1,400	1,400	1,500		
Thailand	81	296	1,044	1,207	1,280		
Turkey	431	1,456	1,888	2,207	1,508		
Turkmenistan	...	...	...	160	125		
Ukraine	...	...	...	1,343	1,200		
United Kingdom	1,894	2,054	2,370	2,086	2,298	8	2
United States	15,535	21,480	18,587	20,350	19,286	2	16
Uzbekistan	...	...	...	636	483		
Venezuela	100	241	427	274	240		
Vietnam	311	196	544	934	1,219		
Zimbabwe	106	173	177	157	171		

Energy

Production, trade and consumption *million tonnes of coal-equivalent*
Consumption – tonnes of c-e per person

	Production	Production	Imports	Imports	Exports	Exports	Consumption per capita	Consumption per capita	Consumption per capita % change	Consumption total
	1980	1994	1980	1994	1980	1994	1980	1994	1980–94	1994
WORLD	**9,264**	**11,893**	**3,256**	**4,222**	**3,221**	**4,233**	**1.92**	**1.99**	**4**	**11,258**
Afghanistan	3.69	0.30	0.49	0.45	3.36	0	0.05	0.04	–27	0.73
Albania	4.99	1.41	0.17	0	0.06	...	1.13	0.30	–73	1.03
Algeria	102.10	153.00	2.38	1.27	70.03	106.64	1.33	1.58	19	43.26
American Samoa	0	0	0.20	0.27	0	0	6.28	2.55	–59	0.14
Angola	11.04	36.46	0.23	0.02	9.21	33.90	0.14	0.08	–39	0.89
Antigua & Barbuda	0	0	0.21	0.22	0	0.01	0.84	2.28	171	0.15
Argentina	51.13	90.75	7.44	7.35	2.06	19.71	1.75	2.15	23	73.51
Armenia	...	0.43	...	1.96	...	0	...	0.61	...	2.16
Australia	112.97	237.00	19.09	27.63	39.35	139.34	6.20	7.61	23	135.93
Austria	9.66	8.46	23.98	26.78	0.90	2.34	4.06	4.16	3	32.95
Azerbaijan	...	21.66	...	4.35	...	0.31	...	2.60	...	19.44
Bahamas	0	0	16.08	4.05	9.87	3.00	5.51	2.97	–46	0.81
Bahrain	7.74	12.07	13.88	14.60	13.63	14.52	12.65	17.06	35	9.37
Bangladesh	1.62	8.22	2.70	3.10	0.03	0	0.04	0.09	100	10.39
Barbados	0.08	0.12	0.42	0.50	0	0.03	1.17	1.58	35	0.41
Belarus	...	4.34	...	36.17	...	4.27	...	3.38	...	34.34
Belgium	7.48	15.53	87.63	90.90	25.46	26.74	6.00	6.86	14	69.16
Belize	0	0	0.11	0.13	0	0	0.63	0.57	–10	0.12
Benin	0	0.44	0.22	0.28	0.02	0.44	0.05	0.05	–12	0.24
Bermuda	0	0	0.27	0.24	0	0	2.86	3.46	21	0.22
Bhutan	0	0.20	0	0.06	0	0.17	0.01	0.05	500	0.08
Bolivia	4.66	6.56	0.02	0.11	2.54	2.89	0.38	0.49	27	3.52
Bosnia-Herzegovina	...	0.69	...	0.42	...	0.05	...	0.36	...	1.27
Brazil	34.50	88.41	70.80	67.29	2.76	7.43	0.76	0.85	11	135.21
British Virgin Islands	0	0	0.01	0.03	0	0	1.00	1.39	39	0.03
Brunei	31.71	25.76	0.10	0	27.60	22.87	19.91	15.23	–24	4.26
Bulgaria	17.06	13.11	33.23	19.66	0.16	2.91	5.25	3.26	–38	28.72
Burkina Faso	0	0.01	0.21	0.46	0	0	0.03	0.05	39	0.47
Burma (Myanmar)	2.84	3.05	0.21	0.58	0.08	0	0.06	0.08	21	3.41
Burundi	0	0.02	0.06	0.11	0	...	0.01	0.02	57	0.13
Cambodia	0.01	0.01	0.02	0.23	0	0	0.01	0.02	200	0.24
Cameroon	4.09	8.15	0.88	0.02	2.34	6.28	0.24	0.14	–42	1.82
Canada	280.88	482.34	59.48	61.12	78.30	218.49	10.55	11.21	6	326.66
Cape Verde	0	0	0.18	0.06	0	0	0.15	0.15	0	0.06
Cayman Islands	0	0	0.05	0.15	0	0	2.88	4.50	56	0.14
Central African Republic	0.01	0.01	0.09	0.13	0	0	0.04	0.04	0	0.13
Chad	0	0	0.13	0.08	0	0	0.02	0.01	–70	0.05
Chile	5.77	7.51	6.20	14.11	0.13	0.15	1.03	1.45	41	20.30
China	615.11	1,142.63	2.70	41.21	28.39	53.37	0.57	0.92	61	1,092.54
Colombia	21.90	63.91	4.86	2.76	2.17	33.89	0.92	1.00	8	34.39
Comoros	0	0	0.02	0.03	0	0	0.05	0.05	13	0.03
Congo	4.62	13.14	0.16	0.02	4.51	11.45	0.10	0.34	246	0.86
Congo (Zaïre)	2.13	2.69	1.30	1.62	1.29	1.71	0.07	0.06	–20	2.36
Costa Rica	0.26	0.86	1.22	2.34	0	0.09	0.55	0.87	58	2.90
Croatia	...	5.42	...	6.81	...	3.77	...	1.59	...	7.16
Cuba	0.43	1.52	15.14	12.36	0.80	0.13	1.39	1.14	–18	12.53
Cyprus	0	0	1.40	2.92	0	0	1.92	3.03	57	2.22
Czech Republic	...	42.67	...	23.42	...	11.66	...	4.97	...	51.21
Denmark	0.44	19.70	30.63	25.74	2.48	17.33	5.25	5.15	–2	26.64
Djibouti	0	0	0.71	0.78	0	0	1.04	0.33	–69	0.19
Dominica	0	0	0.01	0.03	0	0	0.19	0.51	164	0.04
Dominican Republic	0.07	0.23	2.91	5.02	0	0	0.50	0.65	30	5.00
Ecuador	15.32	26.20	0.84	0.67	9.85	19.96	0.71	0.77	9	8.66
Egypt	45.97	82.12	1.92	1.63	13.69	37.36	0.49	0.66	35	40.56
El Salvador	0.18	0.87	1.01	2.07	0	0.03	0.20	0.50	153	2.84
Equatorial Guinea	0	0	0.03	0.06	0	0	0.08	0.15	100	0.06
Estonia	...	4.08	...	4.05	...	0.55	...	4.90	...	7.54
(former) Ethiopia	0.06	0.22	1.23	1.65	0.23	0.23	0.03	0.03	7	1.53
Falkland Islands	0	0.01	0	0.01	0	0	2.50	8.50	240	0.02
Faroe Islands	0.01	0.01	0.20	0.28	0	...	5.00	6.11	22	0.29
Fiji	0	0.05	0.58	0.56	0.10	0.17	0.55	0.47	–13	0.37
Finland	2.98	11.71	29.56	32.21	2.83	5.08	5.51	7.40	34	37.62
France	50.30	159.40	234.73	188.71	22.81	32.07	4.41	5.15	17	297.61
French Guiana	0	0	0.17	0.43	0	0	2.64	2.89	10	0.41
French Polynesia	0	0.01	0.25	0.32	0	0	0.93	1.27	37	0.27
Gabon	13.17	22.81	0.06	0.06	12.17	20.52	0.80	0.87	10	1.12
Gambia	0	0	0.08	0.11	0	0	0.13	0.10	–21	0.11
Georgia	...	0.73	...	4.32	...	0.03	...	0.85	...	4.63
Germany	247.05	200.68	296.58	303.89	38.99	30.08	6.50	5.48	–16	444.98
Ghana	0.78	0.75	1.50	1.85	0.59	0.12	0.13	0.14	4	2.33
Gibraltar	0	0	0.24	1.38	0	0	1.03	3.39	228	0.10
Greece	4.76	11.78	34.47	28.50	14.00	4.88	2.09	3.22	54	33.58

	Production	Production	Imports	Imports	Exports	Exports	Consumption per capita	Consumption per capita	Consumption per capita % change	Consumption total
	1980	1994	1980	1994	1980	1994	1980	1994	1980–94	1994
Greenland	0	0	0.26	0.25	0	0.01	5.51	4.10	−25	0.24
Grenada	0	0	0.02	0.08	0	0	0.22	0.84	274	0.08
Guadeloupe	0	0	0.23	0.76	0	0	0.76	1.54	105	0.65
Guam	0	0	2.63	0.85	0.86	0	8.54	4.70	−45	0.69
Guatemala	0.34	0.79	2.12	2.82	0.09	0.33	0.27	0.29	8	2.97
Guinea	0.01	0.02	0.42	0.53	0	0	0.09	0.08	−6	0.54
Guinea-Bissau	0	0	0.04	0.12	0	0	0.05	0.10	93	0.11
Guyana	0	0	0.74	0.52	0	0	0.84	0.60	−29	0.50
Haiti	0.03	0.02	0.32	0.25	0	0	0.06	0.04	−32	0.26
Honduras	0.10	0.30	0.93	1.38	0.03	0	0.25	0.31	26	1.69
Hong Kong	0	0	9.31	28.03	0.30	7.82	1.45	2.36	63	13.76
Hungary	21.98	17.84	23.75	19.45	2.77	2.54	3.79	3.27	−14	33.26
Iceland	0.38	0.87	0.84	1.05	0	0	4.90	6.70	37	1.78
India	113.53	296.52	32.83	68.13	0.10	0.10	0.20	0.37	85	343.70
Indonesia	134.04	255.31	10.56	18.35	97.39	150.64	0.23	0.47	102	90.45
Iran	117.91	317.54	0.24	7.76	63.35	194.47	1.18	1.88	60	123.55
Iraq	191.58	57.43	0.01	0	178.70	5.58	0.81	1.76	118	35.08
Ireland	2.60	5.34	9.40	11.53	0.40	1.43	3.27	4.31	32	15.24
Israel	0.22	0.04	12.98	23.63	0.79	4.17	2.27	3.26	43	17.80
Italy	26.27	43.40	181.98	211.31	15.03	28.99	3.11	3.95	27	225.80
Ivory Coast	0.34	0.61	2.86	4.85	0.79	0.39	0.20	0.26	29	3.51
Jamaica	0.02	0.01	3.99	4.01	0.06	0.07	1.79	1.66	−7	4.03
Japan	42.26	121.78	440.69	558.84	2.17	11.90	3.73	4.98	34	621.32
Jordan	0	0.01	2.55	5.57	0	0	0.69	1.01	47	5.27
Kazakstan	...	127.52	...	23.23	...	48.34	...	5.93	...	100.95
Kenya	0.13	0.70	4.93	3.71	1.64	0.65	0.14	0.12	−12	3.29
Kiribati	0	0	0.01	0.01	0	0	0.21	0.13	−37	0.01
Korea, North	44.77	90.29	4.12	8.05	0.10	0.44	2.71	4.21	55	98.83
Korea, South	12.91	27.07	45.88	181.56	0.16	16.95	1.37	3.77	175	168.09
Kuwait	131.75	156.61	0	0	115.74	176.31	5.02	9.85	96	16.08
Kyrgyzstan	...	2.07	...	2.65	...	1.13	...	0.76	...	3.56
Laos	0.11	0.11	0.20	0.14	0.09	0.08	0.06	0.04	−35	0.17
Latvia	...	0.61	...	5.43	...	0.22	...	2.30	...	5.94
Lebanon	0.11	0.12	3.18	5.41	0.15	0	0.95	1.83	92	5.32
Liberia	0.04	0.02	0.95	0.17	0	0	0.40	0.06	−86	0.17
Libya	135.08	106.42	0.92	0.01	124.56	87.22	2.46	3.34	36	17.45
Lithuania	...	3.11	...	11.67	...	3.99	...	3.04	...	11.27
Luxembourg	0.04	0.09	5.07	5.37	0.10	0.08	13.43	12.82	−4	5.14
Macau	0	0	0.22	0.61	0	0	0.78	1.50	92	0.60
Macedonia	...	2.73	...	1.24	...	0.02	...	1.90	...	4.07
Madagascar	0.02	0.04	1.06	0.59	0.16	0.03	0.10	0.04	−59	0.57
Malawi	0.05	0.10	0.32	0.31	0	0	0.06	0.04	−38	0.39
Malaysia	19.78	78.78	10.11	17.49	16.48	47.12	0.88	2.29	160	45.11
Mali	0.01	0.03	0.21	0.24	0	0	0.03	0.02	−17	0.25
Malta	0	0	0.61	0.84	0	0	1.25	1.97	58	0.72
Martinique	0	0	0.52	1.22	0.29	0.27	1.01	2.15	113	0.81
Mauritania	0	0	0.31	1.51	0	0	0.18	0.61	242	1.35
Mauritius	0.01	0.01	0.45	1.05	0	0	0.33	0.70	112	0.77
Mexico	198.10	283.07	1.42	14.34	68.85	104.63	1.71	2.03	19	186.57
Moldova	...	0.03	...	7.38	...	0.62	...	1.55	...	6.85
Mongolia	1.71	2.93	0.90	0.91	0	0.17	1.57	1.55	−1	3.67
Morocco	0.98	0.80	6.17	13.04	0.14	0	0.32	0.47	46	12.35
Mozambique	2.07	0.05	1.30	0.51	1.48	0	0.13	0.03	−77	0.47
Nauru	0	0	0.07	0.07	0	0	8.43	5.73	−32	0.06
Nepal	0.02	0.11	0.17	0.64	0	0.05	0.01	0.03	162	0.73
Netherlands	117.89	102.62	103.08	133.27	107.79	111.56	6.54	7.22	10	111.12
Netherlands Antilles	0	0	48.14	22.30	34.18	13.33	16.85	6.26	−63	1.23
New Caledonia	0.03	0.04	0.90	0.79	0	0.02	6.46	4.39	−32	0.78
New Zealand	5.78	16.13	5.68	6.32	0.10	2.55	3.15	5.47	73	19.30
Nicaragua	0.06	0.68	0.96	0.84	0	0.01	0.33	0.36	8	1.52
Niger	0.02	0.17	0.26	0.36	0	0	0.05	0.06	14	0.51
Nigeria	153.77	143.88	0.49	3.30	141.38	114.61	0.14	0.21	54	22.68
Norway	82.66	241.34	15.68	6.87	71.45	210.27	6.42	7.44	16	32.16
Oman	20.40	66.65	1.23	0.06	20.12	55.59	0.73	5.41	646	11.23
Pakistan	11.26	28.79	10.22	18.40	1.14	0.42	0.19	0.33	74	45.35
Panama	0.15	0.29	6.18	3.74	0.42	0.47	0.85	1.20	41	3.10
Papua New Guinea	0.04	8.02	0.89	1.10	0	7.88	0.28	0.29	3	1.20
Paraguay	0.07	4.40	0.52	1.60	0	4.03	0.23	0.38	63	1.83
Peru	16.57	10.90	0.23	3.10	4.65	3.18	0.69	0.46	−34	10.65
Philippines	1.69	9.52	15.80	22.24	0.13	0.74	0.35	0.43	23	28.22
Poland	173.84	134.56	35.36	29.98	29.97	28.29	4.94	3.51	−29	134.45
Portugal	1.10	1.44	14.08	27.74	0.60	5.95	1.15	2.13	85	20.98
Puerto Rico	0.02	0.04	13.58	11.44	4.90	1.04	3.64	3.07	−15	11.20
Qatar	39.33	47.74	0.09	0	32.83	28.68	26.67	35.20	32	19.01
Réunion	0.04	0.06	0.35	0.77	0	0	0.70	1.26	79	0.81
Romania	85.71	44.00	31.83	23.55	12.41	7.17	4.51	2.54	−44	58.31

	Production	Production	Imports	Imports	Exports	Exports	Consumption per capita	Consumption per capita	Consumption per capita % change	Consumption total
	1980	1994	1980	1994	1980	1994	1980	1994	1980–94	1994
Russia	...	1,384.01	...	38.58	...	475.61	...	6.00	...	883.60
Rwanda	0.02	0.02	0.08	0.24	0	0	0.02	0.03	78	0.25
St Kitts & Nevis	0	0	0.03	0.05	0	0	0.48	1.15	138	0.05
St Lucia	0	0	0.05	0.09	0	0	0.44	0.64	44	0.09
St Pierre & Miquelon	0	0	0.05	0.06	0	0	2.83	5.50	94	0.03
St Vincent & Grenadines	0	0	0.02	0.06	0	0	0.20	0.54	168	0.06
São Tomé & Príncipe	0	0	0.02	0.04	0	0	0.20	0.29	46	0.04
Saudi Arabia	741.16	656.07	2.85	0	693.99	507.73	2.75	5.77	110	100.68
Senegal	0	0	2.00	1.72	0.22	0.06	0.19	0.16	−16	1.32
Seychelles	0	0	0.10	0.24	0	0	0.89	1.10	23	0.08
Sierra Leone	0	0	0.49	0.50	0	0	0.08	0.05	−45	0.20
Singapore	0	0	52.67	104.71	30.18	59.84	3.71	9.67	161	27.29
Slovak Republic	...	6.49	...	19.02	...	2.34	...	4.07	...	21.73
Slovenia	...	3.16	...	3.33	...	0.31	...	3.11	...	6.04
Solomon Islands	0	0	0.05	0.08	0	0	0.21	0.20	−4	0.07
Somalia	0	0	0.78	0.55	0.14	0.06	0.10	0.05	−46	0.43
Southern Africa *	93.52	145.45	24.46	24.30	23.53	43.32	2.75	2.73	−1	126.28
Spain	21.25	39.92	82.46	108.67	1.69	12.62	2.36	3.01	28	119.22
Sri Lanka	0.18	0.50	2.84	3.30	0.27	0.13	0.11	0.16	45	2.90
Sudan	0.06	0.12	1.72	1.83	0.02	0.01	0.08	0.06	−27	1.64
Surinam	0.11	0.56	1.11	0.67	0	0.07	3.39	2.01	−41	0.84
Sweden	10.57	34.81	45.99	41.54	7.65	13.06	5.38	6.79	26	59.37
Switzerland	5.80	13.96	21.63	23.57	2.35	4.31	3.36	4.50	34	32.22
Syria	12.50	45.50	8.67	0.65	11.77	26.62	0.84	1.28	53	18.12
Tajikistan	...	2.22	...	2.08	...	0.71	...	0.58	...	3.43
Tanzania	0.07	0.08	0.94	1.06	0.08	0.04	0.04	0.04	−18	1.04
Thailand	0.64	24.44	16.89	40.38	0.02	1.62	0.37	1.07	188	62.43
Togo	0	0	0.73	0.32	0.50	0.01	0.11	0.08	−32	0.31
Tonga	0	0	0.02	0.06	0	0	0.20	0.51	158	0.05
Trindad & Tobago	20.98	17.61	10.68	2.48	22.51	9.82	6.99	7.53	8	9.73
Tunisia	8.75	6.77	2.91	5.40	6.71	5.09	0.64	0.75	17	6.55
Turkey	14.40	26.66	20.53	48.59	0.20	0.31	0.72	1.16	61	70.25
Turkmenistan	...	46.99	...	0.13	...	30.49	...	3.68	...	14.77
Uganda	0.08	0.10	0.32	0.47	0.04	0.02	0.03	0.03	0	0.55
Ukraine	...	146.65	...	95.37	...	4.46	...	4.39	...	226.12
United Arab Emirates	137.85	190.62	4.73	0.56	124.21	150.25	17.19	21.03	22	39.13
United Kingdom	280.16	347.70	95.22	107.82	78.93	145.11	4.85	5.33	10	311.00
United States	2,045.68	2,447.50	534.03	736.97	101.49	114.65	10.39	11.39	10	2,968.74
US Virgin Islands	0	0	40.15	24.47	26.46	18.49	44.58	44.34	−1	4.61
Uruguay	0.43	0.92	2.99	2.30	0.15	0.21	0.95	0.78	−18	2.47
Uzbekistan	...	65.25	...	13.35	...	12.90	...	2.94	...	65.61
Vanuatu	0	0	0.06	0.03	0.00	0	0.25	0.18	−72	0.03
Venezuela	193.94	261.26	0.24	0.29	139.35	171.54	3.14	3.75	19	80.07
Vietnam	5.35	17.67	1.71	5.60	0.50	11.98	0.12	0.16	30	11.55
Wake Island		0		0.59		0	...	29.00	...	0.03
Western Sahara	0	0	0.08	0.10	0	0	0.57	0.34	−41	0.09
Western Samoa	0	0	0.05	0.06	0	0	0.31	0.37	20	0.06
Yemen	0	23.28	3.58	0.53	0.97	18.63	0.40	0.33	−18	4.56
Yugoslavia (Serbia)	...	11.90	...	2.09	...	0.05	...	1.22	...	13.15
Zambia	1.61	1.27	1.13	0.81	0.46	0.25	0.40	0.19	−54	1.72
Zimbabwe	3.26	5.76	1.33	1.79	0.33	0.03	0.57	0.70	22	7.65

* Southern Africa includes Botswana, Lesotho, Namibia and Swaziland.

World trade

The total value of the imports and exports for the year stated is shown in the left-hand column of figures. These total figures are divided into percentages for the ten basic groups of the Standard International Trade Classification (SITC). These are the latest figures divided into the SITC groupings that are available.

In the next column to the right, the latest total figure for imports and exports is given. This figure is usually for 1995, but if earlier the numeral in the next column gives the year. In the extreme right-hand column the latest available trade figure has been divided by the population, giving the value of imports and exports per capita.

SITC GROUP	Year		Total million $US	**Percentages** Food and live animals 0	Beverages and tobacco 1	Crude materials (inedible) excluding fuels 2	Mineral fuels, lubricants & related materials 3	Animal and vegetable oils and fats 4	Chemicals 5	Manu-factured goods 6	Machinery and transport equipment 7	Misc. manu-factured goods 8	Misc. transactions and goods 9	Trade total for 1995 (or latest available year) million $US	Latest year (if not 1995)	Trade per capita
Afghanistan	1981	Imports	622	12.5	0.7	1.3	17.9	4.2	7.2	25.3	23.9	3.5	3.5	616		19
	1991	Exports	694	33.9	0.0	38.9	12.6	0.0	0.6	13.5	0.0	0.5	0.0	188		6
Algeria	1994	Imports	9,599	29.7	0.8	3.9	0.6	2.3	10.7	21.7	26.8	3.4	0.1	10,250		375
		Exports	8,594	0.4	0.0	0.3	97.1	0.0	1.1	0.9	0.2	0.0	0.1	10,240		375
Angola	1981	Imports	1,678	24.5	1.4	1.6	0.8	4.3	12.1	20.2	20.9	14.2	0.0	2,042	1993	198
	1992	Exports	3,698	0.1	0.0	7.3	92.6	0.0	0.0	0.0	0.0	0.0	0.0	3,179		309
Antigua & Barbuda	1991	Imports	246	12.3	3.3	2.0	9.9	0.0	6.2	27.0	26.8	12.3	0.2	661		9,443
		Exports	39.8	2.8	1.2	0.3	25.0	0.0	7.1	8.4	30.2	24.9	0.0	248		3,543
Argentina	1994	Imports	21,581	4.6	0.4	2.7	3.0	0.0	13.6	13.2	51.8	10.4	0.2	20,122		579
		Exports	15,839	35.3	1.0	9.1	10.5	9.6	5.8	13.2	11.2	4.1	0.3	20,967		603
Australia	1994	Imports	52,082	3.6	0.7	2.3	4.5	0.3	8.9	13.8	43.4	14.3	8.3	60,317		3,342
		Exports	49,097	13.2	0.7	13.7	14.4	0.3	3.4	11.5	11.1	3.4	28.3	53,097		2,942
Austria	1994	Imports	55,290	4.8	0.4	4.2	4.5	0.0	9.9	19.5	37.9	18.1	0.6	66,272		8,253
		Exports	40,159	2.9	0.5	3.9	1.2	0.0	8.6	29.1	39.0	14.3	0.5	57,540		7,166
Bahamas	1991	Imports	1,091	18.6	2.5	2.1	11.0	0.0	9.0	16.3	24.0	15.8	0.7	1,243		4,439
		Exports	225	25.6	15.4	12.6	16.2	0.0	14.1	5.4	8.7	1.8	0.2	1,517		5,418
Bahrain	1994	Imports	3,737	7.9	1.6	1.4	33.4	0.8	8.6	15.1	21.6	7.7	1.9	3,716		6,298
		Exports	3,454	0.8	0.0	0.4	64.4	1.1	2.2	25.6	1.6	3.5	0.3	4,113		6,971
Bangladesh	1993	Imports	2,709	8.4	0.6	30.7	9.6	5.4	6.7	17.9	13.6	6.4	0.8	6,501		55
		Exports	2,138	12.1	0.1	3.7	0.9	0.0	2.4	21.6	0.0	58.9	0.3	3,173		27
Barbados	1994	Imports	611	17.0	2.3	4.1	8.7	0.5	12.4	17.1	24.0	13.6	0.2	766		2,946
		Exports	185	24.7	6.7	0.8	14.9	0.0	14.1	13.7	17.5	7.1	0.5	238		915
Belgium–Lux.	1994	Imports	125,762	8.8	1.3	5.1	6.9	0.5	13.0	22.7	25.5	11.0	5.3	155,109		14,702
		Exports	137,394	9.1	0.9	2.3	3.1	0.4	16.7	27.4	28.1	8.5	3.6	169,620		16,078
Belize	1994	Imports	260	15.1	3.0	0.9	11.3	0.0	10.1	20.5	25.5	13.3	0.3	256		1,164
		Exports	143	67.7	2.8	3.0	2.4	0.0	1.4	1.6	5.8	15.3	0.0	162		736
Benin	1989	Imports	207	19.4	7.1	3.7	15.3	0.8	7.1	30.7	14.5	0.0	1.3	694		125
		Exports	97.5	0.7	0.0	64.4	21.3	6.3	0.4	4.4	2.0	0.0	0.5	189		34
Bermuda	1993	Imports	535	15.9	3.7	0.8	5.8	0.0	13.9	12.0	23.3	24.2	0.3	630		10,000
	1992	Exports	84.3	0.0	0.0	0.0	0.0	0.0	90.0	0.0	0.0	0.0	10.0	53		841
Bhutan	1988	Imports	127	11.6	3.2	1.1	8.1	1.8	3.6	13.9	48.4	4.9	3.5	630		384
		Exports	74.9	18.7	2.4	22.0	32.6	0.0	7.6	16.4	0.0	0.2	0.0	53		32
Bolivia	1994	Imports	1,196	9.4	0.4	3.6	5.1	0.1	12.8	17.0	43.1	7.0	1.5	1,424		192
		Exports	1,124	14.0	0.3	29.3	9.5	1.9	0.6	14.0	2.6	16.9	10.8	1,101		149
Brazil	1994	Imports	35,553	9.0	0.4	5.6	14.9	1.0	16.3	8.9	38.2	5.7	0.0	53,783		345
		Exports	43,558	21.1	2.6	12.5	1.8	2.2	5.8	24.7	20.6	7.1	1.5	46,506		298
Brunei	1991	Imports	1,208	12.9	2.4	1.2	0.6	0.3	6.3	27.4	38.3	10.1	0.5	1,695	1994	6,054
		Exports	2,682	0.4	0.0	0.0	96.7	0.0	0.0	0.4	1.3	0.9	0.3	2,296		8,200
Bulgaria	1993	Imports	4,962	5.9	2.4	4.1	35.1	0.1	9.2	12.4	18.8	5.9	6.2	5,026		598
		Exports	3,500	8.6	9.5	5.7	8.7	0.8	14.6	25.1	17.2	9.8	0.0	5,091		606
Burkina Faso	1991	Imports	536	19.4	2.2	1.9	11.6	2.1	18.5	23.5	20.8	0.0	0.0	549		54
		Exports	105	12.8	0.1	69.6	0.0	1.6	0.0	14.9	1.0	0.0	0.1	537		53
Burma (Myanmar)	1992	Imports	880	2.7	0.3	0.3	1.6	7.4	11.5	16.1	27.7	3.1	29.4	1,335		30
		Exports	599	36.0	0.0	33.4	0.0	0.0	0.0	7.7	0.0	3.3	19.7	851		19
Burundi	1993	Imports	205	9.9	0.4	2.7	12.4	0.5	14.1	21.0	21.3	4.0	13.7	234		39
		Exports	68.7	76.1	3.1	6.0	0.0	0.0	1.4	6.4	0.0	0.0	7.0	108		18
Cameroon	1991	Imports	2,306	13.6	1.2	7.1	3.4	1.2	14.7	24.0	27.1	7.4	0.3	1,245		94
		Exports	2,892	18.9	0.5	14.0	47.5	1.9	7.0	8.2	7.5	0.8	0.3	2,047		154
Canada	1994	Imports	147,851	5.3	0.5	3.2	3.5	0.0	7.6	13.0	51.5	12.1	3.3	168,053		5,676
		Exports	165,837	6.1	0.5	11.8	9.7	0.0	5.3	15.3	40.0	4.8	6.4	192,204		6,491
Cape Verde Islands	1990	Imports	136	21.2	3.6	2.9	7.5	3.0	6.1	18.0	30.7	6.9	0.0	210	1994	551
		Exports	28.6	18.1	0.0	0.3	65.1	0.0	0.9	1.2	11.1	3.2	0.2	5		13
Cayman Is.	1991	Imports	267	18.9	4.9	2.4	10.1	0.0	5.9	13.0	25.8	17.9	1.2	399		13,300
		Exports	2.9	0.0	0.0	0.0	0.0	0.0	0.0	0.0	0.0	0.0	100.0	4		133
Central African Rep.	1989	Imports	159	14.3	3.6	1.7	6.7	1.1	14.0	17.8	33.2	7.4	0.2	175		54
		Exports	140	28.8	1.7	24.9	0.0	0.0	0.0	42.2	0.0	0.0	2.4	171		52
Chad	1975	Imports	110	11.6	2.0	2.1	14.2	0.8	16.4	18.4	28.9	5.4	0.2	220		67
		Exports	40	14.9	0.3	68.6	7.9	0.0	0.5	1.6	5.4	0.0	0.8	252		77
Chile	1994	Imports	11,149	5.7	0.0	2.5	9.9	1.0	11.7	15.2	42.5	9.9	1.7	15,914		1,121
		Exports	11,369	24.0	1.5	25.6	0.2	0.4	4.6	33.5	2.7	3.0	4.4	16,039		1,130
China	1994	Imports	115,614	2.7	0.1	6.2	3.5	1.6	10.4	24.9	44.4	5.6	0.6	129,113		106
		Exports	121,006	8.3	0.8	3.4	3.4	0.4	5.1	19.7	18.0	40.7	0.3	148,797		122
Colombia	1994	Imports	11,889	7.2	0.3	3.6	2.7	0.7	16.3	15.9	41.0	6.4	5.8	13,853		395
		Exports	8,917	35.4	0.4	5.8	20.1	0.0	5.9	13.9	5.8	11.9	0.8	10,126		288

	Year		Total million $US	Percentages Food and live animals	Beverages and tobacco	Crude materials (inedible) excluding fuels	Mineral fuels, lubricants & related materials	Animal and vegetable oils and fats	Chemicals	Manufactured goods	Machinery and transport equipment	Misc. manufactured goods	Misc. transactions and goods	Trade total for 1995 (or latest available year) million $US	Latest year (if not 1995)	Trade per capita
Comoros	1993	Imports	67.8	25.9	0.0	0.0	10.7	0.0	2.0	9.8	9.0	2.3	40.4	69	1992	118
		Exports	25.1	81.8	0.0	0.0	0.0	0.0	13.3	0.0	0.0	0.0	4.8	22		38
Congo	1990	Imports	594	12.2	1.1	0.0	0.0	0.0	12.9	14.7	34.5	4.2	20.3	670		259
		Exports	978	1.5	0.0	5.6	84.9	0.0	0.0	2.4	0.0	0.0	5.6	842		325
Congo (Zaïre)	1986	Imports	1,332	19.4	1.0	2.5	9.9	0.0	10.0	14.7	38.2	3.2	1.0	382		8
	1978	Exports	899	28.0	0.0	11.2	1.4	1.0	0.2	55.7	0.6	0.0	1.8	419		9
Costa Rica	1992	Imports	2,789	6.2	0.4	2.6	8.7	0.0	16.3	20.4	25.5	8.7	11.4	3,253		977
		Exports	1,834	59.7	0.0	5.0	0.5	0.5	5.6	9.5	3.3	7.5	8.4	2,702		811
Croatia	1993	Imports	4,666	7.7	0.8	3.7	9.9	0.3	12.0	27.3	24.1	14.0	0.0	7,583		1,586
		Exports	3,904	9.5	1.4	6.1	9.7	0.3	14.1	15.7	14.2	28.2	1.3	4,633		969
Cuba	1989	Imports	8,122	11.0	0.0	3.4	32.4	1.0	6.2	9.6	27.5	4.0	5.0	2,825		258
		Exports	5,392	80.1	1.9	9.7	0.0	0.0	1.2	0.9	0.8	0.4	5.0	1,600		146
Cyprus	1994	Imports	3,014	8.6	8.5	2.0	8.4	0.8	8.1	20.6	27.2	10.3	5.4	3,690		4,986
		Exports	961	14.5	27.3	1.8	3.9	1.3	6.6	13.5	12.2	18.8	0.1	1,229		1,661
Czech Rep.	1994	Imports	14,788	6.9	1.3	4.8	10.2	0.4	12.5	16.8	34.8	12.2	0.1	25,313		2,450
		Exports	14,318	5.1	1.2	7.0	5.7	0.0	9.7	31.7	26.0	13.1	0.6	21,686		2,099
Denmark	1994	Imports	33,937	11.0	1.3	4.0	4.4	0.5	10.9	18.1	32.4	14.0	3.4	43,231		8,266
		Exports	39,835	24.6	1.1	3.7	2.6	0.4	9.3	10.7	25.8	15.3	6.6	49,045		9,378
Djibouti	1992	Imports	220	19.9	5.6	10.7	8.1	1.5	6.8	16.0	19.2	8.2	4.1	219	1992	401
		Exports	15.9	21.3	0.3	4.5	0.0	0.3	0.1	5.2	7.9	0.5	59.8	16		29
Dominica	1991	Imports	110	18.6	4.8	2.1	7.9	2.4	12.0	22.4	21.6	8.2	0.0	96	1994	1,352
		Exports	54.2	65.7	0.7	1.2	0.0	0.0	23.7	2.3	4.3	2.0	0.0	45		634
Dominican Republic	1985	Imports	1,248	6.4	0.2	3.5	35.3	3.9	11.6	13.7	23.1	2.3	0.0	2,976		376
	1991	Exports	658	45.6	2.9	0.0	0.0	0.5	49.2	34.2	0.0	0.0	−32.5	765		97
Ecuador	1993	Imports	2,553	3.9	0.6	2.8	1.7	0.4	15.3	17.5	49.0	8.2	0.7	4,193		366
		Exports	3,020	46.6	0.3	2.2	41.4	0.0	1.1	2.8	2.3	1.0	2.3	4,307		376
Egypt	1994	Imports	9,592	23.6	1.5	7.5	1.4	2.0	12.0	19.0	29.0	3.9	0.0	11,760		199
		Exports	3,475	7.7	0.0	8.8	39.2	0.0	4.6	30.1	0.5	8.8	0.3	3,450		58
El Salvador	1994	Imports	2,262	11.4	0.6	3.6	9.5	2.6	16.5	17.7	30.8	7.2	0.1	2,853		504
		Exports	813	49.1	1.0	1.7	0.5	0.4	12.0	21.1	3.0	11.0	0.1	998		176
Equatorial Guinea	1990	Imports	61.6	7.0	5.2	4.2	7.7	0.5	3.9	6.4	58.2	4.4	2.5	50		125
		Exports	61.7	10.9	5.2	32.4	0.0	0.0	0.1	2.2	44.7	0.7	3.7	86		215
Ethiopia	1993	Imports	772	12.2	0.5	1.5	21.6	3.4	13.8	16.1	27.1	3.9	0.0	1,033	1994	19
		Exports	202	68.7	0.0	26.2	4.0	0.4	0.1	0.1	0.0	0.6	0.0	372		7
Fiji	1994	Imports	830	13.7	0.6	0.6	11.3	0.8	7.0	23.7	30.9	9.7	1.7	860		1,075
		Exports	544	44.2	0.0	4.6	7.4	0.5	0.9	4.9	8.0	20.9	8.6	614		768
Finland	1994	Imports	23,358	6.0	0.6	6.6	11.6	0.0	12.4	14.9	35.9	11.1	0.9	28,114		5,502
		Exports	29,765	2.9	0.4	9.9	2.3	0.0	6.4	39.4	31.8	6.8	0.1	39,573		7,744
France	1994	Imports	228,269	9.4	1.2	3.5	7.7	0.4	11.7	16.2	35.2	14.3	0.3	276,981		4,763
		Exports	233,284	11.2	3.2	2.4	2.5	0.0	14.3	16.5	39.3	10.2	0.5	287,334		4,941
French Guiana	1994	Imports	676	13.2	4.5	0.3	6.8	0.4	7.0	12.6	41.5	11.6	2.1	752		5,013
		Exports	149	29.3	0.0	1.9	0.0	0.0	0.9	23.9	25.3	8.1	10.5	131		873
Gabon	1983	Imports	686	13.9	3.4	1.5	1.8	0.7	7.5	22.1	38.5	10.0	0.5	881		667
		Exports	1,475	0.4	0.0	14.2	79.5	0.0	1.2	3.8	0.6	0.3	0.0	2,712		2,055
Gambia	1991	Imports	202	30.4	4.6	0.9	10.7	2.1	6.8	18.1	14.7	10.6	1.2	140		130
		Exports	39.8	14.1	0.0	16.9	0.0	5.2	0.0	0.0	0.0	0.0	63.9	16		15
Germany	1994	Imports	377,992	8.2	1.0	4.4	7.0	0.0	8.5	16.4	33.7	15.9	5.0	444,554		5,445
		Exports	423,995	4.2	0.8	1.8	1.2	0.0	13.0	16.2	49.0	10.7	3.1	508,398		6,227
Ghana	1987	Imports	1,076	5.2	0.4	1.7	14.0	0.5	12.0	22.2	28.1	14.6	1.2	2,175	1992	129
	1985	Exports	623	67.3	0.0	7.4	0.0	0.0	0.0	3.4	0.0	0.3	21.6	1,252		74
Greece	1994	Imports	20,841	12.8	2.1	3.3	9.8	0.4	12.4	18.3	28.5	11.4	0.9	21,489		2,056
		Exports	9,119	20.1	5.5	6.4	10.3	3.7	3.9	20.4	6.1	21.2	2.3	9,392		899
Greenland	1993	Imports	347	12.4	4.1	1.4	11.2	0.0	4.1	18.0	22.5	12.4	13.9	421		7,017
		Exports	312	92.5	0.0	0.0	1.2	0.0	0.0	0.0	1.6	1.4	3.3	364		6,067
Grenada	1991	Imports	117	23.9	1.8	2.6	7.4	0.4	8.5	20.2	24.2	11.1	0.0	107		1,189
		Exports	23.2	67.0	0.0	0.7	0.0	0.0	4.1	9.2	7.4	11.3	0.3	20		222
Guadeloupe	1994	Imports	1,539	17.5	4.6	1.9	1.7	0.6	9.8	15.3	30.5	15.8	2.3	1,890		4,500
		Exports	152	55.7	5.6	0.7	0.0	0.0	1.0	3.6	29.9	3.4	0.1	159		379
Guatemala	1994	Imports	2,647	10.7	0.5	1.6	11.5	1.8	17.4	18.1	31.2	7.0	0.1	3,293		310
		Exports	1,502	57.2	2.3	6.6	1.8	0.6	11.5	12.0	1.8	6.0	0.0	2,156		203
Guinea-Bissau	1980	Imports	55.0	17.0	2.2	2.3	6.2	0.8	5.6	23.9	36.4	3.7	1.9	71		66
		Exports	39.9	1.6	44.7	0.0	0.0	1.2	0.3	6.9	0.0	0.0	5.4	24		22
Guyana	1981	Imports	436	0.0	1.1	0.0	21.9	0.0	1.1	0.0	3.9	0.0	72.1	485	1993	594
	1991	Exports	267	48.5	1.0	31.2	0.0	1.5	0.5	0.5	0.0	0.0	16.8	455		558
Haiti	1984	Imports	472	18.4	1.9	2.8	12.9	7.1	9.1	19.6	19.5	8.0	0.6	654		91
		Exports	179	35.8	0.0	0.0	0.0	0.0	3.2	15.5	0.0	37.6	7.9	112		16
Honduras	1994	Imports	1,335	13.3	0.5	1.5	13.0	0.4	16.8	18.2	28.9	7.4	0.0	1,219		205
		Exports	614	77.1	1.6	5.7	0.1	1.1	2.2	6.2	0.5	5.4	0.2	1,061		178
Hong Kong	1994	Imports	165,894	3.9	1.5	1.8	1.9	0.0	6.5	20.5	34.6	26.2	3.1	192,774		31,143
		Exports	151,479	1.6	1.5	1.5	0.8	0.0	5.5	16.7	31.3	40.3	0.8	173,754		28,070

World trade continued

Country	Year		Total million $US	Percentages Food and live animals	Beverages and tobacco	Crude materials (inedible) excluding fuels	Mineral fuels, lubricants & related materials	Animal and vegetable oils and fats	Chemicals	Manuf-actured goods	Machinery and transport equipment	Misc. manuf-actured goods	Misc. transactions and goods	Trade total for 1995 (or latest available year) million $US	Latest year (if not 1995)	Trade per capita
Hungary	1994	Imports	14,554	5.7	0.6	3.7	11.8	0.0	12.7	19.8	34.1	11.3	0.3	15,046		1,472
		Exports	10,701	16.5	2.0	5.2	4.0	0.9	11.2	16.6	25.6	17.9	0.1	12,435		1,217
Iceland	1994	Imports	1,472	9.4	1.9	4.5	8.3	0.3	8.8	17.4	31.4	17.6	0.4	1,755		6,500
		Exports	1,627	76.6	0.5	1.9	0.0	1.9	0.0	13.7	4.1	0.9	0.4	1,803		6,678
India	1994	Imports	28,655	5.0	0.0	8.3	23.8	0.9	14.6	17.0	19.0	3.0	8.3	34,525		37
		Exports	26,309	14.3	0.4	4.6	2.0	0.6	8.1	40.8	7.1	20.5	1.6	30,640		33
Indonesia	1994	Imports	31,983	5.9	0.4	8.5	7.8	0.3	14.9	16.8	42.0	3.1	0.2	40,948		211
		Exports	40,053	8.9	0.3	8.1	26.3	3.4	2.5	23.8	7.6	18.7	0.4	45,417		234
Iran	1990	Imports	18,722	11.4	0.3	4.0	2.3	1.7	15.4	27.5	33.5	3.6	0.3	30,676	1992	537
		Exports	17,927	2.2	0.0	0.5	92.7	0.0	0.0	3.3	0.0	0.0	1.3	19,868		348
Iraq	1990	Imports	4,834	27.9	1.9	1.6	0.4	0.2	8.8	23.2	30.3	5.7	0.1	4,834	1990	278
		Exports	392	19.9	3.9	40.0	0.5	0.4	22.8	8.5	0.9	3.1	0.0	6,659		383
Ireland	1994	Imports	25,314	8.1	1.2	2.3	3.9	0.4	12.6	11.6	38.6	12.5	8.9	33,068		9,237
		Exports	29,905	20.9	2.1	2.6	0.6	0.0	23.2	6.2	32.4	12.1	0.1	44,638		12,469
Israel	1994	Imports	23,779	5.5	0.4	2.5	6.1	0.4	8.6	31.7	34.6	8.2	2.0	29,568		5,337
		Exports	16,934	4.8	0.0	2.8	0.5	0.4	13.7	35.7	30.6	11.6	0.3	19,038		3,436
Italy	1994	Imports	167,979	10.3	1.1	7.7	8.2	0.8	12.6	16.9	28.2	9.3	5.0	204,047		3,562
		Exports	190,008	5.1	1.3	1.0	1.6	0.3	7.2	22.8	36.7	23.1	0.9	231,331		4,038
Ivory Coast	1989	Imports	2,185	21.0	1.7	1.1	21.3	0.0	14.8	22.8	16.4	0.0	1.0	2,929		231
		Exports	2,931	59.7	0.3	13.5	9.6	2.0	3.4	8.1	2.9	0.0	0.5	3,818		301
Jamaica	1994	Imports	2,171	11.1	1.2	2.9	15.2	0.8	9.9	15.9	24.3	16.4	2.2	2,756		1,089
		Exports	1,224	17.9	3.4	50.6	0.5	0.8	2.0	1.7	2.4	21.4	0.1	1,380		545
Japan	1994	Imports	274,742	15.2	1.7	10.8	17.5	0.0	7.1	11.4	19.1	14.6	2.5	335,991		2,684
		Exports	395,600	0.4	0.0	0.6	0.6	0.0	5.8	10.8	71.8	7.8	2.0	443,265		3,540
Jordan	1994	Imports	3,382	17.3	0.6	3.0	12.6	3.5	11.9	18.3	25.4	6.5	0.9	3,697		680
		Exports	1,424	10.4	0.4	21.5	0.0	6.3	27.6	10.8	15.8	5.8	1.4	1,769		325
Kenya	1993	Imports	1,696	9.0	0.4	3.0	15.0	4.2	20.4	15.9	26.8	5.1	0.2	3,006		98
		Exports	1,392	48.8	2.8	8.4	9.3	0.5	4.2	13.7	1.4	9.9	1.1	1,890		62
Kiribati	1992	Imports	36.7	21.1	5.0	1.2	7.8	0.2	3.0	8.0	47.3	5.9	0.4	34		425
		Exports	4.7	11.3	0.0	71.2	0.0	0.0	0.0	1.5	0.0	0.2	15.8	7		88
Korea, South	1994	Imports	102,343	4.6	0.3	9.1	15.2	0.3	9.3	15.9	36.5	7.6	1.1	135,119		3,013
		Exports	96,008	2.4	0.0	1.5	1.8	0.0	6.5	24.2	49.0	13.8	0.8	125,058		2,788
Kuwait	1994	Imports	6,680	14.8	1.6	1.6	0.7	0.4	7.4	19.3	38.1	15.6	0.5	7,790		4,609
		Exports	768	3.3	0.1	5.8	4.4	0.6	19.7	14.8	44.8	6.5	0.1	12,944		7,659
Latvia	1994	Imports	1,241	8.2	1.8	1.6	28.9	0.0	11.0	13.2	22.8	9.6	3.0	1,749		697
		Exports	990	10.5	1.8	17.7	1.8	0.0	7.8	25.4	19.1	12.9	2.8	1,304		520
Liberia	1988	Imports	272	17.4	1.1	0.6	20.3	0.7	5.6	17.6	30.2	5.7	0.8	272	1988	116
		Exports	396	3.0	0.0	91.3	0.0	0.0	0.0	2.2	0.0	0.0	1.9	460		197
Libya	1991	Imports	5,358	20.0	0.4	2.4	0.4	3.1	7.6	22.7	33.8	9.2	0.3	5,356	1991	1,240
		Exports	11,212	0.5	0.0	0.2	95.4	0.0	3.4	0.5	0.0	0.0	0.1	11,213		2,596
Lithuania	1994	Imports	2,589	6.5	1.7	4.8	31.6	0.4	10.1	15.1	21.9	6.8	1.1	3,649		984
		Exports	2,029	16.1	6.1	6.6	15.9	0.4	12.7	15.6	15.5	10.8	0.4	2,705		729
Macau	1994	Imports	2,089	6.7	6.6	3.6	4.7	0.0	4.3	42.5	20.3	10.3	1.1	2,026		4,824
		Exports	1,872	0.8	2.8	2.3	0.0	0.0	1.2	12.4	4.2	76.2	0.0	1,983		4,721
Madagascar	1994	Imports	432	12.3	0.3	1.4	14.9	2.7	13.0	15.6	30.1	8.1	1.6	529		36
		Exports	327	77.9	0.0	7.4	0.6	0.0	1.3	5.1	0.3	6.1	1.4	366		25
Malawi	1991	Imports	647	6.6	0.0	1.5	10.9	1.3	20.0	19.5	33.1	6.1	1.1	475		49
		Exports	472	16.4	76.9	3.1	0.0	0.0	0.3	1.9	0.2	1.0	0.2	405		41
Malaysia	1994	Imports	59,594	4.3	0.3	2.4	2.6	0.4	6.6	14.0	60.0	5.5	3.9	77,614		3,751
		Exports	58,754	2.9	0.0	7.4	7.3	6.8	2.6	9.1	53.5	9.5	0.9	73,715		3,563
Maldives	1991	Imports	161	19.3	5.1	12.1	14.6	1.2	5.4	12.3	21.8	7.7	0.6	268		1,072
		Exports	53.1	65.6	0.0	3.8	0.0	0.3	0.0	0.0	0.0	30.3	0.0	50		200
Mali	1990	Imports	602	21.1	3.6	1.5	19.5	0.9	10.7	17.1	22.2	2.9	0.6	755		70
		Exports	330	32.1	0.0	65.1	0.0	1.2	0.0	0.6	0.9	0.0	0.2	452		42
Malta	1993	Imports	2,173	8.5	1.1	1.4	4.7	0.0	6.6	16.0	50.1	10.6	1.1	2,942		7,951
		Exports	1,355	2.1	0.9	0.5	2.2	0.0	2.5	7.2	57.1	27.1	0.3	1,913		5,170
Martinique	1994	Imports	1,642	17.9	2.8	1.4	7.8	0.5	10.0	14.4	27.5	15.3	2.4	1,963		5,166
		Exports	219	36.7	16.3	1.2	28.8	0.0	2.4	2.4	10.3	2.0	0.1	224		589
Mauritania	1984	Imports	246	28.7	0.6	2.3	8.0	1.0	3.5	15.0	35.0	5.0	0.9	599	1992	284
		Exports	297	9.3	0.0	90.6	0.0	0.0	0.0	0.0	0.0	0.0	0.1	471		223
Mauritius	1994	Imports	1,895	12.3	0.6	2.8	6.2	1.2	6.8	34.6	25.7	9.1	0.6	1,959		1,797
		Exports	1,325	28.5	0.0	0.7	0.0	0.0	0.7	6.7	2.2	60.7	0.4	1,537		1,410
Mexico	1994	Imports	80,170	6.1	0.4	3.8	1.9	0.6	8.4	16.2	39.3	12.7	10.6	45,977		508
		Exports	61,964	6.1	0.8	2.2	11.9	0.0	4.4	9.7	53.6	11.0	0.3	47,056		520
Moldova	1994	Imports	669	5.2	1.0	2.9	55.9	0.0	6.4	11.3	12.6	4.6	0.2	822		185
		Exports	566	40.7	23.4	3.3	2.5	2.0	2.1	7.9	11.5	6.5	0.0	720		162
Morocco	1994	Imports	7,194	9.7	1.5	9.0	15.5	2.3	1.3	18.8	27.0	4.2	10.7	8,539		315
		Exports	4,034	28.0	0.3	14.5	2.1	0.0	20.2	9.3	4.1	21.4	0.1	4,664		172

	Year		Total million $US	Percentages Food and live animals	Beverages and tobacco	Crude materials (inedible) excluding fuels	Mineral fuels, lubricants & related materials	Animal and vegetable oils and fats	Chemicals	Manu- factured goods	Machinery and transport equipment	Misc. manu- factured goods	Misc. transactions and goods	Trade total for 1995 (or latest available year) million $US	Latest year (if not 1995)	Trade per capita
Mozambique	1989	Imports	808	10.5	0.0	0.2	9.9	0.0	1.9	2.7	13.1	0.0	61.7	784		45
		Exports	115	60.9	0.0	9.0	9.1	0.8	0.0	0.0	0.0	0.0	20.2	169		10
Nepal	1993	Imports	696	4.4	0.9	11.7	11.8	3.3	12.0	18.8	16.6	4.5	15.9	1,378		64
		Exports	355	9.0	0.0	3.4	0.0	0.0	0.6	59.3	0.0	24.3	3.4	349		16
Netherlands	1994	Imports	130,512	11.4	1.4	5.4	8.2	0.8	12.1	15.3	31.3	13.4	0.8	176,426		11,419
		Exports	145,825	17.3	2.6	5.6	7.6	0.9	14.9	12.2	24.9	9.5	4.5	195,912		12,680
Netherlands Antilles	1993	Imports	1,947	10.1	0.9	0.6	57.4	0.0	4.4	6.8	12.3	7.5	−0.1	1,947	1993	9,985
		Exports	1,399	6.5	0.2	0.9	89.0	0.0	0.7	0.6	1.5	0.0	0.5	1,283		6,579
New Caledonia	1993	Imports	855	17.4	2.0	0.0	9.8	0.0	7.4	20.7	35.0	0.0	7.7	912		5,067
		Exports	377	0.0	0.0	32.6	0.0	0.0	0.0	56.4	0.0	0.0	11.0	515		2,861
New Zealand	1994	Imports	11,901	5.9	1.1	3.3	5.6	0.4	12.6	15.7	41.7	13.6	0.1	13,988		3,951
		Exports	12,185	41.7	0.5	18.7	2.0	0.7	7.6	13.8	8.2	4.4	2.4	13,741		3,882
Nicaragua	1994	Imports	852	14.4	0.6	1.4	12.8	4.3	16.1	16.0	26.4	8.0	0.0	962		212
		Exports	351	74.1	1.1	9.2	1.0	0.0	1.4	3.4	1.7	6.7	1.3	520		115
Niger	1988	Imports	387	24.3	1.5	3.4	5.5	1.0	12.1	25.5	26.6	0.0	0.0	373		41
		Exports	289	7.1	0.3	88.9	0.0	0.0	0.0	1.8	2.0	0.0	0.0	259		28
Nigeria	1992	Imports	7,149	8.2	0.2	2.5	0.5	0.7	18.1	23.0	41.8	4.9	0.1	7,513	1993	71
		Exports	11,787	1.3	0.0	0.7	96.9	0.0	0.3	0.2	0.0	0.0	0.6	9,923		94
Norway	1994	Imports	27,295	5.7	0.7	7.5	3.4	0.3	9.3	18.9	37.0	16.4	0.8	32,973		7,563
		Exports	34,744	8.7	0.0	2.9	49.7	0.0	6.5	16.3	12.2	3.2	0.6	41,994		9,632
Oman	1994	Imports	3,915	12.7	6.4	2.5	1.1	0.8	5.8	14.3	42.7	6.8	6.9	4,248		1,994
		Exports	5,418	2.1	2.2	0.3	76.5	0.3	0.3	2.4	12.8	2.1	0.9	5,713		2,682
Pakistan	1994	Imports	8,897	7.1	0.0	8.1	18.4	8.9	16.3	9.9	28.4	2.5	0.5	11,461		88
		Exports	7,370	9.5	0.0	2.6	0.8	0.0	0.6	58.4	0.5	27.3	0.3	7,992		62
Panama	1994	Imports	2,404	9.0	0.6	1.3	13.0	0.8	12.9	19.1	30.8	12.4	0.2	2,511		955
		Exports	524	74.5	2.7	0.9	2.5	0.5	5.3	6.5	0.0	6.4	0.8	625		238
Papua New Guinea	1990	Imports	1,233	16.7	1.3	0.8	6.8	0.4	7.0	19.2	38.3	8.6	1.0	1,452		357
		Exports	2,625	5.8	0.0	36.8	30.6	3.7	0.0	0.5	2.5	0.2	19.9	2,650		651
Paraguay	1994	Imports	2,425	6.2	8.2	0.7	8.3	0.0	11.1	13.0	41.2	10.7	0.6	3,144		669
		Exports	817	16.8	1.0	52.9	0.3	7.8	2.5	16.9	0.9	1.0	0.0	919		196
Peru	1994	Imports	5,626	15.2	0.6	2.3	6.5	1.7	13.3	14.6	38.9	6.8	0.0	9,224		392
		Exports	4,389	30.7	0.0	17.6	4.0	1.7	2.2	29.2	0.7	6.0	7.8	5,575		237
Philippines	1994	Imports	22,738	6.6	1.0	4.3	9.5	0.0	9.5	14.0	33.3	3.4	18.3	28,337		403
		Exports	13,483	9.9	0.3	3.0	1.6	3.6	2.2	6.5	21.6	14.7	36.5	17,502		249
Poland	1994	Imports	21,433	8.1	0.9	5.1	10.6	0.7	14.1	20.6	29.0	10.3	0.0	29,050		753
		Exports	17,194	10.0	1.4	4.7	9.1	0.7	6.6	28.1	19.8	19.9	0.4	22,892		593
Portugal	1994	Imports	26,603	11.6	1.1	4.5	8.8	0.5	9.8	19.3	34.3	9.5	0.6	32,349		3,261
		Exports	17,540	3.7	2.9	6.2	4.1	0.4	4.8	25.0	21.2	31.5	0.2	22,622		2,280
Qatar	1993	Imports	1,891	12.8	1.3	2.5	0.7	0.5	7.4	19.3	42.4	13.0	0.1	1,891	1993	3,383
		Exports	3,245	0.3	0.0	0.0	81.4	0.0	8.8	6.5	1.3	1.4	0.3	3,181		5,691
Réunion	1994	Imports	2,358	16.2	2.6	1.6	5.0	0.4	10.2	14.7	31.5	15.6	2.1	2,711		4,171
		Exports	171	73.0	3.9	0.7	0.0	0.0	1.4	3.5	12.5	4.8	0.3	209		322
Romania	1994	Imports	7,109	7.5	1.0	5.7	23.7	0.3	8.8	19.5	25.1	7.3	1.2	10,278		453
		Exports	6,151	5.0	0.4	4.5	10.0	0.8	9.6	26.5	14.3	27.4	1.6	7,910		349
Rwanda	1990	Imports	291	11.6	0.7	3.9	15.3	3.9	10.2	16.3	16.1	8.3	13.7	236		46
		Exports	132	68.7	0.0	8.0	0.0	0.0	0.0	0.6	0.0	0.5	22.2	50		10
St Kitts & Nevis	1991	Imports	110	16.7	2.9	1.9	7.8	0.9	8.3	23.1	23.4	14.5	0.5	118	1993	281
		Exports	27.5	40.7	6.1	0.1	0.0	0.0	0.0	5.0	30.4	16.7	1.0	27		64
St Lucia	1993	Imports	300	20.3	3.6	2.7	7.6	0.1	9.1	19.2	22.8	14.2	0.2	300	1993	2,143
		Exports	120	50.2	4.3	0.4	0.0	1.3	1.3	9.0	8.6	24.8	0.0	120		857
St Pierre & Miquelon	1989	Imports	83.6	14.5	3.6	0.6	18.6	0.0	2.8	9.4	38.4	6.9	5.2	71	1994	11,833
		Exports	20.0	93.2	0.0	0.0	0.0	0.0	0.0	0.0	6.8	0.0	0.0	12		2,000
St Vincent & Grenadines	1991	Imports	140	21.4	1.9	2.8	8.7	0.0	11.7	22.0	21.7	9.7	0.1	136		1,236
		Exports	67.1	82.2	0.0	0.0	0.0	0.2	1.0	5.3	4.4	5.8	1.1	43		391
Saudi Arabia	1992	Imports	33,273	9.6	0.3	1.8	0.0	0.4	7.8	19.2	45.1	10.7	5.0	28,091		1,539
		Exports	50,287	0.8	0.0	0.3	92.5	0.0	4.5	0.9	0.8	0.2	0.1	42,614	1994	2,335
Senegal	1991	Imports	1,097	23.4	1.4	2.6	11.0	4.6	14.1	15.3	22.7	4.8	0.0	1,302		156
		Exports	521	29.2	0.5	10.3	16.8	6.6	19.7	7.8	6.7	2.4	0.0	861		103
Seychelles	1993	Imports	242	15.7	3.5	1.4	14.2	0.8	5.9	18.5	25.0	14.9	0.1	233		3,329
		Exports	51.6	29.3	0.7	0.5	55.1	0.0	0.0	0.0	7.8	6.2	0.4	53		757
Sierra Leone	1990	Imports	164	31.1	2.0	2.2	16.2	2.3	8.3	12.4	20.8	4.7	0.0	135		30
		Exports	143	9.9	0.6	75.7	0.0	0.0	0.0	9.1	0.0	0.0	4.7	25		6
Singapore	1994	Imports	102,590	3.3	1.4	1.2	8.8	0.4	6.3	10.6	56.5	10.0	1.5	124,502		41,639
		Exports	96,749	2.4	1.7	1.5	9.6	0.4	5.6	6.0	63.9	7.7	1.3	118,263		39,553
Slovenia	1994	Imports	7,304	7.6	0.6	6.3	7.2	0.4	11.8	20.1	31.8	10.7	3.4	9,490		4,793
		Exports	6,828	4.0	0.7	1.9	1.1	0.0	10.1	28.6	30.3	22.9	0.3	8,315		4,199
Solomon Islands	1991	Imports	91.4	16.5	3.2	0.0	12.9	0.0	5.4	24.7	25.0	9.3	3.0	142	1994	374
		Exports	84.0	52.5	0.0	30.7	0.0	8.0	0.0	0.0	0.0	0.0	8.7	168		442

World trade continued

	Year		Total million $US	Percentages Food and live animals	Beverages and tobacco	Crude materials (inedible) excluding fuels	Mineral fuels, lubricants & related materials	Animal and vegetable oils and fats	Chemicals	Manu- factured goods	Machinery and transport equipment	Misc. manu- factured goods	Misc. transactions and goods	Trade total for 1995 (or latest available year) million $US	Latest year (if not 1995)	Trade per capita
Somalia	1982	Imports	330	16.4	3.8	6.6	14.4	2.1	5.4	17.9	23.9	7.0	2.6	228	1992	26
		Exports	199	93.8	0.0	0.7	1.1	0.0	0.0	0.5	0.0	0.0	3.9	44		5
Southern	1994	Imports	22,361	4.0	0.7	3.0	0.4	1.2	11.6	18.4	45.4	8.2	7.1	29,608		718
Africa	1993	Exports	23,930	5.7	0.6	7.9	6.9	0.0	4.7	24.8	7.0	2.3	40.1	26,918		653
Spain	1994	Imports	92,058	10.7	1.6	5.7	9.4	0.5	11.4	14.1	35.3	10.9	0.3	113,317		2,890
		Exports	73,031	12.9	1.6	2.1	2.2	1.3	7.9	19.5	42.1	9.1	1.2	91,533		2,334
Sri Lanka	1994	Imports	4,483	14.0	1.1	2.5	6.2	0.6	8.5	37.3	23.3	5.7	0.7	5,307		296
		Exports	3,210	19.8	1.2	4.2	0.7	0.0	0.9	15.5	2.6	53.1	2.0	3,798		212
Sudan	1985	Imports	905	14.8	1.3	1.4	37.8	0.7	10.0	11.8	17.9	2.6	1.7	1,185		44
		Exports	227	25.2	0.0	73.0	0.0	0.0	0.0	1.7	0.0	0.0	0.2	556		21
Surinam	1992	Imports	640	5.7	1.8	1.1	13.5	0.8	12.8	15.7	38.7	9.6	0.0	640	1992	1,565
		Exports	357	17.9	0.0	67.8	1.3	0.0	0.0	12.6	0.1	0.0	0.2	357		873
Sweden	1994	Imports	51,778	6.3	1.2	3.5	7.7	0.0	11.0	16.4	37.7	15.3	0.9	64,447		7,299
		Exports	61,360	1.6	0.4	7.9	2.5	0.0	9.3	24.5	45.0	8.2	0.6	79,919		9,051
Switzerland	1994	Imports	66,653	5.4	1.3	2.5	3.4	0.0	13.7	20.0	30.7	21.9	1.1	77,006		10,938
		Exports	68,904	2.3	0.7	1.1	0.0	0.0	24.6	16.6	29.6	24.1	1.1	78,062		11,088
Syria	1992	Imports	3,490	16.9	0.0	3.2	3.9	1.6	12.8	26.5	31.3	3.0	0.9	4,616		325
		Exports	3,093	13.0	0.2	8.1	69.6	0.0	0.2	4.2	0.3	4.4	0.0	3,970		280
Taiwan	1996	Imports	102,370	4.5	0.0	13.5	4.7	0.0	10.7	22.1	27.6	0.0	17.0	102,370		4,768
		Exports	115,942	0.9	0.0	8.8	0.0	0.0	2.8	39.7	46.6	0.0	1.1	115,942		5,400
Tanzania	1989	Imports	998	2.9	0.0	2.3	18.8	1.6	11.8	18.2	39.1	5.0	0.3	1,679		55
		Exports	371	49.8	4.1	28.4	3.8	0.0	1.3	9.6	0.9	0.8	1.4	685		23
Thailand	1994	Imports	54,340	3.7	0.4	5.1	6.9	0.0	10.1	19.0	46.8	5.7	2.3	73,426		1,236
		Exports	45,167	20.6	0.4	4.9	0.8	0.0	2.8	12.2	33.3	24.3	0.8	56,191		946
Togo	1991	Imports	444	16.3	5.7	2.0	9.8	1.1	11.9	17.7	28.3	6.4	0.8	385		94
		Exports	253	17.2	0.0	73.7	2.3	0.3	1.1	3.1	1.0	1.2	0.1	209		51
Tonga	1992	Imports	62.6	21.6	3.9	4.8	12.8	0.0	6.1	22.7	19.3	8.3	0.6	77		770
		Exports	12.8	79.8	0.0	0.6	0.0	2.5	0.2	7.1	3.5	5.3	0.9	15		150
Trinidad	1994	Imports	1,136	15.0	0.6	9.8	0.7	0.7	13.5	22.2	29.6	7.5	0.5	1,714		1,329
& Tobago		Exports	1,960	5.8	2.0	0.0	49.2	0.0	26.5	12.4	1.7	2.0	0.5	2,456		1,904
Tunisia	1994	Imports	6,484	7.4	0.8	5.7	7.7	1.5	8.5	28.5	29.2	10.4	0.4	7,903		886
		Exports	4,584	4.9	1.3	1.8	9.5	6.6	11.5	12.2	8.6	43.8	0.0	5,475		614
Turkey	1994	Imports	23,268	2.0	0.7	9.8	16.5	2.0	13.5	17.5	32.9	4.9	0.4	35,710		579
		Exports	18,106	18.2	2.6	3.3	1.4	1.0	4.0	31.5	9.4	28.5	0.1	21,600		350
Tuvalu	1986	Imports	2.8	29.5	6.9	0.9	13.9	0.2	6.6	12.4	15.1	12.8	1.7	38	1986	350
	1985	Exports	0.02	0.0	0.0	0.0	0.0	0.0	0.0	0.0	0.0	0.0	100.0	0	1985	13
Uganda	1992	Imports	524	4.0	0.5	4.2	13.4	5.8	8.3	21.9	32.2	9.4	0.2	1,055		50
		Exports	171	68.4	2.8	23.9	3.0	0.0	0.0	0.4	0.9	0.4	0.2	461		22
(former) USSR	1990	Imports	120,651	13.0	1.2	1.7	1.7	0.3	8.4	9.0	41.5	11.5	11.8	43,458	1991	150
		Exports	104,177	1.7	0.0	7.4	40.5	0.0	3.6	6.2	18.7	1.4	20.5	46,274		160
United	1992	Imports	12,952	9.4	0.9	1.8	1.7	0.3	5.5	26.1	35.1	19.2	0.1	19,520	1993	16,186
Arab Emirates		Exports	899	5.6	1.9	4.5	5.8	0.0	5.0	44.9	6.8	25.4	0.2	24,756		20,527
United	1994	Imports	222,152	8.2	1.5	3.7	4.1	0.4	9.5	16.4	40.8	14.7	0.8	265,321		4,527
Kingdom		Exports	200,511	4.6	2.8	1.7	6.7	0.0	13.8	14.7	41.3	13.0	1.3	242,036		4,130
United States	1994	Imports	689,030	4.0	0.8	2.8	8.7	0.0	5.1	12.2	45.6	17.2	3.6	770,852		2,929
		Exports	512,337	6.9	1.6	5.3	1.8	0.3	10.0	8.8	49.2	11.0	5.1	584,743		2,222
Uruguay	1994	Imports	2,707	8.8	1.3	3.5	8.4	0.7	14.6	15.8	37.0	9.9	0.0	2,867		899
		Exports	1,918	40.2	0.3	6.4	0.0	0.4	5.3	25.6	11.7	9.8	0.3	2,106		660
Vanuatu	1992	Imports	81.1	17.4	4.1	0.8	9.0	0.5	6.6	14.9	27.5	10.6	8.6	95		559
	1990	Exports	13.8	41.4	0.4	45.5	0.0	0.0	1.8	0.9	2.5	7.4	0.0	28		165
Venezuela	1994	Imports	8,037	10.0	1.2	4.7	1.5	1.7	13.5	14.6	44.6	8.1	0.0	11,961		553
		Exports	16,650	2.0	0.6	1.7	75.9	0.0	3.0	11.4	3.1	0.5	1.7	18,489		854
Western	1990	Imports	81.7	24.3	2.1	2.4	11.4	0.7	4.7	19.3	28.9	6.1	0.0	95		559
Samoa		Exports	8.0	58.0	8.5	8.2	0.0	21.8	0.0	1.8	0.4	1.3	0.0	9		53
Yemen	1992	Imports	2,588	28.1	1.9	3.6	6.1	2.1	6.6	24.2	21.8	5.4	0.1	2,087	1994	165
		Exports	329	11.0	1.1	10.1	74.4	0.9	1.5	0.3	0.0	0.4	0.2	934		74
(former)	1990	Imports	18,915	10.3	0.8	7.6	17.0	0.4	12.6	16.0	26.6	8.4	0.4	11,804	1991	1,135
Yugoslavia	1990	Exports	14,391	6.3	0.9	6.9	2.5	0.0	9.5	28.0	29.9	15.6	0.4	9,548		918
Zambia	1986	Imports	714	3.5	0.0	1.5	21.9	0.2	14.9	16.2	32.5	3.3	5.9	97	1992	12
		Exports	666	0.1	0.1	0.0	0.0	0.0	0.0	97.0	0.0	0.0	2.8	781	1994	94
Zimbabwe	1993	Imports	1,818	8.4	0.3	5.0	14.7	2.0	13.7	14.8	35.0	4.1	1.9	2,661		231
		Exports	1,323	11.3	29.8	14.0	0.6	0.0	2.9	28.1	3.0	9.5	0.8	2,115		183

* Southern Africa includes Botswana, Lesotho, Namibia and Swaziland.

Gross National Product

	GNP 1995 (million $US)	GNP per capita 1995 ($US)	GDP share agriculture 1995 (%)	GDP share industry 1995 (%)	GDP share manufacture 1995 (%)	GDP share services 1995 (%)	Average annual growth of real GNP per capita 1985–95	Consumer price index Jan. '97 (1990=100)
Afghanistan	5,000	300	52	32	26	16	–6	...
Albania	2,199	670	56	21		23	–7	294
Algeria	44,609	1,600	13	47	9	40	–2.6	420
American Samoa	210	3,500	...	...	...	...	...	119
Angola	4,422	410	12	59	3	29	–6.1	204,000
Antigua & Barb.	490	7,000	3	11	5	86	2.7	...
Argentina	278,431	8,030	6	31	20	63	1.9	323,000
Armenia	2,752	730	44	35	25	21	–15.1	...
Aruba	1,120	16,000	...	...	...	...	6	107
Australia	337,909	18,720	3	28	15	70	1.4	117
Austria	216,547	26,890	2	34	24	64	1.9	120
Azerbaijan	3,601	480	27	32	...	41	–16.3	...
Bahamas	3,297	11,940	3	9	3	88	–1	121 ('95)
Bahrain	4,525	7,840	1	42	15	57	0.6	106
Bangladesh	28,599	240	31	18	10	51	2.1	128
Barbados	1,745	6,560	5	17	8	78	–0.2	107
Belarus	21,356	2,070	13	35	22	52	–5.2	432,638
Belgium	250,710	24,710	2	31	23	67	2.2	117
Belize	568	2,630	19	36	14	45	4.4	119
Benin	2,034	370	34	12	7	54	–0.4	...
Bermuda	1,620	27,000	...	...	...	...	–1.2	113 ('94)
Bhutan	295	420	41	28	11	31	4	...
Bolivia	5,905	800	17	30	16	53	1.7	168
Bosnia	11,650	2,600	...	...	...	...	1.8	...
Botswana	4,381	3,020	5	46	4	49	6	207
Brazil	579,787	3,640	14	37	24	49	–0.7	84,000
Brunei	4,205	14,500	3	51	5	46	–1	118
Bulgaria	11,225	1,330	13	34		53	–2.2	21,375
Burkina Faso	2,417	230	34	27	21	39	–0.1	137 ('96)
Burma (Myanmar)	45,100	1,000	63	9	7	28	0.4	396
Burundi	984	160	56	18	12	26	–1.3	162
Cambodia	2,718	270	51	14	6	35	2	...
Cameroon	8,615	650	39	23	10	38	–7	...
Canada	573,695	19,380	3	30	18	67	0.4	115
Cape Verde Is.	366	960	21	29	6	50	2.1	170
Central Afr. Rep.	1,123	340	44	13	7	43	–2	140 ('96)
Chad	1,144	180	44	22	16	35	0.5	132
Chile	59,151	4,160	8	34	17	58	6.1	212
China	744,890	620	21	48	38	31	8	...
Colombia	70,263	1,910	14	32	18	54	2.8	388
Comoros	237	470	39	12	5	49	–1.4	...
Congo	1,784	680	10	38	6	52	–3.2	156
Congo (Zaïre)	5,313	120	51	16	7	33	–8.5	...
Costa Rica	8,884	2,610	17	24	19	59	2.9	137
Croatia	15,508	3,250	12	25	20	63	–20	59,469
Cuba	13,700	1,250	...	...	...	...	–10	...
Cyprus	8,510	11,500	6	43	34	51	4.6	132
Czech Rep.	3,990	3,870	6	39		55	–1.8	177
Denmark	156,027	29,890	4	29	21	67	1.5	114
Djibouti	600	1,000	3	18	5	79	–1	...
Dominica	218	2,990	18	18	6	64	4	119
Dominican Rep.	11,390	1,460	15	22	15	63	2.1	...
Ecuador	15,997	1,390	12	36	21	52	0.8	650
Egypt	45,507	790	20	21	15	59	1.1	208
El Salvador	9,057	1,610	14	22	19	64	2.9	209
Equat. Guinea	152	380	45	25	2	30	2.3	...
Eritrea	1,750	500	11	20	11	69	...	...
Estonia	4,252	2,860	8	28	17	64	–4.3	246
Ethiopia	5,722	100	57	10	3	33	–0.5	177
Fiji	1,895	2,440	21	18	12	61	2.3	110
Finland	105,174	20,580	6	37	28	57	–0.2	113
France	1,451,051	24,990	2	27	19	71	1.5	115
French Guiana	975	6,500	...	...	...	...	...	113
French Polynesia	1,650	7,500	5	15	7	80	5.3	109
Gabon	3,759	3,490	9	59	22	32	–1.6	124 ('94)
Gambia, The	354	320	28	15	7	57	0.3	138 ('96)
Georgia	2,358	440	67	22	18	11	–17	...
Germany	2,252,343	27,510	1	30	23	69	1.9	118
Ghana	6,719	390	46	16	6	38	1.5	527
Gibraltar	225	7,500	...	...	...	...	5	127
Greece	85,885	8,210	21	36	21	43	1.2	215
Greenland	720	12,000	...	...	...	...	4.1	...
Grenada	271	2,980	12	18	7	70	3.9	120
Guadeloupe	3,990	9,500	...	...	...	...	...	114
Guatemala	14,255	1,340	25	19		56	0.3	234
Guinea	3,593	550	24	31	5	45	1.4	166
Guinea-Bissau	265	250	46	24	7	30	1.8	...
Guyana	493	590	50	35	10	15	0.8	...
Haiti	1,777	250	44	12	9	44	–5.2	242 ('96)
Honduras	3,566	600	21	33	18	46	0.2	196 ('94)
Hong Kong	142,332	22,990	0	17	9	83	4.8	170
Hungary	42,129	4,120	8	33	24	59	–1	405
Iceland	6,686	24,950	13	29	17	58	0.3	122
India	319,660	340	29	29	19	42	3.1	188
Indonesia	190,105	980	17	42	24	41	6	170
Iran	328,000	4,800	25	34	14	41	0.5	449
Iraq	36,200	1,800	28	20	4	52	...	...
Ireland	52,765	14,710	9	37	...	54	5.2	116
Israel	87,875	15,920	3	32	22	65	2.5	212
Italy	1,088,085	19,020	3	31	21	66	1.7	133
Ivory Coast	9,548	660	31	20	18	49	–4.3	145 ('95)
Jamaica	3,803	1,510	9	38	18	53	3.7	700
Japan	4,963,587	39,640	2	38	24	60	2.9	107
Jordan	6,354	1,510	8	27	14	65	–2.8	132
Kazakhstan	22,143	1,330	12	30	6	58	–8.6	59,000
Kenya	7,583	280	29	17	11	54	0.1	320
Kiribati	73	920	24	9	2	67	–0.3	...
Korea, North	24,000	1,000	...	...	...	...	–8	...
Korea, South	435,137	9,700	7	43	27	50	7.6	143
Kuwait	28,941	17,390	0	53	11	47	0.9	...
Kyrgyzstan	3,158	700	44	24		32	–6.9	10,500
Laos	1,694	350	52	18	14	30	2.7	...
Latvia	5,708	2,270	9	31	18	60	–6.6	4,500
Lebanon	10,673	2,660	7	24	10	69	2.7	...
Lesotho	1,519	770	10	56	18	34	1.5	210
Liberia	2,300	850	...	...	...	...	1.5	...
Libya	38,000	7,000	8	48	8	44	1	...
Liechtenstein	1,020	34,000	...	...	...	...	...	...
Lithuania	7,070	1,900	11	36	30	53	–11.7	18,000
Luxembourg	16,876	41,210	1	33	24	66	1	117
Macau	6,700	16,000	...	...	...	...	12	155
Macedonia	1,813	860	19	44	38	37	–15	290
Madagascar	3,178	230	34	13	13	53	–2	345
Malawi	1,623	170	42	27	188	31	–0.7	577
Malaysia	78,321	3,890	13	43	33	44	5.7	128
Maldives	251	990	21	17	6	62	6.7	...
Mali	2,410	250	46	17	6	37	0.6	147
Malta	4,070	11,000	3	28	25	69	5.1	116 ('95)
Martinique	3,800	10,000	...	...	...	...	...	120
Mauritania	1,049	460	27	30	13	43	0.5	...
Mauritius	3,815	3,380	9	33	23	58	5.7	155
Mexico	304,596	3,320	8	26	19	66	0.1	200
Moldova	3,996	920	50	28	26	22	–8.2	18,000
Mongolia	767	310	21	46	...	33	–3.8	...
Montserrat	45	4,500	...	...	...	...	4.3	...
Morocco	29,545	1,110	14	33	19	53	0.8	140
Mozambique	1,353	80	33	21	8	46	3.6	...
Namibia	3,098	2,000	14	29	9	57	2.8	200
Nepal	4,391	200	42	22	10	36	2.4	192
Netherlands	371,039	24,000	3	27	18	70	1.8	118
Neths Antilles	2,100	10,500	...	...	...	...	2	118
New Caledonia	2,880	16,000	2	26	13	72	2.4	117
New Zealand	51,655	14,340	7	25	17	68	0.6	115
Nicaragua	1,659	380	33	20	16	47	–5.8	...
Niger	1,961	220	39	18	...	43	–2.1	...
Nigeria	28,411	260	43	27	9	30	1.2	920
Norway	136,077	31,250	3	36	13	61	1.6	116
Oman	10,578	4,820	3	48	5	49	0.3	105
Pakistan	59,991	460	26	24	17	50	1.2	165
Panama	7,235	2,750	11	18	9	71	–0.4	110

	GNP 1995	GNP per capita 1995	GDP share agriculture 1995	GDP share industry 1995	GDP share manufacture 1995	GDP share services 1995	Average annual growth of real GNP per capita 1985–95	Consumer price index Jan. '97 1990=100
	million $US	$US	%	%	%	%		
Papua N. Guinea	4,976	1,160	26	38	8	36	2.1	156 ('96)
Paraguay	8,158	1,690	24	22	16	54	1.1	181 ('96)
Peru	55,019	2,310	7	38	24	55	-1.6	2,100
Philippines	71,865	1,050	22	32	23	46	1.5	182
Poland	107,829	2,790	6	39	26	55	-0.4	724
Portugal	96,689	9,740	6	40	29	54	3.7	132
Puerto Rico	27,750	7,500	1	42	39	57	2.1	128
Qatar	7,448	11,600	1	49	11	50	-2.6	...
Réunion	2,925	4,500	6	27	12	67	...	118
Romania	33,488	1,480	21	49	45	30	-4	7,100
Russia	331,948	2,240	7	38	31	55	-5.1	290,000
Rwanda	1,128	180	37	17	3	46	-5	...
St Kitts & Nevis	212	5,170	7	26	12	67	4.6	...
St Lucia	532	3,370	12	20	7	68	3.9	122
St Vincent & G.	253	2,280	16	25	9	59	3.9	123
São Tomé & P.	45	350	28	33	8	39	-2.1	...
Saudi Arabia	133,540	7,040	6	51	8	43	-1.9	112
Senegal	5,070	600	20	18	12	62	-1.2	150
Seychelles	487	6,620	4	20	11	76	4.2	108
Sierra Leone	762	180	42	27	6	31	-3.4	...
Singapore	79,831	26,730	0	36	27	64	6.2	116
Slovak Rep.	15,848	2,950	6	33	...	61	-2.6	183
Slovenia	16,328	8,200	5	39	1	56	-1	634
Solomon Is.	341	910	48	9	4	43	2.2	192
Somalia	4,625	500	65	9	4	26	-2.3	...
South Africa	130,918	3,160	5	31	24	64	-1	191
Spain	532,347	13,580	3	31	23	66	2.6	136
Sri Lanka	12,616	700	23	25	16	52	2.7	202
Sudan	20,000	750	36	18	11	46	0.6	...
Surinam	360	880	22	23	14	55	0.7	6,800
Swaziland	1,051	1,170	10	25	29	65	0.6	214
Sweden	209,720	23,750	2	32	23	66	-0.1	122
Switzerland	286,014	40,630	3	32	27	65	0.2	118
Syria	15,780	1,120	18	43	39	39	1	190
Taiwan	252,000	12,000	3	42	32	55	7	...
Tajikistan	1,976	340	27	45	36	28	-13	...
Tanzania	3,703	120	58	17	8	25	0.9	450
Thailand	159,630	2,740	11	40	29	49	8.4	136
Togo	1,266	310	38	21	9	41	-2.8	...
Tonga	170	1,630	33	8	4	59	0.2	121 ('94)
Trinidad & Tob.	4,851	3,770	3	42	9	55	-1.6	149
Tunisia	16,369	1,820	12	29	19	59	1.8	140
Turkey	169,452	2,780	16	31	21	53	2.2	3,900
Turkmenistan	4,125	920	9	79	7	12	-9.6	...
Uganda	4,668	240	50	14	6	36	2.8	268
Ukraine	84,084	1,630	18	42	37	40	-9.2	...
United Arab Em.	42,806	17,400	2	57	8	41	-3.5	...
United Kingdom	1,094,734	18,700	2	32	21	66	1.4	122
United States	7,100,007	26,980	2	26	18	72	1.4	122
Uruguay	16,458	5,170	9	26	18	65	3.3	1,548
Uzbekistan	21,979	970	33	34	18	33	-3.9	...
Vanuatu	202	1,200	21	13	6	66	-1.1	123
Venezuela	65,382	3,020	5	38	17	57	0.5	1,550
Vietnam	17,634	240	28	30	22	42	4.2	...
Western Samoa	184	1,120	...	...	...	...	-0.4	144
Yemen	4,044	260	22	27	14	51	3.1	...
Yugoslavia	14,750	1,400	26	36	29	38	1.8	...
Zambia	3,605	400	22	40	30	38	-1	...
Zimbabwe	5,933	540	15	36	30	49	-0.6	430

The Gross National Product (GNP) is a measure of a country's total production of goods and services including the net income from overseas. Owing to difficulties in the use of exchange rates and individual nation's methods of calculating the GNP, the figures must be used cautiously. Gross Domestic Product (GDP) is the value of domestic production and excludes net overseas income. Note that manufacturing is also included within the industry percentage. Services also includes items which cannot be included in the other groups.

Social indicators

	Adult illiteracy F%	Adult illiteracy M%	Population per doctor 1993	Fertility rate 1995 children	Real GDP per capita 1995 $US	WDR order PPP$
Afghanistan	85	53	7,000	6.9	...	
Albania	0	0	735	2.6	...	45
Algeria	51	26	1,062	3.5	5,300	69
American Samoa	4	4	2,000	4.2	...	
Angola	71	44	23,725	6.9	1,310	33
Antigua & Barbuda	...	...	1,600	1.7	...	
Argentina	4	4	330	2.7	8,310	105
Armenia	2	1	261	1.8	2,260	49
Australia	...	...	500	1.9	18,940	117
Austria	0	0	231	1.5	21,250	127
Azerbaijan	4	1	257	2.3	1,460	37
Bahamas	2	1	700	2	14,710	
Bahrain	21	10	700	3.1	13,400	
Bangladesh	74	51	12,884	3.5	1,380	13
Barbados	3	2	1,000	1.8	10,620	
Belarus	3	1	236	1.4	4,220	77
Belgium	0	0	274	1.6	21,660	124
Belize	30	30	1,450	3.9	5,400	
Benin	74	51	14,216	6	1,760	29
Bermuda	3	3	1,100	1.8	...	
Bhutan	72	44	11,000	5.3	1,260	
Bolivia	24	10	2,348	4.5	2,540	52
Bosnia	23	3	600	1	...	
Botswana	40	20	5,151	4.4	5,580	89
Brazil	17	17	844	2.4	5,400	96
Brunei	17	7	1500	2.9	...	
Bulgaria	3	1	306	1.2	4,480	61
Burkina Faso	91	71	34,804	6.7	780	11
Burma	22	11	12,528	3.4	...	
Burundi	78	51	17,153	6.5	630	4
Cambodia	47	20	9,374	4.7	...	21
Cameroon	48	25	11,996	5.7	2,110	43
Canada	2	2	464	1.7	21,130	119
Cape Verde Is.	36	19	4,000	4	1,870	
Central African Rep.	48	32	25,920	5.1	1,070	26
Chad	65	38	30,030	5.9	700	6
Chile	5	5	942	2.3	9,520	101
China	27	10	1,063	1.9	2,920	42
Colombia	9	9	1,105	2.8	6,130	75
Comoros	50	36	7,500	5.9	1,320	
Congo	33	17	3,713	6	2,050	46
Congo (Zaïre)	32	13	15,150	6	490	
Costa Rica	5	5	1,133	2.8	5,850	81
Croatia	5	1	500	1.5	...	92
Cuba	5	4	275	1.7	...	
Cyprus	7	2	450	2.2	...	
Czech Rep.	0	0	273	1.3	9,770	98
Denmark	0	0	360	1.8	21,230	130
Djibouti	67	40	5,250	5.8	...	
Dominica	10	10	2,100	2.3	...	
Dominican Rep.	18	18	949	2.9	3,870	65
Ecuador	12	8	652	3.2	4,220	64
Egypt	61	36	1,316	3.4	3,820	51
El Salvador	30	27	1,515	3.7	2,610	70
Equatorial Guinea	32	10	3,500	5.9	...	
Eritrea	...	...	50,000	6.5	...	
Estonia	0	0	253	1.3	4,220	87
Ethiopia	75	55	32,499	7	450	2
Fiji	11	6	1,800	2.7	5,780	
Finland	0	0	406	1.8	17,760	120
France	1	1	334	1.7	21,030	125
French Guiana	18	16	650	3.4	...	
French Polynesia	5	5	600	3	...	
Gabon	47	26	1,987	5.2	...	95
Gambia, The	75	47	14,000	5.3	930	25
Georgia	1	0	182	1.9	1,470	34
Germany	0	0	367	1.2	20,070	129
Ghana	47	24	22,970	5.1	1,990	31
Gibraltar	1	1	950	2.2	...	
Greece	7	2	312	1.4	11,710	107
Greenland	0	0	700	2.2	...	

	Adult illiteracy		Population per doctor 1993	Fertility rate 1995 children	Real GDP per capita 1995 $US	WDR order PPP$
	F%	M%				
Grenada	15	15	1,500	3.7	...	
Guadeloupe	9	10	700	2.1	...	
Guatemala	51	38	3,999	4.7	3,340	63
Guinea	78	50	7,445	6.5	...	39
Guinea-Bissau	58	32	3,500	6	790	16
Guyana	2	1	3,000	2.4	2,420	
Haiti	58	52	10,855	4.4	910	17
Honduras	27	27	1,266	4.6	1,900	40
Hong Kong	12	4	760	1.2	22,950	121
Hungary	1	1	306	1.6	6,410	100
Iceland	0	0	360	2.1	20,460	
India	62	35	2,459	3.2	1,400	27
Indonesia	22	10	7,028	2.7	3,800	56
Iran	24	22	3,142	4.5	5,470	
Iraq	55	29	1,659	5.4	...	
Ireland	0	0	632	1.9	15,680	112
Israel	7	3	220	2.4	16,490	113
Italy	4	2	207	1.2	19,870	118
Ivory Coast	70	50	11,739	5.3	1,580	44
Jamaica	11	19	6,420	2.4	3,540	67
Japan	0	0	608	1.5	22,110	132
Jordan	21	7	554	4.8	4,060	68
Kazakstan	4	1	254	2.3	3,010	62
Kenya	30	14	21,970	4.7	1,380	22
Kiribati	10	10	7,500	3.8	...	
Korea, North	5	5	370	2.2	...	
Korea, South	2	2	951	1.8	11,450	108
Kuwait	25	18	600	3	23,790	114
Kyrgyzstan	4	1	303	3.3	1,800	47
Laos	56	31	4,446	6.5	...	28
Latvia	0	0	278	1.3	3,370	79
Lebanon	10	5	537	2.8	...	82
Lesotho	38	19	24,095	4.6	1,780	50
Liberia	78	46	25,000	6.5	...	
Libya	37	12	957	6.1	...	
Liechtenstein	0	0	950	1.4	...	
Lithuania	2	1	235	1.5	4,120	74
Luxembourg	0	0	460	1.7	37,930	
Macau	15	6	800	1.8	...	
Macedonia	16	6	427	2.2	...	53
Madagascar	27	12	8,385	5.8	640	12
Malawi	58	28	44,205	6.6	750	5
Malaysia	22	11	2,441	3.4	9,020	99
Maldives	7	7	5,200	6.6	3,080	
Mali	77	61	18,376	6.8	550	18
Malta	4	4	410	1.9	...	
Martinique	7	8	600	2	...	
Mauritania	74	50	15,772	5.2	1,540	36
Mauritius	21	13	1,165	2.2	13,210	94
Mexico	13	8	615	3	6,400	93
Micronesia	13	33	2,100	4.6	1,500	
Moldova	6	1	250	2	...	54
Mongolia	23	11	371	3.4	1,950	23
Montserrat	...	...	...	1.9	...	
Morocco	69	43	4,665	3.4	3,340	58
Mozambique	77	42	36,225	6.2	810	1
Namibia	26	22	4,328	5	4,150	76
Nepal	86	59	13,634	5.3	1,170	9
Netherlands	0	0	399	1.6	19,950	123
Neths Antilles	7	6	700	2.1	...	
New Caledonia	42	43	1,000	2.5	...	
New Zealand	1	1	518	2.1	16,360	111
Nicaragua	33	35	2,039	4.1	2,000	30
Niger	93	79	53,986	7.4	750	10
Nigeria	53	33	5,208	5.5	1,220	19
Norway	0	0	308	1.9	21,940	131
Oman	76	42	1,131	7	8,140	102
Pakistan	76	50	1,923	5.2	2,230	35
Panama	10	9	562	2.7	5,980	84
Papua New Guinea	37	19	12,754	4.8	2,420	60
Paraguay	9	7	1,231	4	3,650	72
Peru	17	6	939	3.1	3,770	80
Philippines	6	5	8,273	3.7	2,850	57
Poland	2	1	451	1.6	5,400	86
Portugal	13	13	353	1.4	12,670	109
Puerto Rico	10	10	350	2.1	...	
Qatar	20	21	800	3.9	17,690	
Réunion	20	24	610	2.2	...	
Romania	5	1	538	1.4	4,360	66
Russia	3	0	222	1.4	4,480	78
Rwanda	48	30	24,967	6.2	540	7
Saudi Arabia	50	29	749	6.2	...	104
Senegal	77	57	18,192	5.7	1,780	41
Seychelles	14	17	1,100	2.4	...	
Sierra Leone	82	55	11,000	6.5	580	8
Singapore	14	4	714	1.7	22,770	126
Slovak Rep.	0	0	287	1.5	3,610	88
Slovenia	0	0	500	1.3	...	106
Solomon Is.	55	38	6,100	5.1	2,190	
Somalia	52	39	13,300	7	...	
South Africa	18	18	1,500	3.9	5,030	91
Spain	6	2	261	1.2	14,520	110
Sri Lanka	13	7	6,843	2.3	3,250	48
St Kitts & Nevis	10	10	1,100	2.4	9,410	
St Lucia	20	20	2,000	2.9	...	
St Vincent & G.	4	4	2,500	2.3	...	
Sudan	65	42	10,000	4.8	...	
Surinam	9	5	1,200	2.6	2,250	
Swaziland	24	22	9,250	4.6	2,880	
Sweden	0	0	394	1.7	18,540	122
Switzerland	0	0	580	1.5	25,860	133
Syria	44	14	1,159	4.8	5,320	59
São Tomé & Príncipe	61	30	1,800	4.8	...	
Taiwan	10	3	800	1.8	...	
Tajikistan	3	1	424	4.2	920	
Tanzania	43	21	22,000	5.8	640	3
Thailand	8	4	4,416	1.8	7,540	83
Togo	63	33	11,385	6.4	1,130	24
Tonga	7	7	2,000	3.3	...	
Trinidad & Tobago	3	1	1,520	2.1	8,610	97
Tunisia	45	21	1,549	2.9	5,000	73
Turkey	28	8	976	2.7	5,580	85
Turkmenistan	3	1	306	3.8	...	
Uganda	50	26	22,399	6.7	1,470	14
Ukraine	3	0	227	1.5	2,400	71
United Arab Emirates	20	21	1,208	3.6	16,470	115
United Kingdom	0	0	300	1.7	19,260	116
United States	5	4	421	2.1	26,980	128
Uruguay	2	3	500	2.2	6,630	103
Uzbekistan	4	1	282	3.7	2,370	55
Vanuatu	52	43	8,000	5	2,290	
Venezuela	10	8	633	3.1	7,900	90
Vietnam	9	4	2,279	3.1	...	15
West Bank & Gaza	...	...	1,500	6.2		
Western Samoa	0	0	2,500	4.2	2,030	
Yemen	74	47	4,498	7.4	...	20
Yugoslavia (Serbia)	11	2	232	1.9	...	
Zambia	29	14	10,917	5.7	930	32
Zimbabwe	20	10	7,384	3.8	2,030	38

The WDR order PPP$ represents the position of a country in the World Development Report, based on the purchasing power of the local currency. In this case, the higher the number, the greater the purchasing power of the local currency.

Production statistics

Agricultural, forest and fishing products

Apples *thousand tonnes*

	1970	1980	1990	1994	1995	Rank	%
WORLD	28,308	34,580	40,518	47,282	49,682		
Algeria	8	20	54	49	50		
Argentina	435	946	980	1,070	920		
Armenia	...	...	...	95	95		
Australia	430	317	319	345	320		
Austria	293	300	338	334	335		
Azerbaijan	...	...	...	275	275		
Belarus	...	...	...	290	200		
Belgium	279	262	235	528	455		
Brazil	15	87	543	700	693		
Bulgaria	389	371	411	76	90		
Canada	413	470	540	553	485		
Chile	142	251	700	810	850		
China	396	2,765	4,332	11,137	14,016	1	28.2
Croatia	...	...	70	47	45		
Czech Rep.	...	...	...	244	246		
Denmark	121	94	30	80	80		
Egypt	5	18	62	313	350		
France	3,895	2,268	2,326	2,566	2,488	3	5.0
Georgia	...	...	...	215	350		
Germany	2,399	2,132	2,221	896	573		
Greece	230	307	342	346	280		
Hungary	700	1,071	945	657	600		
India	277	714	1,093	1,200	1,200	8	2.4
Iran	89	629	1,524	2,008	2,000	6	4.0
Iraq	36	93	75	86	90		
Israel	71	119	113	86	134		
Italy	1,923	1,890	2,050	2,233	2,127	4	4.3
Japan	1,037	886	1,053	989	900		
Kazakstan	...	...	...	90	86		
Korea, N.	135	460	645	660	660		
Korea, S.	217	459	629	617	650		
Kyrgyzstan	...	...	...	30	65		
Latvia	...	...	...	19	50		
Lebanon	98	101	200	162	165		
Lithuania	...	...	...	31	75		
Macedonia	...	...	88	70	70		
Mexico	128	283	457	448	663		
Moldova	...	...	...	439	350		
Morocco	168	70	221	270	270		
Netherlands	482	393	431	600	570		
New Zealand	131	211	361	415	475		
Norway	51	46	50	45	45		
Pakistan	34	107	240	533	533		
Peru	73	81	118	104	166		
Poland	636	891	812	1,441	1,228	7	2.5
Portugal	89	111	178	212	213		
Romania	265	511	683	363	457		
Russia	...	...	...	1,142	1,142	9	2.3
Slovak Rep.	...	...	...	57	38		
Slovenia	...	...	94	108	60		
South Africa	214	395	530	552	496		
Spain	535	1,052	657	774	843		
Sweden	137	145	150	70	67		
Switzerland	400	342	346	325	262		
Syria	25	90	205	224	240		
Tajikistan	...	...	...	80	80		
Tunisia	8	17	42	68	65		
Turkey	716	1,410	1,900	2,095	2,050	5	4.1
Turkmenistan	...	...	...	30	80		
Ukraine	...	2,174	1,968	651	1,046	10	2.1
UK	524	317	310	350	350		
USA	2,962	3,732	4,398	5,217	5,031	2	10.1
Uruguay	30	28	48	40	40		
Uzbekistan	...	...	...	350	350		
Yugoslavia	...	...	235	148	160		

Asses *thousand head*

	1970	1980	1990	1994	1995	Rank	%
WORLD	42,285	37,920	43,128	43,710	43,762		
Afghanistan	1,283	1,303	1,240	1,160	1,160	9	2.7
Albania	58	52	103	113	113		
Algeria	335	511	307	226	230		
Argentina	94	90	90	90	90		
Bolivia	653	680	630	631	631		
Botswana	51	124	174	231	235		
Brazil	1,400	1,334	1,343	1,370	1,370	8	3.1
Bulgaria	301	338	329	297	291		
Burkina Faso	200	200	411	445	455		
Cameroon	84	33	35	36	36		
Chad	343	262	264	253	252		
China	11,623	7,567	11,129	10,886	10,923	1	25.0
Colombia	327	630	704	710	710		
Dom. Rep.	129	119	143	145	145		
Ecuador	179	207	251	264	265		
Egypt	1,361	1,706	1,356	1,650	1,680	6	3.8
Ethiopia	3,837	3,925	5,000	5,200	5,200	2	11.9
Greece	375	241	137	110	110		
Haiti	173	206	215	210	210		
India	1,000	1,000	1,450	1,600	1,600	7	3.7
Iran	2,021	2,200	1,911	1,900	1,900	5	4.3
Iraq	549	439	327	162	164		
Ireland	78	28	15	14	14		
Italy	287	135	69	33	32		
Jordan	47	19	19	19	19		
Kazakstan	...	...	45	40	40		
Lesotho	74	97	152	152	152		
Libya	95	60	62	55	55		
Mali	470	488	561	611	611		
Mauritania	215	144	151	155	155		
Mexico	3,380	3,212	3,187	3,200	3,200	4	7.3
Morocco	990	1,032	909	880	880		
Namibia	56	67	68	71	71		
Niger	328	467	431	450	450		
Nigeria	840	700	936	1,000	1,000	10	2.3
Pakistan	1,900	2,423	3,421	3,901	3,901	3	8.9
Peru	507	488	497	520	520		
Portugal	168	182	170	160	160		
Saudi Arabia	95	106	104	98	97		
Senegal	178	235	310	364	364		
South Africa	218	210	210	210	210		
Spain	394	193	93	90	90		
Sudan	627	682	675	675	678		
Syria	240	240	168	201	205		
Tanzania	160	163	174	178	178		
Tunisia	180	204	226	230	230		
Turkey	1,910	1,349	1,063	841	809		
USA	4	22	53	52	52		
Uzbekistan	...	...	150	150	150		
Venezuela	493	452	440	440	440		
Yemen	673	695	500	500	500		
Zimbabwe	85	95	103	104	104		

Bananas *thousand tonnes*

	1970	1980	1990	1994	1995	Rank	%
WORLD	30,938	37,087	47,230	53,842	54,467		
Angola	283	303	280	275	275		
Argentina	196	122	260	142	171		
Australia	130	126	165	235	220		
Bangladesh	645	651	624	630	630		
Belize	3	18	34	68	45		
Bolivia	214	159	415	279	273		
Brazil	4,809	4,348	5,502	5,722	5,679	2	10.4
Burundi	810	1,096	1,547	1,487	1,421		
Cambodia	118	62	115	129	132		
Cameroon	94	550	510	950	980		
Cen. Afr. Rep	56	80	92	98	100		
China	704	291	1,657	3,282	3,309	4	6.1
Colombia	788	1,075	1,600	2,400	2,500	6	4.6
Comoros	87	31	50	57	58		
Congo (Zaïre)	279	349	404	410	412		
Costa Rica	1,119	1,105	1,740	1,996	1,996	9	3.7
Cuba	44	149	200	180	160		
Dominica	48	29	65	52	52		
Dom. Rep.	242	299	395	283	361		

Bananas continued

	1970	1980	1990	1994	1995	Rank	%
Ecuador	2,895	2,192	3,055	5,086	5,403	3	9.9
Egypt	89	127	408	458	480		
El Salvador	46	52	63	63	65		
Ethiopia	53	73	78	80	80		
Guadeloupe	140	106	86	116	116		
Guatemala	487	476	454	660	535		
Guinea	82	99	165	151	151		
Haiti	160	217	235	230	230		
Honduras	1,426	1,402	1,046	839	839		
India	3,148	4,425	6,734	9,242	9,500	1	17.4
Indonesia	1,574	1,886	2,411	2,300	2,300	7	4.2
Israel	57	67	61	90	105		
Ivory Coast	185	164	146	173	185		
Jamaica	193	110	128	100	85		
Kenya	111	134	200	220	220		
Lebanon	35	19	37	63	63		
Liberia	60	74	80	82	82		
Madagascar	258	274	220	210	210		
Malawi	8	72	89	91	91		
Malaysia	375	455	505	530	530		
Martinique	187	155	246	173	173		
Mexico	934	1,435	1,986	2,295	2,141	8	3.9
Morocco	...	...	51	100	90		
Mozambique	46	65	85	82	84		
Nicaragua	29	139	110	43	66		
Pakistan	76	130	210	63	79		
Panama	1,007	1,044	1,166	899	910		
Papua N.G.	758	916	1,200	640	650		
Paraguay	241	304	310	76	76		
Philippines	893	4,006	2,913	3,112	3,200	5	5.9
Portugal	35	35	46	40	40		
Puerto Rico	113	108	67	54	48		
Somalia	136	66	110	43	45		
South Africa	71	103	182	131	137		
Spain	426	457	416	338	345		
St Lucia	66	56	160	130	130		
St Vincent & G.	35	26	83	30	55		
Sudan	67	90	45	23	21		
Surinam	44	38	48	48	48		
Taiwan	462	214	201	184	173		
Tanzania	539	773	823	834	651		
Thailand	1,200	1,550	1,613	1,700	1,700	10	3.1
Uganda	314	362	560	580	580		
Venezuela	969	892	1,167	1,200	1,210		
Vietnam	399	856	1,200	1,400	1,400		
Yemen	15	28	50	74	74		
Zimbabwe	37	54	74	85	80		

Barley *thousand tonnes*

	1970	1980	1990	1994	1995	Rank	%
WORLD	129,036	156,649	177,670	159,925	142,746		
Afghanistan	363	313	216	258	274		
Algeria	470	592	800	234	540		
Argentina	497	229	303	341	338		
Australia	2,372	3,278	4,055	2,791	5,490	9	3.8
Austria	954	1,288	1,521	1,184	1,065		
Azerbaijan	...	306	446	262	266		
Belarus	...	1,727	2,908	3,013	2,700		
Belgium	608	844	594	407	416		
Bulgaria	1,108	1,439	1,387	1,146	900		
Canada	10,024	11,199	13,441	11,690	13,035	2	9.1
China	6,434	3,133	3,000	3,200	3,500		
Czech Rep.	...	...	...	2,419	2,140		
Denmark	5,175	6,250	4,987	3,446	3,870		
Egypt	93	111	129	129	368		
Estonia	...	535	600	340	480		
Ethiopia	727	1,021	899	1,284	1,417		
Finland	943	1,421	1,720	1,858	1,764		
France	8,865	10,997	10,020	7,698	7,677	6	5.4
Germany	7,312	13,385	13,992	10,903	11,025	3	7.7
Greece	655	838	341	406	448		
Hungary	749	848	1,369	1,558	1,408		
India	2,642	2,020	1,486	1,276	1,534		
Iran	1,042	1,548	3,360	3,045	3,100		
Iraq	692	726	1,854	854	990		
Ireland	854	1,643	1,380	910	1,096		
Italy	326	914	1,703	1,467	1,428		

Barley continued

	1970	1980	1990	1994	1995	Rank	%
Japan	629	392	346	225	210		
Kazakstan	...	6,359	8,500	5,497	2,587		
Korea, N.	353	155	150	110	110		
Korea, S.	1,589	1,059	578	234	300		
Kyrgyzstan	...	513	592	288	220		
Latvia	...	541	697	481	383		
Libya	70	97	141	149	148		
Lithuania	...	1,016	1,197	1,084	1,300		
Mexico	240	486	492	307	550		
Moldova	...	208	419	139	203		
Morocco	2,190	1,712	2,138	3,720	608		
Netherlands	366	265	219	228	218		
New Zealand	222	254	435	405	398		
Norway	545	636	740	588	650		
Pakistan	97	141	131	146	164		
Peru	164	115	80	130	131		
Poland	2,162	3,563	4,217	2,686	3,279		
Romania	615	2,360	2,680	2,134	1,816		
Russia	...	20,250	27,235	27,054	15,786	1	11.1
Saudi Arabia	13	8	350	2,025	1,200		
Slovak Rep.	...	...	...	874	794		
South Africa	27	102	262	275	300		
Spain	3,922	6,571	9,415	7,560	5,194	10	3.6
Sweden	1,836	2,323	2,123	1,662	1,793		
Switzerland	147	220	343	315	298		
Syria	375	1,129	846	1,482	1,722		
Tunisia	126	279	477	145	80		
Turkey	3,720	5,480	7,300	7,000	7,500	7	5.3
Ukraine	...	7,152	9,169	5,945	6,900	8	4.8
UK	8,257	10,058	7,900	14,509	9,633	4	6.7
USA	9,476	8,838	9,192	8,162	7,816	5	5.5
Uruguay	38	71	133	171	200		
Uzbekistan	...	333	385	303	293		
Yugoslavia	...	...	313	290	235		

Beef and veal *thousand tonnes*

	1970	1980	1990	1994	1995	Rank	%
WORLD	**38,871**	**44,110**	**52,109**	**52,739**	**53,217**		
Afghanistan	66	69	65	65	65		
Algeria	24	44	89	101	101		
Angola	40	50	56	56	56		
Argentina	2,503	2,933	2,587	2,484	2,466	5	4.6
Australia	997	1,683	1,643	1,825	1,803	7	3.4
Austria	155	199	224	235	222		
Azerbaijan	...	63	74	35	34		
Bangladesh	141	140	140	145	146		
Belarus	...	421	586	384	430		
Belgium	264	306	323	355	346		
Bolivia	51	100	130	136	140		
Brazil	1,822	2,104	3,700	4,500	4,620	2	8.7
Bulgaria	78	117	120	97	78		
Burma	67	76	85	90	92		
Cameroon	35	50	72	75	75		
Canada	864	977	906	904	960		
Chad	31	30	63	68	68		
Chile	165	171	242	240	258		
China	1,433	229	1,129	3,004	3,474	3	6.5
Colombia	422	607	795	609	615		
Costa Rica	44	80	87	91	92		
Cuba	199	145	141	100	100		
Czech Rep.	...	...	...	170	178		
Denmark	193	245	202	189	187		
Dom. Rep.	32	49	51	81	70		
Ecuador	45	79	103	127	148		
Egypt	119	119	151	198	200		
Estonia	...	74	80	31	25		
Ethiopia	243	214	245	230	231		
Finland	109	115	118	108	96		
France	1,577	1,832	1,870	1,814	1,899	6	3.6
Germany	1,633	1,890	2,082	1,420	1,407	8	2.6
Greece	86	110	82	74	75		
Guatemala	57	56	55	56	53		
Honduras	32	61	46	45	32		
Hungary	122	145	114	36	33		
India	66	845	1,194	1,292	1,292	10	2.4
Indonesia	133	156	173	271	280		
Iran	75	168	210	276	276		
Iraq	42	46	42	33	34		

Beef and veal continued

	1970	1980	1990	1994	1995	Rank	%
Ireland	217	384	515	445	497		
Israel	19	20	36	37	37		
Italy	1,062	1,120	1,165	1,171	1,171		
Japan	270	430	549	602	601		
Kazakstan	...	479	710	648	615		
Kenya	131	183	250	230	240		
Korea, S.	37	93	128	205	210		
Kyrgyzstan	...	52	91	75	68		
Latvia	...	108	125	68	62		
Lithuania	...	181	231	105	175		
Madagascar	114	129	142	143	144		
Mali	38	40	71	83	83		
Mexico	450	743	1,155	1,365	1,329	9	2.5
Moldova	...	79	114	62	45		
Mongolia	49	72	66	64	71		
Morocco	91	113	145	125	125		
Mozambique	31	36	41	38	38		
Namibia	27	33	63	52	44		
Netherlands	337	420	521	600	575		
New Zealand	387	502	479	636	643		
Nicaragua	59	58	38	51	49		
Nigeria	205	325	204	219	267		
Norway	57	73	83	84	84		
Pakistan	155	184	312	330	342		
Panama	35	41	55	57	57		
Paraguay	124	107	148	225	226		
Peru	96	87	117	102	107		
Philippines	73	89	82	99	107		
Poland	513	654	725	421	435		
Portugal	87	107	115	95	82		
Romania	214	297	176	239	240		
Russia	...	3,361	4,329	3,240	2,799	4	5.3
Slovak Rep.	...	...	...	58	61		
South Africa	398	590	661	554	582		
Spain	296	411	514	478	495		
Sudan	126	246	218	238	241		
Sweden	159	156	146	142	145		
Switzerland	133	162	164	147	141		
Tajikistan	...	45	55	35	35		
Tanzania	123	129	195	202	202		
Thailand	89	142	172	248	248		
Turkey	187	209	285	317	317		
Uganda	68	91	77	89	90		
Ukraine	...	1,569	1,965	1,427	1,189		
UK	921	1,063	1,001	916	994		
USA	10,062	10,092	10,465	11,194	11,552	1	21.7
Uruguay	338	331	333	361	335		
Uzbekistan	...	212	295	345	250		
Venezuela	208	341	382	394	418		
Vietnam	33	41	105	80	83		
Yugoslavia	...	...	162	197	198		
Zimbabwe	90	79	78	64	53		

Beer *million hectolitres*

	1970	1980	1990	1992	1993	Rank	%
WORLD	**644**	**900**	**1,099**	**1,153**	**1,182**		
Angola	0.7	1.3	...	...	...		
Argentina	3.6	2.3	6.2	9.5	10		
Australia	16	20	19	19	18		
Austria	7.4	7.7	9.8	10	12		
Azerbaijan	...	0.6	0.5	1.9	1.5		
Belarus	...	3.1	3.3	2.7	2.1		
Belgium	13	14	14	14	14		
Bolivia	0.4	1.2	1.1	1.3	1.3		
Botswana	...	...	1.2	1.2	1.4		
Brazil	9.1	30	44	44	83	6	3.8
Bulgaria	3.0	5.3	6.7	4.7	4.2		
Cameroon	0.7	1.9	...	...	...		
Canada	17	23	23	23	25	8	2.1
Chile	2.1	1.8	2.7	3.3	3.6		
China	1.2	6.9	69	102	119	2	10.1
Colombia	7.1	13	15	15	16		
Congo (Zaïre)	3.4	5.0	4.3	4.3	4.3		
Croatia	...	...	2.8	2.7	2.8		
Cuba	1.0	2.4	3.3	3.3	3.5		
Czech Rep.	21	23	22	19	17		
Denmark	7.1	9.2	9.4	9.7	9.8		

Beer continued

	1970	1980	1990	1992	1993	Rank	%
Dom. Rep.	0.4	1.2	1.2	1.2	1.2		
Ecuador	0.7	0.6	...	1.8	1.8		
Finland	2.4	2.9	4.2	4.7	4.6		
France	21	21	19	19	19		
Gabon	1.0	1.0	0.8	0.8	0.8		
Germany	98	113	115	114	111	3	9.4
Greece	0.8	2.6	3.9	4.0	4.1		
Hungary	5.0	7.8	9.9	9.2	7.9		
India	0.3	0.9	1.9	2.2	3		
Indonesia	1.0	1.0	0.8	1.2	1.1		
Ireland	3.9	5.0	5.2	5.2	5.4		
Italy	5.9	8.7	11	11	11		
Ivory Coast	0.2	1.6	1.5	1.5	1.5		
Japan	31	46	66	70	70	5	5.9
Kazakstan	...	...	30	23	25	9	2.1
Kenya	0.8	2.3	3.3	3.7	1.7		
Korea, S.	6.9	5.8	13	16	15		
Lithuania	...	...	...	1.4	1.2		
Malaysia	...	1.2	1.4	1.4	1.4		
Mexico	14	27	39	42	44	7	3.7
Netherlands	8.8	16	20	20	21		
New Zealand	3.4	3.8	3.9	3.7	3.5		
Nigeria	1.3	4.0	7.8	11	17		
Norway	1.5	2.0	2.3	2.3	2.3		
Panama	1.0	1.0	1.2	1.2	1.2		
Paraguay	...	1.0	1.1	1.1	1.7		
Peru	2.3	5.3	5.7	5.7	5.7		
Philippines	3.5	5.2	...	...	...		
Poland	10	11	11	14	13		
Portugal	1.3	3.8	6.6	6.5	6.9		
Romania	4.4	9.9	11	10	9.9		
Russia	...	...	34	28	25	10	2.1
Slovak Rep.	...	...	4.1	3.7	3.9		
Slovenia	...	...	2.5	1.8	1.8		
South Africa	2.9	7.5	18	18	18		
Spain	12	19	28	24	24		
St Kitts & Nevis	...	...	1.7	1.7	1.7		
Sweden	4.4	4.0	4.7	4.7	4.9		
Switzerland	4.7	4.1	4.1	4.2	3.8		
Taiwan	1.8	4.4	7.0	6.9	6.8		
Thailand	0.4	1.2	2.6	3.3	4.2		
Turkey	0.5	2.5	3.5	4.8	5.5		
Ukraine	...	13	14	11	9.1		
UK	55	65	71	72	73	4	6.2
USA	158	215	236	237	237	1	20.1
Venezuela	4.9	5.0	...	...	...		
Vietnam	1.5	1.0	1.0	1.7	1.6		
(former) Yugo.	6.7	12	11	...	...		
Zambia	2.6	2.8	0.8	0.8	0.8		
Zimbabwe	0.4	1.0	1.5	1.5	1.5		

Buffaloes *thousand head*

	1970	1980	1990	1994	1995	Rank	%
WORLD	**123,487**	**121,731**	**145,792**	**149,591**	**151,514**		
Bangladesh	778	474	772	874	882		
Brazil	118	504	1,380	1,435	1,435		
Burma	1,593	1,896	2,060	2,130	2,203	10	1.5
Cambodia	903	386	750	829	839		
China	29,509	18,269	21,426	22,416	22,633	2	14.9
Egypt	2,014	1,906	2,897	3,200	3,250	7	2.1
India	56,119	66,083	78,380	79,070	79,500	1	52.5
Indonesia	2,956	2,459	3,297	3,109	3,565	5	2.4
Iran	210	242	383	440	440		
Iraq	280	172	148	105	105		
Laos	932	831	1,072	1,308	1,300		
Malaysia	303	276	206	166	157		
Nepal	3,552	2,400	3,020	3,176	3,278	6	2.2
Pakistan	8,828	11,590	17,373	19,219	20,000	3	13.2
Philippines	4,452	2,841	2,751	2,560	2,508	9	1.7
Romania	182	228	180	...	...		
Sri Lanka	744	862	958	880	880		
Thailand	5,642	5,934	5,152	4,982	4,807	4	3.2
Turkey	1,184	1,031	429	316	305		
Vietnam	2,333	2,311	2,871	2,961	3,000	8	2.0

Buffalo meat *thousand tonnes*

	1970	1980	1990	1994	1995	Rank	%
WORLD	**1,142**	**1,568**	**2,212**	**2,569**	**2,638**		
Bangladesh	5	2	3	3	3		
Bulgaria	5	4	2	2	2		
Burma	14	18	21	22	23	10	0.9
Cambodia	5	6	11	12	13		
China	504	69	164	271	301	3	11.4
Egypt	96	120	157	180	180	4	6.8
India	112	824	1,089	1,204	1,204	1	45.6
Indonesia	32	43	50	54	54	8	2.0
Iran	9	7	10	10	10		
Iraq	4	3	3	2	2		
Laos	10	19	23	28	7		
Malaysia	8	7	4	4	4		
Nepal	15	51	95	100	104	5	3.9
Pakistan	139	188	378	477	505	2	19.1
Philippines	30	28	45	46	52	9	2.0
Romania	9	12	5				
Sri Lanka	6	5	5	5	5		
Thailand	58	72	63	63	63	7	2.4
Turkey	56	25	11	8	8		
Vietnam	56	62	86	95	97	6	3.7

Butter and ghee *thousand tonnes*

	1970	1980	1990	1994	1995	Rank	%
WORLD	**5,915**	**6,877**	**7,775**	**6,668**	**6,738**		
Afghanistan	5	12	11	12	12		
Argentina	33	32	35	53	53		
Australia	208	89	106	143	138		
Austria	42	42	41	43	42		
Bangladesh	12	15	13	15	16		
Belarus	...	96	159	74	120		
Belgium	98	101	93	73	75		
Brazil	46	94	75	70	85		
Bulgaria	14	21	22	2	2		
Burma	4	6	10	10	10		
Canada	150	108	104	92	97		
China	71	32	64	74	74		
Colombia	11	12	15	15	15		
Cuba	0.1	10	9	8	8		
Czech Rep.	...	...	...	71	69		
Denmark	133	117	93	59	54		
Ecuador	4	4.2	4.6	46	46		
Egypt	56	67	79	82	82		
Estonia	...	29	29	18	24		
Ethiopia	9	9	10	10	10		
Finland	91	73	62	53	50		
France	489	606	511	444	453	4	6.7
Germany	718	838	637	461	487	3	7.2
Hungary	20	31	39	15	15		
India	492	640	983	1,200	1,280	1	19.0
Iran	43	51	72	1044	105		
Iraq	6	8	8	5	5.9		
Ireland	75	128	148	127	140	10	2.1
Italy	68	76	82	93	97		
Japan	44	66	76	80	70		
Kazakstan	...	59	85	60	62		
Korea, S.	1.4	9	44	51	51		
Kyrgyzstan	...	10	13	7	7		
Latvia	...	33	44	10	5		
Lithuania	...	52	74	31	50		
Macedonia	...	...	...	8	8		
Mexico	18	22	31	33	33		
Moldova	...	18	27	8	6		
Morocco	7	12	15	13	13		
Nepal	7	10	16	18	19		
Netherlands	119	189	174	129	134		
New Zealand	246	262	245	306	310	7	4.6
Nigeria	7	7	8	9	9		
Norway	20	22	22	16	16		
Pakistan	209	170	284	353	372	6	5.5
Poland	198	296	282	150	150	9	2.2
Portugal	6	5	15	17	20		
Romania	37	37	33	14	16		
Russia	...	611	833	488	419	5	6.2
Slovak Rep.	...	...	...	16	16		
Somalia	1	9.5	8	11	11		
South Africa	50	18	16	16	16		

Butter and ghee continued

	1970	1980	1990	1994	1995	Rank	%
Spain	7	19	46	19	25		
Sudan	9	12	13	14	14		
Sweden	53	65	72	56	50		
Switzerland	30	36	38	40	40		
Syria	10	14	12	12	13		
Turkey	113	120	115	116	115		
Ukraine	...	335	444	254	219	8	3.3
UK	63	168	141	155	108		
USA	517	508	610	621	602	2	8.9
Uruguay	7	7	14	10	16		
Uzbekistan	...	12	16	12	11		
Yugoslavia	...	...	11	1	1.5		

Cabbages *thousand tonnes*

	1970	1980	1990	1994	1995	Rank	%
WORLD	**27,751**	**34,817**	**37,306**	**41,289**	**42,110**		
Armenia	...	...	...	60	65		
Australia	71	97	84	90	90		
Austria	101	179	54	42	47		
Azerbaijan	...	...	...	40	50		
Bangladesh	51	50	66	81	81		
Belarus	...	...	...	400	400		
Belgium	52	55	90	157	110		
Bosnia	...	...	84	60	68		
Bulgaria	168	155	115	74	74		
Canada	70	135	158	145	143		
Chile	15	30	63	82	70		
China	4,110	5,848	8,230	9,887	9,887	1	23.5
Colombia	241	455	350	350	350		
Croatia	...	...	104	92	75		
Czech Rep.	...	...	...	113	116		
Denmark	55	49	50	52	52		
Ecuador	84	24	5	6	5		
Egypt	271	362	381	496	498		
Estonia	...	...	49	30	30		
Ethiopia	31	42	49	48	48		
France	406	285	215	252	247		
Georgia	...	...	...	100	110		
Germany	851	857	660	659	664		
Greece	127	159	181	202	180		
Hong Kong	56	81	13	1	2		
Hungary	220	165	139	117	100		
India	380	1,700	2,504	3,300	3,300	3	7.8
Indonesia	150	334	991	1,418	1,418	8	3.4
Ireland	125	31	45	67	67		
Israel	15	29	51	76	69		
Italy	801	517	492	480	497		
Japan	3,753	3,126	2,815	2,628	2,600	5	6.2
Kazakstan	...	...	...	150	180		
Korea, N.	208	660	900	900	900		
Korea, S.	909	3,387	3,129	2,839	3,000	4	7.1
Kyrgyzstan	...	...	...	40	48		
Latvia	...	...	...	130	130		
Lebanon	25	18	50	62	63		
Lithuania	...	...	100	120	120		
Macedonia	...	...	55	53	53		
Malaysia	1	28	21	85	85		
Mexico	29	68	181	204	205		
Moldova	...	...	...	69	100		
Netherlands	229	267	305	300	300		
Norway	49	46	43	37	37		
Pakistan	...	...	50	45	48		
Peru	42	36	51	42	42		
Philippines	44	66	68	85	85		
Poland	1,459	1,493	1,749	1,672	1,866	7	4.4
Portugal	120	143	145	140	140		
Romania	541	833	552	711	824		
Russia	...	...	...	4,680	4,680	2	11.1
Slovak Rep.	...	...	...	97	88		
Slovenia	...	...	69	65	60		
South Africa	109	217	220	217	230		
Spain	718	560	425	359	363		
Sri Lanka	14	42	36	56	56		
Sweden	30	36	29	26	26		
Syria	19	80	52	56	82		
Thailand	174	138	194	205	205		
Turkey	543	573	699	699	676		
Turkmenistan	...	...	...	50	36		

Cabbages continued

	1970	1980	1990	1994	1995	Rank	%
Ukraine	...	1,939	1,891	893	965	10	2.3
UAE	8	7	41	107	110		
UK	926	796	795	769	769		
USA	1,229	1,431	1,400	1,816	1,890	6	4.5
Uzbekistan	...	...	...	1,000	1,200	9	2.8
Vietnam	48	65	95	103	105		
Yugoslavia	...	...	287	277	285		

Camels *thousand head*

	1970	1980	1990	1994	1995	Rank	%
WORLD	**15,965**	**17,102**	**18,779**	**19,017**	**19,241**		
Afghanistan	300	267	265	265	265		
Algeria	173	150	125	114	115		
Azerbaijan	...	...	...	30	30		
Chad	397	432	549	593	600	8	3.1
China	693	597	475	373	356		
Djibouti	22	51	59	62	62		
Egypt	120	91	197	133	133		
Eritrea	...	...	...	69	69		
Ethiopia	981	980	1,050	1,000	1,000	6	5.2
India	1,110	1,050	1,450	1,520	1,520	3	7.9
Iran	135	111	143	140	140		
Iraq	262	72	59	15	16		
Jordan	13	13	18	18	18		
Kazakstan	...	...	...	155	156		
Kenya	507	608	810	810	810	7	4.2
Kyrgyzstan	...	...	...	50	50		
Libya	163	134	140	130	130		
Mali	217	230	245	260	260		
Mauritania	707	734	950	1,080	1,087	5	5.6
Mongolia	636	601	558	400	390	10	2.0
Morocco	205	157	34	36	36		
Niger	340	404	366	374	380		
Nigeria	19	17	18	18	18		
Oman	11	41	87	94	94		
Pakistan	700	844	1,035	1,119	1,119	4	5.8
Qatar	8	10	27	43	45		
Saudi Arabia	107	284	413	415	418	9	2.2
Somalia	4,700	5,883	6,000	6,000	6,200	1	32.2
Sudan	2,495	2,611	2,742	2,886	2,903	2	15.1
Tajikistan	...	...	...	50	50		
Tunisia	233	173	230	231	231		
Turkey	37	12	2	2	2		
Turkmenistan	...	...	...	40	40		
UAE	100	57	113	148	155		
Uzbekistan	...	...	...	20	20		
Yemen	224	158	175	173	173		

Carrots *thousand tonnes*

	1970	1980	1990	1994	1995	Rank	%
WORLD	**7,908**	**10,499**	**13,708**	**14,047**	**14,471**		
Algeria	27	42	101	158	159		
Argentina	94	106	165	213	205		
Australia	85	109	155	175	175		
Austria	20	22	23	31	31		
Azerbaijan	...	...	...	12	14		
Belarus	...	...	...	55	55		
Belgium	67	84	95	116	135		
Bolivia	15	19	29	33	33		
Bosnia	...	...	22	9	6		
Bulgaria	32	28	17	12	12		
Canada	180	237	315	312	315		
Chile	34	84	107	118	132		
China	1,135	1,791	2,749	2,477	2,477	1	17.1
Colombia	86	153	178	147	147		
Croatia	...	...	7	20	18		
Czech Rep.	...	...	...	68	73		
Denmark	50	54	70	60	60		
Dom. Rep.	1	1	8	12	14		
Ecuador	3	10	4	19	31		
Egypt	51	133	92	118	125		
Estonia	...	...	13	8	8		
Finland	15	26	32	60	60		
France	552	503	548	590	641	7	4.4
Germany	335	421	355	245	297		
Greece	22	30	46	40	40		
Hungary	106	107	119	98	100		

Carrots continued

	1970	1980	1990	1994	1995	Rank	%
Indonesia	...	45	172	234	234		
Iraq	9	13	13	10	11		
Ireland	...	38	39	34	33		
Israel	52	49	77	88	71		
Italy	246	275	510	443	468	8	3.2
Jamaica	5	12	16	28	27		
Japan	498	597	655	658	680	6	4.7
Kazakstan	...	...	...	30	45		
Korea, S.	4	78	87	152	160		
Kyrgyzstan	...	...	...	31	40		
Latvia	...	...	17	30	30		
Lebanon	14	10	24	30	30		
Libya	2	9	25	22	22		
Lithuania	...	...	64	40	40		
Mexico	66	85	198	192	200		
Moldova	...	...	...	17	40		
Morocco	38	52	180	166	224		
Netherlands	137	163	390	430	430	9	3.0
New Zealand	31	32	38	52	52		
Nigeria	...	...	...	175	175		
Norway	52	47	48	49	49		
Pakistan	...	...	117	160	172		
Peru	24	47	55	47	47		
Poland	438	595	822	786	814	4	5.6
Portugal	75	82	83	83	83		
Russia	...	...	...	1,250	1,250	3	8.6
Saudi Arabia	1	5	21	25	25		
Slovak Rep.	...	...	...	59	72		
South Africa	65	106	90	86	45		
Spain	38	140	250	288	300		
Sri Lanka	2	5	13	23	23		
Sweden	41	55	66	60	60		
Switzerland	22	49	60	57	57		
Tajikistan	...	...	...	34	34		
Tunisia	25	35	40	46	46		
Turkey	41	72	168	225	250		
Turkmenistan	...	...	...	26	19		
Ukraine	...	...	401	327	409	10	2.8
UK	611	649	569	751	751	5	5.2
USA	838	980	1,323	1,384	1,365	2	9.4
Uruguay	11	12	13	19	19		
Uzbekistan	...	...	...	26	27		
Venezuela	11	28	31	60	60		
Yugoslavia	...	...	58	51	55		

Cassava *thousand tonnes*

	1970	1980	1990	1994	1995	Rank	%
WORLD	**96,760**	**121,472**	**153,963**	**162,838**	**163,776**		
Angola	1,597	1,850	1,617	1,600	1,700		
Argentina	296	202	147	150	160		
Benin	533	631	987	1,146	1,146		
Bolivia	223	204	480	293	299		
Brazil	29,922	24,315	24,176	24,452	25,538	2	15.6
Burundi	843	412	598	527	501		
Cameroon	637	1,273	1,433	1,600	1,300		
Cen. Afr. Rep.	767	920	550	518	402		
Chad	140	205	327	195	195		
China	1,938	3,390	3,282	3,501	3,501	10	2.1
Colombia	1,380	2,070	1,698	1,900	1,920		
Congo	461	631	662	630	630		
Congo (Zaïre)	10,232	12,942	18,738	18,051	17,500	4	10.7
Cuba	217	287	302	290	250		
Dom. Rep.	173	98	154	132	132		
Ecuador	382	216	113	77	77		
Gabon	155	242	207	230	210		
Ghana	1,533	1,894	3,215	6,025	6,899	6	4.2
Guinea	482	480	375	512	512		
Haiti	205	252	331	350	350		
India	4,993	5,921	5,070	5,784	6,000	7	3.7
Indonesia	10,695	13,500	16,300	15,729	15,438	5	9.4
Ivory Coast	546	1,067	1,439	1,564	1,564		
Kenya	510	588	753	830	840		
Liberia	264	300	382	450	450		
Madagascar	1,227	1,641	2,292	2,413	2,420		
Malawi	150	135	156	200	200		
Malaysia	271	347	410	440	440		
Mozambique	2,549	3,100	3,815	3,294	4,178	9	2.6

Cassava continued

	1970	1980	1990	1994	1995	Rank	%
Niger	182	191	213	225	225		
Nigeria	9,473	10,833	20,157	31,005	31,404	1	19.2
Paraguay	1,442	1,977	3,371	2,518	2,600		
Peru	477	453	433	513	547		
Philippines	436	2,226	1,840	1,850	1,870		
Rwanda	333	578	351	150	250		
Senegal	159	28	51	77	56		
Sierra Leone	75	94	121	244	219		
Sri Lanka	376	520	389	298	298		
Sudan	133	125	10	8	9		
Tanzania	3,373	5,547	7,383	7,209	5,969	8	3.6
Thailand	3,208	15,128	21,557	19,091	18,164	3	11.1
Togo	562	404	504	412	469		
Uganda	1,058	2,122	3,406	2,080	2,625		
Venezuela	317	322	344	285	285		
Vietnam	960	3,238	2,439	24,309	2,497		
Zambia	159	183	510	600	600		

Cattle *thousand head*

	1970	1980	1990	1994	1995	Rank	%
WORLD	**1,094,915**	**1,219,756**	**1,284,979**	**1,296,907**	**1,306,476**		
Afghanistan	3,660	3,723	1,650	1,500	1,500		
Algeria	872	1,356	1,393	1,269	1,300		
Angola	2,514	3,117	3,100	3,280	3,280		
Argentina	48,841	55,620	50,582	52,156	53,500	5	4.1
Australia	22,382	26,161	23,191	25,732	26,187	9	2.0
Austria	2,440	2,553	2,562	2,329	2,430		
Azerbaijan	...	1,765	1,900	1,621	1,633		
Bangladesh	25,395	25,053	23,244	24,130	24,340		
Belarus	...	6,800	7,166	5,851	5,403		
Belgium	2,882	3,104	3,257	3,289	3,369		
Bolivia	2,298	4,570	5,538	5,912	5,985		
Botswana	1,660	2,906	2,696	2,800	2,800		
Brazil	75,658	116,645	148,000	156,000	156,500	2	12.0
Bulgaria	1,277	1,782	1,575	750	600		
Burkina Faso	2,556	2,760	3,937	4,261	4,350		
Burma	6,949	8,565	9,298	9,691	9,857		
Cambodia	2,233	831	2,100	2,589	2,589		
Cameroon	2,308	3,521	4,697	4,870	4,900		
Canada	11,678	13,328	12,249	12,254	12,849		
Cen. Afr. Rep.	677	1,662	2,595	2,735	2,797		
Chad	4,500	4,360	4,297	4,621	4,539		
Chile	2,923	3,650	3,336	3,692	3,814		
China	63,168	52,567	79,493	90,906	100,849	4	7.7
Colombia	20,233	24,110	24,550	25,700	26,018	10	2.0
Congo (Zaïre)	968	1,159	1,550	1,475	1,480		
Costa Rica	1,498	2,183	1,762	1,894	1,860		
Cuba	6,146	5,166	4,920	4,200	4,200		
Czech Rep.	...	...	...	2,161	2,030		
Denmark	2,855	2,970	2,241	2,105	2,060		
Dom. Rep.	1,176	1,918	2,240	2,366	2,302		
Ecuador	2,391	2,987	4,359	4,937	4,995		
Egypt	2,108	1,906	2,618	3,070	3,100		
El Salvador	1,164	1,234	1,220	1,236	1,262		
Eritrea	...	...	...	1,290	1,312		
Ethiopia	26,310	26,000	30,000	29,450	29,825	8	2.3
Finland	1,907	1,747	1,363	1,230	1,185		
France	21,669	23,825	21,419	20,099	20,524		
Georgia	...	1,552	1,427	929	800		
Germany	19,281	20,672	20,287	15,897	15,962		
Ghana	902	804	1,145	1,680	1,680		
Guatemala	1,474	1,886	2,032	2,300	1,700		
Guinea	1,300	1,753	1,800	1,780	1,780		
Haiti	800	1,000	1,450	1,234	1,200		
Honduras	1,578	1,980	2,424	2,050	1,980		
Hungary	1,952	1,936	1,598	999	910		
India	177,447	186,500	191,750	103,585	194,655	1	14.9
Indonesia	6,273	6,505	10,550	11,010	11,966		
Iran	5,239	5,450	7,532	7,700	8,200		
Iraq	2,633	1,630	1,675	1,200	1,250		
Ireland	5,940	6,043	5,899	6,308	6,410		
Italy	9,436	8,697	8,746	7,459	7,164		
Japan	3,582	4,261	4,760	4,989	4,916		
Kazakstan	2,642	8,349	9,800	9,347	9,347		
Kenya	8,433	10,418	13,793	12,500	13,000		
Korea, N.	733	945	1,300	1,350	1,350		
Korea, S.	1,244	1,634	2,126	2,945	3,075		

Cattle continued

	1970	1980	1990	1994	1995	Rank	%
Latvia	...	1,400	1,472	678	551		
Lithuania	442	2,200	2,422	1,384	1,152		
Madagascar	8,519	10,147	10,254	10,288	10,309		
Mali	5,400	5,670	5,000	5,542	5,542		
Mauritania	2,250	1,262	1,350	1,100	1,125		
Mexico	24,668	27,706	32,054	30,702	30,162	7	2.3
Mongolia	2,026	2,452	2,693	3,005	3,317		
Morocco	3,617	3,362	3,400	2,238	2,490		
Mozambique	1,274	1,400	1,380	1,270	1,280		
Namibia	2,500	2,403	2,087	2,036	1,890		
Nepal	6,292	6,893	6,281	6,546	6,838		
Netherlands	4,281	5,071	4,926	4,629	4,500		
New Zealand	8,734	8,063	8,065	8,887	8,729		
Nicaragua	2,275	2,373	1,680	1,730	1,750		
Niger	4,077	3,343	1,711	1,968	2,008		
Nigeria	11,183	12,267	14,640	16,316	17,791		
Pakistan	14,584	15,268	17,573	17,814	19,000		
Panama	1,201	1,425	1,388	1,454	1,454		
Paraguay	4,433	5,966	8,254	8,000	8,100		
Peru	3,999	3,958	4,102	4,062	4,513		
Philippines	1,653	1,885	1,629	1,936	2,021		
Poland	10,990	12,494	10,049	7,696	7,306		
Portugal	1,252	1,332	1,335	1,323	1,288		
Romania	4,947	6,351	6,291	3,957	3,481		
Russia	954	58,414	58,800	48,914	39,696	6	3.0
Senegal	2,557	2,424	2,740	2,800	2,850		
Somalia	3,750	4,437	3,800	5,000	5,200		
South Africa	11,114	13,647	13,398	12,584	13,015		
Spain	4,236	4,608	5,126	5,252	5,060		
Sri Lanka	1,601	1,662	1,773	1,703	1,703		
Sudan	12,300	18,376	20,583	21,750	22,000		
Sweden	1,934	1,928	1,718	1,827	1,777		
Switzerland	1,866	2,008	1,855	1,763	1,762		
Tajikistan	...	1,200	1,400	1,250	1,250		
Tanzania	10,141	12,616	13,047	13,376	13,376		
Thailand	4,470	4,228	5,669	7,593	7,593		
Turkey	13,235	15,467	12,173	11,910	11,901		
Uganda	3,987	5,063	4,913	5,150	5,200		
Ukraine	26	25,400	25,195	21,607	19,624		
UK	12,632	13,321	11,922	11,834	11,868		
USA	112,321	112,152	98,162	100,988	102,755	3	7.9
Uruguay	8,730	10,965	8,723	10,614	10,870		
Uzbekistan	2,162	3,500	4,217	5,291	5,291		
Venezuela	8,292	10,527	13,272	13,796	14,231		
Vietnam	1,750	1,646	3,199	3,467	3,604		
Yugoslavia	...	...	...	1,809	1,950		
Zambia	1,580	2,238	2,920	3,300	3,300		
Zimbabwe	5,178	5,378	6,218	4,300	4,500		

Cheese *thousand tonnes*

	1970	1980	1990	1994	1995	Rank	%
WORLD	**7,732**	**11,363**	**14,574**	**14,778**	**14,749**		
Afghanistan	9	19	15	19	20		
Argentina	178	247	258	385	405	7	2.7
Armenia	...	...	...	15	15		
Australia	76	144	182	234	216		
Austria	59	93	112	107	103		
Azerbaijan	...	...	...	43	43		
Belarus	...	...	...	89	79		
Belgium	39	47	68	76	73		
Bosnia	...	...	...	14	14		
Brazil	49	58	60	60	60		
Bulgaria	127	163	185	88	85		
Burma	12	18	26	28	28		
Canada	121	206	286	307	302		
Chile	18	20	32	45	48		
China	171	75	173	217	202		
Colombia	39	44	51	51	51		
Croatia	...	...	...	17	17		
Cuba	1	11	16	15	15		
Czech Rep.	...	...	...	136	137		
Denmark	113	218	286	288	311		
Egypt	204	240	312	341	349	10	2.4
Estonia	...	...	...	34	32		
Finland	40	72	90	92	96		
France	780	1,137	1,465	1,564	1,592	2	10.8
Georgia	...	...	...	25	55		

Cheese continued

	1970	1980	1990	1994	1995	Rank	%
Germany	660	986	1,305	1,367	1,420	3	9.6
Greece	142	195	224	211	221		
Hungary	42	68	90	83	85		
Iran	74	107	184	207	216		
Iraq	25	35	32	20	19		
Ireland	30	58	4	3	3		
Israel	32	55	76	86	86		
Italy	470	608	836	905	899	4	6.1
Japan	40	68	85	102	105		
Kazakstan	...	...	...	81	75		
Kyrgyzstan	...	...	...	21	25		
Latvia	...	...	...	11	17		
Lebanon	7	10	10	14	14		
Lithuania	...	...	...	44	40		
Mexico	77	97	115	132	126		
Moldova	...	...	...	28	28		
Netherlands	284	458	583	648	680	5	4.6
New Zealand	102	93	124	193	197		
Niger	7	16	11	13	14		
Norway	53	71	85	82	85		
Peru	36	34	16	5	6		
Poland	249	379	360	352	351	8	2.4
Portugal	23	38	59	65	65		
Romania	83	129	...	53	55		
Russia	...	...	...	613	477	6	3.2
Slovak Rep.	...	...	...	35	38		
Slovenia	...	...	...	15	16		
South Africa	29	31	41	41	41		
Spain	80	145	166	168	176		
Sudan	38	55	66	74	75		
Sweden	64	101	115	133	129		
Switzerland	87	123	134	137	132		
Syria	27	52	69	64	67		
Tajikistan	...	...	...	16	16		
Turkey	94	128	140	137	136		
Ukraine	...	...	...	118	86		
UK	139	238	297	330	351	9	2.4
USA	1,319	2,262	3,062	3,544	3,471	1	23.5
Uruguay	8	12	17	22	23		
Uzbekistan	...	...	...	46	46		
Venezuela	28	62	84	74	76		
Yemen	13	20	...	9	9		

Cocoa beans   *thousand tonnes*

	1970	1980	1990	1994	1995	Rank	%
WORLD	1,491	1,636	2,511	2,487	2,529		
Bolivia	1	2	4	4	4		
Brazil	183	330	355	330	319	3	12.6
Cameroon	115	120	122	100	100	7	4.0
Colombia	20	35	56	59	62	9	2.5
Congo	2	2	2	1	1		
Congo (Zaïre)	6	5	3	7	7		
Costa Rica	5	7	4	2	2		
Cuba	1	1	2	2	2		
Dom. Rep.	32	32	43	58	59	10	2.3
Ecuador	57	83	97	81	86	8	3.4
Equat. Guinea	25	8	5	4	4		
Gabon	5	4	2	2	2		
Ghana	430	268	284	270	325	2	12.9
Grenada	3	2	2	2	2		
Guatemala	1	2	1	2	1		
Guinea	...	4	2	4	4		
Haiti	3	3	5	6	3		
Honduras	1	1	3	4	4		
India	1	2	6	7	7		
Indonesia	2	11	142	271	243	4	9.6
Ivory Coast	195	427	750	809	860	1	34.0
Jamaica	2	2	2	3	2		
Liberia	2	5	3	3	3		
Madagascar	1	2	4	4	4		
Malaysia	4	38	247	177	131	5	5.2
Mexico	27	35	44	43	52		
Nigeria	261	169	155	130	130	6	5.1
Panama	1	2	1	1	1		
Papua N.G.	27	30	40	30	30		
Peru	2	5	16	13	23		
Philippines	4	4	10	8	8		
São Tomé & P.	10	7	3	5	4		

Cocoa beans continued

	1970	1980	1990	1994	1995	Rank	%
Sierra Leone	5	9	24	12	10		
Solomon Is.	1	1	4	3	3		
Sri Lanka	2	2	4	4	4		
Tanzania	2	1	2	1	1		
Togo	27	14	7	5	5		
Trinidad & Tob.	4	3	2	1	2		
Vanuatu	1	1	2	1	2		
Venezuela	19	16	16	19	19		
W. Samoa	3	2	1	1	1		

Coconuts   *thousand tonnes*

	1970	1980	1990	1994	1995	Rank	%
WORLD	27,614	35,270	43,570	44,439	45,068		
Bangladesh	66	75	82	94	95		
Brazil	331	507	734	902	950	9	2.1
Burma	67	95	183	320	310		
Cambodia	44	28	48	53	53		
China	53	59	65	75	77		
Colombia	35	64	119	90	90		
Comoros	69	53	50	52	52		
Dom. Rep.	57	69	109	185	185		
Ecuador	25	73	36	36	39		
El Salvador	30	55	78	80	80		
Fiji	260	217	239	190	210		
Fr. Polynesia	178	130	110	86	86		
Ghana	257	225	220	264	264		
Guinea-Bissau	31	25	25	25	25		
Guyana	56	30	48	57	64		
India	4,472	4,192	7,207	7,800	8,000	3	17.8
Indonesia	5,892	11,307	14,181	13,868	13,868	1	30.8
Ivory Coast	49	156	363	213	213		
Jamaica	150	172	92	115	115		
Kenya	77	68	42	43	43		
Kiribati	62	73	47	65	65		
Madagascar	19	67	84	80	80		
Malaysia	1,039	1,170	1,190	1,005	1,043	7	2.3
Mexico	998	851	1,169	1,201	1,201	6	2.7
Micronesia	101	203	140	140	140		
Mozambique	400	453	420	438	438		
Nigeria	86	90	118	148	150		
Papua N.G.	741	835	796	700	700	10	1.6
Philippines	7,601	9,142	9,552	9,800	10,300	2	22.9
São Tomé & P.	42	36	42	22	22		
Seychelles	42	22	10	3	3		
Solomon Is.	184	201	180	220	225		
Sri Lanka	1,963	1,692	1,924	1,997	1,997	4	4.4
St Lucia	35	34	29	29	29		
Tanzania	310	310	365	365	365		
Thailand	713	781	1,426	1,476	1,465	5	3.3
Tonga	88	91	25	25	25		
Trinidad & Tob.	105	49	40	30	20		
Vanuatu	247	326	357	260	280		
Venezuela	147	160	177	167	167		
Vietnam	100	287	894	1,190	1,000	8	2.2
W. Samoa	193	162	138	130	130		

Coffee   *thousand tonnes*

	1970	1980	1990	1994	1995	Rank	%
WORLD	4,266	5,287	6,100	5,583	5,603		
Angola	216	27	5	2	3		
Bolivia	11	19	29	19	20		
Brazil	1,197	1,475	1,465	1,306	930	1	16.6
Burundi	21	30	34	41	26		
Cameroon	90	108	101	60	70		
Cen. Afr. Rep.	10	17	14	15	9		
China	4	10	33	44	45		
Colombia	483	740	845	678	810	2	14.5
Congo (Zaïre)	69	90	120	77	76		
Costa Rica	82	106	151	150	153		
Cuba	29	21	27	19	27		
Dom. Rep.	44	58	59	41	42		
Ecuador	60	82	135	187	197	8	3.5
El Salvador	139	183	156	158	151		
Equat. Guinea	7	6	7	7	7		
Ethiopia	172	192	204	207	228	5	4.1
Ghana	6	2	1	3	3		
Guatemala	125	167	202	214	210	7	3.7

Coffee continued

	1970	1980	1990	1994	1995	Rank	%
Guinea	9	14	30	30	30		
Haiti	31	39	37	34	34		
Honduras	39	71	120	126	126		
India	82	126	120	170	170		
Indonesia	186	295	413	348	346	4	6.2
Ivory Coast	243	298	286	148	194	9	3.5
Kenya	57	89	104	80	93		
Laos	1	4	5	6	10		
Liberia	5	10	2	3	3		
Madagascar	63	82	85	79	79		
Malawi	1	1	6	5	5		
Malaysia	6	9	7	11	11		
Mexico	182	228	440	325	408	3	7.3
Nicaragua	38	59	28	41	55		
Panama	5	7	10	8	12		
Papua N.G.	26	51	65	65	65		
Paraguay	5	9	18	5	5		
Peru	68	90	81	91	97		
Philippines	48	129	134	122	135		
Puerto Rico	12	12	13	13	13		
Rwanda	14	23	32	2	22		
Sierra Leone	6	11	26	28	25		
Sri Lanka	9	11	8	11	11		
Tanzania	49	54	53	34	40		
Thailand	1	10	61	72	75		
Togo	11	8	13	26	16		
Uganda	215	112	141	198	220	6	3.9
Venezuela	60	57	76	79	83		
Vietnam	5	6	59	166	185	10	3.3
Yemen	4	4	7	8	9		
Zimbabwe	2	5	14	9	4		

Copra   *thousand tonnes*

	1970	1980	1990	1994	1995	Rank	%
WORLD	3,842	4,441	4,915	4,665	5,528		
Bangladesh	2	3	13	16	16		
Benin	3	3	3	3	3		
Brazil	2	2	9	3	3		
Cambodia	8	5	8	9	10		
Comoros	6	3	4	5	9		
Costa Rica	2	2	3	3	3		
Dom. Rep.	6	6	25	30	30		
Ecuador	4	13	6	6	6		
El Salvador	3	3	3	5	7		
Fiji	30	22	16	8	11		
Fr. Polynesia	24	17	11	10	11		
Ghana	10	7	9	10	10		
Guinea-Bissau	6	5	5	5	5		
Guyana	6	3	5	6	6		
India	354	350	469	455	610	3	11.0
Indonesia	753	1,077	1,267	1,171	1,070	2	19.4
Ivory Coast	6	21	52	34	34		
Jamaica	17	7	8	8	8		
Kenya	6	6	6	7	7		
Kiribati	8	9	8	8	8		
Madagascar	2	10	10	10	10		
Malaysia	186	144	92	61	68	9	1.2
Mexico	146	149	193	215	217	4	3.9
Mozambique	59	72	70	74	74	7	1.3
Nigeria	6	10	16	20	20		
Pacific Is.	12	28	18	18	18		
Papua N.G.	131	145	109	99	122	6	2.2
Philippines	1,582	1,897	1,969	1,886	2,657	1	48.1
St Lucia	6	6	4	2	2		
São Tomé & P.	5	10	1	1	1		
Seychelles	5	4	1	1	1		
Solomon Is.	25	32	30	21	26		
Sri Lanka	209	128	106	60	55	10	1.0
Tanzania	31	29	31	33	34		
Thailand	31	38	65	69	70	8	1.3
Tonga	10	11	2	2	2		
Trinidad & Tob.	13	5	4	3	2		
Vanuatu	25	43	33	30	30		
Venezuela	16	19	17	21	21		
Vietnam	20	58	173	210	208	5	3.8
W. Samoa	15	20	16	11	11		

Cotton lint *thousand tonnes*

	1970	1980	1990	1994	1995	Rank	%
WORLD	**12,010**	**14,352**	**18,443**	**18,672**	**19,799**		
Afghanistan	25	29	9	22	22		
Angola	28	11	11	4	4		
Argentina	114	134	302	249	402	10	2.0
Australia	27	78	289	329	335		
Azerbaijan	...	301	256	90	90		
Bangladesh	2	4	16	17	20		
Benin	9	7	59	103	103		
Brazil	631	555	660	501	515	7	2.6
Bulgaria	13	7	4	2	2		
Burkina Faso	10	25	77	67	67		
Burma	14	20	21	23	28		
Cameroon	21	32	44	48	48		
Cen. Afr. Rep.	20	9	13	12	13		
Chad	40	30	60	45	45		
China	1,988	2,627	4,508	4,341	4,768	1	24.1
Colombia	122	111	119	56	56		
Congo (Zaïre)	21	8	26	26	26		
Egypt	520	504	303	267	315		
El Salvador	49	57	6	4	4		
Ethiopia	13	26	19	14	15		
Ghana	2	3	5	15	37		
Greece	115	115	210	390	420	8	2.1
Guatemala	71	142	41	14	12		
India	1,088	1,280	1,671	2,346	2,380	3	12.0
Iran	155	78	120	118	101		
Israel	37	83	51	31	43		
Ivory Coast	14	54	105	116	93		
Kazakstan	...	236	180	62	50		
Kyrgyzstan		97	102	17	12		
Mali	22	48	99	110	110		
Mexico	354	352	201	119	231		
Mozambique	42	17	28	17	16		
Nicaragua	80	70	23	1	7		
Nigeria	62	31	36	105	115		
Pakistan	595	730	1,637	1,479	1,835	4	9.3
Paraguay	10	85	220	137	137		
Peru	89	86	78	51	65		
Senegal	5	11	11	20	18		
South Africa	19	54	52	28	22		
Spain	52	58	80	38	30		
Sudan	235	116	83	87	131		
Syria	150	126	159	186	222		
Tajikstan	...	60	25	151	135		
Tanzania	70	53	60	48	45		
Thailand	31	57	32	25	24		
Togo	2	7	34	40	40		
Turkey	441	488	655	606	755	6	3.8
Turkmenistan	...	345	437	385	403	9	2.0
Uganda	79	5	4	12	12		
USA	2,225	3,004	3,375	4,281	3,912	2	19.8
Uzbekistan	...	1,660	1,593	1,215	1,306	5	6.6
Venezuela	15	14	31	25	25		
Zimbabwe	43	54	67	60	37		

Cotton seed *thousand tonnes*

	1970	1980	1990	1994	1995	Rank	%
WORLD	**22,440**	**27,738**	**34,635**	**34,142**	**36,101**		
Afghanistan	49	58	29	44	44		
Angola	55	23	8	8	8		
Argentina	220	252	433	392	620	10	1.7
Australia	45	125	581	466	474		
Azerbaijan	...	...	...	221	221		
Bangladesh	4	8	29	34	40		
Benin	18	12	80	132	132		
Brazil	1,197	1,075	1,197	850	915	7	2.5
Bulgaria	26	9	9	4	4		
Burkina Faso	19	40	98	94	94		
Burma	25	39	41	45	47		
Cameroon	33	50	63	71	71		
Cen. Afr. Rep.	33	19	17	16	19		
Chad	65	48	98	75	75		
China	3,977	5,255	9,314	8,682	9,536	1	26.4
Colombia	205	186	198	85	86		
Congo (Zaïre)	42	15	50	50	50		
Egypt	901	817	495	411	495		
El Salvador	80	99	9	6	6		

Cotton seed continued

	1970	1980	1990	1994	1995	Rank	%
Ethiopia	27	58	32	28	30		
Ghana	1	4	8	34	52		
Greece	227	232	403	565	640	9	1.8
Guatemala	138	236	57	21	22		
India	2,176	2,638	3,539	4,693	4,761	3	13.2
Iran	285	170	249	232	198		
Iraq	29	10	9	17	17		
Israel	58	137	65	55	70		
Ivory Coast	20	74	131	133	109		
Kazakstan	...	...	...	116	116		
Kyrgyzstan	...	...	...	40	40		
Malawi	14	20	24	20	45		
Mali	39	79	174	150	150		
Mexico	623	552	285	187	325		
Mozambique	84	34	21	34	32		
Nicaragua	130	110	40	2	10		
Nigeria	125	59	167	218	233		
Pakistan	1,190	1,460	3,516	2,959	3,669	4	10.2
Paraguay	20	169	347	218	176		
Peru	148	166	151	100	130		
South Africa	38	98	102	48	39		
Spain	94	95	125	60	46		
Sudan	442	219	264	174	260		
Syria	241	215	295	332	372		
Tajikistan	...	...	...	401	401		
Tanzania	135	106	139	95	88		
Thailand	62	114	65	49	47		
Togo	4	12	55	61	44		
Turkey	705	781	977	930	1,180	6	3.3
Turkmenistan	...	...	...	830	830	8	2.3
Uganda	173	11	14	25	26		
USA	3,742	5,034	5,314	6,898	6,882	2	19.1
Uzbekistan	...	...	...	2,380	2,380	5	6.6
Venezuela	25	23	48	41	41		
Zimbabwe	86	103	136	109	63		

Cucumbers and gherkins *thousand tonnes*

	1970	1980	1990	1994	1995	Rank	%
WORLD	**8,417**	**11,919**	**14,761**	**19,055**	**19,353**		
Algeria	...	8	45	40	41		
Armenia	...	...	...	22	25		
Australia	10	14	17	14	14		
Austria	45	41	23	19	20		
Bangladesh	17	12	14	16	16		
Belarus	...	...	...	100	100		
Belgium	29	41	48	48	50		
Bulgaria	52	146	149	100	100		
Canada	71	82	95	94	95		
Chile	23	25	29	26	26		
China	1,987	2,662	4,048	8,042	8,042	1	41.6
Croatia	...	20	20	24	19		
Cuba	13	29	45	35	35		
Cyprus	12	11	12	12	12		
Czech Rep.	...	...	...	51	51		
Denmark	22	13	10	8	8		
Egypt	165	290	267	248	250		
Finland	14	22	33	30	30		
France	81	88	122	142	147		
Georgia	...	...	...	20	20		
Germany	116	130	125	106	100		
Greece	96	135	160	185	160		
Honduras	...	...	5	25	25		
Hungary	115	135	96	90	90		
Indonesia	133	165	255	300	300		
Iran	...	693	1,485	1,227	1,250	2	6.5
Iraq	127	210	362	340	345	10	1.8
Israel	48	49	94	85	85		
Italy	103	121	110	105	75		
Japan	976	1,060	931	866	866	5	4.5
Jordan	8	35	54	35	35		
Kazakstan	...	...	...	100	120		
Korea, N.	24	38	65	73	73		
Korea, S.	94	119	216	303	330		
Kuwait	...	...	...	30	36		
Lebanon	28	60	137	158	160		
Libya	...	1	22	16	16		
Lithuania	...	...	23	17	12		
Macedonia	...	...	23	19	21		

Cucumbers and gherkins continued

	1970	1980	1990	1994	1995	Rank	%
Malaysia	1	28	37	50	50		
Mexico	98	194	298	272	274		
Moldova	...	...	...	50	130		
Morocco	...	2	37	26	26		
Netherlands	300	372	448	500	500	7	2.6
Peru	7	6	8	20	20		
Poland	366	415	388	366	370	8	1.9
Romania	103	284	130	120	140		
Russia	...	...	...	130	130		
Saudi Arabia	...	11	90	113	115		
Slovak Rep.	...	...	...	39	22		
South Africa	11	20	28	15	15		
Spain	85	277	330	339	330		
Sri Lanka	3	22	22	25	25		
Sweden	23	28	27	10	10		
Syria	61	240	173	132	150		
Thailand	62	269	206	215	215		
Tunisia	5	13	25	34	33		
Turkey	394	503	1,000	1,140	1,150	3	5.9
Ukraine	...	...	300	518	669	6	3.5
UK	34	54	90	111	111		
USA	705	834	593	986	992	4	5.1
Uzbekistan	...	...	...	350	350	9	1.8
Yugoslavia	...	...	59	50	50		

Dates *thousand tonnes*

	1970	1980	1990	1994	1995	Rank	%
WORLD	**2,072**	**2,581**	**3,429**	**4,083**	**4,182**		
Algeria	145	201	206	317	318	5	7.6
Bahrain	15	40	16	19	20		
Chad	22	29	32	18	18		
China	...	7	15	30	30		
Egypt	360	414	542	646	650	2	15.5
Iran	293	261	516	774	795	1	19.0
Iraq	410	495	545	578	600	3	14.3
Israel	2	5	12	13	12		
Libya	52	91	74	79	68	10	1.6
Mauritania	14	13	13	22	25		
Morocco	92	79	120	62	98		
Niger	5	6	7	8	8		
Oman	44	70	120	133	133	9	3.2
Pakistan	161	202	290	290	290	6	6.9
Qatar	2	4	5	11	11		
Saudi Arabia	237	377	537	564	566	4	13.5
Somalia	5	9	10	10	10		
Spain	16	10	11	8	8		
Sudan	91	138	90	142	140	8	3.3
Tunisia	32	51	81	74	84		
Turkey	2	4	10	9	9		
UAE	8	47	141	236	240	7	5.7
USA	16	20	22	23	23		
Yemen	101	15	21	21	21		

Eggs (hen's) *thousand tonnes*

	1970	1980	1990	1994	1995	Rank	%
WORLD	**20,922**	**26,236**	**35,294**	**41,471**	**41,536**		
Algeria	...	25	130	150	150		
Argentina	182	254	298	248	270		
Australia	185	198	188	155	155		
Austria	86	97	94	98	95		
Azerbaijan	...	40	55	27	28		
Bangladesh	34	39	57	77	82		
Belarus	...	166	203	189	185		
Belgium	229	201	169	218	220		
Brazil	337	765	1,244	1,400	1,400	6	3.4
Bulgaria	89	132	129	84	75		
Burma	17	31	34	41	46		
Canada	328	331	321	325	328		
Chile	58	66	96	93	95		
China	3,309	2,882	6,698	12,092	12,340	1	29.7
Colombia	95	177	236	293	315		
Croatia	...	...	51	50	46		
Cuba	64	99	110	70	70		
Czech Rep.	...	...	...	149	152		
Denmark	84	77	82	90	91		
Dom. Rep.	...	19	35	43	45		
Ecuador	13	43	51	54	55		
Egypt	55	78	141	154	158		

Eggs (hen's) continued

	1970	1980	1990	1994	1995	Rank	%
El Salvador	23	37	46	50	52		
Ethiopia	66	73	79	73	73		
Finland	64	78	76	71	66		
France	644	850	903	982	1,026	8	2.5
Georgia	...	36	43	14	14		
Germany	1,125	1,123	989	843	843	9	2.0
Greece	100	123	132	125	126		
Guatemala	29	41	65	69	69		
Hungary	176	250	254	215	180		
India	262	682	1,229	1,446	1,540	5	3.7
Indonesia	32	178	383	452	452		
Iran	56	155	310	516	525		
Iraq	10	48	64	43	45		
Ireland	40	35	33	31	31		
Israel	74	92	105	117	117		
Italy	549	659	687	672	631		
Japan	1,735	1,998	2,446	2,582	2,571	3	6.2
Kazakstan	...	188	232	183	185		
Kenya	12	20	42	42	42		
Korea, N.	55	104	144	150	150		
Korea, S.	131	256	398	442	442		
Latvia	...	40	46	20	22		
Lebanon	27	41	55	64	65		
Lithuania	...	54	71	40	55		
Malaysia	63	131	287	352	354		
Mexico	334	636	1,066	1,246	1,208	7	2.9
Moldova	...	49	63	28	45		
Morocco	44	73	88	190	190		
Netherlands	268	540	648	609	597		
New Zealand	52	57	46	50	50		
Nigeria	102	180	313	418	320		
Norway	38	45	51	50	50		
Pakistan	15	96	211	270	290		
Paraguay	13	26	34	46	46		
Peru	28	60	104	115	144		
Philippines	117	201	276	292	305		
Poland	387	489	410	301	301		

Eggs (hen's) continued

	1970	1980	1990	1994	1995	Rank	%
Portugal	37	62	85	109	101		
Romania	165	324	354	270	270		
Russia	...	2,193	2,641	2,184	1,869	4	4.5
Saudi Arabia	7	42	113	127	132		
Slovak Rep.	...	...	...	89	89		
South Africa	115	160	213	235	237		
Spain	460	666	649	726	694	10	1.7
Sri Lanka	20	29	47	48	48		
Sudan	17	32	33	39	38		
Sweden	102	114	116	103	103		
Switzerland	39	43	38	35	33		
Syria	16	69	75	102	105		
Taiwan	32	108	216	270	270		
Tanzania	15	35	42	48	54		
Thailand	117	105	430	410	538		
Tunisia	...	36	52	55	63		
Turkey	96	217	369	492	493		
Ukraine	...	850	944	573	532		
UK	878	834	616	632	618		
USA	4,057	4,116	4,005	4,390	4,399	2	10.6
Uzbekistan	...	82	136	88	88		
Venezuela	76	129	119	138	140		
Vietnam	84	55	97	130	136		
Yugoslavia	...	...	98	82	82		

Fish – catch by fishing area *thousand tonnes*

	1970	1980	1990	1995	Rank	%
WORLD	**70,000**	**72,042**	**97,556**	**112,910**		
Marine areas						
WORLD	**60,930**	**64,383**	**82,867**	**91,905**		
18 Arctic Sea	0	0	0	0		
21 Atlantic, NW	4,239	2,867	3,242	2,065	10	2.2
27 Atlantic, NE	666	11,799	9,195	11,794	3	12.8
31 Atlantic, WC	1,440	1,795	1,701	1,895		
34 Atlantic, EC	2,830	3,432	4,095	3,194	7	3.5
37 Med. & Black Sea	1,120	1,649	1,502	1,922		
41 Atlantic, SW	1,081	1,274	2,028	2,402	9	2.6

Fish – catch by fishing area continued

	1970	1980	1990	1995	Rank	%
47 Atlantic, SE	2,460	2,170	1,405	1,295		
48 Atlantic, Antarctic	0	453	388	122		
51 Indian, W	1,620	2,098	3,350	3,903	6	4.2
57 Indian, E	789	1,458	2,595	4,118	5	4.5
58 Indian, Antarctic	0	138	34	10		
61 Pacific, NW	12,997	18,759	25,674	27,249	1	29.6
67 Pacific, NE	2,652	1,975	3,391	3,067	8	3.3
71 Pacific, WC	4,176	5,487	7,525	9,231	4	10.0
77 Pacific, EC	902	2,417	1,520	1,547		
81 Pacific, SW	221	382	1,049	873		
87 Pacific, SE	13,732	6,228	13,974	17,217	2	18.7
88 Pacific, Antarctic	0	3	1	0		

Inland waters

	1970	1980	1990	1995		
WORLD	**9,020**	**7,625**	**14,689**	**21,005**		
1 Africa	1,308	1,404	1,930	1,908		
2 N. America	136	146	551	549		
3 S. America	249	280	335	415		
4 Asia	6,251	4,673	10,395	17,091		
5 Europe	225	373	465	528		
6 Oceania	2	2	24	24		
7 (former) USSR	853	747	988	489		

The figures include the produce from both inland and marine fishing. In 1995 fish from inland waters accounted for 18.5% of the total world catch. The figures in both this and the next table refer to fish caught in the inland waters or the craft of the country. The flag of the vessel rather than the port of landing is the criteria for assigning the catch to a country. All the figures refer to the live weight of the catch. Whales are not included and are shown in the table entitled Whaling. The fishing areas are shown on the map below.

World fishing areas

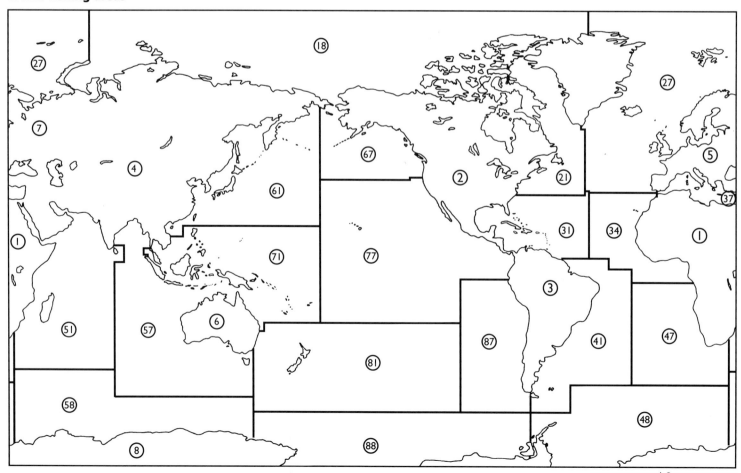

CARTOGRAPHY BY PHILIP'S © GEORGE PHILIP LIMITED

Fish – catch by nation   *thousand tonnes*

	1970	1980	1990	1994	1995	Rank	%
WORLD	70,000	72,042	97,434	110,538	112,910		
Algeria	24	48	91	135	106		
Angola	368	86	107	78	94		
Argentina	215	385	556	949	1,149		
Australia	103	132	220	222	219		
Bangladesh	247	650	848	1,091	1,170		
Brazil	517	818	803	820	800		
Burma	432	580	744	824	832		
Cambodia	52	52	111	103	113		
Canada	1,389	1,347	1,626	1,089	901		
Chad	120	115	60	80	60		
Chile	1,181	2,817	5,195	7,841	7,591	3	6.7
China	6,868	4,235	12,095	20,718	24,433	1	21.6
Colombia	76	76	128	124	167		
Congo (Zaïre)	45	102	162	156	158		
Cuba	106	187	189	88	94		
Denmark	1,227	2,029	1,517	1,916	2,041		
Ecuador	92	644	391	340	592		
Egypt	72	140	313	306	310		
Estonia	...	...	367	124	132		
Faroe Is.	208	275	289	250	297		
Finland	81	143	139	180	185		
France	764	789	863	853	793		
Germany	945	542	391	273	298		
Ghana	172	232	392	337	344		
Greece	78	104	146	223	198		
Greenland	40	104	143	117	129		
Hong Kong	124	195	235	220	204		
Iceland	734	1,515	1,509	1,560	1,616		
India	1,756	2,442	3,791	4,738	4,904	6	4.3
Indonesia	1,229	1,842	3,043	3,917	4,118	8	3.6
Iran	...	44	271	332	368		
Ireland	79	149	219	319	413		
Italy	387	448	520	576	610		
Ivory Coast	58	86	104	74	71		
Japan	9,366	10,434	10,350	7,396	6,758	4	6.0
Kenya	34	48	202	204	194		
Korea, N.	...	1,400	1,750	1,802	1,850		
Korea, S.	934	2,091	2,833	2,701	2,688		
Latvia	...	...	130	139	150		
Madagascar	48	50	105	120	120		
Malaysia	368	737	604	1,182	1,240		
Mali	90	80	65	63	133		
Mexico	387	1,223	1,401	1,264	1,358		
Morocco	256	330	566	752	846		
Namibia	...	24	256	301	286		
Netherlands	301	340	459	530	521		
New Zealand	59	191	560	492	612		
Nigeria	227	480	317	282	366		
Norway	2,980	2,409	1,711	2,551	2,808	10	2.5
Oman	100	79	120	119	140		
Pakistan	158	279	479	552	541		
Panama	42	216	146	170	182		
Peru	12,613	3,735	6,875	11,997	8,943	2	7.9
Philippines	992	1,557	2,209	2,276	2,269		
Poland	469	641	473	460	451		
Portugal	498	279	322	270	266		
Romania	59	174	128	43	69		
Russia	...	...	...	3,781	4,374	7	3.9
Senegal	189	233	298	350	348		
South Africa	1,583	615	536	521	575		
Spain	1,539	1,265	1,450	1,372	1,320		
Sri Lanka	98	186	165	227	236		
Sweden	295	241	260	394	412		
Taiwan	613	936	1,317	1,256	1,298		
Tanzania	185	228	414	343	360		
Thailand	1,448	1,798	2,786	3,537	3,502	9	3.1
Turkey	184	427	385	603	652		
Uganda	129	166	245	213	209		
Ukraine	...	...	1,100	311	425		
UK	1,099	919	811	971	1,011		
USA	2,777	3,635	5,859	5,922	5,634	5	5.0
Uruguay	13	120	91	121	127		
Venezuela	126	185	332	441	505		
Vietnam	817	613	960	1,150	1,200		
Yemen	128	94	78	84	104		

Flax   *thousand tonnes*

	1970	1980	1990	1994	1995	Rank	%
WORLD	753	624	741	573	578		
Argentina	...	1	2	2	2		
Belarus	...	...	...	50	50	4	8.7
Belgium	14	8	11	12	12	9	2.1
Bulgaria	...	2	2	1	1		
Chile	...	2	2	2	2		
China	77	135	259	252	252	1	43.6
Czech Rep.	20	19	...	7	7	10	1.2
Egypt	9	24	15	12	12	8	2.1
Estonia	...	1	1	1	1		
France	49	62	69	64	70	2	12.1
Hungary	...	3	2	1	1		
Latvia	...	3	3	1	1		
Lithuania	...	13	10	4	4		
Netherlands	...	6	35	34	34	6	5.9
Poland	55	49	13	3	3		
Romania	18	23	16	2	2		
Russia	...	...	...	54	54	3	9.3
Slovak Rep.	...	...	...	3	3		
Ukraine	...	...	...	49	48	5	8.3
UK	...	...	...	22	22	7	3.8

Goat meat   *thousand tonnes*

	1970	1980	1990	1994	1995	Rank	%
WORLD	1,995	1,722	2,620	3,150	3,262		
Afghanistan	20	22	23	27	29		
Albania	8	4	4	5	5		
Algeria	7	10	8	8	8		
Angola	2	3	4	4	4		
Argentina	11	6	7	7	7		
Australia	...	2	13	9	9		
Bahrain	2	1	2	2	2		
Bangladesh	31	29	74	98	105	5	3.2
Benin	2	3	3	4	4		
Bolivia	6	5	4	5	5		
Botswana	3	3	6	5	5		
Brazil	22	23	34	35	35		
Bulgaria	4	4	4	7	5		
Burkina Faso	8	6	18	19	19		
Burma	3	3	5	6	6		
Burundi	2	2	3	3	3		
Cameroon	6	7	12	14	14		
Cen. Afr. Rep.	2	3	4	5	6		
Chad	6	9	9	11	11		
Chile	6	5	4	4	4		
China	260	198	520	771	832	1	25.5
Colombia	2	2	4	4	4		
Congo (Zaïre)	6	7	9	10	10		
Cyprus	4	2	4	4	4		
Djibouti	2	2	2	2	2		
Egypt	16	21	33	41	41		
Eritrea	...	...	...	5	5		
Ethiopia	57	58	...	62	62	8	1.9
France	10	8	9	7	8		
Ghana	4	6	5	8	8		
Greece	31	42	48	47	47		
Haiti	4	4	3	3	3		
India	254	302	417	470	474	2	14.5
Indonesia	39	44	53	72	61	10	1.9
Iran	55	45	100	101	101	6	3.1
Iraq	12	9	7	5	6		
Italy	4	5	4	4	4		
Ivory Coast	5	5	4	4	4		
Jamaica	1	2	2	2	2		
Jordan	4	2	2	3	3		
Kazakstan	...	11	...	5	7		
Kenya	13	20	30	29	29		
Korea, N.	1	1	2	2	2		
Korea, S.	...	2	1	3	3		
Kyrgyzstan	...	8	...	7	6		
Lebanon	3	4	3	2	2		
Lesotho	1	2	3	2	2		
Libya	4	2	5	4	4		
Madagascar	2	6	6	7	7		
Malawi	2	2	3	3	3		
Mali	15	24	23	27	27		
Mauritania	5	8	8	8	8		

Goat meat continued

	1970	1980	1990	1994	1995	Rank	%
Mexico	16	31	37	39	40		
Mongolia	20	25	22	16	18		
Morocco	25	18	22	20	20		
Mozambique	2	1	2	2	3		
Namibia	4	5	4	4	4		
Nepal	10	24	29	31	31		
New Zealand	2	1	3	2	2		
Niger	19	27	21	21	21		
Nigeria	82	59	121	130	130	4	4.0
Oman	1	4	4	5	5		
Pakistan	86	162	297	399	430	3	13.2
Peru	10	9	9	8	7		
Philippines	3	13	28	57	63	7	1.9
Portugal	3	4	3	3	3		
Romania	3	4	9	6	6		
Russia	...	6	...	5	5		
Rwanda	2	3	4	3	3		
Saudi Arabia	8	6	20	25	25		
Senegal	4	4	11	14	14		
Somalia	48	38	51	34	36		
South Africa	24	28	34	36	36		
Spain	13	12	17	16	16		
Sri Lanka	1	3	2	2	2		
Sudan	19	41	34	37	37		
Swaziland	2	3	3	3	3		
Syria	5	6	6	5	6		
Tanzania	18	16	22	24	24		
Thailand	...	8	1	1	1		
Togo	1	1	4	4	4		
Tunisia	3	3	6	7	7		
Turkey	101	56	66	62	62	9	1.9
Turkmenistan	...	5	...	34	34		
Uganda	7	10	13	14	15		
Ukraine	...	1	...	5	9		
UAE	2	3	5	5	6		
Venezuela	6	6	7	10	11		
Vietnam	1	3	3	3	3		
Yemen	...	13	17	18	18		
Zimbabwe	6	4	9	9	9		

Goats   *thousand head*

	1970	1980	1990	1994	1995	Rank	%
WORLD	403,895	456,159	573,876	613,227	639,400		
Afghanistan	2,662	2,878	2,150	2,560	2,715		
Albania	868	780	1,100	1,280	1,280		
Algeria	2,546	2,763	2,472	2,544	2,550		
Angola	777	1,273	1,500	1,570	1,570		
Argentina	5,380	3,000	3,300	3,978	3,978		
Bangladesh	8,786	9,309	21,031	28,050	30,330	4	4.7
Benin	578	930	1,017	1,180	1,180		
Bolivia	2,332	2,333	1,440	1,479	1,496		
Botswana	1,055	625	2,092	1,850	1,900		
Brazil	5,742	8,420	11,895	12,200	12,200		
Bulgaria	354	425	433	676	745		
Burkina Faso	2,485	3,467	6,625	7,242	7,242		
Burma	573	655	1,036	1,113	1,164		
Burundi	449	665	927	920	920		
Cameroon	1,500	2,256	3,520	3,770	3,800		
Cen. Afr. Rep.	522	956	1,250	1,340	1,350		
Chad	2,200	2,620	2,800	3,178	3,271		
Chile	843	600	600	600	600		
China	62,501	78,456	95,614	105,990	123,484	1	19.3
Colombia	630	645	959	960	960		
Congo (Zaïre)	2,250	2,680	3,060	4,212	4,220		
Egypt	1,166	1,576	4,442	3,210	3,250		
Eritrea	...	...	...	1,400	1,400		
Ethiopia	17,646	17,177	17,200	16,700	16,700	7	2.6
France	923	1,065	1,240	1,055	1,069		
Ghana	1,408	1,934	2,019	3,337	3,337		
Greece	4,063	4,600	5,904	6,200	6,220		
Haiti	1,134	997	917	910	910		
India	66,529	82,000	110,000	118,347	119,242	2	18.6
Indonesia	6,941	7,813	11,250	11,886	12,527	9	2.0
Iran	13,817	17,372	24,748	25,462	25,700	5	4.0
Iraq	3,233	2,272	1,650	1,080	1,100		
Italy	1,032	989	1,246	1,378	1,448		
Ivory Coast	833	883	888	978	1,002		
Kazakstan	...	649	724	684	684		

Goats continued

	1970	1980	1990	1994	1995	Rank	%
Kenya	4,237	7,761	8,000	7,300	7,400		
Korea, S.	113	208	211	600	650		
Lesotho	880	827	1,050	670	670		
Libya	1,222	1,400	1,100	800	800		
Madagascar	956	1,457	1,256	1300	1,300		
Malawi	618	674	807	890	890		
Mali	5,483	6,428	6,086	7,380	7,380		
Mauritania	3,423	2,577	3,320	3,520	3,526		
Mexico	9,120	9,648	10,439	10,450	10,500		
Mongolia	3,967	4,662	4,959	7,241	8,521		
Morocco	8,467	5,773	5,336	4,431	4,424		
Mozambique	522	335	385	384	385		
Namibia	1,700	2,117	1,860	1,639	1,640		
Nepal	2,267	4,650	5,324	5,525	5,649		
New Zealand	53	57	1,063	470	470		
Niger	6,102	7,010	4,971	5,566	5,716		
Nigeria	23,367	11,297	23,321	24,500	24,500	6	3.8
Oman	148	240	720	735	735		
Pakistan	15,533	26,200	35,446	41,957	43,767	3	6.8
Peru	1,845	1,983	1,722	1,790	2,044		
Philippines	798	1,587	2,125	2,633	2,826		
Portugal	668	747	857	836	819		
Romania	578	378	1,017	776	745		
Russia	...	2,878	2,900	3,097	2,682		
Rwanda	478	884	1,100	950	920		
Saudi Arabia	735	2,270	3,262	4,150	4,200		
Senegal	1,067	982	2,270	3,200	3,250		
Somalia	15,167	17,267	18,000	12,000	12,500	10	2.0
South Africa	5,598	5,744	5,880	6,402	6,457		
Spain	2,656	2,120	3,663	3,157	2,678		
Sri Lanka	548	489	522	588	588		
Sudan	8,900	12,755	14,843	16,400	16,500	8	2.6
Syria	762	1,028	1,008	1,035	1,200		
Tajikistan	...	597	780	826	826		
Tanzania	4,441	5,714	8,526	9,682	9,682		
Togo	501	556	1,851	1,900	1,900		
Tunisia	540	822	1,279	1,350	1,350		
Turkey	20,129	18,755	11,942	10,133	9,564		
Uganda	1,822	2,275	3,251	3,450	3,500		
Ukraine	...	234	458	745	782		
UAE	257	340	657	861	862		
USA	2,640	1,380	1,900	1,960	1,960		
Uzbekistan	...	646	800	968	968		
Venezuela	1,276	1,346	1,530	2,369	2,959		
Yemen	7,607	2,855	3,333	3,232	3,230		
Zimbabwe	1,572	1,191	2,564	2,580	2,615		

Grapefruit   *thousand tonnes*

	1970	1980	1990	1994	1995	Rank	%
WORLD	**3,339**	**4,607**	**4,464**	**4,792**	**5,054**		
Algeria	4	4	3	2	3		
Argentina	129	149	190	229	200	4	4.0
Australia	13	30	26	30	30		
Bangladesh	3	4	7	10	10		
Belize	11	13	40	30	44		
Bolivia	...	14	25	27	27		
Brazil	35	37	50	62	62		
Cambodia	4	1	2	3	3		
Cen. Afr. Rep.	3	3	4	4	4		
China	115	99	295	170	176	5	3.5
Congo (Zaïre)	8	9	13	14	14		
Cuba	15	94	332	310	280	3	5.5
Cyprus	50	49	81	58	69	9	1.4
Dominica	3	8	8	8	8		
Ecuador	18	58	3	5	4		
Greece	...	4	5	10	10		
Haiti	7	11	10	9	9		
Honduras	10	22	36	28	28		
India	20	20	50	70	70	8	1.4
Indonesia	...	2	4	...	...		
Iran	...	10	30	55	58		
Israel	303	501	404	338	404	2	8.0
Italy	1	4	7	4	4		
Jamaica	39	25	40	42	42		
Jordan	1	1	3	5	5		
Kenya	4	7	14	16	16		
Laos	2	2	4	6	6		
Lebanon	5	23	50	55	55		
Madagascar	1	7	9	9	9		

Grapefruit continued

	1970	1980	1990	1994	1995	Rank	%
Malaysia	1	2	2	8	8		
Mexico	32	163	107	137	120	7	2.4
Morocco	9	12	7	8	2		
Mozambique	14	17	17	16	17		
New Zealand	4	7	5	7	7		
Paraguay	19	64	69	65	65	10	1.3
Peru	7	4	4	4	4		
Philippines	28	34	40	42	43		
Portugal	5	7	8	7	7		
Puerto Rico	10	6	3	2	2		
Somalia	5	8	28	18	19		
South Africa	104	109	124	149	160	6	3.2
Spain	6	9	21	27	22		
Sudan	44	46	45	65	63		
Surinam	5	2	1	1	1		
Swaziland	27	41	52	46	45		
Thailand	9	198	255	...	...		
Trinidad & Tob.	20	4	4	6	7		
Tunisia	2	23	51	56	56		
Turkey	7	18	33	54	60		
USA	2,179	2,571	1,794	2,414	2,642	1	52.3
Uruguay	3	8	8	9	9		
Venezuela	6	6	9	9	9		
Vietnam	...	...	...	10	10		
Zimbabwe	...	2	4	5	4		

Grapes   *thousand tonnes*

	1970	1980	1990	1994	1995	Rank	%
WORLD	**54,583**	**66,087**	**66,087**	**54,323**	**53,255**		
Afghanistan	377	452	365	330	330		
Albania	62	68	91	44	46		
Algeria	1,263	398	263	180	180		
Argentina	2,636	3,230	2,342	2,498	1,930	6	3.6
Armenia	...	270	144	130	130		
Australia	620	775	824	920	767		
Austria	337	377	412	354	245		
Azerbaijan	...	1,411	1,196	500	550		
Brazil	528	604	805	807	829		
Bulgaria	1,128	1,029	731	498	450		
Canada	69	74	56	49	53		
Chile	762	1,067	1,171	1,449	1,320	10	2.5
China	155	182	961	1,682	1,901	7	3.6
Croatia	...	...	398	363	360		
Cyprus	190	208	156	92	120		
Czech Rep.	...	...	...	80	43		
Egypt	115	280	585	707	730		
France	9,706	10,470	8,151	6,944	7,085	2	13.3
Georgia	...	902	691	200	480		
Germany	1,049	889	1,107	1,035	850		
Greece	1,569	1,504	1,047	1,115	1,150		
Hungary	809	788	863	614	570		
India	219	195	408	750	750		
Iran	628	1,132	1,424	1,893	1,900	8	3.6
Iraq	75	220	455	282	350		
Israel	69	77	99	80	86		
Italy	10,638	12,396	8,438	9,322	8,433	1	15.8
Japan	240	328	276	246	265		
Kazakstan	...	165	139	37	37		
Korea, S.	35	61	131	212	230		
Kyrgyzstan	...	75	43	28	28		
Lebanon	98	142	280	370	380		
Macedonia	...	...	193	205	191		
Mexico	160	485	429	537	500		
Moldova	...	1,260	940	672	672		
Morocco	213	233	232	282	128		
New Zealand	14	39	70	54	55		
Peru	62	54	53	65	81		
Portugal	1,570	1,620	1,600	917	900		
Romania	1,020	1,518	935	1,033	1,314		
Russia	...	832	612	311	301		
Saudi Arabia	24	60	102	115	119		
Slovak Rep.	...	...	...	101	59		
Slovenia	...	...	214	118	130		
South Africa	820	1,202	1,559	1,510	1,660	9	3.1
Spain	4,048	6,587	6,474	3,167	3,085	5	5.8
Switzerland	129	122	174	153	154		
Syria	221	351	423	362	380		
Tajikistan	...	178	189	85	85		
Tunisia	125	123	77	121	112		

Grapes continued

	1970	1980	1990	1994	1995	Rank	%
Turkey	3,779	3,600	3,500	3,450	3,550	4	6.7
Turkmenistan	...	55	169	147	147		
Ukraine	...	968	836	395	457		
USA	3,325	4,549	5,136	5,326	5,240	3	9.8
Uruguay	129	108	124	95	95		
Uzbekistan	...	524	745	344	344		
Yemen	21	56	142	146	147		
Yugoslavia	...	1,400	273	476	450		

Groundnuts   *thousand tonnes*

	1970	1980	1990	1994	1995	Rank	%
WORLD	**18,347**	**18,277**	**23,410**	**28,738**	**27,990**		
Angola	20	20	20	17	17		
Argentina	280	451	333	299	339	10	1.2
Australia	30	48	21	27	42		
Bangladesh	45	28	42	41	41		
Benin	47	60	79	83	83		
Brazil	876	433	137	159	168		
Burkina Faso	68	70	140	203	203		
Burma	492	390	459	431	501	9	1.8
Burundi	21	56	97	10	13		
Cameroon	206	137	100	110	110		
Cen. Afr. Rep.	68	123	105	84	86		
Chad	95	93	108	207	207		
China	2,634	3,501	6,433	9,763	10,316	1	36.9
Congo	17	14	26	25	25		
Congo (Zaïre)	258	334	425	547	581	8	2.1
Dom. Rep.	76	40	34	1	4		
Egypt	40	26	31	30	32		
Ethiopia	24	27	54	54	54		
Gambia, The	129	79	75	81	84		
Ghana	88	125	193	176	176		
Guinea	25	83	52	128	170		
Guinea-Bissau	36	32	18	18	18		
Haiti	2	35	46	23	23		
India	462	723	930	8,260	7,100	2	25.4
Indonesia	2	3	6	903	903	5	3.2
Israel	17	22	21	24	24		
Ivory Coast	42	73	134	138	147		
Japan	120	61	40	35	35		
Madagascar	42	37	30	28	28		
Malawi	182	176	39	31	32		
Mali	144	136	180	215	215		
Mexico	81	73	133	80	80		
Morocco	3	34	40	30	14		
Mozambique	140	131	113	74	102		
Nicaragua	1	21	12	56	31		
Niger	223	105	60	65	65		
Nigeria	1,660	466	1,166	1,453	1,502	4	5.4
Pakistan	55	60	89	106	106		
Paraguay	17	34	41	42	44		
Philippines	17	43	35	37	37		
Senegal	794	690	703	718	791	6	2.8
Sierra Leone	19	12	20	40	36		
South Africa	364	297	111	142	107		
Sudan	370	760	123	714	630	7	2.3
Syria	18	18	22	29	30		
Taiwan	122	86	85	81	92		
Tanzania	32	54	60	72	72		
Thailand	128	128	162	150	150		
Togo	20	25	26	30	32		
Turkey	40	52	63	70	70		
Uganda	207	80	172	142	143		
USA	1,289	1,550	1,634	1,927	1,578	3	5.6
Vietnam	78	94	218	294	305		
Zambia	24	18	25	35	36		
Zimbabwe	111	101	119	66	52		

Hemp *thousand tonnes*

	1970	1980	1990	1994	1995	Rank	%
WORLD	293	242	165	104	103		
Austria	9	...	...	...	...		
Bangladesh	5	2	2	...	...		
Bulgaria	9	4	...	...	...		
Chile	4	4	4	4	4	5	3.9
China	23	72	31	20	20	2	19.4
France	5	5	2	4	4	6	3.9
Hungary	18	12	2	...	...		
India	62	52	41	38	38	1	36.9
Korea, N.	2	3	10	12	12	4	11.7
Korea, S.	6	1	1	1	1	9	1.0
Pakistan	7	6	5	3	3	7	2.9
Poland	14	4	1	...	...		
Romania	20	26	38	1	1	10	1.0
Russia	...	...	...	15	15	3	14.6
Spain	1	1	1	1	1		
Turkey	8	12	4	3	3	8	2.9
Ukraine	...	...	...	2	1		
Yugoslavia	15	5	2	1	1		

Honey *thousand tonnes*

	1970	1980	1990	1994	1995	Rank	%
WORLD	862	935	1,169	1,189	1,199		
Afghanistan	3	3	3	3	3		
Algeria	1	2	2	2	2		
Angola	16	15	15	21	21		
Argentina	21	35	47	67	70	3	5.8
Armenia	...	...	...	1	1		
Australia	20	21	21	24	24		
Austria	5	3	6	9	9		
Azerbaijan	...	...	...	4	4		
Belarus	...	...	...	50	50	8	4.2
Belgium	1	1	1	1	1		
Brazil	6	7	17	19	19		
Bulgaria	7	9	8	4	4		
Cameroon	2	2	3	3	3		
Canada	24	32	32	30	32	10	2.6
Cen. Afr. Rep.	5	6	9	10	11		
Chad	...	1	1	0.9	0.9		
Chile	7	5	5	5	5		
China	200	139	197	181	182	1	15.2
Colombia	2	2	3	3	3		
Costa Rica	0.3	0.8	1	1	1		
Cuba	5	8	10	11	11		
Czech Rep.	...	...	...	8	8		
Dom. Rep.	1	1	2	1	1		
Egypt	5	8	10	10	10		
El Salvador	1	2	3	4	4		
Ethiopia	17	21	23	24	24		
Finland	0.5	1	2	2	2		
France	11	12	15	18	18		
Georgia	...	...	...	2	2		
Germany	21	16	25	22	24		
Greece	7	11	12	15	16		
Guatemala	3	4	3	3	3		
Hungary	8	14	17	16	16		
India	...	43	51	51	51	7	4.3
Iran	4	6	7	8	8		
Israel	2	2	3	2	3		
Italy	7	14	10	13	9		
Jamaica	1	1	1	1	1		
Japan	7	7	5	4	4		
Kazakstan	...	...	...	28	28		
Kenya	7	11	17	24	25		
Korea, S.	1	5	8	11	11		
Kyrgyzstan	...	...	...	3	3		
Latvia	...	...	3	2	2		
Lebanon	0.2	0.4	2	2	2		
Lithuania	...	...	2	3	3		
Madagascar	10	3	4	4	4		
Mexico	35	66	67	56	51	6	4.3
Moldova	...	...	...	4	4		
Morocco	1	5	3	4	2		
New Zealand	5	7	9	7	7		
Norway	0.5	0.3	2	1	1		
Paraguay	0.5	1	1	1	1		
Poland	9	12	14	9	9		
Portugal	3	3	3	4	4		

Honey continued

	1970	1980	1990	1994	1995	Rank	%
Romania	9	14	11	10	15		
Russia	...	...	...	44	9		3.7
Slovak Rep.	...	...	...	4	3		
Slovenia	...	...	0.1	2	2		
South Africa	0.3	1	0.9	0.9	0.9		
Spain	8	13	23	28	28		
Sweden	2	2	3	2	2		
Switzerland	2	2	2	3	3		
Tajikistan	...	...	...	2	2		
Tanzania	5	10	15	24	25		
Thailand	...	...	2	3	3		
Tunisia	0.2	1	0.9	1	1		
Turkey	15	27	51	54	55	5	4.6
Turkmenistan	...	...	...	4	4		
Ukraine	...	...	...	62	62	4	5.2
UK	3	3	3	3	3		
USA	104	94	90	99	101	2	8.4
Uruguay	1	2	4	6	6		
Uzbekistan	...	...	...	7	7		
Venezuela	0.9	1	0.1	0.8	0.8		
Vietnam	...	0.3	0.7	2	2		
Yugoslavia	...	...	3	2	2		

Hops *thousand tonnes*

	1970	1980	1990	1994	1995	Rank	%
WORLD	98	117	112	123	124		
Australia	2	2	2	2	2		
Austria	...	0.2	0.3	0.3	0.3		
Belgium	2	2	1	0.7	0.7		
Bulgaria	1	1	0.5	1	1		
Canada	1	1	1	4	4	5	3.2
China	...	1	11	12	12	3	9.7
Czech Rep.	...	...	10	9	9	4	7.3
France	2	1	1	1	1		
Germany	29	33	34	29	34	2	27.4
Hungary	...	1	0.4	0.1	0.1		
Ireland	...	1	0.04	0.04	0.04		
Japan	2	2	2	1	1		
Korea, N.	...	1	2	2	2	9	1.6
Korea, S.	...	1	0.3	0.2	0.2		
New Zealand	...	0.3	0.4	0.6	0.6		
Poland	2	2	2	2	3	7	2.4
Portugal	...	0.3	0.2	0.2	0.2		
Romania	...	1	0.2	1	1		
Russia	...	...	...	1	2	10	1.6
Slovak Rep.	...	...	...	1	1		
Slovenia	...	...	...	3	3	8	2.4
Spain	1	2	2	2	2		
Switzerland	...	0.02	0.04	0.4	0.4		
Ukraine	...	...	...	1	2		
UK	11	10	5	4	4	6	3.2
USA	21	32	26	33	35	1	28.2
Yugoslavia	...	...	...	0.5	0.67		

Horses *thousand head*

	1970	1980	1990	1994	1995	Rank	%
WORLD	62,642	59,500	60,929	60,915	61,672		
Afghanistan	400	403	362	300	300		
Albania	43	45	105	58	58		
Algeria	142	173	81	67	67		
Argentina	3,623	3,024	3,400	3,300	3,300	5	5.4
Australia	454	486	310	250	240		
Austria	53	43	48	67	65		
Belarus	...	233	219	215	220		
Belgium	76	38	21	22	23		
Bolivia	291	330	320	322	322		
Bosnia	...	...	100	50	50		
Brazil	4,861	5,070	6,000	6,300	6,300	2	10.2
Bulgaria	183	121	119	113	113		
Burkina Faso	88	20	22	23	23		
Burma	71	112	121	121	122		
Canada	362	363	415	350	350		
Chad	153	166	184	214	218		
Chile	478	450	520	450	550		
China	7,300	11,144	10,300	9,960	10,039	1	16.3
Colombia	1,114	1,683	1,975	2,000	2,450	7	4.0
Costa Rica	109	113	114	114	115		

Horses continued

	1970	1980	1990	1994	1995	Rank	%
Cuba	683	810	629	580	580		
Dom. Rep.	184	204	315	329	329		
Ecuador	242	314	492	515	520		
El Salvador	79	88	94	96	96		
Ethiopia	1,393	1,602	2,650	2,750	2,750	6	4.5
Finland	88	33	44	49	50		
France	691	352	319	332	331		
Germany	411	447	484	600	680		
Greece	251	115	45	43	40		
Guatemala	149	100	113	116	116		
Haiti	335	411	435	470	480		
Honduras	173	165	170	172	174		
Hungary	233	127	75	72	70		
Iceland	34	51	70	79	79		
India	1,010	900	960	990	990		
Indonesia	666	616	687	714	720		
Iran	400	293	255	255	255		
Iraq	98	54	60	21	21		
Ireland	122	69	54	53	53		
Italy	292	271	269	323	326		
Japan	159	23	23	28	28		
Kazakstan	...	1,260	1,619	1,777	1,800	10	2.9
Kyrgyzstan	...	271	310	300	285		
Lesotho	103	102	121	120	120		
Lithuania	...	81	78	78	78		
Macedonia	...	...	66	62	62		
Mali	170	144	77	101	101		
Mexico	5,579	6,195	6,170	6,185	6,200	3	10.1
Mongolia	2,262	2,047	2,200	2,100	2,150	9	3.5
Morocco	380	278	190	165	162		
Netherlands	95	66	65	97	97		
New Zealand	75	71	94	85	85		
Nicaragua	212	275	250	247	246		
Niger	197	270	82	82	82		
Nigeria	325	228	208	204	204		
Pakistan	385	473	368	350	400		
Panama	160	128	151	164	165		
Paraguay	334	316	335	370	370		
Peru	669	650	660	665	665		
Philippines	300	302	200	210	210		
Poland	2,573	1,787	941	622	636		
Romania	686	564	663	751	784		
Russia	7,641	5,623	2,256	2,500	2,400	8	3.9
Senegal	196	222	419	500	502		
South Africa	258	225	230	230	230		
Spain	287	243	241	262	260		
Sweden	60	55	58	86	86		
Syria	70	52	41	27	27		
Thailand	172	28	20	14	15		
Tunisia	96	51	55	56	56		
Turkey	1,103	804	545	450	437		
Ukraine	...	874	754	716	737		
UK	143	147	169	173	173		
USA	7,667	5,053	5,400	6,000	6,000	4	9.7
Uruguay	427	493	465	480	470		
Uzbekistan	...	83	97	120	120		
Venezuela	423	478	495	495	500		
Vietnam	105	123	143	134	134		
Yugoslavia	...	...	97	96	93		

Jute *thousand tonnes*

	1970	1980	1990	1994	1995	Rank	%
WORLD	3,292	3,619	3,556	3,288	3,024		
Bangladesh	1,115	949	886	971	739	2	24.4
Brazil	54	85	26	19	12	8	0.4
Burma	35	97	34	27	35	6	1.2
Cambodia	7	3	9	2	2		
Chile	...	8	10	10	10		
China	301	575	633	355	270	3	8.9
Cuba	2	14	10	10	10	10	0.3
Egypt	14	10	5	2	2		
El Salvador	4	1	1	1	1		
India	1,189	1,469	1,668	1,701	1,720	1	56.9
Indonesia	13	15	10	9	9		
Mozambique	6	4	4	4	4		
Nepal	52	64	16	11	12	9	0.4
Peru	7	3	3	1	1		
Russia	53	48	49	45	45	5	1.5
Thailand	401	234	162	98	128	4	4.2
Vietnam	18	30	28	13	15	7	0.5

Lemons and limes   *thousand tonnes*

	1970	1980	1990	1994	1995	Rank	%
WORLD	3,672	5,259	7,423	8,876	9,073		
Algeria	16	8	11	21	16		
Argentina	198	369	497	681	729	4	8.0
Australia	28	43	34	35	35		
Bangladesh	4	4	7	10	10		
Bolivia	17	45	58	59	59		
Brazil	55	197	392	491	495	7	5.5
Chile	37	69	82	96	100		
China	55	70	138	167	201		
Congo (Zaïre)	5	6	7	8	8		
Cuba	11	25	62	15	19		
Cyprus	28	18	40	31	31		
Dominica	8	6	5	5	5		
Dom. Rep.	12	13	9	9	9		
Ecuador	15	17	22	11	12		
Egypt	85	67	352	296	310	10	3.4
El Salvador	15	19	23	24	24		
Ethiopia	5	5	6	7	7		
Ghana	27	30	30	30	30		
Greece	135	179	193	178	106		
Guatemala	...	...	...	118	122		
Haiti	23	25	25	22	22		
India	450	488	717	1,500	1,700	1	18.7
Iran	29	62	460	649	655	5	7.2
Iraq	22	7	16	16	17		
Israel	41	54	43	26	27		
Italy	813	752	674	552	545	6	6.0
Jamaica	18	22	24	24	24		
Jordan	5	13	53	68	68		
Lebanon	72	60	78	99	99		
Madagascar	4	4	6	5	5		
Mexico	326	577	727	849	984	2	10.8
Morocco	3	14	18	20	12		
Oman	9	14	26	29	29		
Pakistan	18	39	64	77	80		
Paraguay	15	13	19	19	19		
Peru	90	88	221	224	251		
Philippines	9	41	47	48	49		
Portugal	18	19	9	11	11		
South Africa	20	43	65	74	60		
Spain	112	375	603	546	432	8	4.8
Sri Lanka	31	49	17	20	20		
Sudan	34	40	48	58	55		
Syria	5	10	44	65	52		
Thailand	...	...	65	75	75		
Tunisia	13	20	16	18	13		
Turkey	130	284	374	470	420	9	4.6
UAE	...	3	21	20	21		
USA	572	860	718	901	840	3	9.3
Uruguay	6	16	40	43	43		
Venezuela	...	11	15	15	15		
Zimbabwe	5	7	8	9	8		

Linseed   *thousand tonnes*

	1970	1980	1990	1994	1995	Rank	%
WORLD	...	...	...	...	...		
Afghanistan	17	15	14	14	14		
Argentina	545	643	438	152	151	4	5.7
Australia	26	9	2	8	6		
Bangladesh	7	34	50	48	48	8	1.8
Belarus	...	...	...	20	20		
Belgium	8	6	9	7	7		
Brazil	23	13	21	20	20		
Canada	833	575	674	960	...	1	
China	32	78	482	511	500	2	
Czech Rep.	...	...	...	3	3		
Egypt	13	32	26	16	16		
Eritrea	...	...	...	3	3		
Ethiopia	62	25	28	32	32		
France	24	30	31	31	33	10	1.2
Germany	5	0	...	27	48	9	1.8
Hungary	20	10	11	1	1		
India	424	409	339	325	350	3	
Iran	5	3	3	1	1		
Iraq	11	1	1	1	1		
Latvia	...	2	2	2	2		
Lithuania	...	...	...	3	3		
Mexico	31	4	3	3	3		

Linseed continued

	1970	1980	1990	1994	1995	Rank	%
Nepal	...	23	31	25	25		
Netherlands	10	4	8	7	7		
New Zealand	11	8	...	...	...		
Pakistan	3	6	4	4	4		
Poland	66	29	9	3	3		
Romania	46	43	33	25	24		
Russia	...	...	...	54	60	6	2.3
Tunisia	1	3	4	5	5		
Turkey	9	3	2	1	1		
Ukraine	...	42	...	22	25		
UK	...	...	70	112	120	5	4.5
USA	699	229	95	74	56	7	2.1
Uruguay	63	34	5	2	1	.	

Maize   *thousand tonnes*

	1970	1980	1990	1994	1995	Rank	%
WORLD	278,615	423,724	482,711	570,750	514,710		
Afghanistan	707	785	453	500	530		
Angola	467	303	228	201	211		
Argentina	8,717	9,333	5,049	10,360	11,396	6	2.2
Austria	677	1,338	1,561	1,421	1,474		
Benin	201	289	422	492	597		
Bolivia	291	422	407	537	521		
Brazil	13,680	19,265	23,890	32,487	36,276	3	7.0
Bulgaria	2,436	2,626	2,087	1,384	1,792		
Cameroon	283	418	402	450	654		
Canada	2,487	5,901	7,066	7,043	7,251		
Chile	217	471	823	937	984		
China	27,820	60,720	91,674	99,622	112,331	2	21.8
Colombia	856	868	1,177	1,161	1,034		
Congo (Zaïre)	426	604	999	1,198	1,170		
Croatia	...	...	...	1,685	1,735		
Ecuador	239	247	465	581	613		
Egypt	2,370	3,159	4,817	5,549	5,500		
El Salvador	340	517	565	478	640		
Ethiopia	909	1,224	1,636	2,011	2,500		
France	7,394	9,641	11,874	12,943	12,784	5	2.5
Germany	500	752	1,552	2,446	2,395		
Ghana	417	380	733	940	1,042		
Greece	498	1,165	2,131	2,098	1,722		
Guatemala	751	947	1,251	1,188	1,062		
Honduras	339	407	559	583	672		
Hungary	4,542	7,022	4,500	4,761	4,680		
India	6,087	6,486	8,892	8,952	8,277	9	1.6
Indonesia	2,575	4,035	6,374	6,869	8,223	10	1.6
Iran	35	52	126	512	545		
Italy	4,601	6,590	5,864	7,320	8,446	8	1.6
Ivory Coast	257	352	497	517	517		
Kenya	2,292	1,714	2,420	3,085	2,700		
Korea, N.	1,493	3,833	2,393	2,140	2,350		
Malawi	1,066	1,275	1,481	1,040	1,661		
Mexico	9,025	11,866	13,280	18,236	16,187	4	3.1
Moldova	...	...	...	629	978		
Morocco	380	245	391	203	50		
Mozambique	364	383	370	489	692		
Nepal	796	690	1,231	1,273	1,302		
Nigeria	1,215	599	5,529	6,902	7,048		
Pakistan	697	925	1,185	1,318	1,275		
Paraguay	197	535	396	462	816		
Peru	605	569	632	725	715		
Philippines	2,009	3,174	4,600	4,519	4,324		
Portugal	599	486	666	728	766		
Romania	7,354	11,823	6,810	9,343	9,923	7	1.9
Russia	...	...	...	892	1,739		
Slovak Rep.	...	...	...	521	597		
South Africa	6,691	11,322	9,641	13,275	4,670		
Spain	1,804	2,227	3,201	2,344	2,561		
Tanzania	817	1,762	2,634	2,159	2,567		
Thailand	1,979	3,103	3,969	3,965	4,155		
Turkey	1,058	1,263	2,100	1,850	1,900		
Uganda	420	360	598	900	950		
Ukraine	...	...	...	1,539	3,392		
USA	122,649	192,084	194,239	256,629	187,305	1	36.4
Venezuela	698	547	983	1,141	1,200		
Vietnam	272	410	727	1,144	1,177		
Yugoslavia	...	...	3,623	4,724	5,828		
Zambia	786	941	1,345	1,021	738		
Zimbabwe	966	1,829	1,859	2,326	840		

Mangoes   *thousand tonnes*

	1970	1980	1990	1994	1995	Rank	%
WORLD	12,236	13,609	16,115	18,548	19,215		
Australia	...	2	13	27	30		
Bangladesh	424	208	175	184	189		
Brazil	668	443	390	432	435	9	2.3
Cambodia	31	8	23	26	27		
Chad	24	29	32	32	32		
China	161	291	770	1,141	1,185	4	6.2
Colombia	14	21	30	98	98		
Congo (Zaïre)	145	174	208	212	212		
Cuba	18	61	77	44	72		
Dom. Rep.	153	177	190	200	185		
Ecuador	10	25	25	29	31		
Egypt	61	112	144	180	232		
El Salvador	25	15	17	18	18		
Guinea	...	25	53	105	80		
Guinea-Bissau	...	...	4	5	5		
Haiti	240	325	310	225	220		
India	8,300	8,365	8,441	10,000	10,000	1	52.0
Indonesia	300	322	531	567	600	7	3.1
Kenya	10	13	22	24	24		
Madagascar	113	148	205	198	200		
Malawi	19	27	31	32	33		
Malaysia	8	17	32	28	29		
Mexico	298	587	1,100	1,118	1,342	3	7.0
Mozambique	35	30	33	28	30		
Nigeria	...	383	496	500	500	8	2.6
Pakistan	486	545	766	839	884	5	4.6
Panama	23	26	4	5	6		
Paraguay	28	16	19	37	37		
Peru	62	73	60	153	127		
Philippines	143	369	338	366	428	10	2.2
St Lucia	38	43	24	27	27		
Senegal	25	32	58	70	66		
South Africa	7	14	25	28	3,229	2	16.8
Sri Lanka	39	70	76	109	105		
Sudan	45	118	118	140	135		
Tanzania	142	175	186	187	187		
Thailand	...	509	599	665	665	6	3.5
Venezuela	78	102	131	140	140		
Vietnam	...	...	162	136	153		

Milk (cows)   *thousand tonnes*

	1970	1980	1990	1994	1995	Rank	%
WORLD	363,193	420,785	481,840	464,380	465,749		
Afghanistan	521	552	340	300	300		
Albania	150	296	421	647	814		
Algeria	292	514	630	530	530		
Argentina	4,527	5,311	6,400	7,212	7,400		
Armenia	...	501	432	408	420		
Australia	7,468	5,590	6,500	8,327	8,556		
Austria	3,218	3,434	3,350	3,279	3,200		
Azerbaijan	...	800	970	784	826		
Bangladesh	678	833	742	774	782		
Belarus	...	6,082	7,457	5,510	5,300		
Belgium	3,971	4,042	3,900	3,606	3,500		
Bosnia	...	...	907	240	239		
Brazil	7,317	11,378	15,000	16,700	17,400	6	3.74
Bulgaria	1,249	1,843	2,101	1,135	1,000		
Burma	400	283	424	441	448		
Canada	8,247	7,830	7,900	7,750	7,770		
Chile	1,029	1,078	1,353	1,750	1,873		
China	3,233	1,143	4,410	5,578	5,810		
Colombia	2,250	2,187	3,918	4,690	4,690		
Costa Rica	194	318	434	506	506		
Croatia	...	...	917	600	600		
Cuba	672	1,045	1,100	850	850		
Czech Rep.	...	...	...	3,134	3,134		
Denmark	4,588	5,126	4,742	4,442	4,640		
Dom. Rep.	282	427	347	371	429		
Ecuador	705	924	1,539	1,823	1,870		
Egypt	575	648	974	999	1,000		
Estonia	...	1,149	1,208	771	812		
Ethiopia	516	590	748	738	738		
Finland	3,401	3,236	2,730	2,512	2,491		
France	27,467	26,720	26,561	25,322	25,800	5	5.54
Georgia	...	643	630	350	350		
Germany	29,904	31,724	31,307	27,866	28,000	4	6.01
Greece	546	666	619	740	690		

Milk (cows) continued

	1970	1980	1990	1994	1995	Rank	%
Hungary	1,851	2,559	2,846	1,936	1,915		
India	7,633	13,420	26,800	31,000	32,000	3	6.87
Iran	915	1,125	2,480	3,126	3,170		
Ireland	3,685	4,729	5,402	5,409	5,689		
Israel	447	702	952	1,073	1,136		
Italy	9,427	10,546	10,376	10,674	10,674		
Japan	4,703	6,526	8,198	8,389	8,500		
Kazakstan	...	4,490	5,597	5,300	5,300		
Kenya	841	938	2,297	2,080	2,170		
Korea, S.	51	449	1,752	1,986	1,986		
Kyrgyzstan	...	676	1,185	872	864		
Latvia	...	1,668	1,892	1,001	937		
Lithuania	...	2,565	3,157	1,896	2,400		
Madagascar	32	36	473	481	483		
Mexico	3,912	6,949	6,332	7,570	7,820		
Moldova	...	1,189	1,512	904	759		
Morocco	450	753	974	845	830		
Netherlands	8,182	11,832	11,226	10,873	10,900	10	2.34
New Zealand	6,112	6,586	7,572	9,719	9,684		
Norway	1,726	1,926	1,959	1,863	1,863		
Pakistan	2,070	2,189	3,523	4,073	4,223		
Peru	828	796	777	830	858		
Poland	14,951	16,250	15,832	12,222	11,705	9	2.51
Portugal	607	750	1,513	1,485	1,500		
Romania	2,774	3,987	3,242	3,700	3,900		
Russia	...	46,953	55,615	41,951	39,098	2	8.39
Slovak Rep.	...	...	...	1,155	1,186		
Slovenia	...	...	597	577	570		
Somalia	139	477	420	550	560		
South Africa	2,816	2,553	2,475	2,450	2,495		
Spain	4,427	5,984	6,100	5,924	6,000		
Sudan	753	1,352	2,251	2,544	2,592		
Sweden	2,996	3,452	3,400	3,421	3,304		
Switzerland	3,172	3,653	3,866	3,900	3,900		
Syria	197	504	771	764	775		
Tajikistan	...	452	540	450	450		
Tanzania	692	372	516	555	590		
Tunisia	146	216	401	523	565		
Turkey	2,565	7,737	8,183	9,129	9,133		
Turkmenistan	...	311	436	716	666		
Ukraine	...	21,044	24,360	17,935	17,060	7	3.66
UK	13,007	15,917	14,976	14,934	14,668	8	3.15
USA	53,173	58,139	67,274	69,701	70,598	1	15.16
Uruguay	744	811	1,005	1,328	1,328		
Uzbekistan	...	2,123	2,922	3,733	3,686		
Venezuela	947	1,353	1,497	1,611	1,611		
Yugoslavia	...	...	1,957	1,897	1,900		
Zimbabwe	237	455	598	420	420		

Millet   thousand tonnes

	1970	1980	1990	1994	1995	Rank	%
WORLD	29,417	25,610	28,047	28,298	27,000		
Afghanistan	20	33	26	31	33		
Angola	78	49	63	53	62		
Argentina	168	245	91	53	65		
Australia	37	26	27	37	44		
Bangladesh	40	40	64	61	51		
Burkina Faso	352	390	449	831	734	6	2.7
Burma	65	80	126	123	139		
Cameroon	343	98	65	50	66		
Cen. Afr. Rep.	43	11	12	9	10		
Chad	615	182	168	307	228		
China	5,473	5,790	4,576	3,697	4,351	3	16.1
Congo (Zaïre)	22	24	31	35	39		
Egypt	847	643	...	...	...		
Eritrea	...	...	...	73	30		
Ethiopia	117	203	273	172	248		
Gambia, The	40	26	47	53	54		
Ghana	120	117	75	168	201		
Guinea	50	49	60	5	5		
Guinea-Bissau	6	12	17	29	35		
India	10,182	9,189	10,462	11,098	8,970	1	33.2
Ivory Coast	30	37	44	81	85		
Kazakstan	...	...	...	130	39		
Kenya	31	84	62	59	40		
Korea, N.	407	66	60	35	10		
Korea, S.	47	4	2	2	2		
Mali	784	461	737	858	815	5	3.0

Millet continued

	1970	1980	1990	1994	1995	Rank	%
Mauritania	81	3	3	7	8		
Mozambique	10	5	5	29	27		
Namibia	19	34	58	59	37		
Nepal	128	121	232	268	253		
Niger	974	1,311	1,113	1,725	1,729	4	6.4
Nigeria	2,792	2,496	5,136	4,757	4,952	2	18.3
Pakistan	300	255	180	228	188		
Russia	...	...	...	482	488	9	1.8
Senegal	543	555	514	548	667	7	2.5
Sudan	424	436	85	970	388		
Tanzania	140	360	200	218	411	10	1.5
Togo	121	44	58	45	66		
Turkey	54	21	6	4	7		
Uganda	737	473	564	610	643	8	2.4
Ukraine	...	...	...	158	268		
USA	100	107	140	180	180		
Yemen	70	96	50	54	53		
Zambia	79	22	32	63	55		
Zimbabwe	190	153	143	78	21		

Mules   thousand head

	1970	1980	1990	1994	1995	Rank	%
WORLD	11,761	13,362	14,757	14,793	14,812		
Afghanistan	34	30	30	23	23		
Albania	22	22	23	25	25		
Algeria	188	203	105	81	82		
Argentina	200	165	172	175	175	8	1.2
Bolivia	86	86	80	81	81		
Brazil	1,631	1,647	2,030	1,987	1,950	3	13.2
Bulgaria	30	31	22	23	16		
Chile	17	10	10	10	10		
China	1,600	4,019	5,417	5,498	5,552	1	37.5
Colombia	367	576	618	622	586	5	4.0
Cuba	32	24	31	32	32		
Dom. Rep.	92	97	133	135	135		
Ecuador	92	98	131	153	154	10	1.0
El Salvador	23	22	23	24	24		
Ethiopia	1,400	727	590	630	630	4	4.3
France	33	14	12	13	13		
Greece	185	117	65	47	45		
Guatemala	49	38	38	38	38		
Haiti	72	80	86	80	80		
Honduras	65	68	69	69	69		
India	84	128	139	142	142		
Iran	136	143	135	133	137		
Iraq	59	27	21	12	12		
Italy	189	91	43	17	16		
Mexico	3,048	3,155	3,180	3,220	3,250	2	21.9
Morocco	378	450	523	527	540	6	3.6
Nicaragua	43	44	45	46	46		
Pakistan	55	66	72	76	77		
Paraguay	12	13	14	14	14		
Peru	220	217	220	224	224	7	1.5
Portugal	92	92	80	70	70		
Somalia	20	22	24	21	21		
South Africa	20	14	14	14	14		
Spain	568	203	73	60	60		
Syria	64	39	26	18	23		
Tunisia	59	70	78	81	81		
Turkey	288	306	207	172	169	9	1.1
USA	1	26	28	28	28		
Venezuela	76	74	72	72	72		

Oats   thousand tonnes

	1970	1980	1990	1994	1995	Rank	%
WORLD	54,494	40,958	37,665	33,705	28,794		
Algeria	41	92	35	15	50		
Argentina	420	431	657	357	260		
Australia	1,378	1,386	1,620	924	1,937	4	6.7
Austria	281	298	244	172	162		
Belarus	...	515	806	760	638		
Belgium	331	171	57	61	38		
Bosnia	...	...	72	11	11		
Brazil	27	77	210	257	177		
Bulgaria	93	61	64	83	47		
Canada	5,508	2,993	2,677	3,638	2,858	2	9.9
Chile	106	151	205	176	202		
China	1,100	600	733	1,000	700	10	2.4

Oats continued

	1970	1980	1990	1994	1995	Rank	%
Croatia	...	...	62	42	38		
Czech Rep.	...	...	...	208	187		
Denmark	699	166	102	191	150		
Estonia	...	87	93	58	80		
Ethiopia	5	40	71	46	52		
Finland	1,297	1,183	1,436	1,150	1,097	8	3.8
France	2,317	1,850	848	685	612		
Germany	3,567	3,348	1,994	1,663	1,604	5	5.6
Greece	108	80	61	79	88		
Hungary	79	125	149	131	139		
Ireland	222	98	140	128	128		
Italy	488	433	318	355	301		
Japan	63	12	5	3	3		
Kazakstan	...	607	610	822	250		
Korea, N.	97	73	60	30	30		
Latvia	...	104	176	89	73		
Lithuania	...	164	196	69	67		
Mexico	33	62	121	41	36		
Morocco	13	22	47	85	10		
Netherlands	243	106	16	28	15		
New Zealand	57	55	67	56	38		
Norway	215	424	531	388	353		
Poland	3,156	2,387	2,059	1,243	1,495	6	5.2
Portugal	92	79	93	79	58		
Romania	138	57	220	497	404		
Russia	...	10,293	12,326	10,757	8,562	1	29.7
Slovakia	...	...	...	36	42		
South Africa	92	78	39	37	38		
Spain	508	527	474	414	216		
Sweden	1,561	1,635	1,489	991	947	9	3.3
Switzerland	35	53	55	51	48		
Turkey	446	350	247	230	250		
Ukraine	...	997	1,303	1,385	1,116	7	3.9
UK	1,300	587	530	597	617		
USA	13,350	7,234	4,715	3,324	2,351	3	8.2
Uruguay	59	37	43	32	25		
Yugoslavia	...	...	135	126	128		

Olive oil   thousand tonnes

	1970	1980	1990	1994	1995	Rank	%
WORLD	1,553	1,844	2,019	2,055	1,733		
Albania	4	5	1	2	3		
Algeria	21	19	14	23	15	9	0.9
Argentina	17	16	13	10	8		
Croatia	...	3	1	3	2		
Cyprus	2	2	1	2	2		
France	2	2	2	2	2		
Greece	178	309	325	419	355	2	20.5
Iran	1	1	2	2	2		
Italy	553	635	545	523	669	1	38.6
Jordan	3	4	8	16	13	10	0.8
Lebanon	11	7	5	6	5		
Libya	7	28	9	7	5		
Morocco	41	28	63	64	51	7	2.9
Portugal	70	47	46	36	41	8	2.4
Spain	419	435	651	569	321	3	18.5
Syria	23	59	53	108	85	4	4.9
Tunisia	103	101	201	87	68	5	3.9
Turkey	86	130	68	179	67	6	3.9

Olives   thousand tonnes

	1970	1980	1990	1994	1995	Rank	%
WORLD	7,650	9,255	10,791	11,304	9,671		
Albania	33	28	10	30	35		
Algeria	150	154	119	170	131	10	1.4
Argentina	70	92	94	77	89		
Chile	12	10	7	7	9		
Croatia	...	...	4	12	34		
Cyprus	14	12	9	12	14		
Egypt	7	5	41	130	208	9	2.2
France	16	13	9	16	13		
Greece	876	1,465	1,516	1,933	1,730	2	17.9
Iran	10	9	16	18	19		
Iraq	9	3	10	14	15		
Israel	13	24	26	27	37		
Italy	2,530	2,962	2,638	2,640	3,288	1	34.0
Jordan	18	23	43	94	63		
Lebanon	48	37	51	80	50		

Olives continued

	1970	1980	1990	1994	1995	Rank	%
Libya	38	139	68	60	52		
Mexico	10	26	13	10	19		
Morocco	329	269	532	500	436	5	4.5
Peru	9	11	19	21	29		
Portugal	422	271	324	232	260	8	2.7
Spain	1,897	2,025	3,099	2,727	1,618	3	16.7
Syria	110	265	269	518	433	6	4.5
Tunisia	476	521	933	350	350	7	3.6
Turkey	438	727	747	1,400	515	4	5.3
USA	54	65	97	76	70		

Onions   *thousand tonnes*

	1970	1980	1990	1994	1995	Rank	%
WORLD	**15,243**	**21,279**	**29,125**	**33,538**	**37,081**		
Algeria	43	119	239	248	314		
Argentina	215	247	425	458	491		
Australia	94	121	212	200	246		
Austria	23	35	57	62	58		
Bangladesh	182	124	148	144	144		
Belarus	...	...	...	51	53		
Bolivia	36	34	40	52	46		
Brazil	282	721	845	1,019	931	10	2.5
Bulgaria	102	78	76	81	180		
Burma	91	123	171	160	173		
Canada	108	117	135	125	149		
Chile	93	265	270	305	350		
China	2,145	2,646	4,997	7,629	8,030	1	21.7
Colombia	197	277	406	230	230		
Congo (Zaïre)	15	22	31	32	32		
Croatia	...	...	...	41	35		
Czech Rep.	...	...	...	78	94		
Denmark	22	27	28	44	44		
Dom. Rep.	18	14	20	21	26		
Egypt	547	609	526	481	574		
Ethiopia	26	36	42	41	41		
France	186	144	235	264	288		
Georgia	...	...	...	36	40		
Germany	79	128	212	217	236		
Ghana	17	22	28	24	25		
Greece	119	145	122	137	155		
Guatemala	15	21	28	31	33		
Hungary	149	138	160	134	195		
India	1,473	2,551	3,292	4,006	4,058	2	10.9
Indonesia	163	222	468	637	644		
Iran	254	607	1,010	1,112	1,150	6	3.1
Iraq	84	119	119	70	75		
Israel	40	47	62	67	100		
Italy	472	518	469	441	442		
Japan	1,040	1,149	1,298	1,109	1,278	5	3.4
Kazakstan	...	...	...	72	70		
Korea, N.	16	25	85	91	91		
Korea, S.	91	316	498	541	975	9	2.6
Laos	25	30	40	...	...		
Lebanon	34	21	60	71	71		
Libya	21	64	82	75	75		
Macedonia	...	...	...	32	39		
Moldova	...	...	...	40	70		
Morocco	87	157	350	367	406		
Netherlands	336	474	466	611	630		
New Zealand	34	72	...	...	...		
Niger	31	107	80	178	178		
Pakistan	235	424	713	912	1,013	8	2.7
Paraguay	19	19	30	30	30		
Peru	151	134	145	187	185		
Philippines	26	40	61	74	88		
Poland	339	353	600	591	760		
Portugal	70	67	60	57	57		
Romania	241	302	286	311	363		
Saudi Arabia	17	58	17	43	239		
Senegal	10	29	34	45	40		
Slovak Rep.	...	...	...	42	47		
South Africa	109	148	231	247	308		
Spain	920	950	1,101	1,009	1,032	7	2.8
Sri Lanka	38	65	58	48	48		
Sudan	36	33	65	85	80		
Syria	68	163	95	110	124		
Tajikistan	...	...	...	150	150		
Tanzania	46	40	51	52	52		
Thailand	105	124	180	247	250		

Onions continued

	1970	1980	1990	1994	1995	Rank	%
Tunisia	18	21	59	90	90		
Turkey	612	1,017	1,503	1,800	2,850	4	7.7
Turkmenistan	...	...	...	95	105		
Uganda	12	13	33	33	33		
Ukraine	...	...	...	562	568		
UK	164	223	239	257	257		
USA	1,340	1,622	2,289	2,882	2,911	3	7.9
Uzbekistan	...	...	...	163	152		
Venezuela	36	75	63	74	74		
Vietnam	107	130	165	178	180		
Yemen	...	11	69	57	62		
Yugoslavia	243	315	...	121	140		

Oranges   *thousand tonnes*

	1970	1980	1990	1994	1995	Rank	%
WORLD	**25,453**	**38,820**	**50,537**	**53,904**	**57,244**		
Algeria	351	269	194	253	227		
Argentina	892	693	701	748	788		
Australia	263	398	470	517	436		
Belize	33	37	59	82	128		
Bhutan	...	25	58	58	58		
Bolivia	53	85	78	94	92		
Brazil	3,084	10,243	18,087	17,418	19,613	1	34.3
Cambodia	41	22	43	49	50		
Chile	42	58	97	112	110		
China	727	790	1,548	1,836	2,168	5	3.8
Colombia	91	233	249	376	396		
Congo (Zaïre)	126	141	153	156	156		
Costa Rica	59	75	109	165	168		
Cuba	112	251	524	256	275		
Cyprus	119	36	56	46	56		
Dom. Rep.	63	68	60	27	49		
Ecuador	160	521	75	88	86		
Egypt	760	956	1,532	1,513	1,555	9	2.7
El Salvador	38	100	109	123	41		
Gaza	...	152	130	99	105		
Georgia	...	...	...	98	118		
Ghana	107	100	52	50	50		
Greece	418	577	877	932	935		
Honduras	18	38	47	85	85		
India	900	1,170	1,840	2,000	2,000	6	3.5
Indonesia	93	322	292	450	450		
Iran	65	371	1,312	1,584	1,556	8	2.7
Iraq	28	124	247	315	318		
Israel	917	866	664	357	381		
Italy	1,403	1,659	1,890	1,809	1,597	7	2.8
Jamaica	70	36	67	72	72		
Japan	321	352	224	144	136		
Lebanon	167	215	272	137	180		
Libya	19	62	90	82	80		
Madagascar	49	59	84	80	82		
Mexico	1,377	1,811	2,320	3,191	3,572	3	6.2
Morocco	665	705	965	939	673		
Nicaragua	45	53	66	71	72		
Pakistan	312	702	1,124	1,353	1,400	10	2.4
Panama	51	43	28	26	27		
Paraguay	194	280	175	171	175		
Peru	246	137	176	204	228		
Portugal	100	94	160	189	209		
Puerto Rico	32	31	29	18	17		
South Africa	533	581	694	877	731		
Spain	1,884	1,657	2,639	2,698	2,435	4	4.3
Sudan	35	12	13	15	15		
Swaziland	35	46	34	48	29		
Syria	6	35	176	341	309		
Tunisia	58	113	128	105	101		
Turkey	445	690	768	920	842		
USA	7,302	9,519	7,545	9,370	10,538	2	18.4
Uruguay	42	55	108	142	127		
Venezuela	205	350	433	454	451		
Vietnam	43	80	114	286	379		
Zimbabwe	21	30	61	75	70		

Palm kernels   *thousand tonnes*

	1970	1980	1990	1994	1995	Rank	%
WORLD	**1,179**	**1,736**	**3,608**	**4,576**	**4,941**		
Angola	16	12	12	15	15		
Benin	69	29	9	13	13		
Brazil	219	266	206	185	185	4	3.7
Cameroon	40	43	53	55	55	9	1.1
Cen. Afr. Rep.	1	1	1	5	5		
China	28	41	34	37	37		
Colombia	7	17	46	60	76	5	1.5
Congo (Zaïre)	99	68	74	72	72	6	1.5
Costa Rica	3	7	14	18	18		
Ecuador	6	6	25	32	29		
Equat. Guinea	2	3	3	3	3		
Ghana	36	30	29	34	34		
Guatemala	...	...	5	13	13		
Guinea	35	38	40	53	53	10	1.1
Guinea-Bissau	8	9	10	8	8		
Honduras	2	1	14	21	21		
Indonesia	49	130	602	945	1,075	2	21.8
Ivory Coast	19	34	39	31	31		
Liberia	14	8	7	8	8		
Madagascar	...	4	7	5	5		
Malaysia	99	540	1,808	2,203	2,395	1	48.5
Mexico	16	7	2	8	2		
Nigeria	287	343	366	503	543	3	11.0
Papua N.G.	0	17	47	66	60	8	1.2
Paraguay	16	14	17	18	18		
Peru	...	2	4	4	4		
Philippines	1	2	14	17	18		
Senegal	9	5	6	6	6		
Sierra Leone	60	31	27	32	29		
Solomon Is.	1	3	5	7	8		
Tanzania	2	5	6	6	6		
Thailand	...	4	47	67	68	7	1.4
Togo	23	11	15	8	8		

Palm oil   *thousand tonnes*

	1950	1970	1980	1990	1994	1995	Rank	%
WORLD	**1,008**	**1,971**	**5,038**	**11,305**	**14,656**	**15,875**		
Angola	36	40	40	44	52	52		
Benin	34	28	30	18	9	11		
Brazil	1	7	14	63	71	76		
Cameroon	22	63	77	145	125	130		
China	...	108	165	141	150	150	10	0.9
Colombia	...	27	71	256	377	433	4	2.7
Congo	4	8	15	17	14	16		
Congo (Zaïre)	172	232	168	180	181	181	8	1.1
Costa Rica	...	13	33	73	88	93		
Ecuador	9	6	37	150	194	179	9	1.1
Equat. Guinea	4	4	5	5	5	5		
Ghana	30	19	21	85	100	100		
Guatemala	...	...	...	6	19	19		
Guinea	10	44	41	40	50	50		
Guinea-Bissau	8	4	5	5	4	4		
Honduras	1	6	10	78	76	76		
Indonesia	114	218	721	2,345	4,008	4,480	2	28.2
Ivory Coast	6	46	158	212	259	249	6	1.6
Liberia	40	14	26	30	38	38		
Malaysia	49	457	5,030	6,095	7,220	7,810	1	49.2
Mexico	6	13	6	2	7	1		
Nigeria	422	528	667	730	837	860	3	5.4
Papua N.G.	2	0	40	153	225	240	7	1.5
Paraguay	2	7	5	4	3	3		
Peru	...	...	5	22	29	29		
Philippines	...	2	43	46	59	65		
Sierra Leone	35	46	47	50	50	45		
Solomon Is.	...	...	15	23	25	26		
Thailand	...	...	20	220	300	370	5	2.3
Togo	3	17	20	14	14	14		
Venezuela	...	2	2	7	15	15		

Paper and paper board *million tonnes*

	1970	1980	1990	1993	1994	Rank	%
WORLD	**128**	**170**	**240**	**254**	**269**		
Argentina	0.6	0.7	0.9	0.9	0.9		
Australia	1.1	1.4	2.0	2.0	2.2		
Austria	1.0	1.6	2.9	3.3	3.6		
Belgium	1.0	0.9	1.2	1.1	1.1		
Brazil	1.2	3.4	4.9	5.4	5.7		
Bulgaria	0.2	0.4	0.3	0.2	0.2		
Canada	11	13	17	18	18	4	6.8
Chile	0.3	0.4	0.5	0.5	0.6		
China	4.2	6.8	17	24	27	3	10.0
Colombia	0.2	0.4	0.5	0.6	0.7		
Czech Rep.	...	...	...	0.6	0.7		
Denmark	0.3	0.2	0.3	0.3	0.3		
Finland	4.3	5.9	8.9	9.9	11	6	4.1
France	4.1	5.2	7.0	7.9	8.5	8	3.2
Germany	7.0	8.8	13	13	15	5	5.4
Greece	0.2	0.3	0.4	0.8	0.8		
Hungary	0.3	0.4	0.4	0.3	0.3		
India	1.0	1.0	2.2	2.6	2.6		
Indonesia	0.0	0.2	1.4	2.6	3.1		
Iran	0.0	0.1	0.2	0.3	0.3		
Italy	3.5	4.9	5.6	6.0	6.7	9	2.5
Japan	13	18	28	28	29	2	10.6
Korea, S.	0.3	1.7	4.5	5.8	6.4	10	2.4
Malaysia	0.0	0.1	0.3	0.7	0.6		
Mexico	1.0	2.0	2.9	2.4	2.5		
Netherlands	1.6	1.7	2.8	2.9	3.0		
New Zealand	0.5	0.7	0.8	0.8	0.9		
Norway	1.4	1.4	1.8	1.9	2.1		
Pakistan	0.1	0.1	0.2	0.4	0.4		
Peru	0.1	0.2	0.3	0.3	0.3		
Philippines	0.1	0.3	0.2	0.5	0.5		
Poland	1.0	1.3	1.1	1.2	1.3		
Portugal	0.2	0.5	0.8	0.9	0.9		
Romania	0.5	0.8	0.5	0.4	0.3		
Russia	...	...	...	4.5	3.4		
Slovak Rep.	...	...	...	0.3	0.3		
Slovenia	...	...	...	0.4	0.5		
South Africa	0.6	1.1	1.9	1.5	1.7		
Spain	1.3	2.6	3.4	3.3	3.5		
Sweden	4.4	6.2	8.4	8.8	9.3	7	3.5
Switzerland	0.7	0.9	1.3	1.3	1.3		
Taiwan	0.2	0.5	0.9	1.1	1.1		
Thailand	0.1	0.3	0.9	1.3	1.7		
Turkey	0.2	0.5	0.9	1.0	0.8		
UK	5.0	3.8	4.8	5.4	5.8		
USA	46	57	72	77	81	1	30.1
Venezuela	0.3	0.5	0.6	0.6	0.6		

Peaches and nectarines *thousand tonnes*

	1970	1980	1990	1994	1995	Rank	%
WORLD	**6,269**	**7,128**	**9,202**	**10,823**	**10,011**		
Afghanistan	...	...	14	14	14		
Algeria	8	13	37	36	45		
Argentina	254	247	250	243	199	9	2.0
Armenia	...	...	...	10	10		
Australia	117	76	68	80	80		
Austria	7	10	12	11	11		
Azerbaijan	...	...	...	25	20		
Bolivia	22	31	20	35	35		
Brazil	111	108	96	136	135		
Bulgaria	148	94	84	57	72		
Canada	48	34	47	44	56		
Chile	91	104	191	258	270	8	2.7
China	305	386	1,102	2,038	2,172	1	21.7
Ecuador	3	3	4	14	14		
Egypt	13	10	35	58	58		
France	575	459	475	527	540	6	5.4
Germany	44	21	28	20	21		
Greece	184	381	756	1,174	900	4	9.0
Hungary	119	84	72	50	42		
India	10	15	70	85	85		
Iran	...	...	82	123	126		
Iraq	3	28	29	25	26		
Israel	19	30	44	59	59		
Italy	1,086	1,419	1,591	1,790	1,689	2	16.9
Japan	273	253	185	174	163	10	1.6

Peaches and nectarines continued

	1970	1980	1990	1994	1995	Rank	%
Kazakstan	...	...	...	22	22		
Korea, N.	29	64	105	110	110		
Korea, S.	71	90	115	114	120		
Lebanon	11	20	39	44	44		
Libya	1	3	11	9	9		
Madagascar	7	6	7	7	7		
Mexico	161	182	146	154	130		
Moldova	...	...	...	47	50		
Morocco	14	20	30	36	36		
New Zealand	27	22	27	17	17		
Pakistan	9	10	22	37	37		
Peru	31	25	38	35	35		
Portugal	36	31	97	92	87		
Romania	28	60	53	21	13		
Russia	...	...	...	20	20		
South Africa	147	180	158	140	135		
Spain	233	414	708	865	658	5	6.6
Syria	5	21	66	36	21		
Tajikistan	...	...	...	22	20		
Tunisia	7	22	35	76	48		
Turkey	87	242	350	375	375	7	3.7
Ukraine	...	...	...	32	24		
USA	1,507	1,496	1,302	1,204	927	3	9.3
Uruguay	31	10	15	27	25		
Uzbekistan	...	...	...	70	80		
Yugoslavia	...	...	...	41	42		

Pears *thousand tonnes*

	1970	1980	1990	1994	1995	Rank	%
WORLD	**7,936**	**8,616**	**9,524**	**11,504**	**12,414**		
Algeria	10	18	38	36	37		
Argentina	90	148	254	365	320	9	2.6
Australia	162	133	155	142	145		
Austria	158	120	100	82	124		
Azerbaijan	...	...	...	10	10		
Belarus	...	...	...	23	18		
Belgium	73	66	72	155	158		
Bosnia	...	...	...	10	10		
Brazil	54	33	18	17	17		
Bulgaria	130	96	62	35	22		
Canada	35	35	17	16	11		
Chile	31	42	140	230	250	10	2.0
China	516	1,616	2,604	4,159	5,057	1	40.7
Czech Rep.	...	...	...	23	27		
Denmark	12	10	5	8	8		
Ecuador	3	9	5	21	10		
Egypt	17	43	55	90	93		
France	551	452	323	358	336	8	2.7
Georgia	...	...	...	25	20		
Germany	536	410	345	387	395	7	3.2
Greece	112	119	96	107	89		
Hungary	87	92	64	43	41		
India	52	64	131	130	130		
Iran	29	37	143	179	184		
Israel	26	18	19	23	30		
Italy	1,749	1,201	810	929	937	2	7.5
Japan	465	500	439	431	426	5	3.4
Korea, N.	22	64	115	125	125		
Korea, S.	49	66	174	164	165		
Lebanon	8	12	24	46	46		
Lithuania	...	...	...	6	13		
Macedonia	...	...	...	12	9		
Mexico	34	35	26	30	29		
Moldova	...	...	...	33	23		
Morocco	7	14	41	29	26		
Netherlands	120	108	103	140	160		
New Zealand	20	17	25	38	35		
Norway	10	7	3	3	3		
Pakistan	16	31	33	35	35		
Poland	110	92	49	45	83		
Portugal	43	53	94	115	81		
Romania	63	90	74	51	63		
Russia	...	...	...	45	50		
Slovak Rep.	...	...	...	9	10		
Slovenia	...	...	...	15	10		
South Africa	94	132	194	214	210		
Spain	295	480	462	579	469	4	3.8
Sweden	16	20	11	6	6		
Switzerland	155	142	86	91	100		

Pears continued

	1970	1980	1990	1994	1995	Rank	%
Syria	6	10	20	17	20		
Tunisia	4	12	31	36	30		
Turkey	172	310	413	410	410	6	3.3
Ukraine	...	...	...	96	246		
UK	70	55	39	25	25		
USA	612	801	842	949	860	3	6.9
Uruguay	7	10	9	13	15		
Uzbekistan	...	...	...	20	30		
Yugoslavia	...	...	...	73	67		

Pigmeat *thousand tonnes*

	1970	1980	1990	1994	1995	Rank	%
WORLD	**38,619**	**52,000**	**69,883**	**78,537**	**83,539**		
Argentina	221	258	151	181	163		
Australia	173	217	317	344	351		
Austria	263	438	517	534	534		
Belarus	...	...	...	274	263		
Belgium	455	669	843	1,019	1,043		
Brazil	763	953	1,073	1,300	1,450	10	1.7
Bulgaria	160	315	406	214	257		
Burma	60	79	80	94	102		
Canada	600	979	1,133	1,234	1,281		
Chile	44	49	123	161	172		
China	9,639	11,704	23,820	33,250	37,686	1	45.1
Colombia	69	98	105	132	133		
Cuba	34	50	89	62	72		
Czech Rep.	...	...	...	533	575		
Denmark	722	953	1,208	1,521	1,494	9	1.8
Ecuador	28	58	71	82	89		
Finland	109	171	187	171	166		
France	1,388	1,775	1,816	2,116	2,140	5	2.6
Germany	3,061	4,403	4,249	3,606	3,602	3	4.3
Greece	54	144	140	142	141		
Hong Kong	120	178	188	166	158		
Hungary	598	899	988	606	582		
India	52	327	360	408	420		
Indonesia	53	111	537	660	589		
Ireland	147	152	157	215	212		
Italy	590	1,075	1,333	1,369	1,350		
Japan	735	1,434	1,555	1,390	1,322		
Kazakstan	...	...	...	156	113		
Korea, N.	54	113	164	159	159		
Korea, S.	80	276	550	784	877		
Lithuania	...	...	...	82	93		
Malaysia	76	133	219	225	230		
Mexico	240	1,241	765	873	922		
Netherlands	704	1,142	1,619	1,677	1,622	8	1.9
Nigeria	28	37	133	259	259		
Norway	66	83	83	92	92		
Paraguay	42	85	118	128	129		
Peru	64	72	84	98	101		
Philippines	304	415	679	997	1,050		
Poland	1,312	1,617	1,855	1,681	1,962	6	2.3
Portugal	98	164	242	316	305		
Romania	453	970	807	789	792		
Russia	...	...	...	2,103	1,865	7	2.2
Singapore	25	65	76	87	86		
Slovak Rep.	...	...	...	202	199		
South Africa	80	87	125	113	116		
Spain	468	1,115	1,789	2,108	2,175	4	2.6
Sweden	244	317	291	308	311		
Switzerland	201	273	270	253	251		
Thailand	210	265	337	315	301		
Ukraine	...	...	...	916	854		
UK	934	929	955	1,035	1,016		
USA	6,227	7,248	7,131	8,027	8,097	2	9.7
Venezuela	46	76	99	133	140		
Vietnam	332	323	719	958	1,007		
Yugoslavia	...	...	...	571	644		

Pigs *thousand head*

	1970	1980	1990	1994	1995	Rank	%
WORLD	624,272	778,787	854,340	884,717	900,816		
Argentina	4,466	3,751	2,533	3,300	3,100		
Australia	2,414	2,416	2,617	2,775	2,653		
Austria	3,245	3,906	3,773	3,729	3,800		
Belarus	...	...	...	4,181	4,005		
Belgium	3,263	5,083	6,439	6,948	7,053		
Bolivia	900	1,553	2,199	2,331	2,405		
Brazil	30,851	34,102	33,643	35,142	35,350	3	3.9
Bulgaria	2,159	3,803	4,219	2,071	1,986		
Burma	1,562	2,263	2,681	2,728	2,801		
Cambodia	1,162	205	1,601	2,024	2,039		
Cameroon	430	1,139	1,364	1,400	1,410		
Canada	6,624	9,709	10,505	11,476	11,673		
Chile	1,025	1,068	1,144	1,407	1,490		
China	246,320	313,660	360,594	402,846	424,680	1	47.1
Colombia	1,470	2,013	2,627	2,600	2,500		
Congo (Zaïre)	611	685	1,050	1,192	1,170		
Croatia	...	...	...	1,347	1,175		
Cuba	1,483	1,417	2,184	1,750	1,750		
Czech Rep.	...	...	...	4,071	3,867		
Denmark	8,336	9,699	9,282	10,923	11,084		
Dom. Rep.	714	298	543	900	950		
Ecuador	1,918	3,417	2,220	2,546	2,618		
Finland	963	1,430	1,348	1,300	1,295		
France	10,516	11,472	12,233	14,291	14,593	10	1.6
Germany	29,156	34,768	33,350	26,075	24,698	5	2.7
Greece	407	944	1,002	1,143	1,121		
Guatemala	810	737	602	796	889		
Haiti	1,525	1,533	330	360	430		
Hungary	6,271	8,232	7,996	5,002	4,356		
India	6,207	9,433	11,193	11,780	11,900		
Indonesia	3,143	3,234	7,231	8,858	7,825		
Ireland	1,210	1,122	1,125	1,487	1,498		
Italy	8,501	8,885	9,150	8,348	8,023		
Japan	6,403	9,851	11,673	10,621	10,250		
Kazakstan	...	...	...	2,445	1,983		
Korea, N.	1,333	2,100	3,200	3,350	3,350		
Korea, S.	1,287	2,115	4,792	5,955	6,461		
Laos	1,100	1,117	1,385	1,673	1,724		
Lithuania	...	...	...	1,196	1,260		
Madagascar	581	1,090	1,431	1,558	1,592		
Malaysia	1,022	1,869	2,577	3,098	3,282		
Mexico	10,273	16,895	15,715	18,000	18,000	8	2.0
Moldova	...	...	...	1,164	1,061		
Netherlands	5,521	10,058	13,634	14,565	14,397		
Nigeria	844	1,000	3,558	6,926	6,926		
Norway	660	675	696	745	768		
Papua N.G.	1,065	1,363	1,000	1,030	1,030		
Paraguay	601	1,090	2,444	2,500	2,525		
Peru	1,894	2,083	2,400	2,442	2,401		
Philippines	6,619	7,712	7,990	8,227	8,941		
Poland	14,348	20,343	20,056	19,466	20,418	6	2.3
Portugal	1,835	3,367	2,531	2,416	2,402		
Romania	6,061	10,926	12,675	9,262	7,758		
Russia	...	...	...	28,557	24,859	4	2.8
Singapore	995	1,017	300	180	190		
Slovak Rep.	...	...	...	2,179	2,037		
South Africa	1,335	1,339	1,480	1,511	1,628		
Spain	6,657	10,392	16,720	18,345	18,125	7	2.0
Sweden	2,167	2,711	2,264	2,328	2,313		
Switzerland	1,796	2,113	1,787	1,660	1,611		
Taiwan	2,900	4,820	8,565	10,065	10,509		
Thailand	4,814	3,344	4,728	5,341	4,507		
Uganda	57	242	797	910	920		
Ukraine	...	...	...	15,298	13,946		
UK	8,205	7,856	7,519	7,797	7,879		
USA	61,720	64,045	54,557	57,904	59,992	2	6.7
Venezuela	1,563	2,241	2,801	3,150	3,335		
Vietnam	8,844	9,396	12,221	15,569	16,306	9	1.8
Yugoslavia	...	...	...	3,693	4,192		

Pineapples *thousand tonnes*

	1970	1980	1990	1994	1995	Rank	%
WORLD	4,911	8,978	10,775	11,566	11,460		
Angola	19	35	35	34	36		
Australia	139	124	142	139	134		
Bangladesh	97	150	162	150	150		
Bolivia	6	8	10	16	18		
Brazil	437	392	736	974	913	3	8.0
Cambodia	23	5	12	14	15		
Cameroon	5	33	35	42	44		
China	781	299	697	737	792	6	6.9
Colombia	85	119	322	378	380	8	3.3
Congo	...	10	12	12	12		
Congo (Zaïre)	144	128	143	145	145		
Costa Rica	5	10	150	220	250		
Cuba	15	16	22	21	19		
Dom. Rep.	13	21	70	145	116		
Ecuador	57	133	34	62	53		
El Salvador	33	17	15	18	16		
Ghana	28	6	12	21	12		
Guatemala	17	32	70	83	89		
Guinea	14	17	81	67	67		
Honduras	6	33	66	86	90		
India	98	548	840	820	820	4	7.2
Indonesia	107	207	327	542	570	7	5.0
Ivory Coast	127	295	196	205	206		
Jamaica	4	4	9	22	16		
Japan	80	56	32	25	25		
Kenya	28	177	225	270	270		
Laos	25	31	32	34	35		
Liberia	6	7	7	7	7		
Madagascar	39	49	50	48	49		
Malaysia	270	185	210	210	190		
Martinique	25	18	24	30	30		
Mexico	262	530	396	229	281	10	2.5
Mozambique	18	13	16	16	16		
Nicaragua	25	34	42	45	46		
Nigeria	...	...	768	800	800	5	7.0
Panama	5	6	13	16	14		
Papua N.G.	7	9	12	14	14		
Paraguay	32	28	45	35	35		
Peru	63	49	78	102	107		
Philippines	251	861	1,156	1,335	1,469	2	12.8
Puerto Rico	50	37	47	34	24		
South Africa	158	217	197	80	134		
Sri Lanka	38	61	41	45	61		
Swaziland	10	29	55	20	13		
Taiwan	338	229	234	252	256		
Tanzania	37	47	70	73	73		
Thailand	187	2,857	1,934	2,370	2,088	1	18.2
USA	850	597	517	331	313	9	2.7
Venezuela	37	89	81	137	137		
Vietnam	34	309	468	235	185		

Plantains *thousand tonnes*

	1970	1980	1990	1994	1995	Rank	%
WORLD	16,378	21,826	26,468	27,966	29,148		
Bolivia	148	117	143	150	150		
Burma	413	206	238	275	280		
Cameroon	988	1,022	960	950	970	9	3.3
Cen. Afr. Rep.	61	61	67	76	78		
Colombia	2,328	2,328	2,360	2,396	2,783	2	9.5
Congo	34	51	75	95	97		
Congo (Zaïre)	1,442	1,555	2,070	2,424	2,262	3	7.8
Costa Rica	84	87	95	102	103		
Cuba	89	87	115	115	100		
Dom. Rep.	592	592	651	581	442		
Ecuador	730	728	1,065	922	681	10	2.3
Gabon	63	165	235	250	250		
Ghana	872	793	1,000	1,475	1,642	6	5.6
Guatemala	52	52	55	47	35		
Guinea	225	340	400	429	429		
Guinea-Bissau	25	25	31	30	29		
Guyana	21	18	23	24	24		
Haiti	297	288	287	270	270		
Honduras	165	132	166	189	190		
Ivory Coast	808	1,013	1,187	1,300	1,300	7	4.5
Jamaica	18	24	28	35	35		
Kenya	233	233	340	360	370		

Plantains continued

	1970	1980	1990	1994	1995	Rank	%
Liberia	31	31	33	45	45		
Malawi	106	106	180	200	200		
Nicaragua	84	74	64	35	40		
Nigeria	2,217	1,128	1,322	1,665	1,712	5	5.9
Panama	102	82	73	105	105		
Peru	800	708	830	845	1,066	8	3.7
Puerto Rico	86	86	77	93	65		
Rwanda	2,058	2,136	2,629	1,489	2,002	4	6.9
Sierra Leone	21	22	28	28	28		
Sri Lanka	1,679	1,477	548	530	560		
Tanzania	773	992	772	834	651		
Uganda	3,450	5,896	7,791	9,000	9,519	1	32.7
Venezuela	511	427	522	535	566		

Plums *thousand tonnes*

	1970	1980	1990	1994	1995	Rank	%
WORLD	5,707	5,505	6,332	6,699	6,320		
Afghanistan	24	36	34	34	35		
Albania	10	18	10	6	6		
Algeria	10	14	33	24	24		
Argentina	64	71	55	78	56		
Armenia	...	...	...	17	17		
Australia	27	22	20	30	34		
Austria	82	73	51	46	46		
Azerbaijan	...	...	...	30	28		
Belarus	...	...	...	48	60		
Belgium	12	5	6	5	5		
Bosnia	...	...	...	35	35		
Bulgaria	325	164	123	73	100		
Canada	9	8	4	4	5		
Chile	21	17	103	130	128	10	2.0
China	339	436	1,112	1,876	1,959	1	31.0
Croatia	...	...	...	36	40		
Czech Rep.	...	...	...	20	20		
Ecuador	3	1	3	8	8		
Egypt	1	6	45	32	32		
France	184	151	155	221	270	4	4.3
Georgia	...	...	...	6	10		
Germany	589	429	310	382	312	3	4.9
Greece	21	13	8	11	11		
Hungary	216	163	152	116	105		
India	19	28	50	56	56		
Iran	...	...	114	133	137	9	2.2
Iraq	4	29	35	31	32		
Israel	10	18	25	29	29		
Italy	140	166	139	153	108		
Japan	52	58	97	113	113		
Kazakstan	...	...	...	20	20		
Korea, S.	2	14	25	20	35		
Kyrgyzstan	...	...	...	10	12		
Latvia	...	...	...	4	28		
Lebanon	7	11	15	24	24		
Lithuania	...	...	...	12	35		
Macedonia	...	...	...	25	17		
Mexico	75	68	43	62	63		
Moldova	...	...	...	80	70		
Morocco	5	28	41	57	33		
Netherlands	10	6	2	3	3		
Norway	14	14	13	12	12		
Pakistan	29	36	51	70	75		
Poland	15	143	62	77	89		
Portugal	125	6	9	16	16		
Romania	706	615	450	386	253	5	4.0
Russia	...	...	...	112	116		
Slovak Rep.	...	...	...	10	9		
Slovenia	...	...	...	9	6		
South Africa	13	16	18	28	23		
Spain	61	95	140	145	125		
Switzerland	44	52	13	10	10		
Syria	4	24	43	24	25		
Tajikistan	...	...	...	15	15		
Tunisia	6	8	7	12	9		
Turkey	110	152	188	204	205	7	3.2
Turkmenistan	...	...	...	8	8		
Ukraine	...	...	...	105	153	8	2.4
UK	52	37	8	13	13		
USA	532	642	780	796	675	2	10.7
Uzbekistan	...	...	...	90	90		
Yugoslavia	...	...	...	430	229	6	3.6

Potatoes _thousand tonnes_

	1970	1980	1990	1994	1995	Rank	%
WORLD	**275,758**	**258,465**	**267,022**	**270,536**	**285,110**		
Afghanistan	172	283	217	265	280		
Algeria	253	540	962	716	1,200		
Argentina	2,212	1,836	1,852	2,366	1,914		
Armenia	...	...	...	400	451		
Australia	782	840	1,121	1,185	1,122		
Austria	2,787	1,356	810	594	724		
Bangladesh	842	942	1,131	1,438	1,468		
Belarus	...	...	...	8,241	9,504	8	3.3
Belgium	1,631	1,468	1,838	2,303	2,100		
Bolivia	660	794	620	632	642		
Bosnia	...	...	...	180	377		
Brazil	1,557	2,002	2,219	2,480	2,677		
Bulgaria	378	376	495	497	649		
Canada	2,312	2,626	2,903	3,679	3,774		
Chile	707	894	851	900	870		
China	11,029	25,415	31,189	43,836	45,758	1	16.0
Colombia	871	1,931	2,511	2,939	2,899		
Croatia	...	...	...	563	691		
Czech Rep.	...	...	...	1,231	1,330		
Denmark	845	913	1,394	1,359	1,480		
Ecuador	560	323	369	531	473		
Egypt	496	1,142	1,694	1,325	2,599		
Estonia	...	...	...	563	537		
Ethiopia	161	301	380	350	350		
Finland	906	629	845	726	798		
France	8,569	6,735	5,213	5,464	5,839		
Georgia	...	...	...	297	353		
Germany	16,236	19,465	14,039	10,635	10,382	7	3.6
Greece	700	1,036	1,063	968	1,185		
Hungary	1,874	1,504	1,226	946	1,099		
India	4,482	9,377	14,770	17,392	17,900	5	6.3
Indonesia	99	217	571	877	1,002		
Iran	417	1,269	2,387	3,185	2,974		
Iraq	16	96	196	418	420		
Ireland	1,450	902	577	642	620		
Italy	3,632	2,941	2,328	2,021	2,081		
Japan	3,490	3,299	3,583	3,377	3,400		
Kazakhstan	...	...	...	2,040	1,720		
Kenya	206	392	235	162	205		
Korea, N.	960	1,535	2,100	1,600	1,600		
Korea, S.	598	452	472	489	450		
Kyrgyzstan	...	...	...	310	431		
Latvia	...	...	...	1,045	864		
Lebanon	96	129	247	322	325		
Lithuania	...	...	...	1,096	1,594		
Madagascar	106	170	272	270	275		
Malawi	85	270	350	350	376		
Mexico	489	993	1,184	1,167	1,269		
Moldova	...	...	...	475	400		
Morocco	283	503	957	1,038	774		
Nepal	265	279	684	780	839		
Netherlands	5,367	6,329	6,947	7,088	7,340	9	2.6
New Zealand	284	209	264	270	275		
Norway	807	524	452	471	400		
Pakistan	213	412	742	1,056	1,085		
Peru	1,877	1,680	1,432	1,767	2,368		
Poland	45,012	39,508	33,247	23,058	24,891	3	8.7
Portugal	1,222	1,079	1,232	1,324	1,454		
Romania	2,671	4,381	3,186	2,947	3,020		
Russia	...	...	...	33,828	39,900	2	14.0
Rwanda	134	229	334	149	100		
Saudi Arabia	1	3	59	238	406		
Slovak Rep.	...	...	...	399	442		
Slovenia	...	...	...	401	449		
South Africa	583	747	1,247	1,290	1,468		
Spain	4,985	5,615	5,293	3,860	4,195		
Sweden	1,221	1,191	1,132	1,063	1,374		
Switzerland	1,016	924	731	571	569		
Syria	62	279	407	362	489		
Turkey	1,984	2,957	4,300	4,350	4,750		
Uganda	147	157	238	368	386		
Ukraine	...	...	...	16,102	14,729	6	5.2
UK	7,359	6,601	6,333	6,531	6,297	10	2.2
USA	14,483	14,923	17,995	21,185	20,177	4	7.1
Uzbekistan	...	...	...	561	440		
Vietnam	103	710	327	250	230		
Yugoslavia	...	...	...	844	931		

Poultry meat _thousand tonnes_

	1970	1980	1990	1994	1995	Rank	%
WORLD	**17,760**	**27,245**	**40,813**	**51,176**	**54,747**		
Algeria	28	46	185	202	202		
Argentina	182	321	377	566	608		
Australia	128	296	407	491	489		
Austria	47	71	88	102	103		
Bangladesh	61	90	79	100	106		
Belarus	...	...	...	97	69		
Belgium	116	133	190	272	274		
Bolivia	3	9	43	89	96		
Brazil	360	1,345	2,422	3,508	3,752	3	6.9
Bulgaria	94	151	157	82	97		
Burma	16	70	82	100	117		
Canada	542	532	721	863	871	10	1.6
Chile	52	105	125	279	289		
China	1,683	1,725	3,766	8,167	9,994	2	18.3
Colombia	46	107	297	443	553		
Costa Rica	3	5	43	54	64		
Cuba	40	74	94	63	69		
Czech Rep.	...	...	...	119	148		
Denmark	76	100	133	172	173		
Dom. Rep.	28	61	110	131	167		
Ecuador	9	22	69	95	103		
Egypt	80	120	270	383	409		
Ethiopia	54	68	76	72	72		
France	631	1,131	1,627	1,907	2,081	4	3.8
Germany	344	531	555	627	626		
Greece	71	138	158	149	147		
Guatemala	8	19	67	101	106		
Hong Kong	21	48	85	60	56		
Hungary	215	346	406	333	364		
India	83	111	380	507	578		
Indonesia	58	168	498	815	869		
Iran	53	180	409	635	659		
Iraq	16	56	159	110	110		
Ireland	32	52	88	100	105		
Israel	96	153	182	227	227		
Italy	619	1,007	1,092	1,087	1,091	8	2.0
Ivory Coast	9	27	43	48	48		
Jamaica	16	32	48	44	40		
Japan	494	1,115	1,390	1,302	1,280	7	2.3
Jordan	8	26	51	94	95		
Kazakhstan	...	...	...	80	53		
Kenya	16	32	46	48	48		
Korea, N.	20	32	47	50	50		
Korea, S.	46	92	272	373	403		
Lebanon	21	46	52	42	43		
Libya	2	29	63	68	68		
Madagascar	35	55	40	45	48		
Malaysia	53	134	399	684	701		
Mexico	225	440	780	1,155	1,315	5	2.4
Morocco	30	80	143	160	180		
Netherlands	297	343	470	561	604		
New Zealand	17	35	59	90	95		
Nigeria	73	187	169	168	169		
Pakistan	14	46	167	305	317		
Peru	58	148	247	354	411		
Philippines	103	228	250	380	403		
Poland	141	417	346	381	384		
Portugal	54	131	140	184	188		
Puerto Rico	13	28	54	61	62		
Romania	128	413	352	260	294		
Russia	...	...	...	1,068	859		
Saudi Arabia	8	46	264	297	311		
Senegal	6	12	30	55	58		
Singapore	27	66	66	59	61		
Slovenia	...	...	...	54	65		
South Africa	107	233	372	394	394		
Spain	454	798	849	882	941	9	1.7
Sri Lanka	7	9	24	50	54		
Sweden	27	44	46	70	67		
Syria	14	57	62	82	82		
Taiwan	22	51	88	90	90		
Thailand	64	373	674	797	527		
Tunisia	10	40	52	61	66		
Turkey	104	245	406	480	506		
Ukraine	...	...	...	264	235		
UK	574	751	1,000	1,079	1,285	6	2.3
USA	5,979	6,713	10,708	13,248	13,825	1	25.3

Poultry meat continued

	1970	1980	1990	1994	1995	Rank	%
Venezuela	93	247	361	540	572		
Vietnam	70	135	159	174	178		
Yemen	2	7	45	55	55		
Yugoslavia	...	...	...	84	97		

Rapeseed _thousand tonnes_

	1950	1970	1980	1990	1994	1995	Rank	%
WORLD	**2,820**	**6,617**	**11,093**	**25,002**	**29,837**	**34,509**		
Algeria	...	...	34	90	99	99		
Australia	...	31	24	114	264	561	9	1.6
Austria	5	8	7	107	217	268		
Bangladesh	95	132	225	217	239	245		
Canada	9	1,517	2,581	3,567	7,233	6,436	2	18.7
Chile	...	72	55	75	23	26		
China	782	996	2,952	6,610	7,492	9,777	1	28.3
Czech Rep.	...	...	...	452	662	662	8	1.9
Denmark	9	30	204	725	371	312	10	0.9
Ethiopia	20	20	19	77	80	80		
Finland	6	9	68	112	108	127		
France	154	603	871	2,047	1,772	2,789	5	8.1
Germany	193	370	618	2,310	2,896	3,110	4	9.0
Hungary	4	46	71	105	53	89		
India	815	1,629	1,864	4,577	5,328	5,884	3	17.1
Italy	14	5	1	40	29	96		
Japan	129	54	4	2	2	2		
Korea, S.	4	31	25	7	3	3		
Netherlands	33	22	28	23	4	5		
Pakistan	175	249	249	237	197	229		
Poland	100	455	434	1,278	756	1,377	6	4.0
Russia	...	...	...	...	122	123		
Slovak Rep.	...	...	...	...	94	149		
Spain	4	5	15	22	56	55		
Sweden	146	218	313	378	195	218		
Switzerland	4	19	33	49	35	45		
Ukraine	...	...	...	...	18	40		
UK	3	10	274	1,171	1,266	1,235	7	3.6
USA	1	1	1	60	209	250		

Raspberries _thousand tonnes_

	1970	1980	1990	1994	1995	Rank	%
WORLD	**196**	**243**	**324**	**307**	**338**		
Australia	1	1	0.5	0.5	0.5		
Belgium	...	0.3	0.5	0.6	0.6		
Bosnia	...	...	...	1	1		
Bulgaria	11	7	3.9	2.2	3		
Canada	7	9	16.4	18.9	20	6	5.9
Croatia	...	...	...	0.6	0.5		
Czech Rep.	...	...	...	0.8	0.8		
Denmark	1	0.2	0.2	0.2	0.2		
Estonia	...	...	...	0.3	0.3		
Finland	0.2	0.3	0.19	0.2	0.2		
France	5	7	6.3	8.6	7.9	10	2.3
Germany	24	21	28.2	32	32	5	9.5
Hungary	12	18	26.1	17	17	8	5.0
Ireland	1	0.1	0.6	0.6	0.6		
Italy	1	1	1.7	1.5	1.5		
Moldova	...	...	...	3.5	3		
Netherlands	4	0.6	0.3	0.3	0.3		
New Zealand	1	1	2		1.3		
Norway	2	3	3.2	1.8	1.8		
Poland	11	23	34.7	30.2	40	3	11.8
Russia	...	...	...	82.8	85	1	25.1
Slovenia	...	...	...	0.3	0.3		
Spain	...	...	1	1	1		
Ukraine	...	...	...	7	8.1	9	2.4
UK	19	21	20.5	17.4	17.4	7	5.1
USA	15	12	24	33	33	4	9.8
Yugoslavia	...	...	40	56	2	16.6

Rice   *thousand tonnes*

	1970	1980	1990	1994	1995	Rank	%
WORLD	311,469	396,259	517,572	537,338	550,193		
Afghanistan	374	415	329	350	300		
Argentina	347	288	422	606	926		
Australia	267	678	839	1,042	1,016		
Bangladesh	16,540	20,125	26,980	25,248	26,399	4	4.8
Brazil	6,847	8,533	9,318	10,499	11,226	9	2.0
Burma	8,107	12,637	13,658	18,195	19,568	7	3.6
Cambodia	3,016	1,352	2,524	2,223	3,300		
China	111,599	145,665	186,712	178,031	187,334	1	34.0
Colombia	756	1,831	1,986	1,679	1,743		
Cuba	309	455	446	226	223		
Ecuador	165	378	852	1,420	1,291		
Egypt	2,567	2,376	3,098	4,583	4,888		
Guinea	364	438	428	532	631		
India	62,861	74,557	111,290	121,997	119,442	2	21.7
Indonesia	19,136	29,570	44,864	46,641	49,744	3	9.0
Iran	1,041	1,394	2,064	2,259	2,300		
Italy	858	989	1,257	1,361	1,321		
Ivory Coast	335	438	661	988	1,045		
Japan	16,281	13,320	12,688	14,976	13,435	8	2.4
Kazakstan	...	537	579	283	184		
Korea, N.	2,329	4,733	3,151	2,500	2,580		
Korea, S.	5,573	6,780	7,705	6,932	6,343		
Laos	870	1,025	1,373	1,653	1,418		
Madagascar	1,865	2,055	2,381	2,360	2,520		
Malaysia	1,689	2,053	1,980	2,156	2,126		
Mexico	390	528	423	374	367		
Nepal	2,297	2,361	3,377	2,928	2,906		
Nigeria	352	1,027	3,010	2,427	2,920		
Pakistan	3,431	4,884	4,862	5,144	5,920		
Peru	539	580	957	1,401	1,142		
Philippines	5,225	7,747	9,672	10,538	10,541	10	1.9
Russia	...	1,187	896	523	462		
Sierra Leone	474	504	508	405	284		
Spain	384	435	498	408	327		
Sri Lanka	1,463	2,093	2,330	2,684	1,900		
Taiwan	2,663	2,354	1,807	1,679	1,687		
Tanzania	172	251	694	614	723		
Thailand	13,475	16,967	19,398	21,111	21,130	6	3.8
USA	3,953	6,968	7,106	8,971	7,887		
Uruguay	132	289	459	624	804		
Venezuela	208	638	477	589	643		
Vietnam	9,752	11,812	19,281	23,528	24,964	5	4.5

Rubber – natural   *thousand tonnes*

	1950	1970	1980	1990	1994	1995	Rank	%
WORLD	1,740	3,004	3,805	5,012	5,986	5,995		
Bolivia	1	3	5	9	10		
Brazil	22	24	28	29	30	30		
Burma	10	11	16	15	16	27		
Cambodia	16	12	7	31	42	45		
Cameroon	2	13	17	38	54	54		
China	5	5	116	268	374	424	5	7.1
Congo (Zaïre)	10	43	21	13	12	12		
Ghana	0	7	10	4	7	7		
Guatemala	8	10	11	18	22	22		
India	17	90	146	295	435	435	4	7.3
Indonesia	635	838	982	1,256	1,499	1,499	2	25.0
Ivory Coast	10	11	21	69	70	68	10	1.1
Liberia	31	78	81	55	31	31		
Malaysia	722	1,285	1,537	1,321	1,101	1,089	3	18.2
Nigeria	14	63	49	142	105	105	8	1.8
Papua N.G.	2	6	4	3	4	4		
Philippines	1	19	66	179	178	182	6	3.0
Sri Lanka	102	150	137	109	105	105	9	1.8
Thailand	104	295	502	1,099	1,767	1,721	1	28.7
Vietnam	35	36	44	58	121	120	7	2.0

Rye   *thousand tonnes*

	1970	1980	1990	1994	1995	Rank	%
WORLD	31,049	24,684	33,558	22,547	22,672		
Argentina	271	169	55	54	50		
Australia	18	11	26	22	21		
Austria	417	327	376	319	314	8	1.4
Belarus	...	...	...	1864	2143	4	9.5
Belgium	82	43	14	15	12		
Bulgaria	27	29	49	22	20		
Canada	474	638	604	397	310	9	1.4
China	1,233	1,167	967	1,000	700	6	3.1
Czech Rep.	...	...	...	276	262	10	1.2
Denmark	136	221	476	423	495	7	2.2
Egypt	...	...	16	19	22		
Estonia	...	...	...	41	58		
Finland	130	88	156	22	58		
France	297	368	238	176	191		
Germany	4,456	3,828	3,737	3,451	4,533	2	20.0
Greece	9	7	43	39	41		
Hungary	193	117	240	193	171		
Italy	65	35	20	20	20		
Kazakstan	...	...	...	264	84		
Latvia	...	...	...	113	71		
Lithuania	...	...	...	313	239		
Netherlands	196	39	34	27	43		
Poland	7,143	6,166	6,053	5,300	6,288	1	27.7
Portugal	164	128	99	64	35		
Romania	52	38	90	51	43		
Russia	...	...	...	5989	4098	3	18.1
Slovak Rep.	...	...	...	96	89		
Spain	292	239	279	207	174		
Sweden	239	197	273	173	206		
Switzerland	48	35	21	31	42		
Turkey	781	558	229	195	240		
Ukraine	...	...	...	942	1208	5	5.3
UK	14	25	42	40	43		
USA	984	474	284	288	256		

Seed cotton   *thousand tonnes*

	1970	1980	1990	1994	1995	Rank	%
WORLD	34,857	43,076	54,764	53,876	57,928		
Afghanistan	75	87	43	66	66		
Angola	83	34	12	12	12		
Argentina	370	447	777	706	1,125	10	1.9
Australia	82	220	911	795	809		
Azerbaijan	...	...	...	284	250		
Benin	28	19	143	260	369		
Brazil	1,828	1,681	1,921	1,367	1,451	7	2.5
Bulgaria	39	14	13	7	14		
Burkina Faso	31	66	170	177	170		
Burma	39	59	62	68	86		
Cameroon	58	81	112	170	194		
Cen. Afr. Rep.	53	28	28	27	32		
Chad	107	83	161	134	159		
China	5,965	7,882	13,971	13,023	14,304	1	24.7
Colombia	352	291	341	140	146		
Congo (Zaïre)	63	23	77	77	77		
Egypt	1,434	1,341	824	680	640		
El Salvador	135	169	16	11	11		
Ethiopia	40	87	63	42	46		
Ghana	1	7	13	60	92		
Greece	342	356	695	1,221	1,268	9	2.2
Guatemala	190	434	108	40	21		
India	3,264	3,952	5,293	7,064	8,008	3	13.8
Iran	441	258	414	387	523		
Iraq	43	15	13	29	28		
Israel	95	219	104	86	113		
Ivory Coast	37	131	261	253	210		
Kazakstan	...	...	...	207	223		
Malawi	21	30	36	30	68		
Mali	66	129	275	276	347		
Mexico	988	984	526	340	625		
Mozambique	127	51	33	51	49		
Nicaragua	236	220	73	3	20		
Nigeria	185	92	254	330	350		
Pakistan	1,786	2,191	5,274	4,438	5,406	4	9.3
Paraguay	31	268	635	380	461		
Peru	245	265	246	168	217		
South Africa	57	151	166	79	64		

Seed cotton continued

	1970	1980	1990	1994	1995	Rank	%
Spain	155	174	237	130	90		
Sudan	684	342	398	155	235		
Syria	391	342	476	535	600		
Tajikistan	...	...	...	529	417		
Tanzania	210	163	214	147	135		
Thailand	93	170	104	78	81		
Togo	7	19	94	120	140		
Turkey	1,146	1,269	1,606	1,638	2,224	6	3.8
Turkmenistan	...	...	...	1,283	1,293	8	2.2
Uganda	258	17	20	38	39		
USA	5,967	8,038	8,602	11,179	10,030	2	17.3
Uzbekistan	...	...	...	3,938	3,994	5	6.9
Venezuela	41	42	81	52	45		
Zimbabwe	129	158	218	170	101		

Sesame seed   *thousand tonnes*

	1970	1980	1990	1994	1995	Rank	%
WORLD	2,014	2,900	2,244	2,663	2,764		
Afghanistan	33	36	25	24	24		
Bangladesh	29	51	48	48	48	8	1.7
Benin	2	1	4	7	7		
Brazil	3	3	12	13	13		
Burkina Faso	5	7	5	2	2		
Burma	116	159	189	304	297	3	10.7
Cambodia	10	3	6	7	7		
Cameroon	6	8	15	16	16		
Cen. Afr. Rep.	13	11	21	27	29		
Chad	14	10	11	13	13		
China	368	396	415	548	540	2	19.5
Colombia	21	13	8	10	10		
Congo (Zaïre)	5	5	14	15	15		
Egypt	19	16	21	28	28		
El Salvador	1	10	12	9	9		
Eritrea	...	...	...	7	7		
Ethiopia	81	37	35	31	31		
Guatemala	7	13	21	31	33		
Haiti	1	4	4	4	4		
Honduras	1	3	2	2	2		
India	487	461	762	839	925	1	33.5
Iran	6	3	18	20	20		
Iraq	13	6	14	15	15		
Ivory Coast	2	3	3	3	3		
Kenya	3	8	9	12	12		
Korea, S.	10	14	36	28	25		
Laos	...	...	2	5	5		
Mexico	178	145	48	50	50	7	1.8
Mozambique	3	3	3	3	3		
Nicaragua	6	7	9	17	20		
Nigeria	59	73	43	56	50	6	1.8
Pakistan	11	18	22	36	36	9	1.3
Sierra Leone	...	1	2	3	3		
Somalia	7	44	43	22	25		
Sri Lanka	10	11	5	3	3		
Sudan	256	224	106	170	195	4	7.1
Syria	4	19	8	9	10		
Tanzania	11	17	23	25	25		
Thailand	20	26	30	32	32		
Togo	1	2	2	2	2		
Turkey	40	26	40	34	34	10	1.2
Uganda	21	20	56	70	71	5	2.6
Venezuela	101	49	55	16	16		
Vietnam	3	8	23	28	29		
Yemen	6	9	9	12	13		

Sheep   *thousand head*

	1970	1980	1990	1994	1995	Rank	%
WORLD	1,076,956	1,087,985	1,172,107	1,087,289	1,061,717		
Afghanistan	18,900	18,667	14,173	17,000	18,000		
Albania	1,249	1,232	1,645	2,400	2,480		
Algeria	7,940	13,111	17,302	17,842	17,302		
Argentina	42,773	31,473	28,139	23,500	21,626		
Australia	177,491	134,871	165,046	132,569	123,210	1	11.6
Azerbaijan	...	...	4,357	4,376		
Bangladesh	547	1,064	871	1,070	1,155		
Bolivia	6,825	9,050	7,573	7,686	7,884		
Brazil	17,768	18,414	20,061	18,436	18,000		

Sheep continued

	1970	1980	1990	1994	1995	Rank	%
Bulgaria	9,518	10,358	8,226	3,763	3,398		
Burkina Faso	1,657	1,855	5,048	5,686	5,800		
Cameroon	2,000	2,167	3,407	3,780	3,800		
Chad	2,200	2,620	1,926	2,152	2,219		
Chile	6,179	6,059	4,803	4,649	4,625		
China	78,000	101,864	112,299	111,680	117,446	2	11.1
Colombia	1,935	2,399	2,547	2,540	2,540		
Congo (Zaïre)	675	726	934	1,047	1,080		
Ecuador	1,897	2,310	1,417	1,690	1,692		
Egypt	2,000	1,691	3,310	4,000	3,648		
Eritrea				1,520	1,530		
Ethiopia	24,077	23,250	22,960	21,700	21,700		
France	10,023	11,452	11,196	11,505	10,320		
Germany	2,534	3,147	3,824	2,369	2,340		
Ghana	1,324	1,942	2,199	2,279	2,400		
Greece	7,646	8,040	8,684	8,706	9,559		
Hungary	2,966	2,960	2,050	1,252	947		
India	40,657	44,987	43,706	44,809	45,000	5	4.2
Indonesia	3,169	4,124	6,008	6,485	7,169		
Iran	32,000	33,833	44,754	50,285	50,889	3	4.8
Iraq	12,000	10,399	7,804	5,150	5,100		
Ireland	4,092	2,374	5,523	5,991	5,772		
Italy	8,097	9,120	11,088	10,461	10,682		
Ivory Coast	833	1,020	1,137	1,251	1,282		
Jordan	736	950	1,660	2,100	2,100		
Kazakstan	...	...	...	33,524	24,235		
Kenya	3,935	5,100	6,447	5,500	5,600		
Kyrgyzstan	...	...	...	7,077	4,924		
Lesotho	1,610	1,183	1,450	1,200	1,131		
Libya	2,125	5,046	5,100	4,500	4,400		
Macedonia	...	...	...	2,466	2,320		
Mali	5,700	6,247	6,072	5,173	5,173		
Mauritania	4,427	5,098	5,067	5,280	5,288		
Mexico	8,687	6,484	5,862	5,905	5,987		
Moldova	...	...	...	1,366	1,411		
Mongolia	12,678	14,261	14,265	13,787	13,719		
Morocco	17,087	15,228	13,528	13,902	16,586		
Namibia	4,000	5,433	3,289	2,620	2,410		
Nepal	2,156	730	903	914	919		
Netherlands	579	856	1,663	1,766	1,674		
N. Zealand	59,708	67,393	57,861	49,014	49,466	4	4.7
Niger	2,632	2,979	3,100	3,678	3,789		
Nigeria	8,083	9,000	12,477	14,000	14,000		
Norway	1,769	2,033	2,202	2,462	2,400		
Pakistan	13,096	22,580	25,703	28,358	29,065	9	2.7
Peru	16,698	14,565	12,484	12,160	12,570		
Poland	3,236	4,105	3,934	870	713		
Portugal	4,405	4,440	5,531	5,991	6,200		
Romania	13,964	15,766	15,236	11,499	10,897		
Russia	...	...	...	40,616	31,818	7	3.0
Saudi Arabia	1,960	2,888	6,370	7,578	7,753		
Senegal	1,533	1,966	3,500	4,600	4,800		
Somalia	8,967	11,500	12,117	13,000	13,500		
South Africa	35,585	31,625	32,060	29,134	28,784	10	2.7
Spain	18,712	14,721	23,800	23,058	23,018		
Sudan	10,300	17,628	20,179	22,800	23,000		
Syria	5,843	9,311	14,571	11,257	11,800		
Tajikistan	...	...	...	2,078	1,930		
Tanzania	2,823	3,754	3,551	3,955	3,955		
Togo	589	592	1,164	1,200	1,200		
Tunisia	3,200	4,651	5,935	6,137	6,222		
Turkey	36,470	46,199	43,195	37,541	35,646	6	3.4
Turkmenistan	...	...	...	6,000	6,100		
Uganda	799	1,152	1,350	1,850	1,900		
Ukraine	...	...	...	6,118	4,792		
UK	26,332	21,643	29,241	29,484	29,484	8	2.8
USA	20,501	12,670	11,384	9,714	8,860		
Uruguay	19,906	19,219	25,359	22,078	20,299		
Uzbekistan	...	...	...	9,360	9,053		
Venezuela	166	333	551	850	1,160		
Yemen	2,800	3,002	3,682	3,677	3,751		
Yugoslavia	...	...	...	2,635	2,671		

Sheep meat *thousand tonnes*

	1970	1980	1990	1994	1995	Rank	%
WORLD	5,708	5,663	6,951	7,204	7,099		
Afghanistan	86	128	113	137	145		
Albania	16	17	8	12	14		
Algeria	40	61	136	170	170		
Argentina	181	119	85	85	81		
Australia	367	539	613	642	604	2	8.5
Azerbaijan	...	...	...	20	23		
Belgium	7	6	8	5	6		
Bolivia	14	20	13	14	14		
Brazil	36	32	82	84	84		
Bulgaria	71	63	66	40	40		
Burkina Faso	1	6	11	11	11		
Cameroon	9	8	14	16	16		
Canada	8	5	9	10	10		
Chad	7	11	8	10	10		
Chile	24	16	13	12	10		
China	350	237	551	840	1,070	1	15.1
Colombia	2	9	10	10	10		
Ecuador	11	8	4	5	6		
Egypt	29	22	52	63	58		
Ethiopia	80	82	82	78	78		
France	113	170	171	140	139		
Germany	21	43	47	40	41		
Ghana	4	5	6	9	9		
Greece	61	81	88	83	80		
Hungary	6	7	6	2	2		
Iceland	12	15	9	9	9		
India	112	115	169	171	173		
Indonesia	13	23	30	43	45		
Iran	145	229	229	254	256	6	3.6
Iraq	39	46	22	18	15		
Ireland	44	42	80	93	89		
Italy	49	65	79	75	73		
Jordan	5	4	8	12	13		
Kazakstan	...	...	...	250	220	10	3.1
Kenya	13	18	25	22	22		
Kuwait	8	21	20	30	33		
Kyrgyzstan	...	...	...	55	50		
Lebanon	11	8	7	14	14		
Libya	19	49	26	21	20		
Macedonia	...	...	...	13	10		
Mali	18	24	21	24	24		
Mauritania	6	7	13	13	13		
Mexico	16	22	25	30	30		
Mongolia	69	96	108	96	94		
Morocco	47	56	101	105	112		
Namibia	12	17	12	13	10		
Nepal	7	2	3	3	3		
Netherlands	10	18	15	17	16		
New Zealand	563	567	564	552	562	3	7.9
Niger	4	12	12	13	13		
Nigeria	28	31	44	51	51		
Norway	17	20	24	26	27		
Oman	1	2	11	11	11		
Pakistan	67	122	189	238	253	8	3.6
Peru	23	21	19	18	19		
Poland	22	19	29	8	6		
Portugal	19	19	25	24	24		
Qatar	1	3	10	13	14		
Romania	62	72	79	63	75		
Russia	...	...	...	316	255	7	3.6
Saudi Arabia	14	34	62	64	66		
Senegal	6	1	12	15	15		
Somalia	11	22	30	33	34		
South Africa	168	133	133	119	110		
Spain	123	152	216	224	227	9	3.2
Sudan	64	82	70	80	82		
Syria	40	80	115	102	95		
Tajikistan	...	...	...	18	18		
Tanzania	10	10	10	11	11		
Tunisia	27	23	34	38	46		
Turkey	226	253	304	286	273	5	3.8
Turkmenistan	...	...	...	40	45		
Uganda	4	6	7	9	9		
Ukraine	...	...	...	39	33		
UAE	2	4	21	30	32		
UK	221	256	374	351	366	4	5.2
USA	250	143	162	140	123		

Sheep meat continued

	1970	1980	1990	1994	1995	Rank	%
Uruguay	72	37	64	66	80		
Uzbekistan	...	...	...	75	83		
Yemen	15	20	20	20	20		
Yugoslavia	...	...	26	26	...		

Silk *thousand tonnes*

	1970	1980	1990	1994	1995	Rank	%
WORLD	42,146	67,968	85,911	115,796	112,350		
Afghanistan	45	50	50	50	50		
Brazil	270	1,300	1,822	2,450	2,450	4	2.2
Bulgaria	253	199	116	10	10		
China	10,258	34,199	54,736	84,000	80,000	1	71.2
Greece	103	33	10	11	11		
India	2,245	4,926	11,700	14,500	15,000	2	13.4
Indonesia	...	...	120	120	120		
Iran	145	383	537	600	600	10	0.5
Italy	321	20	2	2	2		
Japan	20,562	15,624	5,775	2,400	2,400	5	2.1
Korea, N.	1,400	2,700	4,200	4,700	4,700	3	4.2
Korea, S.	2,876	3,311	947	700	700	8	0.6
Romania	106	120	160	140	140		
Tajikistan	...	...	...	300	300		
Thailand	...	883	1,267	1,600	1,600	7	1.4
Turkey	146	233	240	60	60		
Turkmenistan	...	...	...	500	500		
Uzbekistan	...	...	...	2,000	2,000	6	1.8
Vietnam	233	246	467	600	650	9	0.6

Sisal *thousand tonnes*

	1970	1980	1990	1994	1995	Rank	%
WORLD	312	527	397	319	309		
Angola	65	7	1	1	1		
Brazil	229	234	213	131	118	1	38.2
China	9	20	22	41	42	2	13.6
Cuba	2	5	7	7	7	8	2.3
Ethiopia	2	1	1	1	1		
Haiti	16	12	10	8	7	9	2.3
Indonesia	5	1	1	1	1		
Kenya	46	42	39	34	34	4	11.0
Madagascar	26	15	20	17	16	6	5.2
Mexico	50	86	34	36	37	3	12.0
Morocco	1	1	2	2	2		
Mozambique	28	11	1	1	1		
South Africa	8	6	5	3	3	10	1.0
Tanzania	198	80	34	26	30	5	9.7
Venezuela	12	6	10	10	10	7	3.2

Sorghum *thousand tonnes*

	1970	1980	1990	1994	1995	Rank	%
WORLD	55,629	65,651	57,027	61,957	54,427		
Argentina	3,823	5,641	1,934	2,148	1,649	7	3.0
Australia	759	1,084	980	931	1,272	9	2.3
Benin	52	59	107	113	108		
Bolivia	...	21	58	50	104		
Brazil	2	172	245	292	243		
Burkina Faso	528	620	993	1,232	1,266	10	2.3
Burundi	105	53	66	45	66		
Cameroon	...	301	357	350	460		
Chad	...	210	268	379	437		
China	8,607	7,034	5,135	6,438	4,854	4	8.9
Colombia	153	488	737	680	553		
Congo (Zaïre)	26	32	49	55	55		
Egypt	...	641	631	731	769		
El Salvador	144	145	158	182	199		
Eritrea	...	...	...	127	68		
Ethiopia	827	1,149	880	1,125	1,600	8	2.9
France	203	332	322	263	249		
Ghana	147	140	197	324	390		
Guatemala	46	80	83	43	45		
Haiti	210	121	97	80	90		
Honduras	46	49	73	53	63		
India	8,516	11,380	10,893	10,191	9,550	2	17.5
Italy	15	73	134	236	215		
Kenya	215	160	116	118	94		
Korea, N.	115	18	15	11	11		
Lesotho	57	59	26	60	6		

Sorghum continued

	1970	1980	1990	1994	1995	Rank	%
Malawi	78	20	18	17	45		
Mali	...	341	677	746	807		
Mauritania	...	28	71	147	157		
Mexico	2,573	4,991	5,096	3,169	4,170	5	7.7
Morocco	70	20	15	14	2		
Mozambique	202	181	167	170	194		
Nicaragua	57	80	74	91	58		
Niger	262	347	389	400	266		
Nigeria	3,632	3,341	4,794	6,197	6,184	3	11.4
Pakistan	308	235	242	263	255		
Rwanda	141	178	178	85	72		
Saudi Arabia	185	123	139	185	207		
Senegal	...	131	121	132	127		
Somalia	132	167	243	252	136		
South Africa	376	540	341	520	291		
Spain	168	181	105	74	26		
Sudan	1,525	2,361	2,085	3,648	2,434	6	4.5
Tanzania	156	543	485	478	839		
Thailand	123	237	239	228	194		
Togo	...	87	136	85	124		
Uganda	337	312	357	390	398		
USA	19,314	19,157	14,971	16,485	11,684	1	21.5
Uruguay	53	112	91	64	109		
Venezuela	5	365	529	446	398		
Yemen	878	616	402	444	464		
Zimbabwe	98	71	80	122	29		

Soya beans   *thousand tonnes*

	1970	1980	1990	1994	1995	Rank	%
WORLD	43,487	85,967	106,315	136,154	125,812		
Argentina	39	3,657	9,347	11,715	12,134	4	9.6
Bolivia	2	49	292	710	887	9	0.7
Brazil	1,547	13,468	19,636	24,912	25,651	2	20.4
Canada	257	651	1,314	2,251	2,280	6	1.8
China	8,131	8,266	10,323	16,011	13,511	3	10.7
Colombia	114	130	201	109	94		
Ecuador	2	32	164	194	91		
Egypt	...	110	106	67	64		
France	...	19	237	261	263		
India	2	359	2,300	3,676	4,000	5	3.2
Indonesia	468	679	1,453	1,565	1,689	8	1.3
Iran	15	65	81	132	134		
Italy	...	...	1,592	700	732	10	0.6
Japan	128	192	230	99	119		
Korea, N.	255	340	438	400	400		
Korea, S.	228	243	223	154	160		
Mexico	252	580	764	523	190		
Nigeria	61	60	140	178	192		
Paraguay	46	616	1,604	1,796	2,212	7	1.8
Romania	102	262	208	100	110		
Russia	...	...	...	422	290		
Thailand	51	111	546	528	386		
Turkey	11	7	144	70	75		
USA	31,174	54,861	52,944	68,503	59,243	1	47.1

Strawberries   *thousand tonnes*

	1970	1980	1990	1994	1995	Rank	%
WORLD	1,212	1,768	2,428	2,637	2,600		
Argentina	2	5	8	8	8		
Australia	4	3	6	10	10		
Austria	8	10	14	13	14		
Belgium	34	22	30	31	31		
Bosnia	...	...	...	5	5		
Bulgaria	28	21	18	6	6		
Canada	18	26	27	31	33		
Chile	...	...	13	15	16		
China	...	...	5	5	5		
Colombia	...	...	11	14	15		
Czech Rep.	...	...	...	20	17		
Denmark	11	8	9	9	9		
Ecuador	...	0	3	1	1		
Egypt	2	1	33	25	26		
Finland	3	8	10	10	10		
France	65	81	84	82	82	9	3.2
Germany	41	72	71	56	54		
Greece	5	14	8	9	8		
Guatemala	...	...	3	3	3		
Hungary	20	18	16	11	12		

Strawberries continued

	1970	1980	1990	1994	1995	Rank	%
Iran	...	...	9	13	13		
Ireland	4	5	6	5	5		
Israel	4	8	14	13	13		
Italy	89	201	195	190	190	5	7.3
Japan	138	194	215	198	202	4	7.8
Korea, S.	4	79	102	151	148	6	5.7
Lebanon	0	1	6	8	8		
Macedonia	...	...	...	2	3		
Mexico	112	94	93	129	100	8	3.8
Moldova	...	...	...	11	6		
Morocco	...	...	1	8	10		
Netherlands	32	20	27	30	25		
New Zealand	4	5	4	3	3		
Norway	13	18	15	19	19		
Peru	2	3	7	8	8		
Poland	87	188	258	142	211	3	8.1
Portugal	2	2	3	3	3		
Romania	29	31	21	12	9		
Russia	...	...	...	113	110	7	4.2
Slovak Rep.	...	...	...	11	7		
Slovenia	...	...	...	3	3		
South Africa	2	3	5	4	4		
Spain	10	92	215	282	247	2	9.5
Switzerland	3	3	6	6	6		
Turkey	12	23	51	65	66	10	2.5
Ukraine	...	...	...	19	16		
UK	50	53	50	42	42		
USA	227	314	569	748	729	1	28.0
Venezuela	1	4	4	4	4		
Yugoslavia	...	...	...	20	28		

Sugar   *thousand tonnes*

	1970	1980	1990	1994	1995	Rank	%
WORLD	72,176	88,632	110,019	110,072	118,819		
Angola	74	31	27	20	30		
Argentina	985	1,584	1,245	1,110	1,493		
Australia	2,511	3,243	3,471	5,064	5,006	6	4.2
Austria	315	450	458	438	481		
Bangladesh	90	595	196	241	288		
Barbados	146	113	67	51	39		
Belarus	...	...	...	107	143		
Belgium	711	994	1,078	1,005	1,049		
Belize	62	101	99	107	107		
Bolivia	120	250	272	277	347		
Brazil	5,161	8,191	8,359	12,618	12,594	2	10.6
Bulgaria	218	165	58	8	16		
Canada	130	112	140	171	151		
Chile	217	131	363	464	546		
China	3,878	4,160	7,586	6,793	7,211	3	6.1
Colombia	710	2,117	1,594	1,964	2,069		
Costa Rica	160	214	238	322	331		
Cuba	6,388	7,510	7,821	4,024	3,419		
Czech Rep.	...	...	...	465	537		
Denmark	307	493	543	510	448		
Dom. Rep.	1,010	1,142	710	692	580		
Ecuador	258	402	325	362	324		
Egypt	564	666	994	1,195	1,230		
El Salvador	128	228	221	323	306		
Ethiopia	98	168	186	132	139		
Fiji	329	446	419	517	454		
Finland	60	104	169	154	164		
France	2,872	4,720	4,452	4,988	4,595	7	3.9
Germany	2,645	3,936	4,293	3,672	3,805	9	3.2
Greece	163	286	329	271	312		
Guadeloupe	154	86	52	58	33		
Guatemala	191	448	829	1,130	1,293		
Guyana	354	291	155	257	254		
Haiti	64	135	31	30	30		
Honduras	60	203	185	160	207		
Hungary	321	511	593	462	526		
India	4,188	13,487	11,338	11,660	16,345	1	13.8
Indonesia	760	1,587	2,098	2,452	2,098		
Iran	571	630	676	899	936		
Ireland	164	178	237	232	242		
Italy	1,271	1,956	1,702	1,621	1,618		
Ivory Coast	...	97	145	125	119		
Jamaica	383	247	216	223	249		
Japan	628	789	975	817	898		
Kenya	132	416	475	330	418		

Sugar continued

	1970	1980	1990	1994	1995	Rank	%
Kyrgyzstan	...	...	...	300	300		
Madagascar	103	115	111	83	98		
Malawi	32	140	181	203	222		
Malaysia	...	59	100	114	108		
Mauritius	659	615	613	525	540		
Mexico	2,495	2,864	3,521	3,549	4,274	8	3.6
Moldova	...	...	...	162	173		
Morocco	168	364	489	482	445		
Mozambique	278	189	29	30	43		
Netherlands	769	1,000	1,227	1,050	1,074		
Nicaragua	147	204	199	244	298		
Pakistan	557	738	2,043	3,177	3,263		
Panama	78	184	109	147	123		
Paraguay	50	85	131	120	122		
Peru	782	586	593	542	643		
Philippines	1,859	2,318	1,787	1,873	1,705		
Poland	1,581	1,530	1,920	1,470	1,718		
Puerto Rico	383	158	75	45	41		
Réunion	220	247	193	177	195		
Romania	434	595	579	207	218		
Russia	...	...	...	1,799	2,228		
Slovak Rep.	...	...	...	131	157		
South Africa	1,629	2,011	2,151	1,668	1,667		
Spain	882	934	966	1,150	1,087		
Sudan	85	166	430	445	464		
Swaziland	167	317	525	488	422		
Sweden	233	350	377	369	387		
Switzerland	65	119	150	128	140		
Syria	28	49	59	113	124		
Taiwan	588	830	475	468	408		
Tanzania	100	124	97	124	110		
Thailand	436	2,134	3,871	4,009	5,571	5	4.7
Trinidad & Tob.	229	125	105	131	117		
Turkey	700	1,178	1,792	1,678	1,472		
Uganda	154	14	29	48	76		
Ukraine	...	...	...	3,598	3,804	10	3.2
UK	1,033	1,215	1,351	1,373	1,326		
USA	5,215	5,342	6,281	7,374	6,718	4	5.7
Venezuela	448	351	524	550	516		
Vietnam	7	207	422	326	347		
Yugoslavia	...	...	...	236	183		
Zambia	37	105	137	158	151		
Zimbabwe	155	336	447	507	512		

These figures are raw sugar manufactured from beet and cane.

Sugar beet   *thousand tonnes*

	1970	1980	1990	1994	1995	Rank	%
WORLD	227,615	272,920	302,498	254,018	264,821		
Albania	114	298	163	60	67		
Austria	1,847	2,580	2,552	2,561	2,886		
Belarus	...	...	...	1,078	1,172		
Belgium	4,683	6,652	6,520	5,702	6,081		
Bulgaria	1,664	1,568	802	112	158		
Canada	971	984	953	1,091	1,027		
Chile	1,371	858	2,429	3,547	3,744		
China	6,387	5,257	13,352	12,526	13,984	6	5.3
Croatia	...	...	...	592	691		
Czech Rep.	...	...	...	3,240	3,712		
Denmark	1,968	3,109	3,358	3,138	3,130		
Egypt	...	36	789	825	920		
Finland	410	760	1,053	1,097	1,110		
France	18,469	30,310	29,860	29,036	30,571	1	11.5
Germany	19,218	27,872	27,760	24,211	26,077	3	9.8
Greece	1,258	2,322	2,803	2,564	2,610		
Hungary	2,500	4,196	5,304	3,370	4,199		
Iran	3,750	3,654	4,059	5,295	5,521		
Ireland	1,039	1,266	1,447	1,390	1,547		
Italy	9,622	14,738	13,545	12,629	13,188	8	5.0
Japan	2,204	3,416	3,994	3,853	3,813		
Kazakstan	...	...	...	433	371		
Lithuania	...	...	...	462	692		
Moldova	...	...	...	1,527	2,084		
Morocco	1,199	2,174	2,966	3,144	2,717		
Netherlands	4,922	6,161	7,830	6,149	6,449		
Pakistan	208	375	335	243	194		
Poland	12,207	13,387	14,169	11,676	13,309	7	5.0
Romania	3,560	5,704	4,917	3,273	2,764		
Russia	...	...	...	13,946	19,072	5	7.2

Sugar beet continued

	1970	1980	1990	1994	1995	Rank	%
Slovak Rep.	...	...	...	1,110	1,176		
Slovenia	...	...	...	222	265		
Spain	5,602	6,658	7,124	8,020	7,489		
Sweden	1,579	2,316	2,353	2,350	2,508		
Switzerland	419	786	886	842	825		
Syria	216	452	495	1,452	1,280		
Turkey	4,522	8,897	13,463	12,944	11,171	9	4.2
Ukraine	...	...	...	28,600	29,650	2	11.2
UK	6,772	7,478	7,896	8,016	8,431	10	3.2
USA	24,557	22,086	24,447	28,897	25,460	4	9.6
Yugoslavia	...	...	...	2,238	1,694		

Sugar cane *thousand tonnes*

	1970	1980	1990	1994	1995	Rank	%
WORLD	586,432	769,627	1,050,888	1,089,673	1,167,535		
Angola	776	347	292	240	330		
Argentina	10,213	15,607	16,633	15,500	17,400		
Australia	17,607	23,407	24,225	34,920	37,597	7	3.2
Bangladesh	7,551	6,659	7,271	7,111	7,446		
Barbados	1,325	1,074	584	439	360		
Belize	622	1,007	1,007	1,159	1,091		
Bolivia	1,327	3,101	3,207	3,450	3,697		
Brazil	78,460	147,824	258,735	292,070	303,557	1	26.0
Burma	1,458	1,779	2,217	2,849	2,357		
Cameroon	224	1,072	1,350	1,350	1,350		
China	38,529	33,848	63,930	66,430	70,279	3	6.0
Colombia	13,167	24,667	27,357	31,200	32,000	9	2.7
Congo	672	170	358	340	440		
Congo (Zaïre)	626	832	1,581	1,350	1,300		
Costa Rica	1,837	2,551	2,610	3,200	3,450		
Cuba	60,467	69,322	76,230	39,000	36,000	8	
Dom. Rep.	8,986	9,663	7,099	6,258	5,442		
Ecuador	6,500	6,498	6,095	7,000	6,750		
Egypt	7,096	8,738	11,311	13,822	13,827		
El Salvador	1,662	2,716	3,192	3,929	4,127		
Ethiopia	1,092	1,386	1,627	1,200	1,200		
Fiji	2,603	3,783	3,832	4,064	4,110		
Guadeloupe	1,785	1,001	633	627	376		
Guatemala	2,692	5,610	9,339	11,862	13,780		
Guyana	4,081	3,986	2,725	3,149	3,209		
Haiti	2,702	2,953	1,533	1,300	1,200		
Honduras	1,368	2,809	2,784	3,078	3,139		
India	128,689	144,912	223,217	227,060	259,490	2	22.2
Indonesia	10,352	19,506	27,642	32,834	31,427	10	2.7
Iran	556	1,461	1,500	1,857	1,859		
Ivory Coast	...	1,373	1,517	1,318	1,171		
Jamaica	4,098	2,764	2,505	2,450	2,326		
Japan	2,407	2,214	2,187	1,602	1,616		
Kenya	1,645	4,197	4,725	3,780	4,300		
Madagascar	1,153	1,420	2,020	2,166	2,100		
Malawi	296	1,427	1,790	1,900	1,900		
Malaysia	203	867	1,245	1,541	1,601		
Mauritius	5,400	5,393	5,535	5,000	5,200		
Mexico	33,269	35,324	40,730	40,539	42,562	6	3.6
Mozambique	2,767	2,067	280	300	400		
Nepal	237	412	1,002	1,431	1,469		
Nicaragua	1,866	2,447	2,454	2,593	2,984		
Nigeria	556	828	903	633	636		
Pakistan	23,836	29,061	36,153	44,427	47,168	5	4.0
Panama	1,242	2,353	1,277	1,720	1,669		
Paraguay	1,215	1,605	2,910	2,799	2,576		
Peru	7,915	6,405	6,762	6,100	7,000		
Philippines	16,271	31,600	26,033	28,100	26,000		
Puerto Rico	4,952	1,984	910	570	504		
Réunion	2,026	2,300	1,852	1,656	1,817		
South Africa	14,561	17,345	18,933	15,683	16,782		
Sri Lanka	168	320	821	1,529	1,273		
Sudan	825	1,594	4,129	4,500	4,800		
Swaziland	1,548	2,743	3,846	3,786	3,440		
Taiwan	5,991	8,851	5,581	5,275	4,661		
Tanzania	1,141	1,537	1,353	1,530	1,410		
Thailand	5,856	17,747	36,963	37,823	57,974	4	5.0
Trinidad & T.	2,481	1,561	1,335	1,398	1,326		
Uganda	1,667	350	652	950	1,150		
USA	21,404	24,465	26,554	28,058	27,938		
Venezuela	4,883	4,837	7,259	6,880	6,000		
Vietnam	333	3,938	5,624	7,550	10,711		
Zambia	303	900	1,138	1,311	1,310		
Zimbabwe	1,363	2,878	3,333	3,420	3,943		

Sunflower seeds *thousand tonnes*

	1970	1980	1990	1994	1995	Rank	%
WORLD	13,174	14,412	22,291	21,865	26,277		
Albania	18	32	15	2	2		
Argentina	949	1,447	3,664	4,095	5,604	1	21.3
Australia	26	156	132	105	112		
Austria	1	2	65	88	58		
Bolivia	...	6	13	28	58		
Brazil	3	33	44	30	30		
Bulgaria	471	421	427	602	767		
Burma	10	15	105	83	117		
Canada	39	183	104	117	66		
Chile	26	26	31	12	12		
China	76	860	1,275	1,367	1,269	7	4.8
Croatia	...	...	...	26	37		
Czech Rep.	...	...	...	31	32		
Egypt	6	11	31	51	68		
France	55	280	2,389	2,053	1,987	4	7.6
Germany	...	30	82	311	137		
Greece	2	4	43	29	33		
Hungary	122	500	732	667	789	10	3.0
India	...	86	929	1,204	1,400	6	5.3
Iran	39	20	44	48	50		
Iraq	2	10	33	56	63		
Italy	9	66	355	545	534		
Kazakstan	...	...	...	97	99		
Kenya	3	15	16	15	15		
Moldova	...	...	...	149	232		
Morocco	12	18	119	48	11		
Pakistan	1	1	31	50	86		
Paraguay	1	1	21	40	42		
Portugal	1	14	47	40	26		
Romania	769	833	608	764	933	8	3.6
Russia	...	...	...	2,553	4,200	2	16.0
Slovak Rep.	...	...	...	55	81		
South Africa	106	390	532	366	468		
Spain	146	515	1,088	979	575		
Sudan	10	15	22	57	65		
Tanzania	13	37	27	30	32		
Turkey	383	638	970	740	900	9	3.4
Ukraine	...	...	...	1,700	2,860	3	10.9
USA	121	2,347	1,156	2,194	1,817	5	6.9
Uruguay	55	41	50	62	110		
Venezuela	...	...	87	27	27		
Yugoslavia	...	...	...	299	296		
Zambia	1	20	15	10	22		
Zimbabwe	3	11	64	49	22		

Sweet potatoes *thousand tonnes*

	1970	1980	1990	1994	1995	Rank	%
WORLD	111,469	134,365	124,132	125,876	136,141		
Angola	147	180	167	180	185		
Argentina	457	290	297	371	336		
Bangladesh	830	764	513	427	435		
Brazil	2,155	769	647	656	655	9	0.5
Burundi	831	488	664	601	674	8	0.5
Cameroon	134	133	151	180	200		
China	89,845	114,257	105,543	107,651	117,606	1	86.4
Congo (Zaïre)	264	333	377	385	407		
Cuba	237	320	253	190	220		
Egypt	87	92	95	152	165		
Ethiopia	110	133	152	155	155		
Guinea	80	70	85	143	130		
Haiti	280	276	220	185	185		
India	2,260	1,479	1,265	1,265	1,181	5	0.9
Indonesia	2,215	2,122	2,078	1,845	2,138	3	1.6
Japan	2,590	1,378	1,346	1,264	1,181	6	0.9
Kenya	230	351	538	630	630	10	0.5
Korea, N.	273	374	502	450	450		
Korea, S.	2,053	1,199	467	247	250		
Laos	15	84	170	112	111		
Madagascar	348	379	484	560	450		
Nigeria	139	100	36	40	40		
Papua N.G.	346	442	463	450	450		
Peru	167	149	165	142	156		
Philippines	680	1,060	664	593	579		
Rwanda	379	899	876	800	950	7	0.7
Taiwan	3,441	1,055	200	181	196		

Sweet potatoes continued

	1970	1980	1990	1994	1995	Rank	%
Tanzania	234	514	541	277	451		
Thailand	280	223	102	95	90		
Uganda	693	1,257	1,712	2,129	2,235	2	1.6
USA	586	561	532	608	585		
Vietnam	1,108	2,335	1,992	1,906	1,686	4	1.2

Tangerines *thousand tonnes*

	1970	1980	1990	1994	1995	Rank	%
WORLD	5,093	13,000	13,089	14,595	15,676		
Algeria	132	130	84	100	78		
Argentina	237	225	310	422	385		
Australia	21	28	42	59	70		
Bolivia	12	24	42	46	48		
Brazil	238	517	649	760	760	4	4.8
China	150	263	3,900	4,720	5,672	1	36.2
Cuba	10	26	14	15	16		
Cyprus	2	3	13	15	20		
Ecuador	11	31	24	25	25		
Egypt	88	81	232	250	471	10	3.0
Ethiopia	7	7	8	8	8		
France	7	28	26	22	27		
Greece	32	42	91	101	94		
Haiti	8	9	9	8	8		
Iran	40	87	425	629	599	7	3.8
Iraq	12	41	46	45	45		
Israel	57	89	130	100	130		
Italy	284	333	430	456	451		
Jamaica	12	9	18	16	16		
Japan	2,359	3,110	1,750	1,246	1,378	3	8.8
Jordan	10	13	76	85	47		
Korea, S.	150	172	600	549	625	6	4.0
Laos	6	8	14	18	18		
Lebanon	15	32	53	23	24		
Mexico	105	126	86	219	271		
Morocco	140	266	319	343	276		
New Zealand	1	4	11	12	15		
Pakistan	116	256	420	503	520	8	3.3
Paraguay	30	59	25	30	30		
Peru	14	20	46	73	83		
Philippines	22	33	44	46	47		
Portugal	16	21	22	28	35		
Spain	332	810	1,456	1,785	1,566	2	10.0
Syria	...	...	10	13	14		
Thailand	1	1	634	650	650	5	4.1
Tunisia	18	31	46	38	40		
Turkey	66	166	345	430	453		
USA	480	633	404	516	482	9	3.1
Uruguay	35	29	39	56	50		
Venezuela	...	...	45	66	66		

Tea *thousand tonnes*

	1970	1980	1990	1994	1995	Rank	%
WORLD	1,341	1,859	2,526	2,615	2,581		
Argentina	26	29	48	50	42	10	1.6
Azerbaijan	...	5	8	4	4		
Bangladesh	25	38	43	51	52	9	2.0
Bolivia	1	2	2	3	3		
Brazil	6	10	10	10	10		
Burundi	1	2	4	7	7		
Cameroon	1	2	3	3	3		
China	246	334	561	613	609	2	23.6
Congo (Zaïre)	8	6	3	3	3		
Georgia	...	121	125	62	39		
India	416	558	717	744	715	1	27.7
Indonesia	65	104	152	136	155	5	6.0
Iran	18	32	36	56	54	8	2.1
Japan	91	101	89	86	90	7	3.5
Kenya	38	93	194	209	245	4	9.5
Malawi	18	31	40	35	34		
Malaysia	3	3	6	6	6		
Mauritius	4	5	6	5	5		
Mozambique	17	20	4	2	3		
Papua N.G.	1	8	8	9	9		
Russia	...	2	2	1	2		
Rwanda	1	6	13	5	5		
South Africa	1	8	12	11	12		
Sri Lanka	215	203	227	242	246	3	9.5
Taiwan	28	24	22	25	21		

Tea continued

	1970	1980	1990	1994	1995	Rank	%
Tanzania	9	17	19	22	25		
Thailand	1	1	5	6	6		
Turkey	34	80	132	134	103	6	4.0
Uganda	18	2	7	13	15		
Vietnam	10	21	31	42	40		
Zimbabwe	3	9	16	13	15		

Tobacco *thousand tonnes*

	1970	1980	1990	1994	1995	Rank	%
WORLD	4,603	5,542	7,187	6,503	6,364		
Albania	12	18	13	4	6		
Argentina	60	61	81	82	79		
Australia	18	15	12	8	7		
Azerbaijan	...	20	62	68	68		
Bangladesh	43	44	37	38	38		
Brazil	246	397	435	519	455	4	7.1
Bulgaria	113	138	77	32	19		
Burma	53	44	52	38			
Cambodia	12	5	8	10	10		
Canada	105	100	72	70	72		
Chile	7	6	13	16	12		
China	801	1,134	2,849	2,257	2,327	1	36.6
Colombia	42	52	34	23	26		
Congo (Zaïre)	5	7	3	3	3		
Croatia	...	...	12	9	8		
Cuba	31	32	43	35	30		
Dom. Rep.	22	41	24	17	29		
France	45	47	28	27	26		
Georgia	...	...	22	3	9		
Germany	8	12	10	8	8		
Greece	88	125	144	154	135	7	2.1
Guatemala	5	10	11	14	10		
Honduras	6	7	5	5	5		
Hungary	20	21	15	12	11		
India	353	458	533	563	587	2	9.2
Indonesia	73	105	82	140	133	8	2.1
Iran	18	24	18	21	14		
Iraq	15	10	3	2	3		
Italy	79	131	202	121	124	10	1.9
Ivory Coast	2	2	5	10	10		
Japan	163	144	75	72	70		
Kenya	2	3	10	10	10		
Korea, N.	40	45	65	65	65		
Korea, S.	60	97	73	99	84		
Kyrgyzstan	...	...	59	58	58		
Macedonia	...	...	17	19	17		
Madagascar	5	3	3	2	2		
Malawi	21	53	100	99	129	9	2.0
Malaysia	3	8	12	6	10		
Mexico	72	74	38	30	14		
Moldova	...	...	73	41	25		
Morocco	3	7	7	4	4		
Nepal	7	5	6	6	6		
Nigeria	13	13	9	10	10		
Pakistan	118	71	74	100	81		
Paraguay	20	19	7	9	9		
Philippines	58	57	82	57	64		
Poland	82	75	57	43	40		
Portugal	10	7	5	5	4		
Romania	26	35	19	13	13		
Slovak Rep.	...	...	...	14	9		
South Africa	35	37	32	21	22		
Spain	24	38	49	44	42		
Sri Lanka	9	15	14	14	16		
Syria	8	13	14	14	23		
Tajikistan	...	...	...	10	10		
Tanzania	12	17	13	18	28		
Thailand	77	78	67	56	53		
Turkey	157	204	269	187	200	5	3.1
Uganda	5	3	4	7	7		
Ukraine	...	18	12	6	5		
USA	819	813	705	718	575	3	9.0
Uzbekistan	...	6	31	16	16		
Venezuela	12	17	14	11	16		
Vietnam	12	20	27	32	32		
Yemen	2	7	6	7	7		
Yugoslavia	...	...	11	14	15		
Zambia	6	4	5	7	7		
Zimbabwe	63	104	146	182	198	6	3.1

Tomatoes *thousand tonnes*

	1970	1980	1990	1994	1995	Rank	%
WORLD	34,823	52,602	74,894	78,962	84,389		
Albania	...	113	58	127	150		
Algeria	110	254	483	695	859		
Argentina	373	490	700	790	920		
Armenia	...	...	...	244	252		
Australia	177	214	339	340	425		
Azerbaijan	...	...	...	300	290		
Bangladesh	75	65	87	86	86		
Belarus	...	...	...	90	96		
Belgium	90	96	268	309	350		
Benin	15	37	68	85	109		
Bolivia	50	28	40	49	43		
Brazil	762	1,496	2,261	2,678	2,734	7	3.2
Bulgaria	711	857	788	477	530		
Cameroon	70	40	58	60	60		
Canada	350	476	573	638	605		
Chile	199	375	622	1,151	1,264		
China	2,584	4,118	7,784	12,028	12,832	1	15.2
Colombia	146	244	437	301	300		
Cuba	64	228	260	96	139		
Dom. Rep.	62	139	132	83	94		
Ecuador	25	38	83	77	64		
Egypt	1,580	2,448	4,009	5,011	5,034	5	6.0
Ethiopia	37	46	49	50	50		
France	514	826	823	799	811		
Georgia	...	...	...	230	235		
Germany	49	68	61	55	27		
Ghana	73	91	91	182	160		
Greece	976	1,719	1,893	2,017	1,798		
Guatemala	71	85	136	121	131		
Hungary	359	447	471	224	231		
India	620	1,533	4,483	4,800	4,800	6	5.7
Indonesia	310	102	227	302	260		
Iran	180	473	1,564	2,088	2,403	9	2.8
Iraq	305	347	623	863	870		
Israel	165	255	483	430	504		
Italy	3,571	4,572	5,665	5,130	5,156	4	6.1
Ivory Coast	10	15	39	129	129		
Japan	811	999	767	758	753		
Jordan	142	180	301	439	440		
Kazakstan	...	...	...	280	310		
Kenya	41	60	30	32	32		
Korea, S.	54	60	86	149	150		
Kyrgyzstan	...	...	...	133	159		
Lebanon	68	103	210	233	236		
Libya	134	197	150	135	135		
Macedonia	...	...	137	121	134		
Mexico	901	1,472	1,878	1,368	1,935	10	2.3
Moldova	...	...	...	250	330		
Morocco	246	394	835	850	624		
Netherlands	365	403	636	561	560		
New Zealand	56	51	57	66	80		
Nigeria	220	403	375	513	569		
Pakistan	...	...	195	254	276		
Paraguay	47	53	44	41	42		
Peru	60	65	85	218	171		
Philippines	97	136	184	151	161		
Poland	339	365	439	375	401		
Portugal	764	570	928	963	929		
Romania	780	1,440	839	716	731		
Russia	...	...	...	1,200	1,407		
Saudi Arabia	87	209	405	440	489		
South Africa	225	323	432	386	476		
Spain	1,687	2,170	2,930	3,109	2,706	8	3.2
Sudan	109	86	157	175	170		
Syria	211	608	472	426	431		
Tajikistan	...	...	...	180	190		
Thailand	13	65	90	110	110		
Tunisia	160	313	517	480	580		
Turkey	1,756	3,550	6,000	6,350	7,250	3	8.6
Turkmenistan	...	...	...	148	163		
Ukraine	...	1,853	1,633	1,195	1,271		
UAE	9	38	55	243	443		
UK	108	132	138	132	132		
USA	5,516	6,952	10,852	12,133	11,719	2	13.9
Uruguay	30	59	21	36	36		
Uzbekistan	...	...	...	1,040	1,000		
Venezuela	76	151	192	244	200		
Yemen	...	45	168	182	199		
Yugoslavia	...	...	181	180	203		

Watermelons *thousand tonnes*

	1970	1980	1990	1994	1995	Rank	%
WORLD	19,720	24,718	34,072	39,422	40,324		
Afghanistan	54	34	86	90	90		
Algeria	194	170	344	401	400		
Argentina	182	152	125	129	130		
Australia	36	24	56	70	70		
Azerbaijan	...	...	180	300	300		
Brazil	466	288	440	410	420		
Bulgaria	289	327	200	357	422		
Chile	159	245	74	100	85		
China	3,127	4,229	11,744	17,396	17,908	1	44.4
Colombia	3	7	41	56	56		
Egypt	919	1,197	967	716	720	7	1.8
El Salvador	41	41	76	57	58		
Georgia	...	400	500	800	800	6	2.0
Greece	555	644	624	650	683	9	1.7
Guatemala	...	...	49	55	50		
Hungary	102	182	92	61	61		
Iran	758	1,700	1,826	2,580	2,650	3	6.6
Iraq	527	465	542	460	450		
Israel	97	82	103	125	125		
Italy	748	719	661	594	611		
Japan	1,048	1,008	735	655	617	10	1.5
Jordan	34	25	59	123	99		
Kazakstan	...	...	148	250	250		
Korea, North	20	55	96	110	110		
Korea, South	130	311	623	858	900	5	2.2
Lebanon	21	31	58	71	72		
Libya	30	159	199	185	180		
Macedonia	...	...	108	111	116		
Malaysia	10	91	62	145	135		
Mexico	246	442	433	470	480		
Moldova	...	393	480	400	400		
Morocco	140	134	381	226	226		
Pakistan	1	1	404	400	420		
Paraguay	62	84	111	116	116		
Peru	48	37	41	42	42		
Philippines	63	245	79	70	75		
Russia	...	1,660	2,200	458	400		
Saudi Arabia	505	247	386	400	400		
South Africa	41	25	47	53	50		
Spain	217	545	716	585	687	8	1.7
Sudan	75	101	111	122	120		
Syria	256	770	199	293	310		
Taiwan	226	341	255	300	300		
Tajikistan	...	127	200	105	105		
Thailand	350	660	380	400	400		
Tunisia	77	205	274	280	230		
Turkey	350	3,157	3,300	3,600	3,600	2	8.9
Turkmenistan	...	...	...	250	250		
Ukraine	...	811	792	182	497		
USA	1,216	1,102	1,100	1,814	1,852	4	4.6
Uzbekistan	...	309	500	578	426		
Venezuela	32	54	81	210	210		
Vietnam	60	94	155	173	180		
Yemen	26	60	168	101	94		
Yugoslavia	...	...	201	198	267		

Whaling *number*

	1970	1980	1990	1994	1995
Minke whale					
WORLD	...	...	432	755	827
Brazil	...	902	0	0	0
Greenland	...	...	95	108	159
Japan	...	3,658	330	330	330
Korea, S.	...	925	0	0	0
Norway	...	2,002	5	280	218
Russia	...	3,879	0	0	0
Bryde's whale					
WORLD	910	522	0	0	0
Japan	0	307	0	0	0
Sei whale					
WORLD	...	102	0	0	0
Iceland	0	100	0	0	0
Fin whale					
WORLD	4,547	472	19	20	13
Greenland	0	0	19	20	12
Iceland	0	236	0	0	0
Spain	0	219	0	0	0

Whaling continued

	1970	1980	1990	1994	1995
Humpback whale					
Denmark	24	15	0	0	0
Baleen whale					
WORLD	...	**217**	**193**	**44**	**133**
Russia	...	178	162	0	84
USA	...	0	31	34	45
Sperm whale					
WORLD	...	**2,210**	**0**	**1**	**5**
Japan	...	1,192	0	0	1
Portugal	...	330	0	0	0
Longfin Pilot whale					
WORLD	...	**2,820**	**829**	**9**	**0**
Faroe Is.	...	2,773	818	1,201	0
Killer whale					
WORLD	...	**971**	**3**	**0**	**6**
Japan	...	...	3	0	0
New Zealand					6
White whale					
WORLD	...	**1,909**	**1,283**	**413**	**143**
Canada	...	774	0	0	0
Greenland	...	889	1,000	0	0
USA	...	...	239	413	143
Russia	...	236	44	0	0
Narwhal					
WORLD	...	**520**	**1,200**	**0**	**0**
Greenland	...	520	1,200	0	0
Toothed whale					
WORLD	...	**24**	...	...	...
Argentina		0	0	117	142
Australia	...	...	17	30	28
Brazil	...	...	0	240	209
Canada	...	339	3	0	0
Ecuador			0	227	0
Faroe Is.	...	...	153	266	0
France	...	...	24	53	16
Japan	...	...	47,311	...	...
Netherlands	...	...	0	103	10
New Zealand	...	...	3	40	0
Peru	...	...	2,087	1,589	0
UK	...	...	5	11	169
USA	...	...	5,151	396	393

Wheat *thousand tonnes*

	1970	1980	1990	1994	1995	Rank	%
WORLD	**329,033**	**437,556**	**559,204**	**527,202**	**541,120**		
Afghanistan	2,150	2,561	1,725	2,050	2,170		
Albania	242	500	508	420	405		
Algeria	1,359	1,270	1,257	714	1,500		
Argentina	5,873	7,993	10,292	11,306	9,185		
Australia	9,014	14,486	13,279	9,036	17,263	9	3.2
Austria	912	1,025	1,381	1,255	1,301		
Azerbaijan	...	755	850	739	598		
Bangladesh	103	803	972	1,131	1,245		
Belgium	848	955	1,418	1,554	1,578		
Brazil	1,743	2,614	3,854	2,092	1,516		
Bulgaria	2,899	3,877	5,071	3,754	3,438		
Canada	13,901	20,430	29,613	22,933	25,017	6	4.6
Chile	1,296	882	1,691	1,271	1,384		
China	31,005	57,965	94,999	99,303	102,211	1	18.9
Croatia	...	...	1,600	750	877		
Czech Rep.	2,300	3,000	4,500	3,713	3,823		
Denmark	509	678	3,616	3,725	4,481		
Egypt	1,509	1,834	3,978	4,437	5,722		
Ethiopia	643	623	860	1,313	1,650		
Finland	445	267	521	337	380		
France	14,112	21,996	33,171	30,549	30,878	4	5.7
Germany	8,471	11,248	15,767	16,481	17,816	8	3.3
Greece	1,867	2,703	2,642	2,417	2,214		
Hungary	3,410	4,862	6,249	4,874	4,614		
India	20,859	34,599	53,031	59,131	65,767	2	12.2
Iran	3,946	5,700	7,605	10,823	11,228		
Iraq	1,080	854	1,055	1,342	1,050		
Ireland	375	240	577	572	588		
Italy	9,756	9,017	8,312	8,166	7,946		
Japan	557	579	898	565	444		
Kazakstan	...	18,203	16,000	9,052	6,490		
Kyrgyzstan	...	662	475	566	677		
Lithuania	...	336	1,200	537	612		

Wheat continued

	1970	1980	1990	1994	1995	Rank	%
Mexico	2,141	2,771	4,122	4,151	3,468		
Moldova	...	1,151	1,100	659	1,348		
Morocco	1,819	1,500	4,160	5,523	1,091		
Nepal	230	444	840	873	942		
Netherlands	675	867	1,022	981	1,167		
New Zealand	357	325	168	227	245		
Pakistan	6,796	10,698	14,433	15,213	17,002	10	3.1
Poland	4,925	4,197	8,919	7,658	8,668		
Portugal	614	331	511	463	360		
Romania	4,433	5,634	6,867	6,135	7,667		
Russia	...	42,783	50,000	32,129	30,118	5	5.6
Saudi Arabia	111	150	3,689	2,818	2,453		
Slovak Rep.	1,100	1,500	2,100	2,145	1,938		
South Africa	1,461	1,966	1,968	1,840	2,125		
Spain	4,734	4,435	5,236	4,302	2,958		
Sweden	958	1,086	1,825	1,345	1,554		
Switzerland	378	403	604	584	631		
Syria	763	1,877	1,743	3,703	4,184		
Tunisia	520	837	1,109	503	530		
Turkey	11,423	17,054	18,887	17,514	18,015	7	3.3
Turkmenistan	...	77	130	1,063	878		
Ukraine	...	19,189	30,500	13,857	16,273		
UK	4,140	8,034	14,143	13,314	14,310		
USA	40,034	66,242	61,204	63,168	59,400	3	11.0
Uruguay	379	377	382	447	421		
Uzbekistan	...	531	550	1,362	2,347		
Yugoslavia	...	...	3,900	3,249	2,949		

Wine *thousand tonnes*

	1970	1980	1990	1994	1995	Rank	%
WORLD	**28,884**	**34,790**	**27,769**	**25,644**	**25,263**		
Algeria	888	274	48	50	50		
Argentina	1,935	2,364	1,628	1,817	1,644	5	6.5
Australia	259	375	446	587	503	10	2.0
Austria	239	265	295	265	223		
Azerbaijan	...	...	...	100	100		
Belarus	...	...	...	50	35		
Brazil	179	258	297	302	313		
Bulgaria	436	455	256	189	220		
Canada	39	45	33	30	30		
Chile	443	591	359	360	317		
China	...	38	275	380	400		
Croatia	...	...	...	189	178		
Cyprus	45	54	58	49	56		
Czech Rep.	...	...	...	50	46		
France	6,298	7,063	5,623	5,464	5,623	1	22.3
Georgia	...	...	...	80	110		
Germany	754	700	1,156	1,041	1,105	6	4.4
Greece	454	447	418	305	384		
Hungary	476	491	460	369	329		
Israel	33	18	13	13	13		
Italy	6,825	8,075	5,833	5,928	5,620	2	22.2
Japan	16	55	57	52	53		
Kazakstan	...	...	...	15	25		
Lebanon	4	4	12	30	30		
Macedonia	...	...	...	88	91		
Mexico	17	187	171	203	147		
Moldova	...	...	...	89	93		
Morocco	100	95	40	40	24		
New Zealand	18	44	50	41	56		
Portugal	959	1,127	976	652	713	8	2.8
Romania	584	880	478	537	550	9	2.2
Russia	...	...	...	296	280		
Slovak Rep.	...	...	...	69	66		
Slovenia	...	...	...	83	78		
South Africa	489	703	964	866	950	7	3.8
Spain	2,485	4,142	2,407	2,100	1,964	4	7.8
Switzerland	91	88	136	119	118		
Tunisia	79	60	30	28	28		
Turkey	44	17	23	27	27		
Ukraine	...	...	...	120	106		
USA	1,183	1,678	1,745	1,615	2,023	3	8.0
Uruguay	86	70	86	71	85		
Uzbekistan	...	...	...	90	90		
Yugoslavia	...	...	...	306	280		

Wood – coniferous roundwood
million cubic metres

	1961–65 av.	1970	1980	1990	1993	1994	Rank	%
WORLD	**959**	**1,081**	**1,190**	**1,406**	**1,121**	**1,111**		
Afghanistan	1.7	2.3	2.4	2.4	2.5	2.7		
Algeria	1.0	0.8	1.1	1.5	1.6	1.6		
Argentina	0.5	0.6	0.9	2.4	2.6	2.6		
Australia	1.8	2.5	4.3	7.5	8.5	9.5		
Austria	9.4	10.0	12.1	14.0	10.5	12.6		
Belarus	...	...	...	...	5.3	5.3		
Belgium	1.4	1.5	1.5	4.0	2.8	2.9		
Brazil	16.9	26.1	38.0	46.4	48.7	49.0	6	4.4
Bulgaria	1.5	1.5	1.2	1.1	0.9	0.9		
Canada	89.9	110.7	145.3	167.0	167.0	175.0	2	15.8
Chile	2.2	3.7	8.0	13.9	20.3	21.1	10	1.9
China	65.2	77.1	112.6	136.0	144.0	146.0	3	13.1
Czech Rep.	...	...	...	...	9.6	11.5		
Denmark	0.9	1.3	1.2	1.5	1.5	1.5		
Estonia	...	...	...	...	1.4	1.4		
Ethiopia	1.8	2.4	2.3	2.9	3.0	3.0		
Finland	34.1	32.6	39.1	35.1	34.6	40.1	7	3.6
France	13.6	15.0	18.1	23.5	20.8	23.3	9	2.1
Germany	23.3	25.1	31.0	30.9	23.4	26.8	8	2.4
Guatemala	3.1	2.8	4.9	9.2	9.1	9.2		
Honduras	2.3	2.4	2.3	2.5	2.4	2.5		
India	3.5	4.3	8.0	9.9	10.3	10.5		
Ireland	0.2	0.3	0.3	1.5	1.8	1.9		
Italy	1.5	1.4	1.7	1.4	1.5	1.6		
Japan	34.7	26.8	21.4	19.0	19.0	19.0		
Kenya	0.8	1.0	1.4	1.8	1.9	1.9		
Korea, N.	2.7	3.1	2.4	2.7	2.9	2.9		
Korea, S.	6.5	7.3	5.6	4.3	4.3	4.3		
Latvia	...	...	...	...	3.8	3.3		
Lithuania	...	...	...	...	1.3	2.6		
Mexico	5.9	7.5	9.3	11.3	10.0	10.2		
Mongolia	1.1	2.0	2.2	1.3	0.5	0.5		
New Zealand	5.5	8.4	9.7	11.8	15.9	16.8		
Norway	8.4	7.7	8.3	10.7	9.0	8.2		
Pakistan	0.7	1.0	1.0	1.6	1.7	1.7		
Poland	14.1	15.3	16.8	13.8	14.1	13.6		
Portugal	4.0	4.5	5.5	6.7	5.3	5.1		
Romania	6.4	7.3	7.0	4.5	2.3	3.9		
Russia	...	...	...	...	116.8	77.0	4	6.9
Slovak Rep.	...	...	...	...	2.9	3.0		
Slovenia	...	...	...	...	0.7	1.2		
South Africa	2.5	4.0	6.3	7.2	8.5	8.3		
Spain	5.7	5.6	7.3	10.2	7.4	7.4		
Swaziland	0.4	0.8	1.4	1.6	1.7	1.7		
Sweden	40.5	53.3	41.7	45.7	47.5	50.8	5	4.6
Switzerland	2.8	3.0	3.1	5.1	3.2	3.5		
Turkey	5.8	10.4	14.2	9.4	8.9	8.2		
UK	1.4	1.8	2.6	5.3	6.6	7.3		
USA	214.0	246.0	262.8	327.0	280.0	275.0	1	24.8

Roundwood is timber as it is felled.

Wood – coniferous sawnwood
million cubic metres

	1961–65 av.	1970	1980	1990	1993	1994	Rank	%
WORLD	**277**	**311**	**334**	**373**	**307**	**304**		
Afghanistan	0.20	0.30	0.40	0.38	0.38	0.38		
Australia	0.70	0.80	1.1	1.4	1.7	1.9		
Austria	4.4	5.1	6.3	7.2	6.6	7.2	10	2.4
Belarus	...	...	...	...	0.94	0.94		
Belgium	0.30	0.40	3.4	0.93	0.90	0.93		
Brazil	2.9	4.5	7.1	7.9	8.6	8.6	9	2.8
Bulgaria	0.70	1.0	1.0	0.86	0.19	0.19		
Canada	21.3	25.4	42.9	53.7	58.7	60.6	2	19.9
Chile	0.50	0.70	2.0	2.9	2.7	2.9		
China	7.0	9.0	13.2	15.1	15.6	15.5	5	5.1
Czech Rep.	...	...	...	...	2.8	2.9		
Denmark	0.30	0.40	0.40	0.50	0.34	0.34		
Finland	6.9	7.1	10.2	7.4	8.3	9.7	8	3.2
France	5.1	5.7	5.7	7.0	6.2	7.0		
Germany	8.8	9.0	10.2	12.4	10.4	12.4	7	4.1
Honduras	0.50	0.40	0.50	0.30	0.33	0.36		

Wood – coniferous sawnwood continued

	1961–65 av.	1970	1980	1990	1993	1994	Rank	%
Hungary	0.30	0.40	0.50	0.33	0.12	0.09		
India	0.50	0.70	1.5	2.5	2.5	2.5		
Ireland	...	0.03	0.10	0.40	0.62	0.70		
Italy	0.80	0.60	1.1	0.88	0.80	0.80		
Japan	23.8	32.8	30.0	26.4	23.3	22.8	3	7.5
Korea, S.	0.50	0.60	1.6	2.9	2.7	2.7		
Latvia	...	...	...	...	0.40	0.75		
Lithuania	...	...	...	...	0.63	0.70		
Mexico	1.0	1.4	1.5	2.0	2.1	2.4		
Mongolia	0.20	0.40	0.50	0.50	0.16	0.16		
New Zealand	1.6	1.8	2.0	2.2	2.8	2.8		
Norway	1.6	2.0	2.5	2.4	2.3	2.4		
Poland	5.9	5.9	5.9	3.4	3.7	3.9		
Portugal	1.1	1.6	2.0	1.8	1.3	1.2		
Romania	2.8	2.8	2.1	1.4	0.86	0.86		
Russia	...	...	...	...	32.8	22.4	4	7.4
Slovak Rep.	...	...	...	...	0.35	0.40		
Slovenia	...	...	...	...	0.38	0.38		
South Africa	0.70	1.1	1.4	1.7	1.3	1.4		
Spain	1.1	1.6	1.6	2.7	2.2	2.2		
Sweden	8.7	12.0	11.1	11.8	12.5	13.6	6	4.5
Switzerland	1.1	1.3	1.5	1.8	1.3	1.2		
Turkey	0.90	1.8	3.6	3.4	3.2	2.3		
UK	0.30	0.30	1.1	1.9	2.0	2.1		
USA	65.5	65.0	66.6	84.5	77.7	77.2	1	25.4
Yugoslavia	...	...	...	...	1.3	1.3		

Sawnwood is timber in its first stage of processing – sawn into rectangular forms.

Wood – nonconiferous roundwood

million cubic metres

	1961–65 av.	1970	1980	1990	1993	1994	Rank	%
WORLD	**1,162**	**1,315**	**1,632**	**1,960**	**2,064**	**2,092**		
Afghanistan	3.5	4.2	3.9	3.7	4.3	4.6		
Albania	1.1	1.6	1.5	1.4	0.6	0.4		
Angola	5.9	7.3	4.3	4.9	5.5	5.7		
Argentina	10.4	11.2	7.3	7.4	7.2	7.2		
Australia	12.1	11.0	12.6	12.4	11.9	9.5		
Austria	1.6	1.8	2.3	2.4	2.3	2.3		
Bangladesh	7.8	...	23.8	28.7	31.0	11.4		
Belarus	...	...	...	...	4.7	4.7		
Benin	1.7	...	3.6	4.8	5.2	5.4		
Bhutan	...	...	3.2	1.3	1.4	1.4		
Bolivia	4.4	4.2	1.4	1.5	2.0	2.0		
Brazil	117	133	146	177	186	189	3	9.0
Bulgaria	3.9	3.6	2.9	2.7	2.7	2.7		
Burkina Faso	3.5		6.6	8.6	9.3	9.4		
Burma	13.4	15.6	18.2	21.5	22.4	10.9		
Burundi	0.7	0.8	3.1	4.2	4.6	4.7		
Cambodia	3.6	4.0	4.7	6.3	6.9	7.1		
Cameroon	6.4	7.6	10.2	13.0	13.6	10.0		
Canada	9.5	10.7	13.6	13.1	12.9	9.9		
Cen. Afr. Rep.	1.9	2.3	3.0	3.5	3.7	3.8		
Chad	2.9	3.3	1.2	1.5	1.6	1.6		
Chile	4.4	4.0	5.6	8.1	9.6	9.9		
China	81.4	95.2	121	145	154	157	5	7.5
Colombia	24.9	26.6	13.9	16.1	16.5	10.5		
Congo	1.7	2.1	2.3	3.7	3.6	3.6		
Congo (Zaïre)	12.0	14.0	26.7	38.0	41.8	12.3	8	2.1
Costa Rica	2.0	2.8	3.4	3.9	4.2	4.3		
Croatia	...	...	...	...	2.1	2.4		
Cuba	2.2	1.8	2.8	2.6	2.6	2.6		
Dom. Rep.	1.7	1.8	0.5	0.6	0.5	0.5		
Ecuador	2.4	2.8	5.6	6.6	3.7	4.3		
Egypt	0.1	0.2	1.8	2.4	2.6	2.6		
El Salvador	2.7	2.4	3.7	5.9	6.2	6.4		
Ethiopia	18.6	20.8	30.1	39.2	42.3	12.1	10	2.0
Finland	12.1	12.5	8.0	8.2	7.6	7.8		
France	19.7	19.8	20.7	21.3	18.6	10.7		
Gabon	2.6	3.0	3.1	4.1	4.4	4.4		
Germany	10.2	10.4	12.3	13.7	9.8	9.3		
Ghana	9.6	10.1	10.6	14.3	19.9	11.1		
Greece	2.5	2.3	2.0	1.9	1.9	1.9		
Guatemala	0.6	4.2	1.1	1.4	3.9	4.1		
Guinea	2.3	2.8	3.2	3.9	4.4	4.5		
Haiti	3.0	3.4	4.0	4.8	5.1	5.2		

Wood – nonconiferous roundwood continued

	1961–65 av.	1970	1980	1990	1993	1994	Rank	%
Honduras	1.3	1.7	2.6	3.6	3.7	3.8		
Hungary	3.7	4.8	5.8	5.5	4.0	4.0		
India	91.2	107	204	252	266	271	1	13.0
Indonesia	86.0	107	145	174	184	186	4	8.9
Iran	6.5	7.0	6.4	6.6	6.9	6.9		
Italy	9.8	13.7	7.3	6.6	7.3	7.9		
Ivory Coast	7.2	9.0	11.2	12.1	12.2	9.8		
Japan	26.0	23.0	13.0	9.8	6.9	6.9		
Kenya	8.8	10.3	15.7	22.2	24.8	11.2		
Korea, N.	1.4	1.6	2.0	2.0	1.9	1.9		
Korea, S.	2.9	3.3	3.0	2.1	2.1	2.1		
Laos	2.4	2.8	2.6	3.6	4.0	4.0		
Latvia	...	...	...	...	1.6	2.9		
Liberia	1.2	1.6	3.3	3.8	3.7	3.7		
Madagascar	3.7	5.3	6.1	8.4	9.0	9.1		
Malawi	3.5	4.2	5.8	8.6	9.7	10.0		
Malaysia	12.9	11.5	34.0	47.3	45.0	12.2	9	2.1
Mali	2.3	2.7	4.1	5.6	6.1	6.3		
Mexico	6.7	9.0	8.8	10.4	10.9	9.4		
Morocco	1.8	2.2	0.9	1.1	1.1	1.1		
Mozambique	7.6	8.5	12.8	15.3	15.4	10.2		
Nepal	7.7	8.8	14.0	18.0	19.5	10.8		
Nicaragua	1.9	1.9	2.6	2.9	3.1	3.3		
Niger	1.9	2.3	3.6	5.0	5.5	5.7		
Nigeria	46.6	56.9	73.0	88.8	96.4	12.6	6	4.7
Pakistan	6.2	17.6	16.3	25.0	26.5	11.3		
Panama	1.6	1.4	1.8	1.0	1.0	1.0		
Papua N.G.	3.8	4.7	7.0	8.1	8.1	8.1		
Paraguay	2.4	3.7	5.8	7.2	7.2	7.2		
Peru	4.7	5.7	8.1	7.7	8.0	9.6		
Philippines	24.9	33.7	34.8	37.0	38.0	11.9		
Poland	2.6	3.2	4.0	3.8	4.5	4.8		
Portugal	1.9	2.0	3.0	4.5	4.9	4.7		
Romania	14.8	15.0	10.7	8.1	6.6	7.9		
Russia	...	...	...	...	57.9	12.5	7	2.1
Rwanda	3.0	3.7	4.8	5.6	5.7	5.7		
Senegal	2.1	2.5	3.0	4.0	4.3	4.4		
Sierra Leone	2.7	2.7	2.4	2.9	3.1	3.2		
Slovak Rep.	...	...	...	...	2.3	2.3		
Somalia	2.4	3.0	4.6	7.5	7.7	7.8		
South Africa	4.1	5.6	12.5	12.8	13.6	10.4		
Spain	9.2	8.1	5.1	5.3	6.4	6.4		
Sri Lanka	4.0	4.7	7.9	9.0	9.3	9.5		
Sudan	19.7	21.0	6.3	8.4	8.9	9.1		
Sweden	6.0	6.7	7.5	7.1	6.5	5.7		
Tanzania	25.9	31.4	22.6	31.0	33.6	11.7		
Thailand	16.0	18.7	30.6	34.0	34.6	11.8		
Tunisia	1.2	1.4	1.7	2.1	2.3	2.3		
Turkey	5.2	6.4	8.4	6.3	10.0	8.6		
Uganda	11.5	14.0	10.0	13.6	15.1	10.3		
UK	1.1	1.5	1.3	1.1	0.7	0.9		
USA	88.6	82.0	147	183	209	212	2	10.1
Uruguay	1.0	1.0	2.2	2.9	3.2	3.2		
Venezuela	5.6	7.0	1.2	1.5	1.8	1.8		
Vietnam	14.9	17.6	22.3	31.7	33.3	11.6		
Yugoslavia	...	...	...	...	2.1	2.4		
Zambia	3.8	4.7	5.0	7.0	7.7	8.0		
Zimbabwe	4.5	5.4	6.0	7.4	7.4	7.5		

Roundwood is timber as it is felled.

Wood – nonconiferous sawnwood

million cubic metres

	1961–65 av.	1970	1980	1990	1993	1994	Rank	%
WORLD	**77.7**	**93.1**	**116**	**132**	**114**	**109**		
Albania	0.10	0.10	0.10	0.30	0.00	0.00		
Angola	0.10	0.20	0.01	0.05	0.05	0.05		
Argentina	0.70	0.60	0.70	0.82	0.64	0.64		
Australia	2.4	2.5	2.1	1.7	1.5	1.6		
Austria	0.20	0.20	0.40	0.30	0.23	0.23		
Bangladesh	0.30	...	0.10	0.08	0.08	0.08		
Belarus	...	...	...	...	0.60	0.60		
Belgium	0.30	0.30	0.30	0.30	0.30	0.30		
Bolivia	...	0.10	0.20	0.10	0.26	0.35		
Brazil	2.8	3.5	7.7	9.3	10.0	10.0	3	9.2
Brunei	...	0.04	0.10	0.09	0.09	0.09		

Wood – nonconiferous sawnwood continued

	1961–65 av.	1970	1980	1990	1993	1994	Rank	%
Bulgaria	0.90	0.70	0.40	0.30	0.07	0.07		
Burma	0.50	0.60	0.70	0.30	0.30	0.30		
Cambodia	0.04	0.03	0.04	0.07	0.12	0.12		
Cameroon	0.10	0.10	0.40	0.49	0.47	0.47		
Canada	1.1	1.3	1.4	1.2	1.1	1.0		
Chile	0.50	0.30	0.30	0.40	0.45	0.44		
China	4.2	5.6	7.8	8.1	9.7	9.7	4	8.9
Colombia	0.90	1.8	0.90	0.57	0.57	0.57		
Congo (Zaïre)	0.20	0.20	0.10	0.10	0.10	0.10		
Costa Rica	0.30	0.40	0.50	0.40	0.79	0.79		
Croatia	...	...	...	...	0.50	0.50		
Czech Rep.	...	...	...	...	0.26	0.26		
Denmark	0.30	0.50	0.40	0.40	0.25	0.25		
Ecuador	0.90	0.70	0.90	1.6	0.16	0.20		
Finland	0.10	0.20	0.09	0.09	0.07	0.08		
France	2.8	3.6	3.9	3.9	3.0	3.2	8	2.9
Germany	2.1	2.3	2.6	2.3	1.2	1.2		
Ghana	0.40	0.40	0.20	0.47	0.48	0.58		
Greece	0.10	0.10	0.20	0.20	0.13	0.13		
Guatemala	...	0.01	0.01	0.01	0.16	0.17		
Hong Kong	0.20	0.20	0.20	0.40	0.40	0.40		
Hungary	0.50	0.50	0.80	0.80	0.36	0.33		
India	1.4	2.0	9.4	14.9	14.9	14.9	2	13.7
Indonesia	1.7	1.7	4.8	9.0	8.2	8.0	6	7.3
Iran	0.20	0.10	0.10	0.17	0.17	0.17		
Italy	1.1	1.7	1.5	1.1	0.90	1.0		
Ivory Coast	0.20	0.30	0.70	0.75	0.57	0.70		
Japan	6.1	9.8	7.0	3.4	3.0	2.9	9	2.7
Korea, S.	0.10	0.50	1.4	1.0	0.50	0.50		
Laos	...	0.03	0.04	0.10	0.20	0.20		
Liberia	0.10	0.10	0.10	0.09	0.09	0.09		
Madagascar	0.10	0.10	0.20	0.20	0.14	0.06		
Malaysia	1.7	2.5	6.4	8.8	9.3	8.8	5	8.1
Mexico	0.10	0.05	0.30	0.34	0.41	0.29		
Nepal	0.20	0.20	0.20	0.60	0.60	0.60		
Netherlands	0.20	0.20	0.30	0.30	0.20	0.20		
Nicaragua	0.10	0.10	0.20	0.05	0.04	0.04		
Nigeria	0.30	1.0	2.8	2.7	2.7	2.7	10	2.5
Pakistan	...	0.70	0.10	1.1	0.90	0.60		
Papua N.G.	2.4	0.10	0.10	0.07	0.07	0.07		
Paraguay	0.10	0.20	0.70	0.20	0.30	0.30		
Peru	0.10	0.20	0.60	0.50	0.59	0.71		
Philippines	1.1	1.3	1.5	0.80	0.40	0.40		
Poland	0.90	1.0	1.3	0.70	0.56	0.66		
Portugal	0.10	0.20	0.20	0.30	0.19	0.43		
Romania	1.8	2.5	2.5	1.6	1.6	0.86		
Russia	...	...	...	...	8.1	5.5	7	5.0
Slovak Rep.	...	...	...	...	0.20	0.30		
Slovenia	...	...	...	...	0.13	0.13		
Somalia	...	0.01	0.01	0.01	0.13	0.13		
South Africa	0.10	0.10	0.20	0.20	0.01	0.01		
Spain	0.60	0.70	0.50	0.60	0.60	0.60		
Sweden	0.20	0.20	0.20	0.20	0.20	0.20		
Switzerland	0.10	0.20	0.20	0.20	0.10	0.10		
Thailand	1.5	1.2	1.5	1.2	0.70	0.70		
Turkey	0.30	0.50	1.0	1.6	2.1	1.7		
UK	0.70	0.50	0.70	0.30	0.16	0.16		
USA	15.9	16.6	17.4	25.3	17.6	16.9	1	15.5
Uruguay	0.06	0.05	0.06	0.20	0.19	0.19		
Venezuela	0.20	0.03	0.30	0.20	0.22	0.22		
Vietnam	0.40	0.50	0.40	0.80	0.60	0.60		

Sawnwood is timber in its first stage of processing – sawn into rectangular forms.

Woodpulp *million tonnes*

	1970	1980	1990	1993	1994	Rank	%
WORLD	**104.4**	**126**	**155**	**151**	**155**		
Argentina	0.2	0.3	0.6	0.7	0.7		
Australia	0.7	0.7	1	1	1		
Austria	1	1.3	1.5	1.4	1.6		
Bangladesh	...	0.04	0.1	0.1	0.1		
Belgium	0.3	0.4	0.5	0.3	0.4		
Brazil	1	3.1	4.3	5.4	5.8	6	3.7
Bulgaria	0.1	0.3	0.1	0.1	0.1		
Canada	16.6	20	23	22.8	24.7	2	15.9
Chile	0.4	0.8	0.8	1.9	1.95		
China	1.2	1.3	2.1	2.4	2.7	8	1.7

Woodpulp continued

	1970	1980	1990	1993	1994	Rank	%
Colombia	0.04	0.1	0.2	0.2	0.2		
Czech Rep.	...	...	...	0.7	0.8		
Denmark	0.1	0.1	0.1	0.1	0.1		
Finland	6.5	7.2	8.9	9.4	10.1	5	6.5
France	1.8	1.8	2.4	2.5	2.7	9	1.7
Germany	2.5	2.7	2.9	2	1.9		
India	0.1	0.5	1	1.1	1.1		
Indonesia	0.001	0.05	0.7	1.3	1.3		
Italy	1	0.7	0.6	0.4	0.5		
Japan	9	0.8	11.3	10.6	10.6	3	6.8
Korea, S.	0.1	0.2	0.3	0.4	0.5		
Mexico	0.3	0.4	0.5	0.2	0.2		
Morocco	0.05	0.1	0.1	0.2	0.2		
Netherlands	0.2	0.2	0.2	0.1	0.1		
New Zealand	0.6	1.1	1.2	1.3	1.3		
Norway	2.2	1.5	2.2	2.1	2.3	10	1.5
Philippines	0.04	0.1	0.2	0.2	0.2		
Poland	0.6	0.6	0.7	0.7	0.8		
Portugal	0.4	0.6	1.4	1.5	1.5		
Romania	0.4	0.7	0.5	0.4	0.2		
Russia	...	...	...	5.1	3.8	7	2.5
Slovak Rep.	...	...	...	0.2	0.2		
South Africa	0.6	1.1	1.9	1.9	1.5		
Spain	0.6	1.3	1.6	1.3	1.5		
Swaziland	0.1	0.2	0.2	0.2	0.2		
Sweden	8.1	8.7	10	10.3	10.4	4	6.7
Switzerland	0.3	0.3	0.3	0.3	0.3		
Turkey	0.1	0.3	0.3	0.3	0.3		
UK	0.4	0.3	0.7	0.6	0.6		
USA	39.5	46.2	57.2	58.3	59.8	1	38.6
(former) Yugo.	0.5	0.7	0.8	0.7	0.7		

Wool – greasy   *thousand tonnes*

	1970	1980	1990	1994	1995	Rank	%
WORLD	2,867	2,784	3,039	2,743	2,587		
Afghanistan	26	23	17	18	19		
Albania	2.0	3.0	2.6	3.0	3.0		
Algeria	13	20	47	50	50		
Argentina	169	152	139	88	80	6	3.1
Armenia	...	4.8	2.8	1.9	1.9		
Australia	899	705	818	831	732	1	28.3
Azerbaijan	...	11	11	8.0	8.0		
Bolivia	7.0	9.0	7.6	7.8	7.8		
Brazil	32	32	29	26	25		
Bulgaria	29	35	27	12	9.0		
Canada	2.0	1.0	1.4	1.6	1.6		
Chile	23	21	17	19	19		
China	60	173	239	255	277	3	10.7
Ecuador	2.0	3.0	1.3	1.7	1.7		
Egypt	3.0	2.0	1.9	2.1	2.1		
Ethiopia	...	12	12	12	12		
Falkland Is.	2.0	2.0	1.6	2.6	2.4		
France	20	22	22	22	22		
Georgia	...	6.2	6.2	2.5	2.0		
Germany	10	16	20	15	15		
Greece	8.0	10	9.7	9.8	10		
Hungary	10	12	6.7	3.9	3.9		
India	37	35	41	44	44		
Indonesia	5.0	12	18	20	22		
Iran	19	33	45	50	51		
Iraq	16	11	21	17	16		
Ireland	10	11	17	13	13		
Italy	12	13	14	13	13		
Jordan	3.0	2.0	3.3	4.2	4.2		
Kazakstan	...	104	108	75	58	9	2.2
Kyrgyzstan	...	33	39	35	35		
Lesotho	4.0	3.0	2.8	5.2	5.2		
Libya	4.0	8.0	7.7	6.8	6.6		
Macedonia	...	...	2.6	3.1	2.9		
Mexico	8.0	7.0	5.1	3.9	4.1		
Moldova	...	2.6	3.1	2.9	2.7		
Mongolia	19	21	21	20	20		
Morocco	16	14	35	36	36		
Namibia	4.0	5.0	1.6	1.9	1.9		
Nepal	4.0	1.0	0.8	0.6	0.6		
Netherlands	4.5	2.0	4.0	4.0	4.0		
New Zealand	332	353	318	284	282	2	10.9
Norway	5.0	5.0	5.0	5.5	5.5		

Wool – greasy continued

	1970	1980	1990	1994	1995	Rank	%
Pakistan	20	40	47	52	53	10	2.1
Peru	13	11	10	9.9	9.8		
Poland	9.0	12	14	3.1	2.5		
Portugal	9.0	9.0	8.9	8.7	8.6		
Romania	30	37	35	25	24		
Russia	...	224	227	122	94	4	3.6
Saudi Arabia	4.0	3.0	6.4	7.3	7.4		
South Africa	137	103	98	70	61	8	2.4
Spain	33	21	30	31	31		
Sudan	10	15	20	28	30		
Syria	14	20	32	24	26		
Tajikistan	...	5.0	4.6	3.0	3.0		
Tanzania	...	4.0	3.6	4.0	4.0		
Tunisia	5.0	9.0	12	13	13		
Turkey	47	61	39	37	37		
Turkmenistan	...	14	16	9.2	9.2		
Ukraine	...	28	30	19	14		
UK	47	50	73	67	67	7	2.6
USA	85	48	40	32	29		
Uruguay	81	68	90	90	85	5	3.3
Uzbekistan	...	24	26	26	26		
Yemen	4.4	3.0	3.7	4.1	4.1		
Yugoslavia	...	...	4.7	3.9	3.9		
Zimbabwe	...	9.0	1.2	0.9	0.9		

Wool – scoured   *thousand tonnes*

	1970	1980	1990	1994	1995	Rank	%
WORLD	1,666	1,671	1,679	1,693	1,641		
Afghanistan	14	13	8.1	9.9	10.5		
Albania	1	2	1.5	1.8	1.9		
Algeria	6	10	26	26	26		
Argentina	91	90	77	48	44	8	2.7
Australia	511	421	672	540	540	1	32.9
Azerbaijan	...	...	...	4.8	4.8		
Bolivia	4	5	3.8	4	4		
Brazil	20	19	18	16	16		
Bulgaria	15	18	13	5.7	3.5		
Canada	1	0.7	0.9	1	1		
Chile	12	10	8.4	9.5	9.4		
China	36	104	122	130	141	3	8.6
Egypt	2	2	1.6	1.8	1.8		
Ethiopia	6	6	6	6	6		
Falkland Is.	1	2	1.7	1.7	1.7		
France	9	11	12	12	12		
Germany	6	7	9.5	7	7		
Greece	4	5	5.5	5.5	5.5		
Hungary	5	5	2.7	1.5	1.1		
Iceland	1	1	0.6	0.5	0.5		
India	23	23	27.7	29	30		
Iran	11	18	25	27	28		
Iraq	7	6	11.5	9	9		
Ireland	8	7	9.2	7.4	7.4		
Italy	6	6	6.8	6.2	6.2		
Jordan	1	1	1.8	2.3	2.3		
Kazakstan	...	...	...	55	54	5	3.3
Kyrgyzstan	...	...	...	21	21		
Lesotho	2	1	1.5	2.6	2.6		
Libya	1	2	2.1	1.8	1.8		
Mexico	4	3	2.5	1.9	2.1		
Moldova	...	...	...	1.7	1.6		
Mongolia	11	12	12	12	12		
Morocco	6	6	16.6	16.5	16.5		
Namibia	2	3	0.9	1.1	1.1		
Nepal	2	0.3	0.4	0.4	0.4		
New Zealand	237	255	238	214	213	2	13.0
Norway	3	3	3.4	3.5	3.5		
Pakistan	12	24	28	31	32	10	2.0
Peru	7	6	5	5	4.9		
Poland	5	8	8.3	1.9	1.5		
Portugal	3	4	3.6	3.5	3.5		
Romania	18	22	21	17	16		
Russia	...	...	...	73.3	56	4	3.4
Saudi Arabia	2	2	3.5	4	4.1		
South Africa	68	51	49	40	35	9	2.1
Spain	13	13	17	18	18		
Sudan	4	6	9.8	14	15		
Syria	7	10	16	12	13		
Tajikistan				1.8	1.8		

Wool – scoured continued

	1970	1980	1990	1994	1995	Rank	%
Tanzania	1	2	1.8	2	2		
Tunisia	2	4	5.5	5.9	6		
Turkey	26	34	26	22	20		
Turkmenistan	...	...	...	5.5	11		
Ukraine	...	...	...	9.3	6.9		
UK	31	38	53	47	47	7	2.9
USA	40	26	21	16	15		
Uruguay	49	42	54	51	48	6	2.9
Uzbekistan	...	...	...	16	16		
Yemen	1	2	2.2	2.3	2.3		
Yugoslavia	7	6	6	6	6		
Yugoslavia	...	...	...	2.4	2.4		
Zimbabwe	2	5	0.7	0.5	0.6		

Yams   *thousand tonnes*

	1980	1990	1994	1995	Rank	%
WORLD	11,579	21,289	32,255	32,899		
Benin	687	1,078	1,250	1,250	4	3.8
Brazil	179	215	215	215		
Burkina Faso	71	42	38	38		
Cameroon	203	81	110	110		
Cen. Afr. Rep.	153	220	250	250	8	0.8
Chad	163	230	240	240	9	0.7
Colombia	143	64	44	44		
Congo	13	12	15	16		
Congo (Zaïre)	222	282	315	315	6	1.0
Dom. Rep.	14	9	9	9		
Ethiopia	276	...	263	263	7	0.8
Gabon	80	107	120	120		
Ghana	614	1,186	1,700	2,234	3	6.8
Guinea	64	85	114	114		
Haiti	112	170	190	190		
Ivory Coast	2,079	2,561	2,824	2,824	2	8.6
Jamaica	142	160	234	234	10	0.7
Japan	144	184	181	181		
Liberia	15	16	30	30		
Mali	15	7	11	11		
Nigeria	17,000	13,396	23,153	23,264	1	70.7
Panama	19	15	14	14		
Papua N.G.	176	212	222	222		
Philippines	21	24	30	32		
Puerto Rico	15	10	7	5		
Solomon Is.	18	21	20	21		
Sudan	114	109	128	125		
Togo	498	391	375	375	5	1.1
Tonga	34	32	31	31		
Venezuela	33	40	56	56		

Mineral and manufactured products

Aluminium *thousand tonnes*

	1970	1980	1990	1994	1995	Rank	%
WORLD	**12,427**	**19,931**	**25,168**	**25,783**	**26,589**		
Argentina	0	140	166	190	198		
Australia	224	342	1,266	1,365	1,330	5	5.0
Austria	97	109	159	53	47		
Bahrain	0	126	213	453	460		
Brazil	62	311	930	1,262	1,279	6	4.8
Cameroon	52	43	88	81	79		
Canada	994	1,133	1,651	2,351	2,269	3	8.5
China	135	350	850	1,498	1,658	4	6.2
Czech Rep.	...	60	40	40	40		
Egypt	0	120	180	182	180		
Finland	5	9	24	31	31		
France	469	602	541	638	586		
Germany	648	1,196	1,259	941	994	8	3.7
Ghana	113	188	174	141	135		
Greece	88	146	150	147	140		
Hungary	66	74	64	30	30		
Iceland	39	75	88	99	178		
India	161	185	433	472	524		
Indonesia	0	0	192	222	228		
Iran	0	18	59	142	119		
Italy	388	537	581	551	590		
Japan	1,050	1,880	1,124	1,190	1,199	7	4.5
Korea, S.	17	25	2	50	50		
Mexico	42	60	68	74	92		
Netherlands	82	312	406	359	408		
New Zealand	0	158	260	269	273		
Norway	527	671	872	906	913	9	3.4
Poland	99	95	46	49	52		
Romania	101	241	168	120	143		
Russia	...	...	...	2,700	2,700	2	10.2
Slovak Rep.	...	...	...	60	60		
Slovenia	...	...	...	80	80		
South Africa	0	114	160	200	261		
Spain	147	325	442	442	469		
Surinam	55	55	31	27	28		
Sweden	86	106	126	104	114		
Switzerland	106	106	106	6	6		
Taiwan	27	83	64	64	64		
Tajikistan	...	...	...	250	250		
Turkey	0	34	61	60	62		
Ukraine	...	...	...	85	85		
UAE	0	38	174	247	240		
UK	289	565	485	479	519		
USA	4,544	6,231	6,473	6,256	6,523	1	24.5
Venezuela	22	338	594	617	659	10	2.5
(former) Yugo.	47	185	401	111	127		

Aluminium ore (bauxite) *thousand tonnes*

	1970	1980	1990	1994	1995	Rank	%
WORLD	**52,650**	**93,300**	**115,670**	**110,000**	**112,000**		
Australia	3,294	27,179	41,391	41,736	42,660	1	38.1
Azerbaijan	...	...	...	0	0		
Brazil	400	4,632	9,876	8,676	10,212	4	9.1
China	500	1,700	3,200	6,624	6,504	5	5.8
Dom. Rep.	1,086	511	85	0	0		
France	2,992	1,925	490	128	131		
Ghana	342	225	381	426	514		
Greece	2,283	3,259	2,496	2,168	2,006	10	1.8
Guinea	2,642	13,911	17,524	13,764	14,400	2	12.9
Guyana	4,103	3,052	1,424	1,991	2,093	9	1.9
Haiti	673	461	0	0	0		
Hungary	2,022	2,950	2,559	836	1,014		
India	1,370	1,785	5,277	4,780	5,230	7	4.7
Indonesia	1,229	1,249	1,206	1,343	905		
Italy	225	23	0	23	11		
Jamaica	12,106	11,978	10,937	9,625	10,858	3	9.7
Kazakstan	...	...	...	2,430	0		
Malaysia	1,139	920	398	162	185		
Romania	792	450	247	184	174		
Russia	...	...	...	3,000	0		
Sierra Leone	443	674	1,445	700	0		
Surinam	6,011	4,893	3,267	3,803	3,596	8	3.2
Turkey	51	547	779	373	440		
USA	2,562	1,559	495	35	35		
Venezuela	0	0	785	4,774	5,360	6	4.8
(former) Yugo.	2,099	3,138	2,951	0	60		

Antimony *thousand tonnes*
metal content

	1970	1980	1990	1994	1995	Rank	%
WORLD	**69**	**63**	**65**	**120**	**118**		
Australia	1	1.4	1.3	1.7	1.7	7	1.4
Austria	0.6	0.7	0.4	...	...		
Bolivia	12	16	8.4	7.1	6.4	3	5.4
Burma	0.1	0.4	...	...	...		
Canada	0.3	2.4	0.7	0.7	0.5		
China	...	...	...	80	90	1	76.3
Guatemala	0.3	0.6	1.2	0.6	0.6	9	0.5
Italy	0.8	0.7	...	...	...		
Kyrgyzstan	...	...	...	2.5	2.5	5	2.1
Mexico	4.5	2.2	2.6	1.8	1.8	6	1.5
Morocco	2.2	0.5	2.6	0.2	0.2		
Peru	1.2	0.7	0.3	0.4	0.4		
Romania	...	...	0.4	0.4	0.4		
Russia	...	...	...	7	7	2	5.9
Slovak Rep.	0.8	0.5	0.5	0.5	0.5		
South Africa	...	...	...	4.5	4.3	4	3.6
Tajikistan	...	...	...	1	1	8	0.8
Thailand	2.5	3.6	0.5	0.7	0.3		
Turkey	3.4	1	1.1	0.1	0.1		
USA	1	0.3	2.3	0.5	0.5	10	0.4
Zimbabwe	...	0.2	0.1	0.1	0.1		

Cars *thousands*

	1970	1980	1990	1994	1995	Rank	%
WORLD	**22,550**	**28,999**	**35,700**	**36,000**	**36,000**		
Argentina*	169	218	114	338	300		
Australia*	391	316	361	310	294		
Austria	1.2	8	14	44	44		
Belgium*	734	891	1,160	1,080	1,080	10	3.0
Brazil*	255	652	268	367	275		
Canada	923	847	941	1,051	1,150	9	3.2
China	...	...	...	258	316		
Colombia*	8.0	32	36	63	65		
Czech Rep.	143	186	191	...	...		
France	2,458	3,487	2,962	3,158	3,042	4	8.5
Germany	3,655	3,688	4,618	4,223	4,536	3	12.6
India	45	47	221	253	240		
Indonesia*	...	43	57	24	24		
Iran	33	...	...	0	0		
Ireland	47	45	...	0	0		
Italy	1,720	1,445	1,873	1,340	1,421	8	3.9
Japan	3,179	7,038	9,948	7,786	7,864	1	21.8
Korea, S.*	13	58	956	1,756	1,999	5	5.6
Malaysia*	21	79	102	173	241		
Mexico*	137	312	614	832	703		
Morocco*	20	15	50	0	0		
Netherlands	85	80	124	84	84		
New Zealand	55	73	...	0	0		
Poland	65	352	266	338	366		
Portugal*	55	22	60	38	36		
Romania	23	89	120	86	88		
Russia	344	1,327	1,259	798	840		
South Africa*	195	268	221	217	275		
Spain	455	1,048	1,736	1,826	1,998	6	5.6
Sweden	272	257	336	353	240		
Taiwan	9.0	133	358	350	350		
Thailand*	0	24	82	126	120		
Turkey*	5.0	52	167	207	219		
Ukraine	...	...	...	84	59		
UK	1,641	924	1,296	1,466	1,532	7	4.3
USA	8,505	6,376	6,052	6,550	6,310	2	17.5
Venezuela	46	...	...	...	...		

* includes assembly

Cement *thousand tonnes*

	1970	1980	1990	1994	1995	Rank	%
WORLD	**582,982**	**869,000**	**1,154,000**	**1,350,000**	**1,350,000**		
Albania	340	1,000	750	200	200		
Algeria	928	4,156	8,000	8,200	8,200		
Argentina	4,770	7,289	3,576	6,312	5,472		
Australia	5,100	5,201	7,068	6,588	6,612		
Austria	4,806	5,455	4,908	4,824	3,840		
Belgium	6,729	7,482	6,924	8,000	8,000		
Brazil	9,002	25,880	25,848	25,248	28,224		
Bulgaria	3,668	5,359	4,716	1,908	2,076		

Cement continued

	1970	1980	1990	1994	1995	Rank	%
Canada	7,283	10,340	11,076	10,500	10,440		
Chile	1,349	1,583	2,100	2,616	3,012		
China	25,720	79,857	209,712	398,412	400,680	1	29.7
Colombia	2,757	4,356	6,360	9,204	9,228		
Croatia	...	...	...	1,700	1,700		
Cuba	742	2,831	3,600	1,000	1,000		
Cyprus	266	1,233	1,000	1,056	1,020		
Czech Rep.	...	...	...	5,256	4,824		
Denmark	2,604	1,917	1,656	2,424	2,580		
Dom. Rep.	493	928	1,300	1,200	1,200		
Ecuador	458	1,389	3,000	2,250	2,250		
Egypt	3,684	3,638	10,740	13,548	14,000		
Finland	1,838	1,787	1,668	876	900		
France	29,009	29,104	26,508	20,196	19,896		
Germany	46,309	46,991	40,000	40,260	37,500	6	2.8
Greece	4,848	11,591	13,944	12,636	13,116		
Hong Kong	430	1,489	1,800	1,932	1,908		
Hungary	2,771	4,660	3,936	2,808	2,868		
India	13,956	17,803	45,720	61,776	66,924	4	5.0
Indonesia	515	5,289	15,972	21,912	23,316		
Iran	2,575	8,114	15,000	20,000	20,000		
Iraq	1,542	5,500	10,000	12,000	12,000		
Ireland	868	1,812	1,300	1,500	1,500		
Israel	1,384	2,092	2,868	4,800	6,204		
Italy	33,076	41,862	40,788	32,700	34,164	9	2.5
Japan	57,189	87,957	84,444	91,524	90,468	2	6.7
Jordan	378	913	1,800	3,084	3,132		
Kazakstan	...	...	...	4,000	4,000		
Kenya	792	1,280	1,512	1,464	1,560		
Korea, N.	4,000	8,000	10,000	17,000	17,000		
Korea, S.	5,782	15,612	33,912	52,080	56,100	5	4.2
Kuwait	...	1,307	1,000	500	500		
Lebanon	1,339	2,200	900	1,000	1,000		
Libya	98	1,787	3,000	2,300	2,300		
Lithuania	...	...	...	1,500	1,500		
Malaysia	1,030	2,349	5,880	9,924	10,680		
Mexico	7,267	16,398	24,504	30,396	24,432		
Moldova	...	...	...	1,500	1,500		
Morocco	...	...	...	6,324	6,396		
Netherlands	3,830	3,745	3,708	3,500	3,500		
New Zealand	829	720	684	0	0		
Nigeria	...	...	3,500	3,084	0		
Norway	2,680	2,206	1,260	1,464	1,644		
Pakistan	2,656	3,343	7,488	7,932	8,328		
Peru	1,144	2,758	2,184	3,1800			
Philippines	...	...	6,360	9,576	10,572		
Poland	12,180	18,428	12,516	13,884	13,884		
Portugal	2,347	5,914	6,000	0	0		
Puerto Rico	1,509	1,282	1,332	1,392	1,404		
Romania	8,127	14,607	13,200	6,672	7,560		
Russia	...	...	...	37,200	36,432	7	2.7
Saudi Arabia	667	2,888	13,000	16,000	16,500		
Singapore	...	1,952	1,848	2,000	2,000		
Slovak Rep.	...	...	...	2,880	3,000		
South Africa	5,752	7,125	7,000	6,660	7,440		
Spain	16,702	28,752	28,092	25,128	26,424		
Sweden	4,061	2,445	2,500	2,100	2,000		
Switzerland	4,797	4,252	5,136	4,000	4,000		
Syria	964	1,995	3,660	4,008	4,464		
Taiwan	4,541	14,062	17,000	22,700	22,500		
Thailand	2,627	5,359	15,000	29,928	34,380	8	2.5
Tunisia	547	1,780	4,140	4,236	4,620		
Turkey	6,373	14,802	24,636	29,472	33,012	10	2.4
Ukraine	...	...	...	11,400	7,620		
UAE	...	...	3,250	3,600	3,600		
UK	17,171	14,805	14,736	15,132	11,808		
USA	67,682	69,589	70,944	77,112	75,324	3	5.6
Uzbekistan	...	...	...	5,000	5,000		
Venezuela	2,318	4,842	6,000	4,560	0		
Vietnam	790	850	2,000	7,250	7,000		
Yugoslavia	...	...	...	1,608	1,692		

Chromium ore *thousand tonnes*
metal content

	1970	1980	1990	1993	1994	Rank	%
WORLD	**2,730**	**9,748**	**12,799**	**9,930**	**10,000**		
Albania	200	760	957	281	223	8	2.2
Brazil	11	313	263	300	360	7	3.6
China	...	...	25	54	50		
Cuba	8.0	29	50	50	50		

Chromium ore continued

	1970	1980	1990	1993	1994	Rank	%
Cyprus	16	17	-	...			
Finland	51	186	489	510	575	5	5.8
Greece	10	34	35	3.0	4.0		
India	135	321	995	1,000	909	3	9.1
Iran	86	80	79	130	130	10	1.3
Japan	11	14	8.0	7	7.0		
Kazakstan	...	...	...	2,900	2,020	2	20.2
Madagascar	43	147	151	144	90		
New Caledonia	...	2.2	7.0	...	...		
Oman	...	...	...	10	6.2		
Pakistan	14	3.1	18	22	23		
Philippines	197	496	198	68	69		
Russia	...	...	...	120	143	9	1.4
South Africa	643	3,414	4,500	2,830	3,590	1	35.9
Sudan	14	26	15	10	10		
Swaziland	14	26	...	...	...		
Turkey	0.0	383	850	570	790	4	7.9
Vietnam	...	16	4.0	...	...		
(former) Yugo.	15	...	...	...	...		
Zimbabwe	181	553	575	252	517	6	5.2

Coal – bituminous *million tonnes*

	1970	1980	1990	1994	1995	Rank	%
WORLD	2,131	2,740	3,300	3,250	3,320		
Australia	44	78	162	227	193	5	5.8
Belgium	11	5.3	1.8	0	0		
Brazil	2.4	5.1	6.2	5.2	5.2		
Canada	12	31	59	44	39		
China	360	590	920	1,206	1,250	1	37.7
Colombia	...	10	20	25	26		
Czech Rep.	28	28	22	18	17		
France	37	18	11	7.5	7.0		
Germany	112	87	70	58	53	10	1.6
Hungary	4.2	3.1	2.0	1.0	0.8		
India	74	109	200	252	266	3	8.0
Indonesia	0.1	0.3	11	31	42		
Japan	40	18	8.6	6.9	6.3		
Kazakstan	...	...	...	104	80	9	2.4
Korea, N.	24	19	48	28	28		
Korea, S.	12	19	17	7.1	5.6		
Mexico	...	5.0	10	9.0	8.5		
Netherlands	4.3	0	0	0	0		
Pakistan	1.3	1.2	2.6	3.2	2.9		
Poland	140	193	148	130	137	7	4.1
Romania	6.4	9.7	4.0	4.5	4.9		
Russia	...	...	...	175	176	6	5.3
South Africa	55	116	180	182	206	4	6.2
Spain	11	13	20	14	14		
Taiwan	4.5	2.6	0.5	0.3	0.3		
Turkey	5.0	6.6	4.0	2.9	6.0		
Ukraine	...	...	...	92	81	8	2.4
UK	145	130	92	48	53		
USA	550	715	623	580	561	2	16.9
Venezuela	...	0.1	2.2	4.4	5.0		
Vietnam	3.0	5.3	5.5	6.2	6.1		
Zimbabwe	3.4	3.1	5.2	4.6	2.1		

Coal – lignite and brown *million tonnes*

	1970	1980	1990	1994	1995	Rank	%
WORLD	793	1,100	1,400	1,230	1,300		
Albania	...	1.4	2.1	0.40	0.40		
Australia	24	33	48	50	48	7	3.7
Austria	3.7	2.9	2.6	1.4	1.3		
Bulgaria	29	30	30	31	31		
Canada	3.5	6.0	9.0	43	36	10	2.8
China	...	9.3	84	0.00	48	8	3.7
Czech Rep.	82	96	85	55	58	5	4.5
Estonia	...	...	...	15	14		
France	2.8	2.6	2.0	1.5	1.4		
Germany	369	388	357	207	193	2	14.8
Greece	7.7	24	52	57	54	6	4.2
Hungary	24	23	16	13	12		
India	3.5	4.5	14	19	22		
Italy	1.4	1.9	0.90	0.26	0.50		
Kazakstan	...	...	...	4.9	3.7		
Korea, N.	...	10	12	9.3	9.7		
Mexico	0	0	3.1	6.8	7.1		
New Zealand	1.9	0.20	0.10	0.25	0.25		
Poland	33	37	68	67	64	4	4.9
Romania	14	28	34	35	36		

Coal – lignite and brown continued

	1970	1980	1990	1994	1995	Rank	%
Russia	...	...	...	83	86	3	6.6
Slovak Rep.	...	...	...	2.1	2.1		
Spain	2.8	15	16	0.00	15		
Thailand	0.40	1.4	13	17	18		
Turkey	4.5	17	42	54	40	9	3.1
Ukraine	...	...	...	2.6	2.6		
USA	5.4	43	310	320	376	1	28.9
Uzbekistan	...	...	...	3.7	3.5		
Yugoslavia	28	47	76	38	35		

Cobalt ore *tonnes*
metal content

	1970	1980	1991	1994	1995	Rank	%
WORLD	24,500	33,700	30,500	18,500	21,000		
Albania	500	600	500	10	...		
Australia	20	3,704	2,200	2,200	2,100	6	10.0
Botswana	0	226	210	200	250		
Brazil	...	...	400	400	400		
Canada	2,372	2,118	5,300	4,300	5,900	1	28.1
China	...	200	250	1,000	1,100	7	5.2
Congo (Zaïre)	13,598	14,482	8,500	2,000	4,100	2	19.5
Cuba	1,542	1,500	1,100	1,000	1,000	8	4.8
Finland	1,650	1,360	1,500	3,000	3,600	3	17.1
Japan	...	...	198	160	222		
Morocco	595	838	325	450	480	10	2.3
New Caledonia	0	2,598	2,500	800	800	9	3.8
Norway	735	0	0	0	0		
Philippines	0	1,331	0	0	0		
Russia	1,500	2,150	2,000	3,300	3,000	4	14.3
South Africa	...	750	350	350	350		
Zambia	2,052	3,310	4,600	3,500	2,900	5	13.8
Zimbabwe	...	115	100	100	100		

Commercial vehicles *thousands*

	1970	1980	1990	1994	1995	Rank	%
WORLD	6,780	10,500	13,200	15,000	15,500		
Argentina*	50	61	14	71	72		
Australia*	88	46	23	25	25		
Austria	7.0	7.0	17	3.6	3.6		
Belgium*	61	43	92	84	84		
Brazil*	161	516	672	1,228	1,378	3	8.9
Canada	236	528	808	900	960	4	6.2
Chile*	4.0	4.0	8.0	16	17		
China	...	...	...	667	714	5	4.6
Colombia*	10	11	13	16	13		
Czech Rep.	28	88	62	...	...		
France	292	505	474	401	442	8	2.8
Germany	345	420	349	290	300	10	1.9
Hungary	10	14	8.0	1.2	1.2		
India	41	66	145	162	216		
Indonesia*	...	131	202	72	72		
Italy	135	167	260	193	259		
Japan	2,125	4,006	3,550	2,764	2,603	2	16.8
Korea, S.*	15	64	322	491	510	7	3.3
Malaysia*	8.0	22	50	37	46		
Mexico*	53	132	124	163	158		
Netherlands*	16	17	30	23	23		
New Zealand*	17	17	14	...	...		
Pakistan*	0	12	16	16	16		
Philippines*	6.0	18	2.0	...	...		
Poland	53	60	43	22	32		
Portugal*	13	69	77	88	72		
Romania	52	41	20	16	16		
Russia	815	874	860	700	700	6	4.5
South Africa*	76	108	120	113	148		
Spain	77	146	302	173	200		
Sweden	32	60	74	...	...		
Switzerland	19	...	...	...	...		
Thailand*	0	51	236	325	312	9	2.0
Turkey*	12	19	42	45	75		
UK	...	389	274	232	236		
USA	1,692	1,667	3,720	5,640	5,713	1	36.9
Venezuela	13	...	22	...	...		
Yugoslavia	46	64	49	4.8	2.4		

* includes assembly

Copper *thousand tonnes*

	1970	1980	1990	1994	1995	Rank	%
WORLD	7,578	7,300	15,569	17,697	18,251		
Argentina	...	10	12	32	32		
Australia	146	182	314	396	320		
Austria	22	43	50	53	54		
Belgium	338	424	332	523	541	8	3.0
Brazil	19	39	184	224	219		
Bulgaria	38	63	24	27	26		
Canada	493	505	552	633	691	6	3.8
Chile	465	811	1,192	1,277	1,490	3	8.2
China	130	295	490	736	844	5	4.6
Congo (Zaïre)	190	144	174	29	33		
Finland	34	41	75	70	73		
France	34	47	161	194	186		
Germany	456	425	772	1,270	1,249	4	6.8
Hungary	12	28	13	11	0		
India	9	23	39	49	40		
Iran	6	1	48	90	90		
Italy	16	12	298	482	508	9	2.8
Japan	705	1,014	1,642	1,837	1,979	2	10.8
Kazakstan	...	...	...	302	300		
Korea, N.	13	23	30	30	30		
Korea, S.	5	73	322	382	393		
Mexico	54	103	152	305	340		
Netherlands	...	...	...	52	52		
Norway	26	26	47	40	35		
Oman	0	0	12	24	21		
Peru	36	224	182	253	282		
Philippines	0	0	126	155	158		
Poland	72	357	346	405	407	10	2.2
Romania	16	65	25	22	22		
Russia	...	...	...	550	550	7	3.0
Slovak Rep.	17	26	25	28	28		
South Africa	75	148	133	130	140		
Spain	80	154	196	252	216		
Sweden	51	56	122	127	135		
Switzerland	...	...	...	31	33		
Taiwan	4	20	56	55	55		
Turkey	14	19	85	83	100		
UK	206	161	248	170	177		
USA	2,035	1,686	2,958	3,717	3,738	1	20.5
Uzbekistan	...	...	...	55	50		
Yugoslavia	...	...	...	110	117		
Zambia	581	607	443	370	314		
Zimbabwe	21	7	24	18	18		

Copper ore *thousand tonnes*
metal content

	1970	1980	1990	1994	1995	Rank	%
WORLD	6,320	7,900	9,040	9,400	10,050		
Albania	7.0	12	13	3.9	4.2		
Australia	142	244	327	381	365	8	3.6
Bolivia	9.0	2.0	0.2	0.1	0.1		
Botswana	0	16	21	23	20		
Brazil	4.0	...	37	45	30		
Bulgaria	43	62	33	76	76		
Canada	610	716	794	617	724	3	7.2
Chile	711	1,068	1,588	2,234	2,506	1	24.9
China	100	165	360	396	396	6	3.9
Congo (Zaïre)	387	462	356	40	29		
Cyprus	17	4.8	0.5	0	0		
Finland	34	53	13	10	9.4		
Germany	10	12	3.6	0	0		
India	10	27	52	46	47		
Indonesia	...	59	170	330	479	5	4.8
Iran	...	1.0	74	120	102		
Ireland	7.7	4.3	0	0	0		
Israel	11	0	0	0	0		
Japan	120	53	13	6.0	2.4		
Kazakstan	...	...	...	285	260		
Korea, N.	13	12	12	12	12		
Malaysia	...	27	24	25	22		
Mexico	61	175	291	303	360	9	3.6
Mongolia	...	44	124	100	0		
Morocco	3.0	8.0	15	14	14		
Namibia	23	39	33	29	25		
Norway	20	29	20	7.4	7.2		
Oman	...	...	14	6.5	...		
Papua N.G.	...	147	170	206	213		
Peru	206	367	318	306	360	10	3.6
Philippines	160	305	181	112	108		
Poland	83	343	329	424	384	7	3.8

Copper ore continued

	1970	1980	1990	1994	1995	Rank	%
Portugal	...	1.0	158	139	130		
Romania	...	28	32	26	24		
Russia	...	...	...	573	590	4	5.9
South Africa	148	201	209	165	200		
Spain	10	48	15	4.9	22		
Sweden	26	43	74	79	84		
Turkey	22	21	40	35	38		
USA	1,560	1,181	1,587	1,810	1,850	2	18.4
Uzbekistan	...	...	...	70	70		
Yugoslavia	...	...	...	85	88		
Zambia	684	610	496	499	342		
Zimbabwe	...	27	15	9.4	7.7		

Diamonds *thousand carats*

	1970	1980	1990	1994	1995	Rank	%
WORLD	47,634	42,000	106,700	107,500	107,900		
Angola	2,396	1,500	1,300	1,400	1,900	6	1.8
Australia	...	36,000	43,800	40,800		1	37.8
Botswana	464	5,146	17,300	15,600	16,800	3	15.6
Brazil	47	667	500	1,500	1,200	8	1.1
Cen. Afr. Rep.	494	342	500	500	600		
China	...	1,000	1,000	1,000	1,000	9	0.9
Congo (Zaïre)	14,057	10,334	24,000	18,000	20,000	2	18.5
Ghana	2,550	1,149	200	600	800	10	0.7
Guinea	74	38	100	500	500		
Guyana	61	10	8	40	50		
Liberia	826	298	300	...			
Namibia	1,865	1,560	800	1,300	1,300	7	1.2
Russia	14,057	10,850	15,000	11,500	12,500	4	11.6
Sierra Leone	2,050	592	700	400	300		
South Africa	8,112	8,520	8,500	10,200	9,100	5	8.4
Tanzania	708	270	...	...			
Venezuela	509	666	80	350	300		
Zimbabwe	...	...	...	500	500		

This table does not include synthetic diamond production.

Fertilizers – nitrogenous *thousand tonnes*

	1970	1980	1990	1994	1995	Rank	%
WORLD	37,825	62,766	84,862	79,379	80,402		
Algeria	50	24	88	80	83		
Australia	182	214	230	230	238		
Austria	230	300	230	233	195		
Bangladesh	92	161	678	1,006	912		
Belarus	...	...	...	464	344		
Belgium	641	743	678	665	695		
Brazil	78	384	748	709	768		
Bulgaria	523	730	926	611	676		
Burma	...	60	88	80	78		
Canada	772	1,755	2,706	3,851	3,852	5	4.8
Chile	108	101	130	130	110		
China	2,245	10,286	14,515	15,572	16,980	1	21.1
Croatia	...	...	...	250	260		
Cuba	2	112	146	70	15		
Czech Rep.	...	...	...	194	247		
Denmark	77	147	200	120	125		
Egypt	152	400	678	863	900		
Finland	243	266	278	231	255		
France	1,476	1,640	1,572	1,524	1,396	10	1.7
Germany	1,899	2,379	2,134	1,267	1,300		
Greece	240	311	407	312	280		
Hungary	374	651	591	167	228		
India	1,054	2,164	6,747	7,231	7,944	3	9.9
Indonesia	60	958	2,369	2,357	2,428	6	3.0
Iran	143	71	308	444	460		
Iraq	26	355	450	150	200		
Ireland	85	190	297	335	321		
Israel	24	62	75	75	60		
Italy	1,046	1,335	1,169	661	619		
Japan	2,199	1,202	946	868	800		
Jordan	...	...	109	85	135		
Kazakstan	...	...	...	95	61		
Korea, N.	230	553	660	660	630		
Korea, S.	418	688	583	621	644		
Kuwait	270	218	386	293	316		
Libya	...	...	124	269	347		
Lithuania	...	...	...	177	184		
Malaysia	31	35	249	292	269		
Mexico	356	739	1,498	1,249	1,300		
Morocco	5	36	273	388	275		

Fertilizers – nitrogenous continued

	1970	1980	1990	1994	1995	Rank	%
Netherlands	1,217	1,624	1,848	1,756	1,800	8	2.2
Nigeria	...	...	272	150	151		
Norway	396	428	494	432	470		
Pakistan	274	580	1,156	1,566	1,617	9	2.0
Philippines	55	34	127	165	169		
Poland	1,147	1,290	1,643	1,143	1,269		
Portugal	150	172	133	79	88		
Qatar	...	286	359	380	395		
Romania	874	1,707	2,035	1,010	927		
Russia	...	...	...	4,477	4,050	4	5.0
Saudi Arabia	69	152	428	832	1,068		
Slovak Rep.	...	...	...	95	179		
South Africa	248	444	400	430	428		
Spain	724	960	967	742	813		
Sweden	169	180	154	111	118		
Taiwan	...	...	380	379	408		
Trinidad & T.	75	41	223	242	229		
Tunisia	...	47	206	197	176		
Turkey	145	672	700	856	650		
Turkmenistan	...	...	...	105	102		
Ukraine	...	...	...	2,215	1,966	7	2.4
UAE	...	...	266	260	230		
UK	751	1,167	1,070	803	803		
USA	8,433	11,825	12,576	14,415	14,017	2	17.4
Uzbekistan	...	...	...	922	673		
Venezuela	10	145	370	362	360		
Zimbabwe	58	72	72	82	94		

Fertilizers – phosphate *thousand tonnes*

	1970	1980	1990	1994	1995	Rank	%
World	23,673	34,515	39,733	31,763	32,779		
Algeria	38	31	45	41	28		
Australia	900	829	511	296	299		
Austria	139	105	85	80	65		
Azerbaijan	...	...	...	40	40		
Bangladesh	...	33	67	51	50		
Belarus	...	...	...	68	28		
Belgium	780	590	333	318	315		
Brazil	278	1,582	1,109	1,231	1,393	5	4.2
Bulgaria	126	217	169	45	51		
Canada	738	724	440	368	364		
China	1,031	2,367	3,808	4,237	5,041	2	15.4
Colombia	40	46	39	24	32		
Croatia	...	...	...	79	70		
Denmark	97	135	136	68	70		
Egypt	116	106	217	114	145		
Finland	213	159	183	130	130		
France	1,611	1,351	1,025	697	497	8	1.5
Germany	1,395	1,056	595	165	200		
Greece	153	170	198	123	127		
Hungary	161	216	220	6	13		
India	330	859	1,834	1,874	2,557	3	7.8
Indonesia	...	220	551	543	484	9	1.5
Iran	62	30	50	107	214		
Iraq	...	...	415	100	100		
Ireland	136	44	...	...	...		
Israel	...	41	180	190	190		
Italy	500	447	266	266	276		
Japan	729	648	445	384	365		
Jordan	...	13	277	216	345		
Kazakstan	...	...	...	282	70		
Korea, N.	105	127	137	130	130		
Korea, S.	163	494	394	447	463	10	1.4
Latvia	...	...	...	60	60		
Lebanon	42	103	15	64	80		
Lithuania	...	...	...	39	69		
Mexico	217	201	448	212	339		
Morocco	154	177	936	1,175	907	6	2.8
Netherlands	351	328	378	319	335		
New Zealand	421	346	206	308	267		
Nigeria	...	5	44	44	28		
Norway	130	143	230	225	210		
Pakistan	8	58	105	93	92		
Philippines	42	37	191	186	205		
Poland	763	843	946	281	328		
Portugal	89	102	77	30	29		
Romania	313	687	648	246	207		
Russia	...	...	...	2,512	1,718	4	5.2
Saudi Arabia	...	...	...	132	165		
Senegal	...	25	27	38	42		

Fertilizers – phosphate continued

	1970	1980	1990	1994	1995	Rank	%
South Africa	340	480	375	376	403		
Spain	576	497	368	365	430		
Sweden	181	132	108	14	18		
Taiwan	...	...	342	341	367		
Tunisia	194	408	754	646	719	7	2.2
Turkey	125	564	468	489	271		
Turkmenistan	...	...	...	35	13		
Ukraine	...	...	...	324	270		
UK	444	326	172	81	90		
USA	5,795	9,500	9,590	10,223	11,055	1	33.7
Uzbekistan	...	...	...	271	129		
Venezuela	10	23	50	42	41		
Vietnam	42	33	55	94	74		
Yugoslavia	...	...	...	37	14		
Zimbabwe	38	42	38	39	42		

Fertilizers – potash *thousand tonnes*

	1970	1980	1990	1994	1995	Rank	%
WORLD	16,690	27,458	28,328	20,492	23,249		
Azerbaijan	...	...	...	30	30		
Belarus	...	...	1,947	2,510		3	10.8
Brazil	...	...	109	174	229		
Canada	3,820	7,337	6,774	7,293	9,104	1	39.2
Chile	...	...	...	38	52		
China	300	20	56	117	115		
France	1,664	1,933	1,199	890	869	9	3.7
Germany	4,956	6,123	5,491	2,860	3,286	2	14.1
Israel	622	812	1,301	1,310	1,260	5	5.4
Italy	131	95	131	...	...		
Jordan	...	...	810	822	930	7	4.0
Russia	...	...	...	2,628	2,498	4	10.7
Spain	636	691	729	890	873	8	3.8
Taiwan	...	...	950	948	1,021	6	4.4
Ukraine	...	...	...	88	78		
UK	...	307	488	555	580		
USA	2,441	2,052	1,007	842	827	10	3.6

Gold *tonnes*

metal content

	1970	1980	1990	1994	1995	Rank	%
WORLD	1,483	1,220	2,135	2,280	2,275		
Australia	19.4	17	243	255	254	3	11.2
Bolivia	...	...	5	15	16		
Brazil	5.6	14	84	73	67	8	2.9
Canada	75	51	167	146	150	4	6.6
Chile	2	6.8	33	43	49		
China	...	45	95	124	136	6	6.0
Colombia	6.3	16	33	26	24		
Congo (Zaïre)	5.5	2.2	3.7	...	...		
Dom. Rep.	0	12	4.4	1.3	...		
Ecuador	0.3	0.1	11	1.5	...		
Ethiopia	...	0.8	3.3	3.3			
Fiji	3.2	0.8	4.5	3.4	3.4		
France	...	...	5.4	3.8			
Ghana	22	11	17	44	52		
India	3.2	2.5	1.8	2.2	2.2		
Indonesia	...	...	13	55	74	7	3.3
Japan	3	3.2	7.3	9.6	9		
Kazakstan	...	...	...	26	26		
Korea, N.	...	5	5	14	14		
Korea, S.	1.6	1.3	21	25	25		
Malaysia	...	...	2.6	4.1	...		
Mali	...	...	5.2	5.5	5.5		
Mexico	6.2	6.1	9	14	20		
Papua N.G.	0.7	15	34	59	55	10	2.4
Peru	3	3.9	5.2	39	52		
Philippines	19	20	37	31	28		
Poland	...	...	30	30	30		
Russia	195	260	280	158	142	5	6.2
Saudi Arabia	...	...	3.5	8	...		
South Africa	1002	673	605	584	522	1	22.9
Spain	...	...	6.8	6	...		
Sweden	1.4	2	6.3	6.5	...		
Tanzania	0.2	0.3	0.2	6	...		
USA	56	30	294	326	330	2	14.5
Uzbekistan	...	...	...	64	64	9	2.8
Venezuela	...	...	7.7	14	17		
Yugoslavia	1.7	3.3	4.6	4	...		
Zimbabwe	16	11	15	23	26		

Iron and ferro-alloys *thousand tonnes*

	1970	1980	1990	1994	1995	Rank	%
WORLD	**436,416**	**520,000**	**543,000**	**670,000**	**690,000**		
Algeria	409	669	1,500	850	850		
Argentina	847	1,095	2,100	1,392	1,524		
Australia	5,769	7,276	6,192	7,212	7,452		
Austria	2,970	3,493	3,444	3,390	3,876		
Belgium	10,950	9,845	9,360	8,976	9,204		
Brazil	4,334	14,774	21,120	24,828	25,044	6	3.6
Bulgaria	1,251	1,583	1,140	1,476	1,608		
Canada	8,424	11,185	7,344	8,112	8,460		
Chile	481	707	732	888	852		
China	17,060	39,014	64,548	99,216	105,096	1	15.2
Czech Rep.	...	...	5,600	5,300	4,992		
Egypt	300	650	1,100	1,100	1,100		
Finland	1,164	2,072	2,280	2,592	2,244		
France	19,575	19,595	14,412	13,008	12,876	10	1.9
Germany	35,985	36,513	30,324	29,976	30,084	5	4.4
Hungary	1,837	2,227	1,692	1,596	1,500		
India	7,338	8,864	12,000	17,300	19,032	8	2.8
Indonesia	...	...	1,300	1,650	1,500		
Iran	...	...	1,270	1,900	1,900		
Italy	8,529	12,411	12,024	11,184	11,808		
Japan	69,728	88,907	81,360	74,640	75,900	2	11.0
Kazakstan	...	...	...	2,500	2,500		
Korea, N.	2,400	5,470	6,570	7,000	7,000		
Korea, S.	35	5,686	15,528	21,384	22,560	7	3.3
Luxem.	4,814	3,568	2,724	1,920	1,032		
Malaysia	...	...	600	1,000	1,000		
Mexico	2,353	5,330	3,840	3,500	3,660		
Netherlands	3,594	4,328	4,956	5,448	5,532		
Norway	1,251	1,991	900	1,056	1,060		
Pakistan	...	...	1,100	1,200	1,200		
Poland	7,111	11,682	8,664	6,936	7,548		
Romania	4,210	9,013	6,492	3,600	4,320		
Russia	...	...	...	36,636	40,284	4	5.8
Saudi Arabia	...	...	1,090	2,100	2,000		
Slovak Rep.	...	...	...	3,000	3,000		
South Africa	4,328	8,542	6,250	6,050	6,000		
Spain	4,278	6,725	5,748	5,448	5,124		
Sweden	2,842	2,612	2,736	3,036	3,024		
Taiwan	...	...	5,500	5,940	6,000		
Trinidad & T.	...	200	700	900	900		
Turkey	1,176	2,048	4,824	4,608	4,368		
Ukraine	...	...	...	20,196	18,000	9	2.6
UK	19,023	6,413	12,492	11,772	11,988		
USA	85,303	63,748	49,700	49,380	50,904	3	7.4
Venezuela	510	2,450	3,100	4,700	4,500		
Zimbabwe	250	862	800	200	200		

Iron ore *million tonnes*

metal content

	1970	1980	1990	1994	1995	Rank	%
WORLD	**417**	**520**	**979**	**975**	**1,020**		
Algeria	1.5	1.9	2.9	1.1	0		
Australia	29	62	114	82	91	3	9.0
Austria	1.3	1.0	2.3	0.5	0		
Brazil	20	41	152	109	121	2	11.9
Canada	29	30	36	22	21	8	2.1
Chile	6.9	5.4	7.8	5.1	5.1		
China	24	33	169	146	153	1	15.0
Egypt	...	...	1.2	1.1	0		
France	18	9.0	8.7	0.7	0.5		
Germany	1.8	0.5	0	0	0		
India	20	26	54	37	42	5	4.1
Iran	...	...	1.8	4.3	...		
Japan	0.9	0.3	0	0	0		
Kazakstan	...	...	...	5.8	...		
Korea, N.	4.0	3.7	9.5	4.9	4.4		
Liberia	15	13	3	...	...		
Mauritania	5.9	5.6	6.8	6.9	7.5		
Mexico	2.6	5.2	8.3	3.5	3.5		
New Zealand	...	...	1.3	0.6	0		
Norway	2.6	2.5	2.1	1.6	1.3		
Peru	6.1	3.4	2.2	5.9	...		
Romania	0.9	0.6	0.6	0.2	0.1		
Russia	...	...	...	44	44	4	4.3
South Africa	5.9	16	20	21	21	9	2.1
Spain	3.5	4.4	1.4	1.2	0		
Sweden	20	17	14	13	13		
Turkey	1.7	1.4	2.7	4.0	3.2		
Ukraine	...	...	...	29	29	7	2.8
UK	3.4	0.3	0	0	0		
USA	53	44	36	37	39	6	3.9
Venezuela	14	10	13	12	15	10	1.5
(former) Yugo.	1.3	1.6	4.1	0	0		
Zimbabwe	0.3	0.9	0.6	0.0	0.1		

Lead *thousand tonnes*

	1970	1980	1990	1994	1995	Rank	%
WORLD	**4,002**	**5,403**	**5,668**	**5,300**	**5,400**		
Algeria	...	...	5.0	9.0	8.6		
Argentina	38	42	25	25	29		
Australia	213	234	228	232	232	8	4.3
Austria	14	18	21	18	22		
Belgium	94	106	92	124	121		
Brazil	20	85	77	64	50		
Bulgaria	99	118	67	62	59		
Burma	7.6	5.9	1.8	1.9	1.3		
Canada	186	235	184	252	277	7	5.1
China	110	175	287	384	422	2	7.8
Czech Rep.	18	20	24	19	19		
Denmark	16	25	0	0	0		
France	170	219	260	261	297	5	5.5
Germany	335	398	394	332	314	3	5.8
Greece	16	21	0	4.0	4.0		
India	1.9	26	42	60	62		
Indonesia	...	2.0	30	30	30		
Iran	0	0	10	51	46		
Ireland	...	7.0	15	10	10		
Italy	79	134	171	204	180	10	3.3
Japan	209	317	327	292	287	6	5.3
Kazakstan	...	...	...	170	170		
Korea, N.	55	65	65	50	50		
Korea, S.	3.6	15	80	130	162		
Macedonia	...	...	...	21	17		
Malaysia	0	2.5	16	33	34		
Mexico	180	160	173	219	216	9	4.0
Morocco	25	42	67	64	62		
Namibia	68	43	44	24	27		
Netherlands	18	32	44	24	20		
New Zealand	...	7.0	5.0	6.0	6.0		
Peru	72	87	69	88	90		
Philippines	0	4.8	12	17	17		
Poland	55	82	65	63	66		
Portugal	0.6	2.0	5.0	13	13		
Romania	40	41	21	16	15		
Russia	...	...	...	34	30		
Slovenia	...	...	...	12	15		
South Africa	...	35	37	32	32		
Spain	76	121	124	75	81		
Sweden	57	42	76	83	91		
Switzerland	...	...	5.4	6.0	6.0		
Taiwan	...	17	27	36	36		
Thailand	0	5.0	16	17	19		
Tunisia	23	19	0	0	0		
Turkey	3.5	3.0	11	4.0	5.1		
Ukraine	...	...	...	9.0	9.0		
UK	287	325	329	337	306	4	5.7
USA	748	1,151	1,292	1,320	1,320	1	24.4
Venezuela	...	10	14	16	15		
Yugoslavia	...	...	...	4.8	11		
Zambia	28	10	4.7	0.5	0.5		

Lead ore *thousand tonnes*

metal content

	1970	1980	1990	1994	1995	Rank	%
WORLD	**3,400**	**3,600**	**3,345**	**2,800**	**2,700**		
Argentina	36	33	23	10	11		
Australia	459	397	561	505	455	1	16.9
Austria	6.0	5.0	1.5	...	...		
Bolivia	26	17	20	20	20		
Brazil	18	22	9.2	4.0	6.0		
Bulgaria	96	100	45	32	32		
Burma	4.0	6.0	2.3	2.4	1.7		
Canada	358	297	241	166	211	5	7.8
China	100	160	315	470	400	2	14.8
Finland	...	...	1.8	...	...		
France	29	29	1.2	...	...		
Germany	41	32	8.6	...	...		
Greece	10	22	26	20	20		
Greenland	...	30	17	...	...		
Honduras	15	14	4.2	2.8	2.5		
India	3.0	14	26	31	29		
Iran	23	12	9.3	18	16		
Ireland	63	58	35	46	46		
Italy	35	24	16	13	14		
Japan	64	43	19	10	10		
Kazakstan	...	...	...	160	140	7	5.2
Korea, N.	70	100	70	55	55		
Korea, S.	11	11	19	2.2	10		
Macedonia	...	...	...	20	20		
Mexico	177	145	187	175	169	6	6.3

Lead ore continued

	1970	1980	1990	1994	1995	Rank	%
Morocco	85	115	67	72	70	10	2.6
Namibia	71	48	19	21	29		
Peru	157	189	188	227	230	4	8.5
Poland	157	189	45	52	52		
Romania	42	23	25	24	21		
Russia	...	...	...	25	23		
South Africa	...	86	69	96	87	9	3.2
Spain	60	87	62	24	30		
Sweden	78	72	84	113	100	8	3.7
Thailand	1.0	11	22	7.4	9.1		
Tunisia	22	9.0	1.8	2.0	2.8		
Turkey	5.0	8.0	12	10	11		
UK	4.0	4.0	...	1.2	1.1		
USA	519	550	497	370	384	3	14.2
Uzbekistan	...	...	...	18	18		
Yugoslavia	127	121	83	9.0	11		
Zambia	33	14	12	7.6	0.6		

Magnesite *thousand tonnes*

metal content

	1970	1980	1990	1994	1995	Rank	%
WORLD	**8,836**	**11,900**	**10,500**	**8,500**	**8,500**		
Australia	24	32	60	275	260	9	3.1
Austria	1,609	1,318	1,100	600	600	4	7.1
Brazil	236	317	300	250	250	10	2.9
Canada	...	...	200	180	180		
China	1,000	2,000	2,000	1,500	1,500	1	17.6
Colombia	0.3	1.6	20	10	9.0		
Greece	718	1,501	700	250	200		
India	354	380	500	500	500	7	5.9
Iran	4.4	4	1.4	40	40		
Korea, N.	1,633	1,850	1,500	1,500	1,500	2	17.6
Nepal	...	40	25	...	...		
Poland	39	20	23	13	13		
Russia	...	...	1,600	600	600	5	7.1
Slovak Rep.	631	666	560	600	600	6	7.1
South Africa	84	78.8	100	69	70		
Spain	222	506	450	400	400	8	4.7
Turkey	300	826	845	1,000	1,000	3	11.8
USA	...	100	100	...	...		
Yugoslavia	512	262	252	70	70		
Zimbabwe	...	78.2	30	6.0	6.0		

Manganese ore *thousand tonnes*

metal content

	1970	1980	1990	1993	1994	Rank	%
WORLD	**7,400**	**10,000**	**9,250**	**7,000**	**7,000**		
Australia	397	969	915	1,040	980	4	14.0
Brazil	830	1,027	950	716	897	5	12.8
Bulgaria	...	11	11	4	0		
Chile	11	11	13	19	18		
China	300	480	800	1,170	1,180	2	16.9
Gabon	729	1,073	1,120	595	670	6	9.6
Georgia	...	...	...	200	200	8	2.9
Ghana	191	100	100	115	110		
Hungary	35	25	18	18	17		
India	616	592	574	617	607	7	8.7
Iran	...	9.0	12	19	13		
Italy	15	2.8	2.0	2	2		
Japan	79	28	0.0	0	0		
Kazakstan	...	...	...	150	150	9	2.1
Mexico	99	161	165	135	112	10	1.6
Morocco	60	65	25	22	16		
Philippines	2.5	1.1	15	0	0		
Romania	27	18	45	27	34		
South Africa	1,182	1,200	1,910	1,080	1,210	1	17.3
Turkey	5.5	17	7.0	13	16		
Ukraine	...	...	...	1,328	1,050	3	15.0
USA	47	21	4.0	0	0		

Mercury *tonnes*

	1970	1980	1990	1994	1995	Rank	%
WORLD	**8,810**	**6,818**	**6,000**	**2,900**	**4,050**		
Algeria	0	841	637	450	290	4	7.2
China	690	800	930	408	547	3	13.5
(former) Czech.	17	159	126	50	50	9	1.2
Finland	3	75	140	89	90	7	2.2
Germany	68	190	...	...	...		
Italy	1,530	3	...	...	...		
Japan	58	222	...	...	...		

Mercury continued

	1970	1980	1990	1994	1995	Rank	%
Kyrgyzstan	...	...	...	250	250	5	6.2
Mexico	1,043	145	735	10	10	10	0.2
Russia	...	...	...	600	600	2	14.8
Slovenia	...	...	37	...	...		
Spain	1,570	1,721	962	390	1,497	1	37.0
Turkey	324	154	47	...	...		
Ukraine	...	...	...	250	250	6	6.2
USA	941	1,058	500	70	70	8	1.7

Molybdenum *tonnes*
metal content

	1970	1980	1990	1993	1994	Rank	%
WORLD	82,340	110,000	110,000	93,600	104,000		
Armenia	...	...	...	500	500		
Bulgaria	...	150	150	120	100		
Canada	15,319	11,889	12,000	9,700	9,540	4	9.2
Chile	5,701	13,668	13,600	14,900	16,000	3	15.4
China	1,500	2,000	15,700	18,300	17,500	2	16.8
Iran	...	500	542	1,000	1,000	9	1.0
Japan	265	56	100	...	...		
Kazakstan	...	...	...	600	500		
Korea, S.	251	302	130	...	...		
Mexico	85	74	2,000	1,700	2,600	7	2.5
Mongolia	...	487	2,000	2,000	2,000	8	1.9
Norway	303	0	0	0	0		
Peru	607	2,407	2,500	3,000	3,000	6	2.9
Russia	...	...	...	4,800	4,500	5	4.3
USA	50,508	68,350	61,000	37,000	47,000	1	45.2
Uzbekistan	...	...	...	700	700	10	0.7

Natural gas *thousand terajoules**

	1970	1980	1990	1995	1996	Rank	%
WORLD	38,455	53,938	74,920	80,200	84,100		
Afghanistan	95	102	110	...	...		
Algeria	64	759	1,855	2,291	2,483	7	3.0
Argentina	209	326	674	946	1,093		
Australia	56	359	779	1,122	1,122		
Austria	77	78	46	53	53		
Azerbaijan	...	...	348	230	222		
Bahrain	14	114	218	272	272		
Bangladesh	0	45	180	281	285		
Bolivia	1.3	80	113	117	121		
Brazil	3.3	41	142	188	201		
Brunei	7.9	399	335	436	436		
Burma	2.2	13	29	59	110		
Canada	2,113	2,790	4114	5,586	5,766	3	6.9
China	144	555	536	662	750		
Colombia	55	151	155	168	176		
Denmark	0	0	117	201	243		
Egypt	3.3	41	255	415	436		
France	271	289	116	139	...		
Germany	479	774	599	607	657		
Hungary	114	237	159	155	151		
India	19	50.6	465	708	771		
Indonesia	46	607	1,709	2,416	2,508	6	3.0
Iran	45	278	871	1,323	1,436		
Iraq	31	50	117	89	68		
Ireland	0	34	88	111	115		
Israel	4.8	5.6	1.2	766	762		
Italy	498	477	648	773	750		
Japan	10	85	84	91	95		
Kazakstan	...	...	251	209	226		
Kuwait	80	133	159	226	226		
Libya	80	134	218	235	235		
Malaysia	3	10	670	1,089	1,332		
Mexico	451	1,035	1,009	1,059	1,177		
Netherlands	1,116	3,205	2,282	2,525	2,856	5	3.4
New Zealand	4.2	39	192	188	200		
Nigeria	4.3	52	151	172	176		
Norway	0	1,065	1,047	1,173	1,541	10	1.8
Oman	...	...	96	142	151		
Pakistan	96	246	436	528	574		
Poland	186	193	104	147	150		
Qatar	39	176	239	511	511		
Romania	990	1,455	955	632	616		
Russia	...	...	22,538	20,934	21,147	1	25.1
Saudi Arabia	...	49	1,152	1,441	1,558	9	1.9
Thailand	0	0	205	377	423		
Trinidad & T.	73	146	197	230	268		
Turkmenistan	...	...	3,086	1,135	1,240		

Natural gas continued

	1970	1980	1990	1995	1996	Rank	%
Ukraine	...	...	988	641	645		
USA	9	471	758	1,126	1,319		
UK	434	1,454	1,717	2,680	3,187	4	3.8
USA	22,860	19,256	19,380	20,159	20,611	2	24.5
Uzbekistan	...	...	1,436	1,709	1,721	8	2.0
Venezuela	382	643	829	1,122	1,206		

* A terajoule is a measure of energy equivalent to 23.88 tonnes of oil or 34.12 tonnes of coal.

Nickel *thousand tonnes*

	1970	1980	1990	1994	1995	Rank	%
WORLD	607	733	860	837	920		
Albania	...	4.5	4.3	0.1	0.1		
Australia	1.0	35	43	67	77	4	8.4
Austria	...	0.5	3.3	2.1	2.1		
Brazil	2.5	2.5	13	17	16		
Canada	207	134	127	105	122	3	13.3
China	...	11	28	31	38	7	4.1
Colombia	...	...	18	21	26		
Cuba	2.5	20	21	14	22		
Dom. Rep.	...	18	29	31	31	9	3.4
Finland	4.0	13	17	16	15		
France	11	10	8.5	10	10.4		
Germany	1.8	3.0	1.3	...	...		
Greece	8.6	14	16	16	17		
Indonesia	...	4.4	5.2	5.8	11		
Japan	90	109	103	113	135	2	14.7
Korea, S.	...	...	8.2	...	...		
New Caledonia	28	33	32	40	42	6	4.6
Norway	39	37	58	68	53	5	5.8
Philippines	...	23	...	...	...		
Poland	18	1.8	...	...	...		
Russia	...	...	...	192	203	1	22.1
South Africa	9.0	18	28	30	30	10	3.3
Taiwan	...	...	10	10	10		
Ukraine	...	...	3.0	3.0		
UK	37	19	27	28	35	8	3.8
USA	14	40	3.7	...	8.0		
(former) Yugo.	...	...	4.9	11	8.9		
Zimbabwe	5.0	15	19	20	17		

Nickel ore *thousand tonnes*
metal content

	1970	1980	1990	1994	1995	Rank	%
WORLD	651	738	881	868	967		
Albania	...	4.8	8.5	...	...		
Australia	18	74	67	79	99	5	10.2
Botswana	–	15	20	19	18		
Brazil	2.9	4.3	13	17	16		
Canada	278	185	196	150	181	3	18.7
China	–	11	26	37	31	7	3.2
Colombia	–	–	18	21	26		
Cuba	35	38	41	31	31	8	3.2
Dom. Rep.	...	18	29	31	31	9	3.2
Finland	6.7	6.4	12	6.8	3.5		
Germany	...	2.7	0.9	...	...		
Greece	–	14	19	16	17		
Indonesia	18	41	69	81	87	6	9.0
New Caledonia	138	87	85	96	133	4	13.8
Norway	–	0.6	2.2	3.3	3.6		
Philippines	...	35	16	15	17		
Poland	2.0	1.1	...	...	...		
Russia	...	...	280	240	240	1	24.8
South Africa	12	26	30	30	30	10	3.1
Ukraine	...	...	5.5	4.0	4.0		
USA	17	10	0.3	2.5	2.5		
(former) Yugo.	–	0.5	3.0	5.4	3.7		
Zimbabwe	11	13	13	14	12		

Oil – crude *million tonnes*

	1970	1980	1990	1995	1996	Rank	%
WORLD	2,244	2,829	3,180	3,266	3,362		
Algeria	51	51	58	57	60		
Angola	4.5	7.5	24	30	35		
Argentina	19	24	26	38	41		
Australia	8.7	19	28	25	27		
Azerbaijan	...	...	13	9.2	9.1		
Bahrain	3.8	2.4	2.1	2.2	2.2		
Brazil	8.0	9.1	33	36	40		

Oil – crude continued

	1970	1980	1990	1995	1996	Rank	%
Brunei	7.4	12	7.4	8.6	8.1		
Cameroon	0.1	2.9	7.8	5.4	5.2		
Canada	63	70	92	112	114		
China	25	106	138	149	159	7	4.7
Colombia	11	6.2	23	30	32		
Congo	...	2.8	8.0	9.3	11		
Croatia	...	6.6	6.1	1.5	1.5		
Denmark	0.0	0.3	6.0	9.2	10		
Ecuador	0.2	11	15	20	20		
Egypt	16	30	46	47	45		
France	2.3	1.3	3.0	2.2	1.8		
Gabon	5.4	9.0	14	18	18		
Germany	7.3	4.5	3.6	3.1	3.1		
India	6.9	9.1	35	37	35		
Indonesia	43	79	72	74	77		
Iran	166	73	161	183	183	4	5.4
Iraq	77	131	105	26	29		
Italy	1.5	1.8	4.7	5.2	5.4		
Kazakstan	...	27	26	21	23		
Kuwait	136	69	62	104	107		
Libya	165	89	69	69	69		
Malaysia	...	14	30	34	34		
Mexico	21	95	147	151	164	5	4.9
Netherlands	1.8	1.2	3.9	3.0	2.3		
Nigeria	54	102	90	98	106		
Norway	...	26	82	139	156	8	4.6
Oman	17	14	34	43	44		
Papua N.G.	...	...	...	4.7	5.0		
Peru	3.6	9.5	6.6	6.2	6.1		
Qatar	18	24	21	21	22		
Romania	13	12	8.1	7.0	6.8		
Russia	...	582	516	307	301	3	9.0
Saudi Arabia	177	480	341	427	429	1	12.8
Syria	4.1	8.2	21	31	31		
Tajikistan	...	...	...	55	55		
Trinidad & T.	7.0	11	7.7	7.0	6.9		
Tunisia	4.4	5.5	4.5	4.3	4.2		
Turkey	3.4	2.2	3.8	3.1	3.2		
Ukraine	...	...	...	4.1	2.9		
UAE	97	85	105	114	117	10	3.5
UK	0.1	81	92	130	130	9	3.9
USA	480	427	417	384	383	2	11.4
Uzbekistan	...	...	2.8	7.5	7.5		
Venezuela	185	108	116	152	162	6	4.8
Vietnam	...	...	2.7	7.7	8.6		
Yemen	...	4.2	8.7	17	18		

Petroleum products* *million tonnes*

	1970	1980	1990	1994	1995	Rank	%
WORLD	2,032	2,762	3,500	2,936	2,963		
Algeria	2.3	13	38	40	40		
Argentina	19	24	19	22	21		
Australia	22	28	26	33	34		
Austria	5.5	8.8	7.4	8.5	8.2		
Azerbaijan	...	...	...	6.3	...		
Bahamas	2.3	8.3	...	...	...		
Bahrain	11	11	...	11	...		
Belarus	...	...	...	11	...		
Belgium	26	30	23	25	24		
Brazil	24	48	44	55	55		
Bulgaria	5.8	12	...	6.0	...		
Canada	57	98	64	87	87	6	2.9
Chile	3.6	5.0	5.4	7.1	7.6		
China	22	64	85	107	114	4	3.8
Colombia	6.2	7.7	10	13	13		
Croatia	...	...	...	4.5	4.5		
Cuba	4.2	5.5	6.5	4.5	4.5		
Czech Rep.	...	...	...	4.4	4.7		
Denmark	9.4	6.2	7.2	8.7	9.6		
Ecuador	1.1	4.5	5.8	6.5	6.6		
Egypt	3.2	13	22	26	26		
Finland	7.0	11	8.7	11	11		
France	89	103	63	69	69		
Germany	105	116	82	100	95	5	3.2
Greece	4.6	13	15	15	16		
Hungary	5.0	8.9	6.0	6.4	6.4		
India	14	19	37	44	44		
Indonesia	10	24	32	45	46		
Iran	24	33	33	46	46		
Iraq	3.3	8.2	16	22	22		

Petroleum products* continued

	1970	1980	1990	1994	1995	Rank	%
Israel	5	5.6		11			
Italy	104	85	76	83	80	10	2.7
Japan	...	185	137	186	186	2	6.3
Jordan	...	...	2.4	2.9	3.1		
Kazakstan	...	...	...	13	...		
Korea, S.	8.8	22	33	68	74		
Kuwait	17	18	24	34	37		
Lebanon	...	...	0.4	...	...		
Libya	0.4	5.3	12	13	...		
Lithuania	...	...	...	3.8	3.0		
Malaysia	4	5.6	8.9	11	13		
Mexico	21	56	58	84	81	9	2.7
Morocco	1.4	3.8	4.5	5.7	5.3		
Netherlands	52	52	43	60	63		
Neths Antilles	46	26	...	9.9	...		
New Zealand	2.7	2.7	3.6	5.0	5.1		
Nigeria	0.9	6.2	12	5.2	5.5		
Norway	5.5	7.5	11	15	12		
Oman	...	...	...	3.9	...		
Pakistan	4	3.9	5.1	5.8	6.0		
Peru	4.1	7.2	...	7.2	...		
Philippines	8.1	8.8	9.9	11	12		
Poland	6.1	13	9.8	13	13		
Portugal	3.3	7.1	9.4	12	12		
Puerto Rico	9.4	10	...	6.3	...		
Qatar	...	...	...	5.2	...		
Romania	14	25	20	13	13		
Russia	...	...	...	162	160	3	5.4
Saudi Arabia	26	37	63	88	86	7	2.9
Singapore	11	25	...	48	...		
Slovak Rep.	...	...	...	3.7	...		
South Africa	7.7	13	...	16	18		
Spain	29	44	42	47	47		
Sweden	10	17	16	17	17		
Switzerland	4.9	4.4	2.7	4.7	4.6		
Syria	1.7	5.1	11	11	11		
Taiwan	5.9	20	24	29	31		
Thailand	3.2	7.2	...	21	...		
Trinidad & T.	22	12	4.3	4.9	4.5		
Turkey	6.8	11	19	22	24		
Ukraine	...	...	...	11	...		
UAE	0	1.5	...	15	...		
UK	91	78	76	86	85	8	2.9
USA	496	677	572	704	713	1	24.1
US Virgin Is.	13	23	...	15	...		
Uzbekistan	...	...	...	7.9	...		
Venezuela	61	46	44	55	56		
Yemen	6.3	1.9	...	3.3	...		
Yugoslavia	6.4	14	11	...	...		

* The principal products are aviation gasolene, fuel oils, diesel oil, jet fuel, kerosene liquefied petroleum gas, natural gasolene, motor gasolene and residual fuel oil.

Phosphates   thousand tonnes

	1970	1980	1990	1993	1994	Rank	%
WORLD	61,077	138,000	155,385	119,427	128,422		
Algeria	492	1,025	1,128	730	738		
Brazil	700	2,612	2,817	2,967	3,336	8	2.6
China	1,200	10,726	17,300	22,500	26,000	2	20.2
Christmas I.	1,064	1,638	34	298	260		
Egypt	584	658	1,256	537	632		
Finland	...	400	546	628	700		
India	172	543	553	1,085	1,177		
Iraq	...	...	600	300	300		
Israel	1,162	2,307	2,472	3,680	3,961	7	3.1
Jordan	913	3,911	6,080	4,129	4,216	6	3.3
Kazakstan	...	...	...	4,100	2,080		
Korea, N.	300	500	500	500	500		
Mexico	46	387	636	...	237		
Morocco	11,424	18,824	21,396	18,192	19,764	3	15.4
Nauru	2,200	2,087	926	634	613		
Russia	...	...	...	10,381	7,922	4	6.2
Senegal	998	1,290	2,250	1,688	1,587		
South Africa	1,685	3,282	3,165	2,466	2,545	9	2.0
Syria	...	...	1,633	931	1,203		
Togo	1,508	2,933	2,314	1,794	2,149	10	1.7
Tunisia	3,021	4,502	6,259	5,500	5,698	5	4.4
USA	10,884	54,415	45,764	35,138	41,555	1	32.4
Venezuela	...	3	...	183	150		
Vietnam	...	90	274	362	470		
Zimbabwe	...	130	150	155	155		

Potash   thousand tonnes
potash content

	1970	1980	1992	1994	1995	Rank	%
WORLD	18,388	27,900	23,915	22,650	24,500		
Belarus	...	...	3,300	2500	2,800	3	11.4
Brazil	...	...	45	230	225		
Canada	3,103	7,303	7,247	8,150	9,000	1	36.7
Chile	22	25	35	35	65		
China	...	12	100	60	90		
France	1,904	2,039	1,150	900	850	8	3.5
Germany	5,064	6,159	3,470	3,250	3,300	2	13.5
Israel	530	797	1,290	1,300	1,300	6	5.3
Italy	241	130	120	0	0		
Jordan	...	...	790	925	1,050	7	4.3
Russia	...	...	3,500	2,500	2,800	4	11.4
Spain	598	791	580	685	650	9	2.7
Ukraine	...	...	200	200	200		
UK	...	321	530	580	600	10	2.4
USA	2,476	2,239	1,658	1,500	1,500	5	6.1

Radio receivers   thousands

	1970	1980	1990	1993	1994	Rank	%
WORLD	110,000	165,000	135,594	113,069	136,015		
Algeria	76	112	213	109	107		
Armenia	...	...	296	8	8		
Australia	729	199	268	268	268		
Belarus	...	499	979	768	545		
Belgium	1,943	2,246	986	408	400		
Brazil	809	6,769	5,151	4,097	4,665	6	3.4
China	...	30,038	21,030	17,542	41,320	1	30.4
Czech Rep.	...	...	187	...	...		
Egypt	148	209	59	13	52		
Finland	174	219	...	71	70		
France	2,921	2,141	2,059	2,083	2,804	9	2.1
Germany	7,536	4,622	6,477	4,623	5,404	5	4.0
Hong Kong	22,096	48,262	8,182	6,000	6,000	4	4.4
Hungary	215	271	83	...	...		
India	1,771	1,918	647	152	150		
Indonesia	393	1,530	4,436	3,882	3,500	8	2.6
Iran	165	57	232	...	...		
Italy	3,300	...	...	...	...		
Japan	32,618	15,343	15,647	8,317	7,299	3	5.4
Korea, S.	1,088	3,972	1,462	550	28		
Latvia	...	...	1,567	124	33		
Malaysia	...	5,000	37,019	34,537	36,310	2	26.7
Mexico	1,015	1,029	1,000	1,000	1,000		
Poland	987	2,695	1,433	329	309		
Portugal	517	593	1,435	1,500	1,500		
Romania	455	863	384	70	28		
Russia	...	...	5,760	2,806	1,087		
Singapore	...	593	...	...	...		
South Africa	313	861	775	500	500		
Taiwan	6,247	9,490	5,893	3,800	3,775	7	4.4
Thailand	...	1,113	1,105	1,000	1,000		
Turkey	198	52	100	74	32		
Ukraine	...	315	778	797	...		
UK	1,313	439	...	...	...		
USA	13,628	7,672	3,014	2,720	2,500	10	1.8

Rubber – synthetic   thousand tonnes

	1970	1980	1990	1994	1995	Rank	%
WORLD	5,055	6,515	7,300	7,800	8,200		
Argentina	39	33	58	49	54		
Australia	42	46	41	45	48		
Belgium	50	115	125	126	133		
Brazil	96	287	252	280	295	9	3.6
Bulgaria	6	30	...	...	...		
Canada	218	256	213	197	175		
China	...	250	315	494	492	5	6.0
Czech Rep.	...	...	...	74	78		
Finland	...	...	29	33	36		
France	343	528	520	518	619	3	7.6
Germany	442	540	524	643	495	4	6.0
India	30	23	52	62	62		
Italy	155	250	300	305	310	8	3.8
Japan	760	1,161	1,426	1,338	1,498	2	18.3
Korea, S.	5.1	76	184	340	372	6	4.5
Mexico	91	132	119	122	109		
Netherlands	200	212	240	209	185	10	2.3
Poland	62	118	103	84	104		

Rubber – synthetic continued

	1970	1980	1990	1994	1995	Rank	%
Romania	61	150	102	26	42		
South Africa	29	39	46	51	57		
Spain	39	81	66	76	86		
Sweden	7.8	13	...	...	...		
Turkey	0	23	39	43	53		
UK	345	227	298	291	320	7	3.9
USA	2,436	2,302	2,114	2,390	2,510	1	30.6

Salt – unrefined   thousand tonnes

	1970	1980	1990	1993	1994	Rank	%
WORLD	143,200	169,800	191,000	185,000	180,000		
Argentina	958	1,004	800	1,033	1,000		
Australia	2,053	5,665	7,400	9,000	7,800	6	4.3
Austria	563	672	650	716	785		
Bahamas	756	684	900	700	700		
Bangladesh	400	463	400	400	400		
Brazil	1,826	3,932	4,300	8,200	5,300	10	2.9
Burma	165	268	200	200	200		
Canada	4,862	7,423	11,100	11,200	11,500	4	6.4
Chile	517	441	1,800	1,443	3,178		
China	16,000	17,280	28,600	29,500	29,700	2	16.5
Colombia	763	838	700	700	700		
Cuba	...	200	230	200	200		
Czech Rep.	...	...	185	180	180		
Denmark	436	347	550	591	634		
Egypt	440	636	900	972	1,116		
France	11,004	6,543	8,000	6,100	5,400	9	3.0
Germany	23,202	15,783	16,300	12,600	12,700	3	7.1
India	5,588	8,009	9,000	9,500	9,500	5	5.3
Indonesia	63	690	600	650	650		
Iran	390	600	700	720	900		
Israel	100	130	400	400	400		
Italy	8,596	5,267	4,400	3,700	3,100		
Japan	951	1,112	1,400	1,400	1,400		
Kazakstan	...	...	...	763	600		
Korea, N.	544	570	550	550	550		
Korea, S.	405	455	1,000	1,000	1,000		
Mexico	4,063	6,575	7,900	7,200	7,500	7	4.2
Netherlands	2,871	3,464	3,700	3,500	3,500		
Neths Antilles	...	400	225	300	300		
Pakistan	900	687	700	700	700		
Peru	191	457	350	238	238		
Philippines	210	346	500	500	500		
Poland	5,808	4,533	5,600	4,000	3,800		
Portugal	401	620	700	650	650		
Romania	2,862	5,056	5,400	2,190	2,201		
Russia	...	...	...	3,500	3,000		
South Africa	420	573	700	613	282		
Spain	4,160	3,508	3,200	3,700	3,400		
Switzerland	333	360	260	267	305		
Thailand	200	177	170	362	530		
Tunisia	300	460	450	435	528		
Turkey	649	1,179	1,300	1,527	1,354		
Ukraine	...	...	...	4,000	3,500		
UK	18,217	7,154	5,700	6,200	5,700	8	3.2
USA	83,271	36,606	35,700	38,700	39,500	1	21.9
Venezuela	266	243	500	500	500		
Vietnam	270	435	300	600	600		
Yemen	150	210	200	250	250		

Ships   thousand gross registered tons

merchant vessels launched

	1970	1980	1990	1996	Rank	%
WORLD	21,690	15,397	14,680	15,476		
Argentina	18	60	10	8		
Australia	54	8	25	25		
Belgium	155	99	57	...		
Brazil	100	615	105	...		
Bulgaria	53	152	81	132		
Canada	33	80	3	...		
China	...	...	453	602	5	3.9
Croatia	...	...	...	292		
Denmark	514	227	405	36		
Finland	222	198	161	296	10	1.9
France	960	328	108	360	9	2.3
Germany	2,021	802	863	1,200	3	7.8
Greece	73	22	3	...		
India	29	74	1	10		
Italy	598	168	352	520	6	3.4

Ships continued

	1970	1980	1990	1996	Rank	%
Japan	10,476	7,288	6,531	9,640	1	62.3
Korea, S.	...	629	3,295	5,000	2	32.3
Netherlands	461	125	163	199		
Norway	639	319	83	60		
Peru	35	17	...	7		
Poland	463	395	136	448	8	2.9
Portugal	16	167	24	20		
Romania	...	31	5	12		
Russia	...	...	...	40		
Singapore	...	...	...	32		
Singapore	6	27	42	...		
Spain	926	509	383	463	7	2.9
Sweden	1,711	338	27	...		
Taiwan	217	572	1,212	780	4	5.1
Turkey	11	14	8	100		
Ukraine	...	...	...	150		
UK	1,237	244	78	272		
USA	338	558	12	4		

Silver   *tonnes*
metal content

	1970	1980	1990	1994	1995	Rank	%
WORLD	**9,393**	**11,101**	**14,650**	**12,800**	**13,800**		
Argentina	64	73	83	38	48		
Australia	855	767	1,173	1,045	920	6	6.7
Bolivia	186	190	311	352	425	10	3.1
Brazil	11	45	60	170	170		
Bulgaria	...	24	59	29	29		
Burma	17	30	3.4	5.6	4.4		
Canada	1,376	1,070	1,502	768	1,245	4	9.0
Chile	74	299	655	959	1,036	5	7.5
China	25	60	150	225	225		
Congo (Zaïre)	53	79	84	1.0	1.0		
Czechoslovakia	...	35	26	...	...		
Dom. Rep.	...	48	23	9.2	0		
Finland	23	48	30	26	27		
France	150	74	21	2.9	2.9		
Germany	205	85	41	1.8	1.8		
Greece	...	60	63	45	45		
Honduras	119	22	31	28	30		
India	2.0	11	34	50	40		
Indonesia	9.0	22	67	106	161		
Iran	...	...	38	133	60		
Ireland	62	20	8.8	17	14		
Italy	33	43	14	14	14		
Japan	343	268	150	134	100		
Kazakhstan	...	...	900	800	800	7=	5.8
Korea, N.	22	290	280	200	200		
Korea, S.	53	63	16	8.6	0.2		
Malaysia	...	22	13	13	11		
Mexico	1,332	1,557	2,170	2,334	2,495	1	18.1
Morocco	21	98	241	333	333		
Namibia	38	105	93	64	69		
New Zealand	...	23	4.8	28	30		
Papua N.G.	1.0	37	106	78	65		
Peru	1,239	1,315	1,762	1,667	1,908	2	13.8
Philippines	53	61	45	32	31		
Poland	...	766	833	800	800	7=	5.8
Portugal	...	2.0	42	32	39		
Romania	25	28	24	18	18		
Russia	...	...	800	800	800	7=	5.8
Saudi Arabia	...	...	3.0	17	18		
South Africa	110	232	161	196	174		
Spain	51	178	270	175	175		
Sweden	123	166	225	275	268		
Thailand	10	15	21	11	...		
Turkey	...	...	27	60	60		
USA	1,400	1,006	2,125	1,480	1,450	3	10.5
Yugoslavia	...	...	105	32	32		
Zambia	48	24	19	12	8.4		
Zimbabwe	2.0	30	21	11	11		

Steel   *thousand tonnes*

	1970	1980	1990	1994	1995	Rank	%
WORLD	**593,791**	**690,000**	**685,000**	**730,000**	**750,000**		
Algeria	...	...	836	1,000	800		
Argentina	1,859	2,556	3,624	3,036	4,212		
Australia	6,874	7,895	6,684	7,632	8,052		
Austria	4,079	4,624	4,548	4,404	4,920		
Belarus	...	...	...	876	850		

Steel continued

	1970	1980	1990	1994	1995	Rank	%
Belgium	12,609	12,321	11,424	11,268	11,544		
Brazil	5,390	7,940	20,580	25,752	25,032	9	3.3
Bulgaria	1,800	2,565	2,184	2,496	2,724		
Canada	11,198	15,901	21,684	27,240	28,308	7	3.8
Chile	547	695	768	996	948		
China	17,790	37,120	64,656	93,144	93,840	2	12.5
Czech Rep.	...	...	...	7,080	7,188		
Egypt	304	500	1,000	2,600	2,600		
Finland	1,167	2,509	2,856	3,420	3,168		
France	23,773	23,176	19,020	18,024	18,132		
Germany	5,093	51,146	38,436	40,836	42,048	5	5.6
Greece	435	935	996	852	936		
Hungary	3,108	3,766	2,808	1,932	1,860		
India	6,286	9,427	14,964	13,356	13,356		
Indonesia	...	...	2,000	3,200	3,500		
Iran	...	...	2,500	4,500	4,700		
Italy	17,277	26,501	25,452	26,148	27,720	8	3.7
Japan	93,322	111,395	110,328	95,556	101,640	1	13.6
Kazakstan	...	...	...	5,000	5,000		
Korea, N.	2,200	3,500	7,000	7,000	6,000		
Korea, S.	481	5,760	24,468	33,744	36,744	6	4.9
Libya	...	...	...	900	900		
Luxembourg	5,462	4,620	3,480	3,072	2,616		
Mexico	3,846	7,003	8,220	8,760	9,948		
Netherlands	5,042	4,959	5,412	6,168	6,408		
N. Zealand	...	...	...	800	800		
Norway	869	853	396	468	504		
Poland	11,750	18,648	13,620	11,112	11,892		
Portugal	...	...	744	744	828		
Romania	6,517	13,175	6,216	5,796	6,552		
Russia	...	...	75,000	48,768	48,816	4	6.5
Saudi Arabia	...	...	1,500	2,400	2,500		
Slovak Rep.	...	...	...	3,972	3,500		
South Africa	4,674	8,976	8,628	8,304	8,688		
Spain	7,394	12,563	12,624	13,440	13,932		
Sweden	5,494	4,231	4,452	4,956	4,920		
Switzerland	524	929	1,000	1,000	1,000		
Taiwan	607	3,651	11,541	18,816	18,380		
Turkey	1,312	1,700	9,408	12,180	12,816		
Ukraine	...	...	40,000	24,096	22,296	10	3.0
UK	28,316	11,277	16,464	17,244	17,208		
USA	119,309	101,456	98,016	88,812	93,588	3	12.5
Venezuela	927	1,784	3,180	3,516	3,636		
Zimbabwe	250	804	1,000	1,000	1,000		

Tin   *thousand tonnes*

	1970	1980	1990	1994	1995	Rank	%
WORLD	**272**	**283**	**227**	**213**	**206**		
Australia	5.7	4.8	0.6	0.3	0.2		
Belgium	5.7	2.8	...	5.0	5.0	7	2.4
Bolivia	0.7	18	13	20	18	4	8.6
Brazil	3.5	9.0	37	19	15	5	7.5
China	22	15	28	68	61	1	29.6
Congo (Zaïre)	1.4	0.5	0	0	0		
Germany	12	5.7	3.5	0	0		
Indonesia	5.2	31	30	38	44	2	21.4
Italy	3.0	3.5	...	...	...		
Japan	1.4	1.3	0.8	0.7	0.6		
Korea, S.	0.3	0.4	2.5	1.1	1.0		
Malaysia	90	71	49	38	39	3	19.1
Mexico	1.4	1.4	5.0	2.3	2.1	10	1.0
Netherlands	8.5	1.1	6.1	...	...		
Nigeria	8.1	2.7	0.3	0.3	0.3		
Portugal	0.4	0.4	0.1	0.1	0.1		
Russia	...	...	...	5.0	5.0	8	2.4
Singapore	0	4.0	0.6	...	...		
South Africa	1.5	2.2	2.1	0	0		
Spain	4.5	4.8	1.3	2.0	2.0		
Thailand	22	35	16	7.6	8.2	6	4.0
UK	32	18	12	0	0		
USA	25	6.4	0.2	0.1	0.2		
Vietnam	0	0	0.5	2.3	2.4	9	1.2
Zimbabwe	0.6	0.9	0.4	0.1	0		

Includes recovery from scrap in Western countries.

Tin ore   *thousand tonnes*
metal content

	1970	1980	1990	1994	1995	Rank	%
WORLD	**186**	**236**	**209**	**188**	**195**		
Australia	8.9	12	7.4	7.4	8.7	7	4.4
Bolivia	30	28	17	16	14.5	5	7.4
Brazil	4.3	6.9	39	20	19	4	9.9
Burma	0.3	1.1	0.5	0.6	0.6		
Canada	0.1	6.9	3.8	0	0		
China	...	16	36	54	54	1	27.7
Congo (Zaïre)	6.5	3.2	1.6	0.5	0.7		
Germany	...	1.8	1.8	0	0		
Indonesia	19	33	30	31	46	2	23.6
Japan	0.8	0.5	...	0	0		
Kazakhstan	...	...	...	0.4	0.4		
Laos	1.4	0.6	0.3	0.2	0.8		
Malaysia	74	61	29	6.5	6.4	8	3.3
Mexico	0.5	0.1	...	0	0		
Namibia	1.0	1.0	0.9	0	0		
Nigeria	8.0	2.7	0.2	0.2	0.3		
Peru	0	1.1	5.1	20	22	3	11.4
Portugal	0.4	0.3	1.4	4.3	4.6	9	2.4
Russia	...	...	...	11	9.0	6	4.6
Rwanda	1.3	1.6	0.7	0.2	0.2		
South Africa	2.0	2.9	1.1	0	0		
Spain	0.4	0.4	0.1	0	1.8		
Thailand	22	34	15	3.1	1.8		
UK	1.7	3.3	3.4	1.6	1.9		
USA	...	16	0.1	0.1	0.1		
Vietnam	...	0.4	0.8	4.0	3.6	10	1.8
Zimbabwe	0.6	0.9	0.8	0.1	0.1		

Tungsten   *tonnes*
metal content

	1970	1980	1991	1994	1995	Rank	%
WORLD	**43,990**	**52,000**	**38,000**	**30,000**	**30,000**		
Argentina	181	35	...	...	...		
Australia	1,760	3,575	300	11	...		
Austria	165	2,150	1,400	...	650	7	2.2
Bolivia	2,411	2,664	1,100	540	665	6	2.2
Brazil	1,463	1,104	300	90	30		
Burma	278	848	300	115	250	9	0.8
Canada	1,690	3,178	0	0	0		
China	10,100	15,000	25,000	17,400	17,500	1	58.3
Congo (Zaïre)	237	134	20	...	...		
France	88	577	0	0	0		
Japan	854	700	200	...	...		
Kazakstan	...	...	500	100	450	8	1.5
Korea, N.	2,700	2,200	3,200	900	900	3	3.0
Korea, S.	2,822	2,737	700	...	...		
Malaysia	92	35	...	2	...		
Mexico	288	266	150	60	120		
Mongolia	...	1,500	1,500	250	40		
Peru	1,014	549	1,000	330	700	5	2.3
Portugal	1,860	1,580	1,000	1,000	870	4	2.9
Russia	...	...	...	4,250	3,300	2	11.0
Rwanda	410	323	150	65	85		
Spain	514	448	20	...	...		
Sweden	0	364	...	...	...		
Tajikistan	...	...	200	100	100		
Thailand	895	1,615	650	125	60		
Turkey	0	400	400	...	...		
Uganda	153	20	40	60	...		
UK	0	40	40	...	...		
USA	5,326	2,754	200	20	30		
Uzbekistan	...	...	300	360	250	10	0.8
Zambia	0	90	...	...	...		

Television receivers   *thousands*

	1970	1980	1990	1993	1994	Rank	%
WORLD	**44,000**	**71,000**	**128,716**	**134,500**	**135,000**		
Algeria	30	94	283	258	165		
Argentina	194	454	687	1,612	1,523		
Australia	320	332	158	...	...		
Austria	369	...	...	...	...		
Azerbaijan	...	...	...	8,681	2,280	10	1.7
Belarus	...	...	1,302	610	473		
Belgium	505	746	1,084	559	...		
Brazil	726	3,254	3,196	3,638	5,522	6	4.1
Bulgaria	193	91	219	26	•	...

Television receivers continued

	1970	1980	1990	1993	1994	Rank	%
Canada	543	444	...	...	...		
China	...	2,492	26,847	30,330	32,833	1	24.3
Denmark	70	77	122	...	...		
Egypt	64	318	333	269	234		
Finland	146	341	412	321	339		
France	1,511	1,928	2,838	2,523	2,796	8	2.1
Germany	3,316	5,003	4,227	2,800	3,234	7	2.4
Hong Kong	27	108	1,177	...	...		
Hungary	364	417	492	204	272		
India	...	88	1,322	1,540	1,500		
Indonesia	5	607	700	1,000	1,000		
Iran	125	246	598	750	750		
Italy	2,030	1,984	2,325	2,432	2,780	9	2.1
Japan	12,488	15,205	15,132	12,840	11,192	4	8.3
Korea, S.	114	6,819	16,184	15,956	17,102	2	12.7
Kyrgyzstan	...	...	...	1,694	1,500		
Lithuania	...	...	...	423	181		
Malaysia	44	157	3,238	6,629	7,702	5	5.7
Mexico	431	964	633	477	498		
Moldova	...	...	...	167	106		
New Zealand	45	126	...	...	...		
Nigeria	6	208	...	...	...		
Norway	103	...	...	...	...		
Pakistan	...	74	200	162	113		
Philippines	44	206	...	...	...		
Poland	616	900	748	855	888		
Portugal	64	467	329	...	...		
Romania	280	541	401	464	452		
Russia	...	...	4,717	3,987	2,240		
Singapore	...	1,889	2,500	...	...		
Slovak Rep.	...	...	...	165	150		
South Africa	338	377	373	321	...		
Spain	618	763	2,466	...	...		
Sweden	178	308	284	...	...		
Taiwan	1,254	7,041	3,703	1,900	1,900		
Thailand	...	248	2,351	...	...		
Turkey	4	327	2,005	1,922	1,490		
Ukraine	...	...	3,774	1,919	...		
UK	2,214	2,364	...	...	...		
USA	8,298	10,320	13,982	13,679	13,881	3	10.3

Tyres   *thousands*

	1970	1980	1990	1994	1995	Rank	%
WORLD	**600,000**	**700,000**	**860,000**	**861,000**	**900,000**		
Argentina	3,530	5,297	4,956	7,332	7,176		
Australia	7,227	7,674	6,000	8,500	8,500		
Belarus	...	...	...	1,027	1,000		
Brazil	7,847	22,102	29,160	33,396	30,720	9	3.4
Bulgaria	546	1,532	1,800	552	648		
Canada	19,109	22,335	1,795	552	500		
Chile	676	878	1,632	2,280	2,328		
China	4,250	11,460	31,488	73,104	83,484	3	9.3
Colombia	875	1,899	1,408	...	...		
Czech Rep.	2,500	5,000	5,000	3,500	3,500		
Ecuador	120	...	102	912	900		
Egypt	807	1,113	1,176	1,176	1,200		
Finland	1,037	1,127	...	...	...		
France	39,415	50,601	57,516	57,696	59,268	4	6.6
Germany	42,240	44,866	48,240	46,416	48,348	6	5.4
India	3,058	4,720	8,076	10,368	12,036		
Indonesia	358	3,821	7,848	15,000	15,000		
Iran	...	...	6,012	6,000	6,000		
Israel	1,392	1,242	780	972	924		
Italy	22,383	29,681	38,292	29,604	40,872	7	4.5
Japan	66,556	116,384	162,936	142,104	150,300	2	16.7
Korea, S.	899	12,327	27,900	47,100	53,472	5	5.9
Luxembourg	2,974	2,138	...	...	...		
Malaysia	3,067	4,634	6,744	10,152	11,148		
Mexico	3,369	8,749	11,772	12,312	11,004		
N. Zealand	1,433	1,663	1,550	...	...		
Pakistan	109	204	912	828	850		
Peru	609	717	637	784	...		
Philippines	598	1,637	2,208	...	...		
Poland	2,995	6,533	5,808	7,608	9,492		
Portugal	1,400	1,833	2,976	1,800	1,800		
Romania	2,457	5,003	3,708	2,796	3,024		
Russia	...	...	...	17,400	17,412		
Slovak Rep.	...	...	...	3,797	4,800		
Slovenia	...	...	...	4,632	4,500		

Tyres continued

	1970	1980	1990	1994	1995	Rank	%
South Africa	3,600	5,254	7,476	5,172	5,760		
Spain	8,909	15,626	23,361	25,000	25,000	10	2.8
Sweden	5,379	2,691	2,162	2,500	2,500		
Thailand	714	1,762	4,188	5,500	6,500		
Turkey	1,139	2,929	4,596	8,664	10,524		
Ukraine	...	...	...	8,000	8,000		
UK	30,545	26,346	29,376	31,800	32,052	8	3.6
USA	190,251	158,435	210,660	243,600	255,156	1	28.4
Venezuela	1,577	3,483	3,948	4,968	5,000		
Yugoslavia	...	...	...	1,332	1,620		

Uranium   *tonnes*
metal content

	1970	1980	1991	1994	1995	Rank	%
WORLD	**24,000**	**52,000**	**43,000**	**32,200**	**33,030**		
Argentina	50	242	10	64	65		
Australia	299	1,561	3,750	2,183	3,712	2	11.2
Belgium	...	...	40	40	40		
Brazil	...	...	...	50	50		
Bulgaria	...	...	400	50	20		
Canada	3,639	6,739	8,200	9,694	10,515	1	31.8
China	...	...	1,250	780	780		
Czech Rep.	...	...	1,700	541	600		
France	1,476	2,845	2,500	1,025	950	10	2.9
Gabon	472	1,034	540	650	630		
Germany	0	41	1,200	395	274		
Hungary	...	...	450	400	200		
India	0	150	210	200	200		
Kazakstan	...	...	3,600	2,240	1,500	9	4.5
Mongolia	...	...	130	100	100		
Namibia	0	4,036	2,450	1,900	2,010	6	6.1
Niger	54	4,132	3,000	2,975	2,970	3	9.0
Portugal	95	68	30	24	24		
Romania	...	...	150	120	100		
Russia	...	...	3,250	2,400	2,250	5	6.8
South Africa	3,737	6,186	1,700	1,700	1,550	7	4.7
Spain	60	167	200	255	255		
Ukraine	...	...	800	500	500		
USA	11,538	16,800	3,000	1,400	2,300	4	7.0
Uzbekistan	...	...	3,000	2,010	1,500	8	4.5

Vanadium   *tonnes*
metal content

	1970	1980	1990	1993	1994	Rank	%
WORLD	**12,050**	**34,800**	**37,000**	**33,000**	**34,000**		
Chile	...	270	4,500	5,000	5,000	3	14.7
Finland	1,196	4,500	...	...	...		
Hungary	...	...	300	200	200	7	0.6
Japan	...	...	700	250	300	5	0.9
Namibia	600	...	...	...	...		
New Zealand	...	...	...	200	200	6	0.6
Norway	1,080	490	...	...	...		
Russia	...	...	12,000	10,000	10,000	2	29.4
South Africa	4,257	12,700	17,100	15,000	15,700	1	46.2
USA	4,825	4,360	2,300	2,850	2,750	4	8.1

Zinc   *thousand tonnes*

	1970	1980	1990	1994	1995	Rank	%
WORLD	**6,126**	**7,455**	**8,073**	**8,785**	**8,757**		
Algeria	...	25	24	24	24		
Argentina	39	40	34	37	38		
Australia	264	361	304	315	320	8	3.7
Austria	18	23	29	1.6	1.6		
Belgium	233	258	307	310	250		
Brazil	13	97	155	187	197		
Bulgaria	76	91	74	77	77		
Canada	413	592	592	693	720	2	8.2
China	100	155	526	1,017	1,015	1	11.6
Congo (Zaïre)	64	44	38	0.6	0.6		
Finland	56	147	175	173	179		
France	258	264	289	309	310	9	3.5
Germany	372	485	488	627	462	5	5.3
India	23	44	99	176	166		
Italy	157	217	254	266	267		
Japan	763	977	851	927	664	3	7.6
Kazakstan	...	...	...	175	175		
Korea, N.	90	105	199	100	100		
Korea, S.	2.3	76	257	272	279	10	3.2
Macedonia	...	...	...	32	32		

Zinc continued

	1970	1980	1990	1994	1995	Rank	%
Mexico	85	144	199	357	355	7	4.0
Netherlands	46	170	208	213	206		
Norway	62	91	138	154	146		
Peru	69	64	118	151	128		
Poland	209	218	132	156	167		
Romania	60	46	12	18	29		
Russia	...	...	...	160	150		
South Africa	27	81	92	94	99		
Spain	88	162	265	315	362	6	4.1
Taiwan	0	0	107	...	...		
Thailand	0	0	71	71	56		
Turkey	...	13	20	19	20		
Ukraine	...	...	...	10	10		
UK	239	149	146	148	160		
USA	1,174	674	604	625	612	4	7.0
Uzbekistan	...	...	...	60	60		
Vietnam	...	10	10	10	10		
Zambia	54	33	11	0.1	...		

Includes recovery from scrap in Western countries.

Zinc ore   *thousand tonnes*
metal content

	1970	1980	1990	1993	1994	1995	Rank	%
WORLD	**5,520**	**6,192**	**7,366**	**6,758**	**6,830**	**6,728**		
Algeria	17	8.0	4.0	3.0	3.0	4.0		
Argentina	39	34	39	31	27	28		
Australia	496	495	939	1,000	955	937	2	13.9
Austria	16	22	17	20	0	0		
Bolivia	47	50	108	138	101	146		
Brazil	12	70	113	138	140	146		
Bulgaria	76	89	35	30	30	29		
Canada	1,239	1,059	1,203	984	1,011	1,113	1	16.5
Chile	1.0	1.0	25	29	31	36		
China	106	180	619	729	990	758	3	11.3
Congo (Zaïre)	104	67	62	10	0.6	0.8		
Finland	69	58	52	23	17	17		
France	19	37	24	14	0	0		
Germany	127	121	58	0	0	0		
Greece	9.0	27	27	22	17	13		
Greenland	0.0	86	48	...	23	24		
Honduras	5.0	16	29	24	23	24		
India	8.0	32	70	170	148	151		
Iran	58	30	15	77	75	80		
Ireland	97	229	167	194	195	184	7	2.7
Italy	110	57	42	297	22	23		
Japan	280	238	127	119	101	95		
Kazakstan	...	...	...	207	170	155	9	2.3
Korea, N.	130	130	195	110	90	90		
Korea, S.	23	56	23	14	7.0	8.0		
Macedonia	...	...	...	29	26	26		
Mexico	266	243	307	359	381	378	6	5.6
Morocco	16	6.0	18	66	79	78		
Namibia	46	32	38	28	33	30		
Norway	10	28	17	14	16	10		
Peru	321	468	584	668	682	689	4	10.2
Poland	242	217	155	151	151	154	10	2.3
Romania	...	40	36	35	35	35		
Russia	...	...	...	154	147	131		
South Africa	...	82	75	78	76	74		
Spain	98	179	258	170	170	172	8	2.6
Sweden	93	167	160	167	160	140		
Thailand	0.5	1.0	81	69	59	14		
Tunisia	12	9.0	7.3	1.3	13	44		
Turkey	24	23	39	32	34	35		
USA	485	349	543	488	570	601	5	8.9
Uzbekistan	...	...	...	33	21	34		
Vietnam	...	10	10	12	12	12		
Yugoslavia	...	...	...	11	7.3	12		
Zambia	66	43	35	20	1.0	0		

Key world developments

Political changes

Africa

The currencies of Kenya, Tanzania and Uganda were declared mutually convertible on 1 July 1996 in an attempt to boost regional trade and investment. An East African Co-operation grouping was established in March 1996 between the three.

Algeria

The government has declared that English will replace French as the official second language. Legislation has also been passed to enforce the use of Arabic in public life.

Antarctica

Faraday, the oldest base on the Antarctic peninsula, and a home to British scientists since 1934, was given to the Ukrainian Antarctic Survey on 8 February 1996. The base will now be known as Vernadsky and will continue its programme of research into the ionosphere. The UK has four remaining Antarctic bases: Rothera, Halley, Signy and Bird Island.

Arctic

On 19 September 1996, the seven countries bordering the Arctic Ocean (Canada, Iceland, Denmark [Greenland], Norway, Sweden, Russia and the US), plus Finland, formed a new Arctic Council.

ASEAN

Laos and Burma (Myanmar) were admitted into the Association of South-East Asian States in July 1997. The decision brings 457 million people under ASEAN's umbrella. The admission of Cambodia was put on hold after a military coup.

Belarus / Russia

The two countries signed a treaty creating a Commonwealth of Sovereign States on 2 April 1996. The treaty is the most significant step towards reintegration since the collapse of the Soviet Union. It came four days after another Kremlin ceremony in which the leaders of Kazakstan and Kyrgyzstan signed an economic pact with Russia and Belarus, creating an inner core within the CIS.

Bosnia-Herzegovina

Leaders of Bosnia, Serbia and Croatia signed a comprehensive US-sponsored peace agreement on 14 December 1995. It was decreed that Bosnia would remain a single state, with a central government in a united Sarajevo and free, supervised elections. The state consists of two entities: a Muslim-Croat Federation and a Bosnian Serb Republic. The last obstacle to the deal was the Serbian-held Posavina corridor, which marks Bosnia's frontier with Croatia, and is a guarantee to Belgrade that Serb communities outside Serbia can be sustained.

The World Bank has agreed to admit Bosnia-Herzegovina to membership before the country pays off its share of the former Yugoslavia's debts and arrears to the organization.

The fragile Moslem-Croat federation was bolstered by the creation of a customs union in March 1996. The agreement provides for a single state budget, a unitary banking system and a new federation flag.

A new national flag was officially introduced in February 1998. It is blue, with a diagonal sequence of white stars and an inverse yellow triangle.

Bulgaria

The provinces of Mikhaylovgrad and Razgrad have changed their names to Montana and Ruse, respectively.

Canada

A new region, the first in Newfoundland, has been established to encompass the area of Fogo Island.

On 2 January 1998, six former cities around Toronto were combined to form a larger unified city of Toronto.

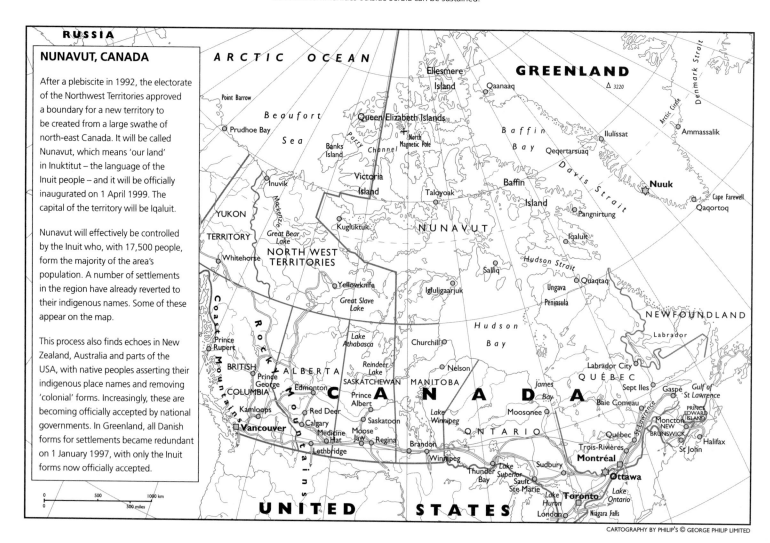

NUNAVUT, CANADA

After a plebiscite in 1992, the electorate of the Northwest Territories approved a boundary for a new territory to be created from a large swathe of north-east Canada. It will be called Nunavut, which means 'our land' in Inuktitut – the language of the Inuit people – and it will be officially inaugurated on 1 April 1999. The capital of the territory will be Iqaluit.

Nunavut will effectively be controlled by the Inuit who, with 17,500 people, form the majority of the area's population. A number of settlements in the region have already reverted to their indigenous names. Some of these appear on the map.

This process also finds echoes in New Zealand, Australia and parts of the USA, with native peoples asserting their indigenous place names and removing 'colonial' forms. Increasingly, these are becoming officially accepted by national governments. In Greenland, all Danish forms for settlements became redundant on 1 January 1997, with only the Inuit forms now officially accepted.

CARICOM
The Caribbean Community (CARICOM) doubled its population with the accession of Haiti. The country becomes the second non-English speaking member, following the admission of Surinam in 1995.

China
The Municipality of Chongqing no longer comes within the jurisdiction of Sichuan province. It now forms a province in its own right. As a result, Sichuan's population was cut by 30 million to 84.28 million. Shandong is now the second most populous Chinese province after Henan.

An agreement fixing a common border between the eastern provinces of Xinjiang and Tibet was signed on 9 April 1996. All of China's internal boundaries are to be properly defined over the next four years, in an attempt to avoid disputes over valuable natural resources.

Hong Kong (Xianggang) was officially handed back to China on 1 July 1997. The Chinese government will almost certainly remove colonial-style names from Hong Kong and these will be standardized into Pinyin, as will the existing Cantonese forms, which formerly had a unique system of transcription. To give some well-known examples: Aberdeen to Xianggangzai, Stanley to Chizhu Cun, Victoria Peak to Cheqi Shan, Wan Chai to Wanzai, and Kowloon to Jiulong.

Commonwealth
Mozambique was admitted into the Commonwealth in November 1996 as a 'unique and special case'. The accession of the former Portuguese colony marks a precedent for the Commonwealth because its existing members all have former colonial links with the UK.

Fiji officially rejoined the Commonwealth on 1 October 1997. Its membership lapsed a decade ago after a racially motivated coup.

Council of Europe
Russia was elected as the 39th member of the Council of Europe on 25 January 1996. Russian accession is seen as an antidote to destabilization, particularly in the Caucasus.

The Council of Europe admitted Croatia as its 40th member in October 1996, after a delay of six months caused by human rights issues.

Croatia
The region of Eastern Slavonia, under the control of UN peacekeeping forces since 1991, was returned to Croatia on 15 January 1998. Many thousands of Serb residents have moved away from the region, fearing for their future under the Croatian government.

Democratic Republic of the Congo
In September 1996, the civil war in Rwanda spilled over into the Zaïrean province of Kivu. Rwandan Tutsi soldiers joined forces with ethnic Zaïrean Tutsis to fight the poorly motivated Zaïrean army whose leader, President Mobutu, was being treated for cancer. The rebel leader, Laurent Kabila, entered

Kinshasa on 20 May 1996, after routing government forces in an eight-month push through the country. He immediately erased the country name (Zaïre) adopted by President Mobuto in 1972 and introduced a new currency, the Congolese franc. A new flag was also unveiled, with a royal blue background, six gold stars down the hoist and one larger star in the middle.

Kabila's rise to power is seen by many analysts as a significant indication of the waning influence of the French in the region, with a network of truly independent African leaders now stretching from Angola to Eritrea.

Eritrea
It was announced on 15 July 1997 that a new currency, the nacfa, would replace the Ethiopian Birr in the country.

Ethiopia
The flag of Ethiopia now includes the national emblem (which consists of a blue disc with a pentangle) in the centre. The symbol is supposed to represent the common will of the 68 ethnic groups within the country.

European Union
The EU is preparing to bow out of its arrangements with the Lomé group of African, Caribbean and Pacific countries. A deal signed on 4 November 1995 will continue to give them trade privileges and aid until the year 2000. From then on, the Lomé convention will effectively cease to exist.

A decision has been reached on the naming of the future single currency. Finance ministers and central bankers agreed to call it the Euro, which will be made up of 100 cents. Member states will be able to choose whose head to put on 'their' side of the coins and there will be a competition to design the pan-European side.

After a week of intensive debate, the EU decided that Estonia and Slovenia should join Poland, Hungary, Cyprus and the Czech Republic in the first wave of countries negotiating to join the EU. The other hopefuls will all have their applications reviewed annually, with the exception of Turkey, whose membership application is in limbo.

The current status of applications to join the EU is as follows:
Applicants: Czech Republic, Slovak Republic, Slovenia, Poland, Hungary, Romania, Bulgaria, Lithuania, Latvia, Estonia, Cyprus.
Application suspended: Turkey.
Application withdrawn: Malta, Switzerland, Norway.

Greenland
As from 1 January 1997, Inuit forms alone will be official for names in Greenland. Danish forms will no longer be used.

Guatemala
The government and left-wing URNG rebels signed a detailed peace accord in December 1996, which ended 36 years of civil war. More than 150,000 Guatemalans were killed in the conflict, which was arguably the worst in modern Latin America.

IMO
The International Maritime Organization has a new, landlocked member: Mongolia. Western Samoa was admitted on 25 October 1996 as the 155th member.

India
The national government officially recognized the name change of Bombay to Mumbai in May 1996, shortly after the alteration was sanctioned by recently elected Hindu extremists in Maharashtra state.

The Tamil Nadu Assembly approved a bill changing the name of the state capital, Madras, to Chennai, on 31 August 1996. The central government in Delhi later approved the change. Chennai is the historic and traditional Tamil form.

A decision was taken in September 1996 to create a new state called Uttarakhand from the mountainous northern part of Uttar Pradesh. No firm date was set for its creation.

Indonesia
The province of Irian Jaya is to be split into three regional support areas, rather than into three separate provinces as many had predicted. The first step in the new development was the inauguration of Sorong into an 'administration city'.

Israel
On 6 and 7 March 1996, Israel deployed tanks along the border separating it from the West Bank for the first time since the territory was seized from Jordan in 1967. The deployment coincided with a clampdown on Hamas after a series of suicide bombings.

Yasser Arafat was sworn in as the first elected Palestinian president on 20 January 1996.

Israel / Oman
On 1 October 1995, Oman became the first Gulf state to establish formal trade links with Israel.

Japan / China
After a series of provocative acts by both sides, Tokyo dispatched 17 police vessels to a group of disputed islands in the East China Sea on 22 September 1996. The islands are called the Diaoyu in Chinese and the Senkaku in Japanese (by whom they have been held since 1922). They are claimed by China, Taiwan and Japan.

Kazakstan
The Central Asian republic abandoned the transliterated Russian spelling (Kazakhstan) of their country's name in April 1995.

Kazakstan acceded to the Organization of the Islamic Conference (OIC) on December 12 1995. An official bulletin said that total OIC membership now stood at 52.

In an effort to weld together a nation containing over 100 ethnic groups, the Kazak president has drafted a new law

Political changes continued

that would require all citizens to be able to speak, read and write in the Turkic Kazak language. Ethnic Kazaks have until 2001 to master the language, with ethnic Russians given until 2006.

The capital of Kazakstan officially changed from Almaty (Alma Ata) to Aqmola, in the north of the country, on 10 December 1997. Northern Kazakstan is dominated by Russians, and the move is seen by the government as a method of bringing a sense of Kazak national identity to the area.

Kiribati

Amidst the continuing controversy about where the sun will 'first' rise on the first day of the new millennium, Kiribati has changed the name of Caroline Island (which it claims will see dawn first) to Millennium Island. They have also redrawn the international dateline in their favour.

Moldova

An agreement has been signed to end the seven-year-old separatist dispute in the Transdniester region. The ethnically Slav (mostly Russian) area will remain part of non-Slavic (mostly Romanian) Moldova, although it will have a high degree of autonomy.

Mongolia

All tariffs and trade taxes were abolished on 1 May 1997, making Mongolia the only country in the world to levy no taxes at all on trade.

Montserrat

Plans for a new capital in the volcano-devastated island have been presented to the British government. The former capital, Plymouth, was submerged by pyroclastic flows from the Soufrière volcano (see page 111). The exact location, should the plans be accepted, will be a 280-acre site around Carr's Bay and Little Bay in the north of the island.

New Zealand

Mount Cook should now be officially referred to by both its 'colonial' form and its original Maori form, Aoraki, according to the New Zealand board for geographic names.

Nigeria

Six new states have been created in a government reorganization. The six are:
Bayelsa (capital: Yenogoa, created from Rivers State);
Eboniyi (capital: Abakaliki, created from Abia and Enugu States); Ekiti (capital: Ado-Ekiti, created from Ondo State); Gombe (capital: Gombe, created from Bauchi State); Nassarawa (capital: Lafia, created from Plateau State); and Zamfara (capital: Gusau, created from Sokoto State).

OECD

The Czech Republic was admitted as the 26th member of the OECD in November 1995. Hungary followed in March 1996, with South Korea accepted in November 1996.

OPEC

Following the example of Ecuador in 1992, Gabon made the decision to withdraw from OPEC in June 1996.

Panama

The government has granted autonomy to the region inhabited by the Guaymi Indians, near the border with Costa Rica.

Portugal

Leaders of the world's seven Portuguese-speaking nations have launched a lusophone commonwealth intended to expand their economic and cultural influence. The Community of Portuguese-Speaking Countries (CPLP) will include Angola, Brazil, Cape Verde, São Tomé and Príncipe, Guinea-Bissau, Mozambique and Portugal.

Clocks were not moved forward on 31 March 1996, thereby aligning Portugal with GMT and not Central European Time.

Romania

The Central European Free Trade Agreement (CEFTA) received another member with the accession of Romania on 1 April 1997. The other members of CEFTA are Hungary, Poland, Slovenia, the Czech Republic and the Slovak Republic.

Russia

A peace deal was signed on 27 May 1996 with the Chechen leader, Zelimkhan Yandarbiyev. The agreement fell short of a comprehensive constitutional settlement and certainly did not provide for full independence. Moscow now refers to Chechenia as a 'sovereign state' within the Russian Federation, and it has been granted a special status, with many more powers than the other republics. Moscow has also promised a referendum on full independence at some point in the future. The Chechen separatists (who refer to their country as Ichkeria), declared independence in 1991, however. The death toll from the war has reached 90,000, according to Russian sources.

Japan dropped its opposition to Russia becoming a member of the G7 group of leading industrial countries in May 1997. The G7 summit in Denver (June 1997) was consequently called the 'The Summit of the Eight'.

Estonia, Latvia and Russia have agreed on the position of the point at which their state borders converge. The tripoint is on the Pededze river, which borders Latvia's Aluksne district.

All Russian regions, apart from Chechenia, have now joined a series of eight new 'economic associations', intended to group similar regions together. The eight associations are: Siberia, Far East, Greater Volga, Urals, Black Earth, Central Russia, North-West and North Caucasus.

On 1 January 1998, the Russian government redenominated the rouble by removing three zeros from its value.

Rwanda

The constitution was amended on 16 January 1996 to recognize English as the third official language, along with Kinyarwanda and French.

Seychelles

A new flag came into general use on 5 June 1996. The change followed the abolition of one-party rule and the introduction of a new constitution. The previous flag was in the colours of the ruling party, whereas the new flag has diagonal sections of blue, gold, red, white and green.

Slovak Republic

The government has drawn up a new administrative map which has been criticized by the Hungarian minority in the south. They claim that the new regions deliberately under-represent them politically. In another controversial move, the government convened a law to make Slovak the only official language and restricting the use of others in public. The eight new administrative regions are: Bratislavsky, Trnavasky, Trenciansky, Nitriansky, Zilinsky, Banskobystricky, Presovsky, Kosicky

South Africa

The province of Eastern Transvaal has changed its name to Mpumalanga.

South Africa was accepted as the 77th member of the African Development Bank on 13 December 1995.

South America

The five countries of the Andean Pact have announced the creation of an 'Andean Community' in an ambitious attempt to revitalize their flagging 27-year-old trading bloc. Within five years, the new Act of Trujillo, signed by Peru, Bolivia, Colombia, Venezuela and Ecuador, is scheduled to provide the community with a directly elected parliament and a genuine customs union.

Sri Lanka

The national army captured the last Tamil Tiger-held territory on the Jaffna peninsula on 16 May 1996, claiming that they had virtually eliminated the rebels from the country. Two months later, Tamil forces launched a surprise attack on an army garrison in Mullaittivu, killing hundreds of government troops. The conflict continued into 1998, with Tamil rebels capturing a government base in Kilinochchi on 31 January 1998. The government, however, claimed that it had killed 350 rebels during the battle for the base.

Switzerland

The traditionally neutral country joined Nato's Partnership for Peace in October 1996, in an attempt to promote security in post-Cold War Europe.

Tajikistan

Nizhniy Pyandzh has changed its name to Panji Poyon.

Turkmenistan

At the 11th summit meeting of the Non-Aligned Movement, held in Colombia, the membership of Turkmenistan was formally endorsed.

The PCGN have approved the following name changes: Krasnowodsk to Turkmenbashi, Hasan Guli to Esenguly,

Firyuza to Pöwrize, Tashkepri to Dashköpri, and Ostrov Ogurchinskiy to Turkmen Adasy.

Tuvalu

The old Tuvalu flag has been reinstated after an 18-month flirtation with a republican version.

Ukraine

The new hryvna currency went into general circulation on 2 September 1996, replacing the karbovanet.

UK

The old two-tier system of local government was replaced in Wales and Scotland on 1 April 1996. Wales was split into 22 new unitary authorities, with 32 authorities designated in Scotland.

On the same day, the first 11 unitary authorities were created in England, from the former counties of Cleveland, Humberside and Avon, as well as the City of York. A year later, on 1 April 1997, a further 12 English unitary authorities were created: in the Midlands, Bedfordshire and the South Coast.

England's turbulent five-year local government review ended in March 1996 when the Department of the Environment officially approved the final eight new unitary councils. These will be Blackburn with Darwen, Blackpool, Halton, Peterborough, Telford and Wrekin, Thurrock, Warrington, and the Medway Towns. These will come into existence in April 1998. Among those to remain as districts within a two-tier system will be Huntingdonshire and Rushcliffe.

The following unitary authority name changes occurred in Wales shortly after they were inaugurated on 1 April 1996: Caernarfonshire and Merionethshire changed to Gwynedd, Aberconwy and Colwyn to Conwy, and Cardiganshire to Ceredigion.

Similarly, in Scotland, three unitary authority name changes occurred shortly after they were inaugurated. Borders changed to Scottish Borders, Perthshire and Kinross to Perth and Kinross, and City of Dundee to Dundee City.

The English Unitary Authority of Thamesdown (implemented in 1997) has changed its name to Swindon. In addition, Blackburn (to be implemented in 1998) will now be called Blackburn with Darwen, and The Wrekin will be known as Telford and Wrekin.

Referenda for devolution in Wales and Scotland took place in September 1997. Both countries voted for the proposals, with 50.3% in favour in Wales and 74.3% in favour in Scotland.

The first elections to the Scottish Parliament and the Welsh Assembly will probably be held in 1999 and they are both scheduled to convene in 2000. The respective powers of the Parliament and the Assembly will differ in several respects:
• The Scottish Parliament will have the power to overturn UK legislation and introduce legislation in areas not retained by Westminster. The Welsh Assembly can only amend Westminster legislation in the limited areas devoted to it.
• The Scottish Parliament will also have powers to vary the basic rate of income tax, while the Welsh Assembly will have to rely on funding by central government.

The map shows the 6 counties in Northern Ireland, the 32 unitary authorities in Scotland, the 22 unitary authorities in Wales and the 87 unitary authorities in England as of 1 April 1998. Authorities which are too small to name on the map are numbered and listed separately.

The Channel Islands and the Isle of Man are dependencies of the Crown and have their own parliaments. They are not part of the United Kingdom.

AREA DATA

	Area in square kilometres
England	130,439
Wales	20,768
Scotland	77,167
Northern Ireland	13,483
United Kingdom	**241,857**
Isle of Man	**572**
Channel Islands	**195**
Ireland	**68,896**

CARTOGRAPHY BY PHILIP'S. COPYRIGHT GEORGE PHILIP LTD

SCOTLAND	WALES	ENGLAND	ENGLAND cont.
1. ABERDEEN CITY	15. SWANSEA	25. HARTLEPOOL	45. NORTH SOMERSET
2. DUNDEE CITY	16. NEATH PORT TALBOT	26. DARLINGTON	46. CITY OF BRISTOL
3. WEST DUNBARTONSHIRE	17. BRIDGEND	27. STOCKTON-ON-TEES	47. BATH AND NORTH EAST SOMERSET
4. EAST DUNBARTONSHIRE	18. RHONDDA CYNON TAFF	28. MIDDLESBROUGH	48. SWINDON
5. CITY OF GLASGOW	19. MERTHYR TYDFIL	29. REDCAR AND CLEVELAND	49. READING
6. INVERCLYDE	20. CAERPHILLY	30. BLACKPOOL	50. WOKINGHAM
7. RENFREWSHIRE	21. BLAENAU GWENT	31. BLACKBURN WITH DARWEN	51. WINDSOR AND MAIDENHEAD
8. EAST RENFREWSHIRE	22. TORFAEN	32. HALTON	52. SLOUGH
9. NORTH LANARKSHIRE	23. CARDIFF	33. WARRINGTON	53. BRACKNELL FOREST
10. FALKIRK	24. NEWPORT	34. KINGSTON UPON HULL	54. THURROCK
11. CLACKMANNANSHIRE		35. NORTH EAST LINCOLNSHIRE	55. SOUTHEND-ON-SEA
12. WEST LOTHIAN		36. STOKE-ON-TRENT	56. MEDWAY TOWNS
13. CITY OF EDINBURGH		37. TELFORD AND WREKIN	57. PLYMOUTH
14. MIDLOTHIAN		38. DERBY CITY	58. TORBAY
		39. CITY OF NOTTINGHAM	59. POOLE
		40. LEICESTER CITY	60. BOURNEMOUTH
		41. RUTLAND	61. SOUTHAMPTON
		42. PETERBOROUGH	62. PORTSMOUTH
		43. MILTON KEYNES	63. BRIGHTON AND HOVE
		44. LUTON	

Political changes continued

• The Scottish Parliament will be directly involved in Westminster's decision-making on EU matters and may have a representative office in Brussels.
• Both are to be elected through the Additional Member System, whereby each elector casts two votes: one for a constituency MP and one for the party of their choice.

The Hebridean island of Eigg became the property of its inhabitants for the first time in 700 years on 12 June 1997. The islanders raised £1.5 million to make Eigg the first community-owned island in the UK.

USA / Europe
The Cold War was finally consigned to the history books after an accord cementing a new security partnership was signed by Russia and NATO. Poland, Hungary and the Czech Republic are expected to join NATO in July 1999. Russia has signed away its right to veto NATO's actions.

Vietnam
Douglas Peterson, shot down in a bombing raid during the war, became the first US ambassador to Hanoi in April 1997.

Western Samoa
According to the embassy in Brussels, the government signed an act to change the name of the country to Samoa on 4 July 1997. It was also announced on Samoan television on 13 July 1997 that the full name of the country had been changed to the Independent State of Samoa.

Yemen
On 28 July 1996, Oman handed over two parcels of land totalling 5,000 sq km [3,107 sq miles] to Yemen. The move follows a 1993 agreement to transfer the Shihan and Sarfit border areas.

Yugoslavia
The PCGN have approved the following place name changes: Titovo Uzice to Uzice, Ivangrad to Berane, and Titova Mitrovica to Kosovska Mitrovica.

Raw materials and primary production

Coal

Bangladesh
The first undergound coal mine in the country is under construction in Barapukuria, 300 km [186 miles] north-west of Dhaka.

China
A new mine based on a reserve of high-quality coal began production in Yingshang County, Anhui Province, in September 1996.

Colombia
Three new areas, near the Atlantic coast, have been opened for coal exploration. Colombia is South America's leading coal producer and this announcement confirms its importance to the world market.

Egypt
The first coal mine in Egypt commenced operations in October 1995. The 600,000 tonnes per year Maghara mine is located in a very isolated and hostile part of the northern Sinai peninsula.

Indonesia
Four new coal mines are being developed in South Sumatra to supply the expanding Suralaya power station in West Java.

Russia
Eight uneconomic mines in the Kuznetsk coal basin in south-west Siberia were closed in late 1996, leaving over 3,000 miners unemployed. The first of the mines to close, Shevyakov, was the scene of one of Russia's worst mining accidents when 25 people were killed in an explosion in 1993.

UK
The Maltby coal mine set a new weekly British production record of 36,842 tonnes in mid-February 1997.

USA
Three new coal mines have opened in Virginia. The 240,000 tonnes per year Blair/Tiller mine, the 285,000 tonnes per year Cherokee mine, and the unimaginatively named Mine no. 23, which has a capacity of 350,000 tonnes per year.

Copper

Chile
The El Abra mine produced its first batch of copper in August 1996. Annual output is expected to be approximately 225,000 tonnes.

Peru
A 40,000 tonnes per year copper plant at Toquepala was inaugurated at the start of July 1996.

Spain
A copper deposit, found at Las Cruces in November 1995, was hailed as the most important find in the Iberian peninsula for many years. Las Cruces is expected to yield almost a million tonnes of pure copper.

Diamonds

USA
Commercial production has started at the Kelsey Lake diamond mine, 75 km [47 miles] from Fort Collins in northern Colorado. Kelsey Lake lies at an altitude of 2,400 m [7,874 ft] in the Rocky Mountains.

Gold

Brazil
A large gold find near the town of Curionópolis is expected to produce 10 tonnes a year. Even if no more gold is located (and much prospecting remains to be done), the site will still become Latin America's biggest gold mine, and one of the five largest in the world. Over 30,000 wildcat miners, known as garimpeiros, headed to the village of Vila da Serra Pelada shortly after the discovery. The area was the scene of one of the century's biggest gold rushes in the 1980s, when 80,000 garimpeiros arrived at the Serra Pelada open mine.

Chile
Production has begun at the newly constructed Fachinal gold and silver mine in southern Chile. The mine, located near the town of Chile Chico at a latitude of 46' 20" south, is the most southerly gold mine in the world. In its first full year of production, the mine is expected to produce 1.2 million g. [44,000 oz.] of gold and 76.5 million g. [2.7 million oz.] of silver.

The first gold has been poured at the newly completed Refugio mine on the edge of the Atacama Desert. The $127 million project is one of the largest open-pit heap leach mines in the world with a projected production of 6.6 million g. [233,000 oz.] per year of gold.

Egypt
A surprise discovery of huge gold deposits at Jabal Kamel, near the border with Libya, has dwarfed all other deposits in the country. The seams are between 4 m [13 ft] and 76 m [250 ft] thick.

Greece
A Canadian company has discovered a new gold resource near Skouries, which is estimated to contain 198 million g. [7 million oz.] of gold.

Guyana
The controversial Omai gold mine is scheduled to be reopened, with considerably improved environmental protection measures. The mine was closed in August 1995 after a disastrous leak of cyanide-tainted water into nearby rivers.

Indonesia
The biggest mining fraud in history was uncovered in early 1997, in connection with the Busang 'gold deposit' – supposedly the world's largest – on Borneo. Share values in the Canadian Bre-X company crashed after they were found to have circulated false samples from the site.

Mexico
The Lluvia de Oro project poured its first gold in August 1996. Full production was forecast to reach 425,000 g. [15,000 oz.].

Philippines

A new gold mine has opened near Sipalay town on the island of Neglos. The mine will have an annual capacity of 2.8 million g. [100,000 oz.] of gold.

Spain

A new shallow zone of gold mineralization has been discovered south of the Boinas West open pit at the Valle deposit in Asturias. The gold of the Asturias region provided the Roman Empire with much of its wealth.

Uganda

According to preliminary mineral surveys, the Karamoja region in north-eastern Uganda holds gold reserves second only to those in the Australian outback.

USA

The Meikle gold mine in Nevada has been officially opened. The $180 million operation is designed to produce around 11.3 million g. [400,000 oz.] per year of gold over an 11-year life, making it the largest underground gold producer in the US.

World

Demand for physical gold reached a record 3,550 tonnes in 1995, well above the previous peak of 3,416 tonnes seen in 1992.

New gold mines capable of producing 534 million g. [18.8 million oz.] of gold between them each year will start up in the next few years, adding 25% to 1996 gold output of 2.1 billion g. [75 million oz.].

Oil and gas production

Azerbaijan

The country became an oil exporter for the first time in January 1997, when a transport agreement with a Russian pipeline operator came into operation.

In November 1997, Azerbaijan began to pump oil from the Caspian Sea, thus beginning a process that will inevitably change the face of global oil production. The area has enormous potential and the new Sangachal terminal is likely to be the first of many.

China

The largest gasfield in China, the Yacheng 13-1 field, located 100 km [62 miles] off the coast of Hainan province, came on stream in January 1996. The field, which has 100 billion cu. m [328 billion cu. ft] of gas reserves, will supply Hong Kong with gas for 20 years via a pipeline 780 km [485 miles] long.

The Liuhua 11-1 oilfield in the Pearl River Mouth Basin came on stream on 29 March 1996. The field is 200 km [77 miles] south-east of Hong Kong and is the largest oilfield yet found in the South China Sea.

New discoveries and more efficient exploitation of fields in remote desert regions contributed to record production of oil and gas in China in 1995. Gas production topped 16 billion cu. m [52 billion cu. ft] in 1995.

UK oilfield statistics   *Offshore fields under production*

Field name	Discovery date	Year of first production	Estimated recoverable reserves orig. present (million tonnes)	First year of peak production	1995 production (thousand tonnes)	1996 production (thousand tonnes)	Cumulative total from 1975 (thousand tonnes)
Alba	1984	1994	50.7	1995	3,767	3,804	9,871
Alwyn North	1975	1987	29.0	1989	1,323	929	26,009
Andrew	1974	1996	15.7	1996	0	855	855
Arbroath	1969	1990	14.7	1991	1,660	1,450	10,522
Argyll	1971	1975	9.7	1977	0	0	9,878
Auk	1971	1975	14.3	1977	606	458	14,197
Balmoral	1975	1986	13.3	1987	633	410	12,312
Beatrice	1976	1981	20.7	1985	472	437	19,380
Beryl	1972	1976	78.6	1980	4,377	4,234	88,472
Birch	1985	1995	4.0	1995	285	1,024	1,309
Blenheim	1990	1995	3.1	1995	1,096	845	1,941
Brae Central	1976	1989	9.0	1990	486	405	4,181
Brae East	1980	1993	37.3	1995	3,318	2,735	8,707
Brae North	1975	1988	26.4	1989	540	468	14,988
Brae South	1977	1983	40.0	1985	532	522	30,562
Brent	1971	1976	262.4	1984	9,009	9,348	229,960
Bruce	1974	1993	24.0	1995	1,710	1,732	6,385
Buchan	1974	1981	13.0	1983	491	535	14,125
Chanter	1985	1992	1.0	1994	92	124	474
Claymore	1974	1977	77.2	1984	2,255	2,151	60,835
Clyde	1978	1987	17.7	1988	795	666	13,821
Cormorant North	1974	1982	55.1	1985	2,059	1,460	42,265
Cormorant South	1972	1979	27.2	1986	811	964	21,182
Crawford	1975	1989	0.5	1989	0	0	539
Cyrus	1979	1990	1.7	1990	0	202	812
Deveron	1972	1984	2.7	1988	54	58	2,009
Don	1976	1989	4.2	1992	233	169	1,632
Donan	1987	1992	2.8	1993	357	282	1,828
Dunbar	1973	1994	15.8	1997	1,754	2,241	4,036
Duncan	1981	1983	2.5	1985	0	0	2,262
Dunlin	1973	1978	49.1	1979	950	746	46,157
Eider	1976	1988	13.3	1989	905	814	11,741
Emerald	1981	1992	3.0	1993	422	41	2,365
Everest	1982	1993	4.6	1994	262	276	908
Forties	1970	1975	332.8	1978	5,444	5,142	312,409
Fulmar	1975	1982	71.7	1986	1,240	1,039	69,515
Gannet A	1978	1993	9.0	1999	997	1,313	2,916
Gannet B	1979	1992	–	1996	196	97	469
Gannet C	1982	1992	8.1	1993	1,615	1,638	5,976
Gannet D	1987	1992	4.0	1994	362	408	1,421
Glamis	1982	1989	2.3	1990	152	72	2,275
Gryphon	1987	1993	14.1	1994	2,201	1,877	6,002
Hamish	1988	1990	0.3	1990	5	3	402
Heather	1973	1978	13.7	1982	294	285	14,240
Highlander	1976	1985	9.9	1986	306	272	8,377
Hudson	1987	1993	11.2	1996	1,767	1,515	2,281
Hutton	1973	1984	27.4	1986	1,185	900	23,851
Hutton NW	1975	1983	15.5	1984	339	296	15,620
Ivanhoe	1975	1989	7.6	1990	618	519	7,462
Joanne	1981	1995	9.3	1996	39	322	361
Kittiwake	1981	1990	6.7	1992	1,363	1,055	8,167
Leven	1981	1992	1.0	1993	83	59	591
Linnhe	1988	1989	0.1	1990	0	0	101
Lomond	1972	1993	1.6	1994	152	181	594
Lyell	1975	1992	4.0	1993	448	436	2,130
Machar	1975	1994	8.1	1994	837	443	1,905
Magnus	1974	1983	102.1	1985	5,355	4,540	81,570

UK oilfield statistics continued   *Offshore fields under production*

Field name	Discovery date	Year of first production reserves orig. present (million tonnes)	Estimated recoverable peak production	First year of (thousand tonnes)	1995 production (thousand tonnes)	1996 production from 1975 (thousand tonnes)	Cumulative total
Maureen	1973	1983	28.0	1984	515	447	28,727
Medwin	1989	1994	0.1	1994	53	7	144
Miller	1983	1992	32.0	1993	6,413	6,458	27,775
Moira	1988	1990	0.6	1991	38	29	529
Montrose	1969	1976	13.1	1979	127	90	11,231
Murchison (UK)	1975	1980	51.1	1983	585	680	34,444
Nelson	1988	1994	64.1	1995	6,639	6,851	18,613
Ness	1986	1987	4.8	1988	91	80	3,637
Ninian	1974	1978	157.0	1982	2,760	2,420	139,998
Osprey	1974	1991	9.4	1992	1,417	1,297	7,922
Petronella	1975	1986	4.4	1991	296	137	4,175
Piper	1973	1992	135.6	1994	4,023	3,144	124,753
Rob Roy	1984	1989	11.1	1990	1,410	1,075	12,139
Saltire	1988	1992	18.7	1994	1,761	1,829	6,109
Scapa	1975	1984	11.7	1991	846	946	11,199
Scott	1984	1992	60.3	1994	8,757	7,028	25,380
Staffa	1985	1992	0.8	1992	0	0	511
Statfjord (UK)	1975	1979	445.7	1986	3,479	3,395	64,783
Strathspey	1975	1993	11.2	1994	1,686	1,810	4,904
Tartan	1975	1981	15.0	1987	452	474	12,320
Tern	1975	1989	28.1	1992	3,322	2,777	21,804
Thistle	1973	1978	60.3	1982	664	535	51,651
Tiffany	1979	1992	16.8	1993	1,952	1,762	5,662
Toni	1977	1992	5.3	1993	1,462	1,056	3,135
Others	–	–	–	–	97	51	542
TOTAL					**116,743**	**116,524**	**1,924,745**

UK oilfield statistics   *Offshore fields under production*

Field name	Discovery date	Year of first production reserves orig. present (million tonnes)	Estimated recoverable peak production	First year of (thousand tonnes)	1995 production (thousand tonnes)	1996 production from 1975 (thousand tonnes)	Cumulative total
Beckingham W	1985	1987	0.01	1988	0	1	12
Crosby Warren	1986	1987	0.45	1987	2	3	69
Farley's Wood	1983	1985	0.03	1986	1	1	31
East Glentworth	1987	1993	0.04	1993	0	1	3
East Herriard	–	–	–	–	4	4	40
Horndean	1983	1988	0.14	1989	18	17	149
Humbly Grove	1980	1986	0.91	1987	51	40	609
Kirklington	1985	1991	0.01	1991	0	0	4
Long Clawson	1986	1990	0.36	1991	7	8	59
Nettleham	1983	1984	0.23	1990	0	1	163
Palmers Wood	1983	1990	0.42	1992	36	24	293
Rempstone	1985	1991	0.36	1991	5	3	17
Scampton North	1985	1989	0.20	1990	7	13	123
Singleton	1989	1991	0.20	1993	35	36	183
Stainton	1984	1987	0.03	1988	1	1	20
Stockbridge	1984	1990	0.28	1991	91	86	423
Wareham	1964	1991	0.70	1992	56	42	427
Welton	1981	1985	3.30	1990	126	153	1,423
West Firsby	1988	1991	0.16	1991	14	26	83
Whisby	1985	1990	0.12	1990	4	3	27
Wytch Farm	1973	1979	41.10	1991	4,536	4,728	27,256
Others	–	–	–	–	57	57	1,592

Congo

The large Nkossa oil field began production in June 1996 and output is expected to reach 120,000 barrels per day by 1997. At 170 m [558 ft], Nkossa is the deepest water field to begin production in the Gulf of Guinea.

Equatorial Guinea

The country's first commercial oil field was formally opened on 29 October 1996. Offshore production from the Zafiro field has already begun and many optimistic claims have been made about the possibility of other finds.

Iran

The $1.5 billion Nar-Kangan gas-processing plant has been inaugurated, adding an extra one third to the country's domestic gas supplies. The plant can produce 80 million cu. m [262 million cu. ft] per day of gas and is intended to supply 240 cities.

Peru

The largest ever single investment in Peru has been made by a Shell/Mobil consortium to develop the gas and hydrocarbon deposits of Camisea, 483 km [300 miles] south-east of Lima.

Qatar

Oil production began at the Al-Rayah field in September 1996, at a rate of 35,000 barrels per day. The field also has significant potential for gas production.

Spain

A 1,400 km [868-mile] pipeline from the Algerian Sahara to Cordoba began operation on 1 November 1996.

Sudan

The government says that the country became an oil producer in late June 1996, when the first consignment of crude from the Heglig field was taken 300 km [186 miles] by road to a small plant at El Obeid. Eight wells at Heglig are claimed to be capable of producing a total of 10,000 barrels per day.

Thailand

The $2 billion, 145,000 barrels per day Rayong oil refinery opened on 20 June 1996. It has significantly reduced Thailand's dependence on imports of refined products.

South Africa

The country's first oil field, the small E-BT discovery located 140 km [87 miles] off Mossel Bay, began production in February 1997. Around 13.4 million barrels are expected over three years.

UK

The government has given the go-ahead to a £1.6 billion project to develop seven oil and natural gas fields in the eastern trough area, 240 km [150 miles] east of Aberdeen. First production is expected in the second half of 1998. The six fields have combined reserves of 400 million barrels of oil, 35 million barrels of natural gas liquids, and 305 billion cu. m [1,000 billion cu. ft] of gas.

Vietnam

The first oil was recovered from the new Ruby oilfield in autumn 1997. The field is expected to yield 200 million barrels and production is due to peak in 2003.

General mining

Canada

One of the largest antimony mines outside China opened in early 1997 near Gander, Newfoundland.

China

According to the China Daily newspaper, China became the world's top steel producer in 1996 with an output of 100 million tonnes.

Uganda

A new cobalt mining project in Uganda has been initiated by the investment of a Canadian mining company. The $100 million Kasese cobalt project is expected to produce 5% of the world's cobalt.

Agriculture, irrigation and water supply

China

Meat consumption in China has climbed from 8 kilograms per person in 1977 to 32 kilograms per person in 1994. The amount of land available for food production, meanwhile, has dropped by 5 million hectares since 1990.

Egypt

The government claims that it has completed the construction of the largest water-pumping station in the world, which will channel water via a new canal from Lake Nasser in the south to Egypt's western desert. The New Delta project aims to change the Nile-hugging inclinations of the rapidly growing Egyptian population by moving them to the desert.

The Al Salam canal was completed in late 1997. It carries Nile water across the northern Sinai peninsula.

Iran

The Zarivar storage dam has been formally completed. The dam is situated near the town of Marivan in the province of Kordestan.

The Alavian dam and reservoir were inaugurated in January 1996, one year ahead of schedule. The $70 million project will provide water for the town of Marageh.

Syria

The Thawrah (Revolution) dam on the Snobar River is ready for commissioning, allowing the full irrigation of agriculture in an extensive coastal strip near the port of Lattakia.

Gasfield statistics *Offshore fields under production*

Field name	Discovery date	Year of first production	Estimated recoverable reserves orig. present (thousand million m³)	First year of peak production	1995 production (million m³)	1996 production (million m³)	Cumulative total production to end of 1996 (million m³)
Alwyn North	1975	1987	27.0	1989	1,876	1,826	24,150
Amethyst	1972	1990	23.9	1992	991	1,416	8,586
Anglia	1985	1991	6.7	1992	615	439	2,722
Ann	1966	1993	3.6	1994	399	428	1,468
Audrey	1976	1988	22.0	1990	1,179	1,197	14,764
Baird	1993	1993	1.8	1993	219	459	217
Barque	1983	1990	8.9	1992	577	1,829	5,532
Bruce	1974	1993	78.0	1995	5,175	6,577	17,953
Bure	1983	1987	–	1988	58	55	1,771
Caister	1967	1993	8.5	1994	745	649	2,219
Camelot C & S	1987	1989	7.2	1990	526	403	3,804
Camelot N	1967	1989	2.3	1990	246	84	810
Camelot NE	1988	1992	0.9	1992	10	204	438
Cats	–	1993	–	–	1,941	2,334	7,201
Cleeton	1983	1988	7.9	1989	997	1,587	8,325
Clipper	1983	1990	14.2	1992	621	1,190	5,755
Esmond	1982	1985	9.0	1986	36	0	8,866
Flags	–	–	–	–	6,214	6,459	81,906
Forbes	1970	1985	1.4	1986	0	0	1,473
Frigg	1972	1977	69.0	1980	474	466	71,501
Fulmar	1975	1982	75.8 mt	1986	1,854	1,716	9,155
Galleon	1969	1994	46.4	1995	518	1,398	2,186
Gordon	1969	1985	4.1	1986	22	0	3,994
Guinevere	1988	1993	2.1	1994	358	243	1,056
Hewett & Della	1966	1969	116.7	1977	1,290	2,188	111,665
Hyde	1967	1993	4.2	1993/4	346	369	1,301
Indefatigable	1966	1971	128.7	1986	1,133	2,139	120,778
Johnston	1990	1994	5.0	1995	543	585	1,264
Lancelot	1986	1993	5.6	1993	868	685	2,936
Leman	1966	1968	324.2	1974	4,049	3,468	283,262
Markham	1984	1992	7.4	1994	933	807	3,283
Miller	1983	1992	33.7	1993	2,467	2,534	10,349
Morecambe S	1974	1985	127.0	1992	7,675	7,099	53,772
Murdoch	1985	1993	9.0	1993	1,110	1,127	3,588
Orwell	1990	1993	6.9	1995	1,470	789	3,619
Pickerill	1984	1992	22.9	1992	1,790	1,345	7,259
Piper/Tartan	1973	1993	2.6 mt	1995	1,037	939	11,326
Ravenspurn N	1984	1990	53.1	1992	1,716	2,942	16,176
Ravenspurn S	1983	1989	18.0	1991	852	1,253	8,192
Rough	1968	1985	110.2	1988	0	0	4,370
Sean E	1983	1994	4.1	1995	501	512	1,078
Sean N & S	1969	1986	16.4	1990	428	942	4,637
Thames	1969	1986	8.4	1987	61	157	6,116
Tristan	1976	1992	0.8	1992	206	27	854
Valiant North	1970	1988	7.8	1991	144	277	3,305
Valiant South	1970	1988	7.5	1991	177	349	5,214
Vanguard	1982	1988	2.6	1991	30	109	1,995
Victor	1972	1984	26.0	1984	1,399	1,657	18,208
Viking	1965	1972	80.1	1974	466	628	77,536
Vulcan	1983	1988	25.5	1991	415	656	10,506
Welland NW	1984	1990	}8.1	1991	411	358	3,689
Welland S	1984	1990		1991	208	117	1,545
West Sole	1965	1967	53.8	1971	1,214	822	45,298
Yare	1969	1987	–	1987	63	51	1,607
Others	–	–	–	–	3,160	3,222	38,773
TOTAL					**75,483**	**89,840**	**1,196,599**

Agriculture, irrigation and water supply continued

UK

After government scientists finally admitted a link between BSE (mad cow disease) and the fatal human brain condition Creutzfeldt-Jakob disease, consumer confidence in British beef plummeted. The EU temporarily suspended imports of British beef. Hundreds of thousands of older cows from the UK's 11-million-strong herd were slaughtered, in an attempt to restore public confidence. By September 1997, 20 people in the UK had died from Creutzfeldt-Jakob disease. In December 1997, the Labour government banned the sale of beef on the bone. Scientists have been unwilling to speculate on whether an epidemic is imminent.

General power and energy projects

Hydroelectric power

Austria

The Freudenau hydroelectric plant on the Danube started operation on 20 October 1997. The plant is the world's most advanced hydroelectric power station, and will ultimately supply half of Vienna's domestic power requirements.

Burma (Myanmar)

Since 1988, Burma has built six power stations. Three of these are hydropower stations: Sedawgyi, Beluchaung and Zawgyi. The others are natural gas power stations: Ahlone, Hlawga and Thakayta.

China

The sacred Yamdrok Tso lake in Tibet is now being tapped for power by a four-turbine HEP scheme. As a result, the lake will gradually drain away over the next 500 years.

The Bailongtan HEP station, the seventh on the Hongshui river in the Guangxi Zhuang autonomous region, went into operation at the end of 1995.

The Yangtze was successfully dammed near Sandouping on 8 November 1997, in readiness for the Three Gorges project which is due to begin operation in 2009.

Congo

A 1,000 MW hydroelectric plant is nearing completion. It is part of a development programme aimed at dramatically increasing the country's indigenous electricity production capacity.

Iran

The multi-purpose Ghadir dam is now in operation. The 100 MW dam is located near Saveh, 130 km [81 miles] south-west of Tehran, and will also irrigate 23,000 hectares of land.

Morocco

The Al Wahda dam across the Ouergha River, 60 km [37 miles] from Fes, has been officially inaugurated. The dam is designed to irrigate over 100,000 hectares of land in the Gharb plain and lower Ouergha valley whilst generating 400 million kWh of electricity per year.

Syria

The Tishreen dam on the Euphrates River, near Aleppo, was officially opened in December 1997.

Turkey

The 672 MW Birecik hydroelectric dam on the Euphrates is nearing completion. The dam is part of the south-eastern Anatolian Project, a vast irrigation and hydroelectric scheme that uses water from the Euphrates and the Tigris.

Thermal, solar, wind and tidal

China

There are currently 130,000 wind driven generators and four major windpower stations in China. There is a plan to increase wind-generated capacity to 8 million kilowatts by 2020.

Mongolia

Photovoltaic cells have been attached to numerous *yurts* throughout Mongolia. Solar technology is proving ideally suited to the nomadic lifestyle.

UK

The biggest wind farm in Europe, a 56-turbine development near Carno, Powys, was switched on in early October 1996. The National Wind Power project will generate enough electricity to power 25,000 homes.

World

New figures show that wind power is the fastest growing source of energy globally, while the commissioning of new nuclear power stations has almost ceased. Experts suggest that the world's nuclear capacity will probably peak at only one tenth that predicted by the International Atomic Energy Agency two decades ago. By contrast, although it currently provides only 1% of the world's energy, wind power grew by 33% in 1995. Half the extra capacity comes from Germany, aided by government incentives. The Indian government has offered tax incentives for renewable energy and is already the world's second largest user of wind power.

Nuclear energy

China

Four new nuclear reactors are under construction and will be completed by 2000. Another ten will be built by 2010.

Currently, nuclear power accounts for less than 1% of China's energy supplies.

Japan

In the first referendum ever to take place in Japan, the 31,000 residents of Maki, in Niigata prefecture, rejected a government-backed plan to build a nuclear reactor in the town.

Romania

The first nuclear power plant in Romania has opened at Cernavoda, 170 km [106 miles] south of Bucharest. So far, only one 700 MW reactor has been installed, but eventually five reactors will generate electricity at the site.

Sweden

One of the world's boldest and most expensive environmental pledges – the Swedish government's promise to decommission the country's 12 nuclear power plants – is now under way. Nuclear power accounts for half of all Swedish electricity production and some put the cost of abandoning it at £30 billion.

General power and energy projects

Germany

The world's first air-powered car was unveiled by Daimler-Benz on 14 May 1996. The vehicle is powered by fuel cells, which use hydrogen and oxygen to turn an electric motor.

Spain

The world's largest power plant incorporating pressurized coal gasification has begun operation in Puertollano, 200 km [124 miles] south of Madrid.

Tanzania

A new wood-fired power station has been opened near Njombe in the southern highlands.

UK

British Gas and Scottish Hydro-Electric have agreed to build a £315 million gas-fired power station near Bristol. The two companies will jointly own the 755 MW Seabank power station. Commercial operation is due to start towards the end of 1998.

Major tourist developments

Israel / Jordan

Shimon Peres and Prince Hassan signed the Aqaba/Eilat agreement in January 1996. The intention is to build a Red Sea Riviera spanning three countries, with a promenade stretching 19 km [12 miles] from Taba (Egypt), through Eilat to a series of new holiday villages in Aqaba. The scheme is also supported by the EU.

World

Over 593 million people travelled abroad in 1996, an increase of 4.6% over 1995. This figure is set to rise, with cheaper airfares and an increasingly affluent middle class in many countries.

Transport and communications

Air

China

Chep Lap Kok airport in Hong Kong, the world's largest current engineering project, is scheduled for completion in 1998. In addition to the $8.1 billion airport itself, a new town (Tung Chun) is being built near the airport on Lantau island, as well as two new expressways and a tunnel under the Western Harbour.

China / USA

The world's longest non-stop scheduled air service, on which passengers spend 16 hours flying 12,535 km [7,789 miles] from Chicago to Hong Kong (in the 'Pacific' direction), is now in service.

France

A new international airport has opened at Lille, offering an alternative to the congested facilities at Paris and Brussels.

Germany

A new airport opened in Mönchengladbach on 1 April 1996. The airport is called Mönchengladbach-Düsseldorf Express and is situated 20 km [12 miles] from the centre of Düsseldorf and a 10-minute bus ride from Mönchengladbach station.

Iran

A new airport has opened near Sarakhs, aimed at improving links with the Central Asian republics. It will ultimately have capacity for 3 million passengers a year.

Japan

The first new internal airline for 45 years has been launched by the discount travel agency HIS. The airline is hoping to halve fares on the world's busiest air route, between Tokyo and Sapporo. This route carries 7.4 million passengers each year.

Macao

The new $1 billion Macao International Airport has been officially opened. It is located on reclaimed land (effectively a man-made island), just off Taipa island. The airport comes close to dwarfing the tiny colony and, according to some, is destined to become a very costly white elephant with the enormous Chep Lap Kok airport due to be opened in Hong Kong in 1998.

South Africa

The following airport name changes occurred in 1996: Jan Smuts to Johannesburg International, D. S. Malan to Cape Town International, Louis Botha to Durban International, J. B. M. Herzog to Bloemfontain Airport, P. W. Botha to George Airport and B. J. Vorster to Kimberley Airport.

UK

East Midlands Airport opened its new £10 million departures building on 17 April 1996.

British Airways is to stop flying to Orkney, Shetland and the Western Isles after making losses on these routes for 50 years. The routes will be franchised out.

Manchester Airport won approval to build a second runway on 15 January 1997.

Bristol Airport has been renamed Bristol International Airport, as a reflection of its operations. Similarly, Glasgow Airport is now Glasgow International, while Newcastle International has reverted to Newcastle Airport.

World

Airport Ranking by Total Passengers (1995)

City (Airport)	Passengers
Chicago (O'Hare)	67,253,358
Atlanta (Hartsfield Atlanta)	57,734,755
Dallas (Dallas/Ft Worth)	56,490,851
London (Heathrow)	54,452,634
Los Angeles (Los Angeles)	53,909,223
Tokyo (Haneda)	45,822,503
Frankfurt/Main (Rheim/Main)	38,179,543
San Francisco (San Francisco)	36,262,745
Miami (Miami)	33,235,658
Denver (Denver)	31,036,622
Seoul (Kimpo)	30,919,462
New York (John F. Kennedy)	30,379,781
Paris (Charles de Gaulle)	28,355,470
Detroit (Metro Wayne County)	28,200,358
Hong Kong (Hong Kong)	28,043,338
Las Vegas (McCarran)	28,027,239
Phoenix (Sky Harbor)	27,856,195
Minneapolis/St Paul	26,787,287
Paris (Orly)	26,653,878
Newark (Newark)	26,626,231
St Louis (Lambert-St Louis)	25,719,351
Amsterdam (Schipol)	25,355,007
Houston (Intercontinental)	24,726,592
Boston (Logan)	24,358,540
Tokyo (Narita)	24,210,286
Honolulu (Honolulu)	23,672,894

Ports and ferries

China / Taiwan

For the first time in 48 years, direct shipping links have been allowed to link the two countries. The first ship to sail directly to China from Taiwan since 1949 arrived in Xiamen on 25 April 1997.

Denmark

The world's largest container carrying vessel, the *Regina Maersk*, was launched from Odense on 24 January 1996. The vessel can carry 700 refrigerated cargo containers and is the first of a series of 12 sister ships that will eventually serve on Europe-Asia routes.

Burmeister and Wain, the Copenhagen shipyard which built the world's first ocean-going vessel driven by diesel engines, has closed after 152 years of shipbuilding.

Europe

Two of the oldest international shipping lines, P&O of the UK and Royal Nedlloyd of the Netherlands, are merging their container activities to create the world's largest container shipping group.

Faroe Islands / UK

The ferry operator Smyril Lines, based in the Faroes, is reintroducing Lerwick as a port of call. A new service will link Lerwick with Torshavn and Bergen, and connect with P&O's Aberdeen–Lerwick route.

France

The marine counterpart of the TGV entered service on 20 April 1996. The *Navire à Grande Vitesse* runs between Nice and Corsica in three hours, half the time the journey previously took. The vessel is capable of 40 knots and can carry 500 passengers.

Kenya / Tanzania

A ferry carrying 16 passengers from the Tanzanian port of Mwanza docked at Kisumu in Kenya in January 1996. The event marked the resumption of passenger services across Lake Victoria after an 18-year break.

Russia

Environmentalists believe that, in the near future, the sea ice in parts of the Arctic Ocean will have melted so much that Russian icebreakers will be able to open a new shipping channel between the Norwegian Sea and the Bering Strait. This new short-cut would attract large volumes of merchant shipping and inevitably increase pollution in the area.

UK

A new ferry service linking Scotland and Northern Ireland has been launched. The service will link Campbeltown in Kintyre with Ballycastle.

Railways

Asia

In a break with tradition, North Korea has reacted positively to a UN project to build a trans-Asian rail link. The project envisages the construction of 10,000 km [6,214 miles] of track to link South Korea with Rotterdam. North Korea apparently expressed a desire to use the rail link to help develop the Najin-Sonbong free economic trade zone.

Railways continued

Belgium

A TGV service linking Paris, Brussels and Amsterdam was inaugurated in June 1996. The opening of a new section of TGV track, 15 km [9 miles] long, in Belgium means that trains can now bypass Lille.

China

Between 1995 and 1997, five new trunk lines or major cut-offs were completed. All six are of considerable significance, either adding capacity or filling in gaps in the network. The Jing-Jiu line is particularly significant as the largest single project in Chinese Railway history. The last few metres of track on this line (which links Beijing with Hong Kong) were laid in mid-November 1995 when the two lines finally met near Longzhou in Guangdong.

Recently completed major rail links in China

Route	Length (km)
Beijing–Kowloon (Jing Jiu)	2,370
Nanning–Kunming (Nan-Kun)	898
Boaji–Zhongwei (Bao-Zhong)	498
Chengdu–Daxian (Cheng-Da)	389
Houma–Yueshan (Hou-Yue)	365

The State Council has approved the construction of the long-planned South Xinjiang Railway, which is designed to open up the centre of the huge autonomous region of Xinjiang in the far west. The line, 1,449 km [900 miles] long, will run from Turpan to Kashi (Kashgar).

The Tongliao to Jining line, 943 km [586 miles] long, was inaugurated on 30 November 1996.

About one-third of the 5,000 passenger stations in China are to be closed, in an effort to make its overstretched rail system more efficient and market oriented. In addition to closing the 1,500 stations, the speed limit on its main tracks is to be raised from 60 km/h [37 mph] to 140 km/h [87 mph].

China and Vietnam reopened two railway links on 14 February 1996, indicating a gradual warming of relations. The routes have been closed since the two countries were briefly at war in 1979. The links are between Hekou in China's Yunnan province and Lao Cai in Vietnam, and between Pingxiang and the Vietnamese town of Dong Dang. The railway line gives the economically burgeoning Yunnan province easier access to the sea at the port of Haiphong in Vietnam. It is generally felt that the reopening stems not from sentiment but from the countries' pragmatic need to develop their economies and trade.

A rail link, 251 km [156 mls] long, between Jinha and Wenzhou in Zhejiang province was completed in early 1997.

Denmark

The bridge and tunnel link across the Great Belt, the 18 km [11-mile] strait between the islands of Funen and Zealand, opened on 1 June 1997. The link cuts the travelling time between Copenhagen and Jutland by an hour. The £3 billion project will be complete when the road bridge opens in 1998.

France

The last sections of high-speed rail line to be completed this century were opened in summer 1996. The new line benefits services on the 25 km [16-mile] Jonction Ouest route through the south-eastern suburbs of Paris and the remaining section of TGV Nord Europe between Fretin and the Belgian border near Antoing.

Iran

A $216 million rail link re-establishing transport links between the Gulf and south-east Asia was opened on 13 May 1996. The new link revives the traditions of the old silk road and is seen as highly significant for the future economic development of the region. Iran has spent $171 million building the 165 km [103-mile] stretch of railway to link Mashhad and Sarakhs, while Turkmenistan has completed a link to Tejen which gives the land-locked Central Asian countries access to Iranian ports.

Japan

A new bullet train has achieved the fastest ever average speed on a commercial run and has matched the French TGV for top speed during a scheduled service. The Nozomi train averages 262.7 km/h [163.3 mph] between Hiroshima and Kokura, whereas the TGV averages 253 km/h [157 mph] between Paris and Tours. Both achieve a top speed of 301 km/h [187mph].

Journey times between Tokyo and Nagano were halved to 90 minutes with the opening of a new bullet train service on 1 October 1997.

North Korea

A rail link, 100 km [161 miles] long, between Wonsan and Mount Kumgang was inaugurated on 15 April 1997.

Singapore

Almost £10 billion is to be invested on high-quality public transport on the island over the next 15 years. The government has a target of 75% of all journeys to be made by public transport, to prevent traffic gridlock. The Transport Authority also envisages, in the longer term, an electrified mainline link all the way to Bangkok.

Taiwan

The first section of Taipei's mass transit system opened on 28 March 1996, after eight years of construction.

UK

Railtrack removed the lines from Corby's single platform station in March 1996. This leaves Corby as the largest town in Europe (population 55,000) without a passenger rail service.

The newest station on the Docklands Light Railway is now operational. Pudding Mill Lane is located between Stratford and Bow Church.

The final decision on the route of the Channel Tunnel Rail Link has been made after an 11-month hearing. The 108 km [67-mile] link will cost about £2.7 billion. As a result of requests for route changes, the key alterations were in Barking (an extended tunnel), Thurrock (moving and lowering the railway near the Mardyke Park housing estate) and the approach to St Pancras (tunnelling and related changes).

The 06.19 Eurostar from Waterloo became the first to stop (intentionally) in the UK, when it drew up at Ashford International on 8 January 1996. Nine international services will now call daily at the station, with services to Paris and Brussels.

The £100 million station is the first British regional station for 150 years to boast access to the Continent. Around 2 million passengers a year are expected to travel from the station.

A new station opened at Yarm in South Cleveland on 20 February 1996. Yarm is served by trains on the Middlesbrough to York and Manchester Airport route. The station is located to the south of the original Yarm station which was closed in 1960.

The biggest new rail terminus to be built since Marylebone in 1899 opened on 30 September 1996 near Wembley. The seven-platform station is a Royal Mail distribution centre and will not see any passengers.

Filton station in South Gloucestershire was closed on 30 September 1996.

The longest single train journey ever made from a British station was completed on 16 March 1997 when Eurostar ran a direct service from Waterloo to Bourg-St.-Maurice in the French Alps. Previously, the longest non-stop journey made from a British station was the daily 1,101 km [684-mile] Aberdeen to Plymouth service. The new route will take skiers to the heart of the Alps without changing train.

Ashchurch station in Gloucestershire reopened on 29 May 1997, 26 years after it was originally removed from the network. The county council has already reopened Cam and Dursley station, and is targeting Charfield as the next station in line for reinstatement.

The new Rugeley Town station was officially opened on 30 May 1997. Four miles of track have been reinstated for passenger trains from the former limit at Hednesford.

A new £1 million station opened at Euxton, Lancashire on 15 December 1997. The two platform station lies on the West Coast Main Line between Leyland and Wigan.

USA

The federal Surface Transportation Board has sanctioned the $5.4 billion merger of the Union Pacific and Southern Pacific railways, thereby facilitating the creation of the largest rail company in the USA.

Uzbekistan

Construction of a line, 223 km [139 miles] long, linking Guzar, Baysan and Kum-Kurgan began on 11 December 1995. The route is scheduled to be completed by the end of the century.

Roads

Australia

The Glebe Island Bridge was opened in Sydney on 3 December 1995. The 808 m [2,650 ft] long structure is the longest cable-stayed bridge in Australia and will be on the route of the marathons in the 2000 Olympic Games.

Bolivia

A new two-lane highway, 190 km [118 miles] long, has opened from the city of Patacamaya to the Chilean border at Tambo Quemado. The road is the first paved-road link between Bolivia and a neighbouring country, and cuts the travel time for the 520 km [323-mile] trip between La Paz and the Chilean coast from 18 hours to six hours.

Bosnia-Herzegovina

The famous Carinskiy Bridge, which links east and west Mostar, was rebuilt in 1996, after it was destroyed by fighting in 1993. It is now open to traffic and pedestrians again.

Canada

On 22 November 1996, the last section of a new 13 km [8-mile] bridge was lowered into place, and Prince Edward Island became attached to mainland New Brunswick. The bridge won only 60% backing in a 1988 plebiscite called by the province's president, who saw it as a symbol of Canadian unity, and it has been a divisive local issue ever since.

China

The Tsing Ma bridge in Hong Kong, the world's longest road and rail suspension structure, was opened on 27 April 1997. The £555 million bridge is the final part of the transport link to the new airport at Chep Lap Kok.

Croatia

The Zagreb–Belgrade motorway reopened on 7 May 1996 for the first time since June 1991. The reopening of the road is seen as one of the most important steps towards reconciliation between Serbia and Croatia.

France

The first crossing to be built over the Seine for 25 years opened in central Paris on 8 August 1996. The Pont Charles de Gaulle spans the river between the Gare de Lyon and the Gare d'Austerlitz. The bridge is the 37th to be built across the Seine in central Paris.

Israel

A large bypass around Bethlehem was completed on 20 December 1995. The bypass is one of 16 similar roads throughout the West Bank which are part of a $1 billion scheme intended to ensure the safety of the 130,000 Jewish settlers.

Kenya

A major road rehabilitation scheme is under way in various parts of the country. Roads set for construction or improvement include Mombasa–Voi, Kusumu Busia–Kakamega, Kabarnet–Narok and Nyeri–Meru. The entire exercise is expected to cost about $49 million.

Spain

The last stretch of the M40 second Madrid bypass, said to be one of the biggest in the world, has been completed. The M40 is a circular road which connects to the six national roads radiating from the centre of the capital.

Switzerland

The names of all Swiss motorways have been changed from 'N' roads to 'A' roads, bringing them into line with the rest of Europe.

UK

The second Severn bridge was completed on 26 April 1996 and opened to traffic on 5 June 1996.

The Department of Transport has decreed that the A38 dual carriageway between Exeter and Plymouth should become the UK's first official 'expressway'. Cynics have noted that the renaming is a convenient way to improve the motorway network without spending any money. A dotted blue representation was recommended to cartographers as a method of reflecting the road's new status.

The government announced the outcome of its review of the road-building programme in July 1997. It approved five schemes, including a private toll road that will offer drivers an alternative to the congested Birmingham section of the M6. The four other approved schemes are the A2/M2 Cobham to junction 4 widening, the A564 Derby southern bypass, the M66 Denton-Middleton, and the A13 Thames gateway.

USA

The national 89 km/h [55 mph] speed limit, imposed by the federal government in 1974 as a fuel-saving measure, was abolished in December 1995. States are now free to set their own limits. Legal speed limits rose to 113 km/h [70 mph] in California, Missouri and three other states, and 121 km/h [75 mph] in Kansas, Nevada and Wyoming. There is no day-time limit at all in Montana.

Telecommunications

Ireland

A new Gaelic language television channel (*Teilifis na Gaeilge* – literally 'Irish TV') has been initiated, with four hours of programmes a day in the indigenous tongue.

Middle East

The BBC has ceased broadcasting its Arabic language news and information service to the Middle East.

World

The longest and most complex submarine telecommunications cable in the world is currently being laid. The cable will eventually stretch for 38,000 km [23,613 miles] between Europe, Australia and Japan.

By the end of January 1997, there were 16.1 million computers connected to the Internet. A study found that 84% of all users are from North America and Northern Europe, and 69% are male.

Space research

Europe

The Ariane 5 rocket, the largest built in western Europe, was destroyed by ground-safety officers after it veered off course 40 seconds into its maiden flight. The launch cost an estimated £320 million and the failure has thrown European leadership of the £3 billion-per-year commercial space transport industry into doubt.

Russia

The space programme in Russia suffered a major setback when the newly launched Mars-96 craft lost power on 17 November 1996 and crashed to Earth.

NASA scientists provoked worldwide interest with their announcement that they had found evidence of bacteria life inside a meteorite thought to come from Mars that was found in Antarctica in 1984.

The Mars Pathfinder mission landed successfully on 4 July 1997, with giant airbags cushioning its bumpy landing on a plain called Ares Vallis. Spectacular pictures revealed a varied landscape, and the mission probed rocks with a spectrometer. In October 1997 the orbiting Mars Surveyor craft beamed back to Earth pictures of a chasm twice as deep as the Grand Canyon, as it prepared to map the planet's surface.

On 20 February 1997, the *Galileo* spacecraft passed the smallest Jupiter moon of Europa, and revealed lobes of ice on its surface. Apart from Earth, it seems that Europa may be the only body in the Solar System to contain water.

A mini-planet has been discovered at the edge of the Solar System. The object, more than 483 km [300 miles] in diameter, is the brightest object to be found beyond the orbit of Neptune since the discovery of Pluto in 1930. The planet has been prosaically named 1996TL66 and takes 800 years to orbit around the Sun. The object will eventually be given a better name.

Astronomers have discovered an asteroid that is trapped in a complex orbit by the Earth's gravity, making it our planet's second natural companion, after the Moon. The orbit of asteroid 3753 takes 770 years to complete.

Conservation and environment

Antarctica

A huge sub-glacial lake has been found 3 km [2 miles] beneath the Antarctic ice cap. Nearly 241 km [150 miles]

Conservation and environment continued

long by 48 km [30 miles] wide, and possibly 610 m [2,000 ft] deep, the lake has remained undisturbed for at least half a million years. The water could provide many species new to science. The mystery is how the water remains unfrozen under so much ice. Unsurprisingly, gaining access to the lake is problematic.

American researchers using satellite imagery have discovered that the true position of the South Pole is located 46 cm [18 in.] from where previous calculations have placed it.

The section of the Larsen Ice Shelf that lies adjacent to the Antarctic Peninsula has been dramatically reduced in size over the past ten years. In addition, the Sjögren Glacier Tongue, which once joined the peninsula to James Ross Island, has disintegrated. The ice shelf north of Seal Nunataks has also broken up. Large north–south cracks are continuing to create the now famous huge icebergs that then drift northwards to melt.

Brazil

A new bird species – *Acrobatornis fonsecai* – has been discovered in northern Brazil. However, scientists report that it is, ironically, endangered by diminishing cocoa plantations.

Chad

The northern part of Lake Chad is now completely dry, a victim of rapid desertification. The southern part of the lake is now densely vegetated with swamps and open pools.

China

The 'wandering' saline lake of Lop Nur in the Talimankan Desert has now completely drained away, starved of water by dams on the Tarim River and a series of irrigation schemes. Before the dams were built, the river fed meltwater from the Pamirs into the lake. Lop Nur is now covered in waves of salt mud as hard as bricks and moulded into metre-high crests.

A protection scheme for the last genetically pure herds of Bactrian camels in the Gashun Gobi desert has been initiated. A conserved area, called the Lop Nur Nature Sanctuary, will be set up.

Czech Republic

A 400 km [250-mile] long 'Czech Greenway' has been created between Vienna and Prague. The network of footpaths connect castles and towns with the countryside.

Europe

The South Yorkshire section of the European E8 walkway, which links Liverpool with Istanbul, was completed in early July 1996. The formal opening of the completed route took place in a Barnsley supermarket car park. The Trans-European route is one of 11 criss-crossing the continent, but the first to enter the UK. The E4 path (Pyrenees to the Peloponnese) is perhaps the most famous.

Greenland

A huge meteorite landed near the settlement of Qaqortoq

on 9 December 1997. Seismometers recorded a shock lasting ten seconds, while eye witnesses reported seeing a flash followed by a huge cloud of steam. It was estimated that 5 billion tonnes of ice were vaporized by the impact.

Honduras

A meteorite created a 50 m [165 ft] crater after it crashed in a remote part of Honduras, setting fire to large areas of forest.

Indonesia

Ornithologists have rediscovered three bird species that they had thought to be extinct. First to reappear was the aptly named invisible rail, which turned up on the island of Halmahera. Next came the Lompobattang flycatcher, unseen since 1931. Finally, a caerulean paradise flycatcher was found off Sulawesi.

Widespread forest fires destroyed over 200,000 hectares of national forest at the end of the 1997. Reports suggested that many of the fires were started deliberately by companies wishing to expand commercial crop plantations.

Kazakstan

A 600,000-acre national park, Zailisky Alatau, has been created, with the aim of protecting endangered species, particularly the snow leopard.

Madagascar

The royal palaces and necropolis of Antananarivo were burned to the ground on 6 November 1995. To illustrate the scale of this disaster, it was, apparently, as if the Louvre or the British Museum had been incinerated overnight.

New Zealand

The earliest new millennium sunrise visible from a terrestrial, accessible and populated site will be seen from North Head Farm on Pitt Island.

Peru

An international team of scientists has claimed that the source of the Amazon is an underground glacier in the southern Peruvian Andes. This is one of the oldest of all geo-exploratory chestnuts and the recent investigation pinpointed an icy creek called Apachita crevice, 5,169 m [16,958 ft] above sea level, near the city of Arequipa.

Portugal

The Côa Valley Archaeological Park was inaugurated on 10 August 1995, enabling visitors to view the world's largest gallery of open-air Stone Age art. A £194 million dam, destined to flood the area, was cancelled after the engravings were found, but only after a long struggle.

Romania

An underground cave system, cut off from the rest of the world for 4 million years, finally revealed its secrets in 1996 after scientists comprehensively explored its passages. The Movile Cave, near Mangalia, was discovered in 1986, when workmen accidentally broke into the sealed system. The fauna in the cave have a food chain completely independent

of the outside world and the 31 species (new to science) form the first known ecosystem that does not depend ultimately on the sun for its food and energy needs. Not surprisingly, most have huge antennae and no eyes. Geologists believe Movile was formed when the level of the Black Sea dropped suddenly, 5.5 million years ago.

Russia

The largest remaining unfragmented forest area in Europe, the Pechoro-Ilych reserve and its surroundings, was added to the World Heritage list in December 1995. The volcanoes of the Kamchatka area of eastern Russia have also been designated a World Heritage Site, along with the Komi forest, a 3.2-million-hectare virgin forest in western Russia.

Uganda

Over 70,000 tonnes of water hyacinth now fill the bay above Owen Falls on Lake Victoria. The vegetation is so thick that small boys can walk across it. The hyacinth was washed down the Kagera river from Rwanda and is now in danger of clogging the 180 MW turbine at Owen Falls, Uganda's main supplier of electricity. Virtually all access from the shoreline of Lake Victoria is now blocked.

UK

The mouse-eared bat, which has not been seen for five years, is believed to be extinct. It becomes the first British mammal to suffer that fate since the wolf in 1745.

Egrets nested in the UK for the first time in the summer of 1997. Five pairs of little egrets stayed on Brownsea Island in Poole harbour.

The remote island of Gough, 350 km [217 miles] from Tristan da Cunha, has been granted World Heritage status. The island becomes the third natural British site to be so honoured, after it was approved at the Berlin UNESCO meeting in December 1995. Gough has an annual rainfall of over 3 m [118 in.] and is particularly important for its population of rockhopper penguins, yellow-nosed albatrosses and greater shearwaters.

Spurn Head became totally cut off from mainland Britain after a series of violent storms around 18/19 February 1996. The sea defences had not been properly maintained and some experts claimed that the coastal feature would inevitably become Spurn Island at some point in the near future. Soon afterwards, however, a flexible roadway was constructed which linked Spurn Head to the mainland via a series of concrete sheets, which move to more solid ground when the sand beneath them starts to erode. As a result, it remains possible to drive right to the tip of Spurn Head.

The River Darent in Kent, which has run dry during most summers since 1976, has been made 'drought-proof' by the installation of six artificial springs that will feed the chalk river at times of low flow. Several other similar schemes are planned.

The county of Essex has been officially classified as semi-arid by both the Met. Office and the United Nations.

By late October 1996, all British snow patches had melted for the first time since records began. One is the UK's most

THE ARAL SEA

The Aral Sea used to be the fourth largest lake in the world; but many years of drawing water away from it for cotton irrigation have greatly reduced its surface area. The former shorelines are obscured by drifts of alluvial silt that now cover much of the landscape, and extensive areas of dry seabed have been exposed over recent years.

Scientists have determined that 135 of the 173 animal species dependent on the lake no longer exist in the area, and several towns which used to have a fishing industry are now over 60 km [40 miles] from the lake's shore.

This is only the most dramatic and infamous example of a phenomenon which is repeated across Central Asia. The large saline lake of Lop Nur in western China, for example, is now reported to be completely dry. Again, the reason is the systematic use of the lake's principal water source for large-scale irrigation schemes.

Similarly, the lake of Garabogazkol Aylagy, which lies in Turkmenistan and feeds the Caspian Sea, is now less than half the size it was in 1960, when it measured 170 km [101 miles] from north to south.

The deserts of Central Asia are geographically and climatically isolated by high mountain ranges. The area is generally arid, although the Aral Sea once marked the western boundary of the desert area. If the shrinkage continues, surrounding deserts like the Kyzyl Kum and Barsuki are likely to colonize the entire region.

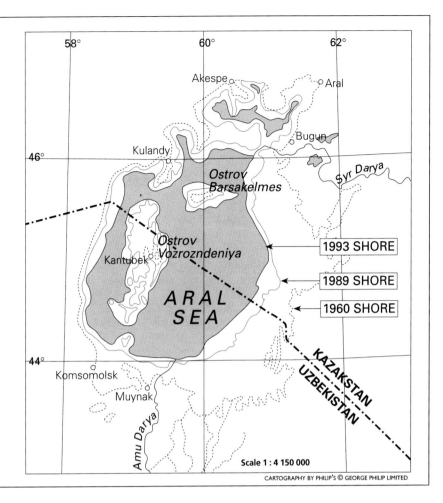

Scale 1 : 4 150 000

CARTOGRAPHY BY PHILIP'S © GEORGE PHILIP LIMITED

---

permanent patch (in the Garbh Choire of Braeriach in the Cairngorms) which, since 1900, has only melted in 1933 and 1959. Another in Observatory Gully on Ben Nevis survives in most years but had completely melted by 28 September 1996. The last patch of all (at the foot of Zero Gully, Ben Nevis) had gone by 26 October 1996. The unique situation did not last long, however, with heavy snow falling on 5 November 1996.

A 250 km [155-mile] stretch of the national cycle network has been opened from Padstow to Bristol. The £43.5 million West Country Way is the fifth of nine routes that will ultimately form the backbone of a 10,460 km [6,500-mile] network. A 299 km [186-mile] network linking Kidwelly Castle with Newport is also nearing completion.

The Council for National Parks has proposed that the New Forest and the South Downs be made national parks. Both areas are near population centres and the South Downs receives 32 million visits each year, compared with 22 million visits to the Peak District, the most frequently visited national park.

USA

The Grand Canyon has been artificially flooded with 117 billion gallons of water from the Colorado River in order to distribute sand and mud more evenly along the canyon floor. This 'periodic disturbance' will cost US$4.3 million.

Nearly 2 million acres of southern Utah has been declared a national park by President Clinton. The decision has, however,

been opposed by members of the Republican Party, because it will block development of the USA's largest coalfield, worth an estimated $1,000 billion.

The former National Monuments of Death Valley and Joshua Tree are now both National Parks.

World

Statistics at the Ramsar Convention on the world's wetlands reveal that US states like Ohio and California have lost 90% of their wetland areas. When the US was first colonized, it contained 90 million hectares of wetlands. The survey also found that France has lost 67% of its wetlands, Italy 66%, Greece 63% and the Netherlands 55%.

The remaining stocks of the smallpox virus, which are held at two centres in Atlanta, USA, and Koltsovo, Russia, are scheduled for destruction in 1999. Destroying the virus is controversial, because it would render a species extinct. However, mankind has now lost most of its natural resistance to smallpox, meaning that an outbreak would be disastrous.

Industrial accidents and pollution

Bolivia

The collapse of a dam at the El Porco zinc mine near Potosi released up to 400,000 tonnes of sludge loaded with heavy metals, which polluted 300 km [186 miles] of river. The

sludge is threatening the livelihoods of 50,000 *campesino* subsistence farmers in the region. The incident is one of the worst environmental disasters ever to strike Latin America.

Japan

A national disaster was declared after a 147,000-tonne supertanker ran aground in Tokyo Bay, causing the worst ever oil spill in Japan's coastal waters, although it later transpired that the slick was not as serious as originally thought. More than 100 ships were mobilized to tackle the slick, which leaked from the Panamanian-registered *Diamond Grace*.

The country's worst nuclear accident occurred on 11 March 1997 as a fire and subsequent explosion hit the Tokaimura reprocessing plant.

Russia

Several major oil spills occurred in December 1995 and January 1996. A pipeline leak in Bashkortostan spilled 2,400 tonnes of oil into the Belaya river. Two leaks on the Ukhta-Yaroslavl pipeline in the Komi republic spilled well over 400 tonnes into the surrounding countryside, while several smaller spills occurred in Krasnodar (where a huge leak was narrowly averted), Samara and Perm.

On 7 March 1996, a huge oil spill saw 12,000 tonnes leak from a damaged pipeline in the Tyumen region of north-west Siberia. The accident was the largest ever in the region.

Industrial accidents and pollution continued

Over 2,000 tonnes of oil escaped from a faulty pipeline in Rostov in June 1997. A 20 km [12-mile] stretch of the Krepkaya river was contaminated and 5 hectares of land heavily polluted. In Atyrau (Kazakstan), a 'serious leak' led to the designation of a disaster area.

Ukraine

New government statistics claim that 3.2 million people were victims of the Chernobyl disaster. In addition, 50,000 of the 357,000 people involved in the clean-up sustained disabilities, and 125,000 of those injured as a result of the accident have died. Between 1990 and 1995, the incidence of thyroid cancer in the region increased between five- and nine-fold. The area of contamination covers more than 50,000 sq km [31,070 sq miles] and includes 2,294 towns and villages. Over 180,000 hectares of arable land and 115,000 hectares of forest have had to be taken out of use.

UK

A supertanker carrying 128,000 tonnes of crude oil ran aground off Milford Haven, Pembrokeshire, on 15 February 1996. At least 6,000 tonnes leaked from the *Sea Empress* within two hours of the accident. The vessel was towed off the rocks after six days, although by then it had already lost almost 70,000 tonnes of crude oil. The spillage is thought to be the worst environmental disaster in the UK since the *Torrey Canyon* in 1967. The final avian death toll was estimated to be about 70,000 birds, and the oil affected the valuable island nature reserves of Skomer and Grassholm.

Uzbekistan

Infant mortality in the semi-autonomous state of Karalpakstan exceeds 80 per 1,000 live births, 50% higher than the Uzbek average. The state is in the grip of an anaemia pandemic, with 97% of the women affected. Kidney disease, cancers, hepatitis and respiratory disorders are all on the increase. Due to the reduction of the Aral Sea, local people are forced to drink polluted drainage water laden with salts and agricultural chemicals (see Aral Sea map on previous page).

Venezuela

In the first four months of 1997, three big oil tankers ran aground at almost the same spot in the channel that connects the Caribbean with Lake Maracaibo, the heart of the country's oil industry. The Greek-registered *Nissos Amorgos* shed 25,000 barrels of heavy crude, and this was followed by the *Olympic Sponsor* and the *Corellis*. There have been over 30 groundings in as many years, with the problem blamed on silt and debris.

Geographical catastrophes

Afghanistan

An avalanche killed at least 100 people when it hit a section of the Salang highway, north of Kabul, on 28 March 1997.

On 4 February 1998, an earthquake measuring 6.1 on the Richter scale destroyed nearly 30 villages in Takhar Province and killed at least 4,200 people. Relief efforts were hampered by the difficult terrain, poor weather and the continuing civil war in the north of Afghanistan. Several subsequent tremors killed 260 people in the region.

Argentina

Fires which began on 22 January 1996 in the southern Chubut and Rio Negro provinces led to the destruction of thousands of hectares of ancient forests in several national parks.

Australia

A landslide destroyed two ski lodges in Thredbo, New South Wales, on 30 July 1997, killing 20 people. The landslide was thought to have been triggered by a gas explosion.

Bangladesh

Over 400 people were killed by a tornado that struck the Tangail district, 112 km [70 miles] north of Dhaka, on 14 May 1996. Officials put the number of injured at 32,000.

At least 95 people were killed and more than 8,000 injured after a 240 km/h [150 mph] cyclone struck the southern coast of Bangladesh on 19 May 1997.

Canada

The worst floods in 42 years left 12,000 people homeless and 12 dead after downpours hit the Chicoutimi and Saguenay river area, 257 km [160 miles] north of Quebec city, in July 1996. In a 72-hour period, 28 cm [11 in.] of rain fell, causing damage estimated at $365 million. It is the worst natural disaster in Canada since 1954, when Hurricane Hazel devastated the city of Toronto.

China

At least 240 people were killed and 3,700 seriously injured on 3 February 1996 by a powerful earthquake centred on the town of Lijiang, near the Tibetan border. The earthquake measured 7.0 on the Richter scale and virtually destroyed the town. More than 150 aftershocks were recorded, with 16 other towns suffering considerable damage.

A series of powerful earthquakes struck Jiashi prefecture in Xinjiang on 21 March 1996. At least 24 people, mostly children, were killed. Over 10,000 people were made homeless. The epicentre of the first and most powerful earthquake, which measured 6.9 on the Richter scale, was Artux, a town 24 km [15 miles] north of the Silk Road town of Kashgar.

Severe flooding in eastern and southern provinces killed at least 1,100 people and left thousands homeless after the heaviest rainfall in nearly 50 years. It is estimated that 2 million homes were destroyed. Up to 28 cm [11 in.] of rain fell in five provinces in late June 1996. Environmentalists claim that the large-scale loss of forest cover and rapid urbanization has exacerbated the impact of the usual torrential rains.

Some 100 miners were reportedly killed and 138 others were missing after landslides on 31 May and 3 June 1997

engulfed gold mines on the Laojinshan mountain in Yunnan province.

The most severe snowstorms to affect China for 30 years left 320,000 people cut off in the north-west, as snow depths reached 2.1 m [7 ft] in January 1997. Temperatures fell as low as −36°C [−33°F] and at least 36 people were killed. A huge landslide swept away four villages in Sichuan province in June 1997, killing at least 150 people and turning areas of the Yangshanzhou region into lakes of mud.

Ecuador

An earthquake registering 5.7 on the Richter scale hit central Ecuador on 28 March 1996, killing 21 people, injuring 66 and leaving 3,000 homeless.

Iceland

A large volcanic eruption in a fissure under the Vatnajökull ice cap finally led to the 'flood of the century' that had been predicted by scientists, and monitored by the world's media, for some time. The fissure had already melted 3,000 cu. m [106,000 cu. ft] of the glacier above in October 1996. The resultant 3 billion tonnes of water lay in the Grimsvotn volcanic crater, under the ice, until the November eruption spewed a 4,270 m [14,000 ft] high column of ash into the air and released the trapped water. The subsequent glacial torrent demolished three of the country's largest bridges as well as several kilometres of the important ring road along the south coast. A number of power lines also collapsed, with house-sized blocks of ice and millions of tonnes of black sulphurous water pouring on to uninhabited regions. All land traffic between east-coast fishing towns and Reykjavik was temporarily forced to go via the rough terrain of the north coast.

India

Monsoon rains in Assam killed 500 people and left 300,000 homeless in June and July 1996. Thirty-two camps were set up to care for the thousands of refugees.

Army helicopters rescued 2,000 pilgrims from the Himalayan foothills as 60,000 people ran into sub-zero temperatures and severe winds on their way to the holy Amarnath cave in August 1996. Devotees worship an ice stalagmite in the cave and several naked holy men were among the 127 dead.

A cyclone killed more than 460 people in Andhra Pradesh in November 1996. Some reports suggest that the death toll could have been closer to 1,000.

A Saudi Airlines Boeing 747 with 312 passengers collided near Delhi with an Ilyushin freighter from Kazakstan carrying 37 people in November 1996. There were no survivors after the world's worst ever mid-air crash.

Indonesia

An earthquake measuring 7.5 on the Richter scale hit Biak island and several coastal areas in the north of Irian Jaya on 18 February 1996. Around 100 people died, but this toll could be an underestimation due to the difficulty of obtaining information from this very remote area.

The island of Sumatra was struck by an earthquake that

registered 7.0 on the Richter scale on 7 October 1995. At least 70 people were killed, several landslides were triggered and 10,000 homes were destroyed.

Iran

On 28 February 1997, an earthquake in Ardabil province killed at least 965 people, injured 3,000 more and destroyed the homes of more than 40,000 people. The quake was thought to measure 6.1 on the Richter scale.

A devastating earthquake measuring 7.1 on the Richter scale struck the desert lands south of Mashhad in Khorasan province on 10 May 1997, killing at least 2,400 people and leaving 50,000 homeless. A hospital wall collapsed in Herat, Afghanistan, killing five and illustrating the huge radius of the tremor. Around 200 villages were destroyed across a swathe of land between Qayen and Birjand, with 10,000 homes destroyed.

Two strong earthquakes hit north-eastern Iran in early February 1997. At least 38 people were killed and 34 villages were flattened around the town of Bojnurd.

Japan

In Hokkaido, a slab of rock 70 m [230 ft] tall, 40 m [131 ft] wide and weighing 50,000 tonnes slid down a mountain during heavy snowfall and crashed into the Toyohama tunnel on 10 February 1996. The rock crushed a bus carrying 19 passengers and a lone motorist was also killed.

Malaysia

Tropical Storm Greg killed 106 people as it hit the eastern state of Sabah on 25 December 1996.

Mexico

The Pacific coast was severely damaged by Hurricane Pauline in October 1997. Oaxaca state was the worst affected, with 69 people killed.

Middle East

A powerful earthquake shook the region from Lebanon to Sudan at dawn on 22 November 1995, killing ten and causing at least 50 injuries and considerable damage to buildings. The epicentre was the Egyptian port of Nuweiba on the Gulf of Aqaba, where a four-storey hotel collapsed.

Mongolia

Over 20 million hectares of forest were destroyed as huge fires spread rapidly across the country in April 1996. An unusually snow-free winter, resulting in a very dry spring, was thought partly to blame.

Montserrat

The Soufrière Hills and Chance's Peak volcanoes became active in July 1995, with a number of explosions. They culminated in a particularly large eruption from Soufrière Hills on 25 June 1997, which killed 27 people and covered the entire island with ash. Five days later, a huge eruption from the Chance's Peak volcano compounded the island's problems. The capital, Plymouth, was virtually destroyed

as molten lava and incandescent rocks, some as large as trucks and travelling at 200 km/h [124 mph], set fire to the buildings.

Nepal

An unusually severe winter storm left over 2 m [6 ft] of snow lying across an area stretching from Bhutan to West Nepal on 10 November 1995. Snow fell continuously for 36 hours and the storm killed over 100 people, including 49 people who were victims of Nepal's worst ever avalanche, which struck the Manang district at an altitude of 5,500 m [18,000 ft]. Many bodies were not retrieved until after the spring thaw.

Pakistan

About 100 people were killed when an earthquake, measuring 7.3 on the Richter scale, hit Harnai in Baluchistan province on 28 February 1997. Most of the victims came from a single village, Mian Kutch.

Papua New Guinea

Almost 500 people were reported to have died from starvation in the Jayawijaya district of Irian Jaya in October and November 1997. The famine was blamed on a prolonged dry season caused by the effects of the El Niño climatic phenomenon.

Peru

Almost 300 people were killed after a mudslide engulfed two Andean villages on 18 February 1997. Heavy rains caused the disaster, with the slide originating from a hill overlooking the villages of Ccoha and Pumaranta, near the town of Abancay.

Poland

The worst floods in several decades hit large areas of Poland and the Czech Republic in July 1997, killing 128 people. Worst affected was the town of Wroclaw, where buildings dating back to the 13th century were damaged. Over 140,000 Poles were forced to leave their homes. Freak downpours over the Krkonose and Jeseniky mountains caused the disaster, with the Oder, Vistula, Neisse and Morava rivers particularly badly affected.

Somalia

Extensive flooding during November 1997 killed at least 1,250 people. The south of the country was worst affected, with the River Jubba submerging entire towns. At one point, the town of Bardera was host to 40,000 displaced people.

South Africa

A rain-swollen river burst its banks outside Pietermaritzburg, sending a flash flood through a black township on Christmas night 1995. The bodies of 130 people were recovered and hundreds more were unaccounted for. Three months previously, the levels of the country's main reservoirs had been declared critically low and wide-ranging restrictions on water use were imposed.

At least 50 people died during widespread flooding in the

north and east of the country in February 1996. Thousands of people were driven from their homes and a crocodile alert was issued in Phalaborwa, Northern Province.

Spain

A flash flood killed 84 people when it swept over a crowded campsite near Biescas in the Pyrenees on 8 August 1996. Some of the bodies were carried up to 16 km [10 miles] downstream on the torrent of mud and rocks.

Tanzania

An estimated 600 people died on 21 May 1996 when an overloaded Tanzanian ferry capsized and sank on Lake Victoria. Forty survivors were rescued.

Venezuela

The country's worst earthquake for three decades killed 59 people and injured hundreds more on 10 July 1997 in Sucre state. The earthquake measured 6.9 on the Richter scale.

Vietnam

Torrential rains hit the north of the country in late August 1996, swelling the Red River and leading to thousands of evacuations from Hanoi. At the same time, a tropical storm left 100,000 hectares of rice underwater in the southern Thanh Hoa province. The toll from the various disasters was at least 194 dead and 200,000 homeless.

Yemen

More than 65 people were killed and hundreds made homeless after 'unprecedented' flooding in eastern Yemen in June 1996.

USA

A swarm of tornadoes devastated parts of central Texas at the end of May 1997. At least 29 people were killed when the town of Jarrell, near Austin, was destroyed by a particularly powerful tornado.

In Texas, and across the south-west, rainfall in 1996 was between 70% and 85% below normal. It is thought that the drought has been the worst natural disaster to hit Texas this century.

At 6.46 pm on 10 July 1996, a huge rockfall occurred on the east side of Glacier Point in the Yosemite valley, killing one person and leaving a large dust cloud over the valley, which blocked out the sun for over an hour. The US Geological Survey reported that a 150 m [495 ft] wide, 6 m [20 ft] thick flake, weighing 162,000 tonnes, detached itself from the wall, creating a subsequent 260 km/h [160 mph] air blast.

World

Natural disasters killed more than 11,000 people and caused over £36 billion of damage in 1996.

World tourism

	International inbound tourism 1994 '000s	International outbound tourism 1994 '000s	Hotel rooms 1994
Albania	28	10	1573
American Samoa	18	...	249
Angola	2	...	232
Antigua & Barbuda	255	...	3317
Argentina	3,866	3,180	111,427
Aruba	582	...	5,854
Australia	3,362	2,354	166,963
Austria	17,894	2,572	311,911
Azerbaijan	321	...	1,990
Bahamas	1,516	...	13,398
Bahrain	2,270	...	3,222
Bangladesh	140	772	3,190
Barbados	426	...	5,685
Belize	129	...	3,504
Bermuda	416	95	4,161
Bhutan	4	...	...
Bolivia	320	263	13,138
Botswana	607	327	1,463
Brazil	1,700	2,100	140,563
Burkina Faso	133	...	2,590
Burma (Myanmar)	80	...	6,213
Burundi	29	...	551
Cambodia	177	...	5,408
Cameroon	81	...	10,739
Canada	15,971	18,344	...
Cape Verde	31	...	1,035
Chad	19	...	334
Chile	1,623	980	36,011
China	5,182	3,734	406,280
Colombia	1,207	949	43,756
Comoros	27	...	438
Congo	30	...	3,398
Congo (Zaïre)	18	...	...
Costa Rica	761	268	10,794
Croatia	2,293	...	85,169
Cuba	617	64	26,358
Cyprus	2,069	302	34,424
Czech Republic	17,000	45,845	66,965
Dominica	57	...	705
Dominican Republic	1,717	...	28,967
Ecuador	482	249	34,880
Egypt	2,356	2,725	61,068
El Salvador	181	259	3,479
Estonia	550	65	4,562
Ethiopia	98	106	3,440
Fiji	319	64	5,093
France	61,312	17,709	596,670
French Polynesia	166	60	3,040
Gambia	78	...	2,553
Germany	14,494	79,200	744,274
Ghana	271	...	8,578
Gibraltar	80	...	...
Greece	10,713	...	269,858
Grenada	109	...	1,428
Guadeloupe	556	...	7,550
Guam	1,087	...	6,873
Guatemala	537	322	11,152
Guinea	93	...	1,443
Guyana	113	...	900
Haiti	70	...	800
Honduras	198	148	8,803
Hungary	21,425	14,374	35,878
Iceland	179	146	4,130
India	1,886	2,735	55,455
Indonesia	4,006	965	176,342
Iran	362	769	18,731
Ireland	4,309	2,368	28,000
Israel	1,839	1,707	35,148
Italy	27,480	...	943,654
Ivory Coast	157	4	5,947
Jamaica	977	...	19,760
Japan	1,915	13,579	241,930
Jordan	858	1,072	9,230
Kenya	863	162	18,000
Kiribati	4	...	102
Kuwait	73	...	2,407
Laos	146	...	2,564
Lebanon	335	...	8,624
Lesotho	97	254	1,041
Libya	54	183	8,463
Liechtenstein	62	...	...
Lithuania	222	2,392	4,761
Luxembourg	762	...	8,092
Macau	4,489	37	8,357
Macedonia	185	...	28,899
Madagascar	66	32	3,040
Malawi	153	...	282
Malaysia	7,197	18,825	65,907
Maldives	280	28	5,133
Mali	28	...	1,239
Malta	1,176	148	...
Marshall Islands	5	...	186
Martinique	419	...	5,090
Mauritius	401	109	5,888
Mexico	17,113	11,796	388,675
Moldova	21	37	2,593
Monaco	217	...	...
Morocco	3,465	1,522	60,817
Namibia	255	...	2,203
Nepal	327	64	9,001
Netherlands	6,178	10,800	71,000
New Caledonia	85	58	1,888
New Zealand	1,323	823	...
Nicaragua	238	256	1,404
Niger	11	16	1,290
Nigeria	192	...	30,000
Norway	2,830	563	59,490
Oman	358	...	2,762
Pakistan	454	...	29,703
Panama	324	183	9,093
Papua New Guinea	39	66	2,631
Paraguay	406	...	4,820
Peru	386	466	63,817
Philippines	1,414	1,318	19,112
Poland	18,800	34,296	52,392
Portugal	9,132	227	89,961
Puerto Rico	3,042	1,192	9,509
Qatar	241	...	1,689
Réunion	263	223	1,687
Romania	2,796	10,105	84,475
Rwanda	2	...	389
St Kitts & Nevis	94	...	1,402
St Lucia	219	...	2,954
St Vincent & G.	55	...	1,215
San Marino	5,353	...	491
São Tomé & Príncipe	5	...	212
Saudi Arabia	996	...	...
Senegal	240	...	7,600
Seychelles	110	26	2,063
Sierra Leone	72	...	1,130
Singapore	6,268	2,447	27,112
Slovak Republic	902	213	16,000
Slovenia	748	...	16,566
Solomon Islands	12	...	511
South Africa	3,897	1,766	43,174
Spain	43,232	17,708	585,696
Sri Lanka	408	405	12,787
Surinam	18	89	1,550
Swaziland	288	...	1,205
Switzerland	12,200	9,561	143,250
Syria	718	2,435	14,664
Taiwan	2,127	4,744	19,600
Tanzania	262	301	6,335
Thailand	6,166	1,681	246,113
Togo	44	...	1,872
Trinidad & Tobago	266	193	3,372
Tunisia	3,856	1,838	74,466
Turkey	6,034	3,447	125,820
Uganda	119	...	3,470
UK	21,300	39,897	...
USA	45,504	47,500	3,080,000
US Virgin Islands	540	...	5,461
Uruguay	1,884	...	15,207
Vanuatu	42	10	463
Venezuela	429	493	61,422
Vietnam	1,018	...	22,287
Yemen	40	...	5,480
Yugoslavia	91	...	37,577

World Heritage Sites

New World Heritage Sites, designated in 1996.

All sites belonging to the UNESCO World Heritage List are considered to be of global importance, either because of their cultural significance or their natural features.

Sites are submitted to UNESCO by the appropriate government ministry within each country. UNESCO then considers each proposal under strict criteria, and adds them to the World Heritage Site list if appropriate.

Some countries are not signatories to the convention, and so the list is not entirely comprehensive worldwide.

The World Heritage Committee added the following sites in 1996:

Site	Country
Monastery of Hagphat	Armenia
Historic Centre of Salzburg	Austria
Palace and Gardens of Schonbrunn	Austria
Belize Barrier Reef Reserve System	Belize
Lushan National Park	China
Okapi Faunal Reserve	Congo (Zaïre)
Lednice-Valtice Cultural Landscape	Czech Republic
Verla Groundwood and Board Mill	Finland
Le Canal du Midi	France
Upper Svaneti	Georgia
The Bauhaus and its sites in Weimar and Dessau	Germany
Cologne Cathedral	Germany
Luther Memorials in Eisleben and Wittenberg	Germany
Archaeological Site of Vergina	Greece
Millenary Benedictine Abbey of Pannonhalma	Hungary
Sangiran Early Man Site	Indonesia
Skellig Michael	Ireland
Castel del Monte	Italy
The Trulli of Alberobello	Italy
Christian Monuments and Mosaics of Ravenna	Italy
Historic Centre of Pienza	Italy
Hiroshima Peace Memorial (Genbaku Dome)	Japan
Itsukushima Shinto Shrine	Japan
Ksour of Ouadane, Chinguetti, Tichitt, Oualata	Mauritania
Pre-hispanic Town of Queretaro	Mexico
Historic City of Meknes	Morocco
Defence Line of Amsterdam	Netherlands
'W' National Park	Niger
Historic Centre of Oporto	Portugal
Volcanoes of Kamchatka	Russia
Lake Baikal	Russia
Historic Walled Town of Cuenca	Spain
'La Lonja de la Seda' of Valencia	Spain
Church Town of Gammelstad	Sweden

UK population

	Area sq km	1961 ('000s)	1961 to 1971 % change	1971 ('000s)	1971 to 1981 % change	Population 1981 ('000s)	1981 to 1991 % change	1991 ('000s)	1991 to 1996 % change	1996 mid-year pop. ('000s)	Density 1996 persons per sq km
England											
Greater London	1,578	**7,992.3**	**–6.8**	**7,452.3**	**–11.3**	**6,608.8**	**–4.9**	**6,679.7**	**5.9**	**7,074.3**	**4,482**
Inner London	321	3,492.8	–13.2	3,031.9	–20.0	2,425.6	–6.6	2,504.5	8.1	2,707.8	8,448
City of London	3	4.8	–12.5	4.2	11.9	4.7	–27.9	4.1	25.1	5.2	1,891
Camden	22	245.7	–15.9	206.7	–22.1	161.1	–5.2	170.4	11.0	189.1	8,707
Hackney	20	257.5	–14.4	220.3	–18.5	179.5	–10.0	181.2	6.9	193.8	9,941
Hammersmith and Fulham	16	222.1	–15.7	187.2	–22.7	144.6	–7.5	148.5	5.5	156.7	9,704
Haringey	30	259.2	–7.4	240.1	–15.6	202.7	–8.9	202.2	6.9	216.1	7,137
Islington	15	261.2	–22.7	201.9	–22.0	157.5	–4.3	164.7	6.9	176.0	11,827
Kensington and Chelsea	12	218.5	–13.9	188.2	33.1	125.9	–7.6	138.4	14.9	159.0	13,320
Lambeth	27	341.6	–10.0	307.5	–20.6	244.1	–11.3	244.8	8.1	264.7	9,708
Lewisham	35	290.6	–7.6	268.5	–14.2	230.5	–7.3	231.0	4.6	241.5	6,953
Newham	36	265.4	–10.6	237.4	–11.9	209.1	–4.7	212.2	7.9	228.9	6,296
Southwark	29	313.4	–16.4	262.1	–20.0	209.7	–6.3	218.5	5.2	229.9	7,993
Tower Hamlets	20	205.7	–19.4	165.8	–15.6	140.0	7.5	161.1	9.7	176.6	8,948
Wandsworth	35	335.4	–9.9	302.3	–16.6	252.2	–6.8	252.4	5.4	266.2	7,631
Westminster, City of	22	271.7	–11.8	239.7	–31.6	163.9	–7.8	174.8	16.7	204.1	9,469
Outer London	1,258	4,499.5	–1.8	4,420.4	–5.4	4,183.1	–3.9	4,175.2	4.6	4,366.4	3,471
Barking and Dagenham	34	177.1	–9.2	160.8	–7.4	149.0	–6.0	143.7	7.0	153.7	4,504
Barnet	89	318.4	–3.7	306.6	–5.3	290.2	–3.0	293.6	8.8	319.4	3,569
Bexley	61	209.9	3.4	217.1	–1.3	214.4	–1.4	215.6	1.7	219.3	3,617
Brent	44	295.9	–5.2	280.6	–10.5	251.2	–10.1	243.0	1.9	247.5	5,603
Bromley	152	293.4	4.1	305.4	–3.6	294.5	–4.2	290.6	1.7	295.6	1,948
Croydon	87	323.9	3.1	333.9	–5.3	316.3	–4.8	313.5	6.5	333.8	3,853
Ealing	55	301.6	–0.2	301.1	–7.4	278.7	–5.7	275.3	7.9	297.0	5,359
Enfield	81	273.8	–2.1	268.0	–4.0	257.2	–3.2	257.4	2.0	262.6	3,237
Greenwich	48	229.8	–5.3	217.7	–3.6	209.9	–5.6	207.7	2.1	212.1	4,448
Harrow	51	209.1	–2.8	203.2	–3.5	196.2	–0.8	200.1	5.3	210.7	4,146
Havering	118	254.6	–2.7	247.7	–3.2	239.8	–6.3	229.5	0.6	230.9	1,961
Hillingdon	110	228.4	2.8	234.9	–3.6	226.4	–0.6	231.6	7.0	247.7	2,246
Hounslow	58	208.9	–1.0	206.9	–3.8	198.9	–2.2	204.4	0.7	205.8	3,570
Kingston upon Thames	38	146.0	–3.8	140.5	–6.6	131.2	–2.0	133.0	6.6	141.8	3,778
Merton	38	189.0	–6.2	177.3	–6.9	165.1	–2.0	168.5	8.2	182.3	4,807
Redbridge	56	250.1	–4.1	239.9	–6.3	224.7	–2.1	226.2	1.9	230.6	4,083
Richmond upon Thames	55	180.9	–3.5	174.6	–9.9	157.3	–1.9	160.7	11.9	179.9	3,256
Sutton	43	169.1	0.2	169.5	–1.2	167.5	–2.0	168.9	3.9	175.5	4,046
Waltham Forest	40	248.6	–5.6	234.7	–8.6	214.6	–6.0	212.0	3.9	220.2	5,555
Metropolitan Counties											
Greater Manchester	1,289	**2,719.8**	**0.3**	**2,728.8**	**–5.6**	**2,575.4**	**–5.5**	**2,499.4**	**3.0**	**2,575.5**	**1,999**
Bolton	140	250.3	3.7	259.5	0.3	260.2	–2.5	258.6	2.7	265.4	1,900
Bury	99	151.8	15.0	174.6	0.5	175.5	–1.4	176.8	2.9	181.9	1,835
Manchester	116	662.0	–17.9	543.8	–19.5	437.7	–12.1	404.9	6.4	430.8	3,710
Oldham	141	215.7	3.8	224.0	–2.0	219.5	–3.2	216.5	1.7	220.2	1,561
Rochdale	160	189.8	7.0	203.1	1.6	206.3	–4.5	202.2	2.7	207.6	1,301
Salford	97	294.4	–4.9	279.9	–13.7	241.5	–11.1	220.5	4.0	229.2	2,368
Stockport	126	256.0	14.1	292.2	–1.1	289.0	–3.6	284.4	2.4	291.1	2,311
Tameside	103	204.2	8.1	220.8	–1.7	217.0	–2.6	216.4	2.0	220.7	2,140
Trafford	106	223.2	2.2	228.0	–3.1	221.0	–6.3	212.7	2.9	218.9	2,074
Wigan	199	272.4	11.2	302.9	1.6	307.7	–1.7	306.5	1.1	309.8	1,558
Merseyside	655	**1,718.3**	**–3.6**	**1,656.5**	**–9.3**	**1,503.1**	**–9.1**	**1,403.6**	**1.2**	**1,420.4**	**2,168**
Knowsley	97	151.4	28.2	194.1	–10.9	173.0	–13.9	152.1	1.3	154.1	1,583
Liverpool	113	745.8	–18.2	610.1	–17.4	503.7	–13.5	452.5	3.4	468.0	4,148
St Helens	133	174.6	8.2	189.0	0.1	189.3	–6.9	178.8	0.4	179.5	1,346
Sefton	153	294.5	4.4	307.5	–3.0	298.2	–5.0	289.5	0.1	289.7	1,895
Wirral	159	352.0	1.1	355.8	–4.7	339.0	–4.8	330.8	–0.5	329.2	2,074
South Yorkshire	1,559	**1,303.3**	**1.5**	**1,322.5**	**–2.3**	**1,292.0**	**–4.1**	**1,262.6**	**3.3**	**1,304.7**	**837**
Barnsley	328	223.8	0.8	225.6	–0.8	223.9	–2.9	220.9	2.8	227.2	692
Doncaster	581	268.1	4.8	281.1	2.1	286.9	–1.1	288.9	1.0	291.8	502
Rotherham	283	226.6	7.3	243.1	3.0	250.4	–1.1	251.6	1.5	255.3	904
Sheffield	367	584.8	–2.1	572.7	–7.3	530.8	–7.8	501.2	5.8	530.4	1,444
Tyne and Wear	537	**1,243.8**	**–2.6**	**1,211.7**	**–6.3**	**1,135.5**	**–5.4**	**1,095.2**	**2.9**	**1,127.3**	**2,099**
Gateshead	143	223.6	0.7	225.1	–6.3	210.9	–7.1	199.6	0.7	201.0	1,403
Newcastle upon Tyne	112	336.4	–8.4	308.3	–11.5	272.9	–7.5	259.5	8.8	282.3	2,526
North Tyneside	84	210.5	–1.2	207.9	–5.0	197.4	–4.4	192.3	0.7	193.6	2,314
South Tyneside	63	184.8	–4.2	177.1	–9.6	160.1	–5.0	154.7	0.9	156.1	2,484
Sunderland	135	288.5	1.7	293.3	0.3	294.1	–3.3	289.0	1.8	294.3	2,172
West Midlands	899	**2,371.8**	**17.8**	**2,793.3**	**–5.9**	**2,628.4**	**–5.5**	**2,551.7**	**3.6**	**2,642.5**	**2,940**
Birmingham	265	1,183.2	–7.2	1,098.0	–9.3	996.3	–7.3	961.0	6.2	1,020.6	3,844
Coventry	97	318.3	5.8	336.7	–7.9	310.2	–7.7	294.4	4.1	306.5	3,176
Dudley	98	254.2	15.6	293.9	1.6	298.5	0.6	304.6	2.5	312.2	3,187
Sandwell	86	339.5	–2.7	330.2	–7.0	307.0	–7.4	290.1	0.7	292.2	3,412
Solihull	179	128.2	49.8	192.1	3.1	198.1	–1.1	199.9	2.0	203.9	1,142
Walsall	106	246.8	10.7	273.3	–2.7	265.9	–3.9	259.5	1.2	262.6	2,483
Wolverhampton	69	261.6	2.9	269.1	–6.2	252.5	–6.0	242.2	0.9	244.5	3,554

Metropolitan Counties continued

	Area sq km	1961 ('000s)	1961 to 1971 % change	1971 ('000s)	1971 to 1981 % change	1981 ('000s)	1981 to 1991 % change	1991 ('000s)	1991 to 1996 % change	1996 mid-year pop. ('000s)	Density 1996 persons per sq km
West Yorkshire	2,034	2,005.4	3.1	2,067.6	–2.2	2,021.6	–2.7	2,013.7	4.8	2,109.4	1,037
Bradford	366	452.8	2.0	461.8	–1.7	454.1	–1.6	457.3	5.7	483.4	1,320
Calderdale	363	201.2	–3.0	195.2	–2.5	190.3	–1.6	191.6	0.7	192.8	531
Kirklees	410	352.9	4.6	369.3	0.3	370.6	–1.3	373.1	4.2	388.8	949
Leeds	562	713.0	3.6	738.9	–5.7	696.7	–5.2	680.7	6.8	726.9	1,294
Wakefield	333	285.5	5.9	302.4	2.5	309.9	–1.3	310.9	2.1	317.3	953

Non-metropolitan Counties

	Area sq km	1961 ('000s)	1961 to 1971 % change	1971 ('000s)	1971 to 1981 % change	1981 ('000s)	1981 to 1991 % change	1991 ('000s)	1991 to 1996 % change	1996 mid-year pop. ('000s)	Density 1996 persons per sq km
Avon	1,332	828.9	9.3	905.9	–0.6	900.4	0.4	932.7	4.9	978.7	735
Bath	29	84.1	0.7	84.7	–8.0	78.0	–2.9	78.7	6.9	84.1	2,934
Bristol	110	438.0	–2.6	426.6	–9.8	384.9	–6.3	376.1	6.1	399.2	3,643
Kingswood	37	67.6	15.1	77.8	8.2	84.2	4.6	89.7	2.9	92.3	2,502
Northavon	460	69.9	50.4	105.1	11.3	117.0	9.4	130.6	7.3	140.2	305
Wansdyke	322	60.8	16.6	70.9	7.3	76.1	3.0	80.0	0.1	80.1	248
Woodspring	375	108.7	29.5	140.8	13.9	160.3	8.0	177.5	3.0	182.7	488
Bedfordshire	1,236	382.7	21.3	464.2	8.1	502.0	1.7	524.1	4.7	548.8	444
Bedford	477	103.8	19.9	124.5	5.4	131.3	–0.5	133.7	2.8	137.5	288
Luton	43	140.1	15.2	161.4	1.1	163.2	1.4	171.7	5.7	181.5	4,186
Mid-Bedfordshire	503	69.1	30.0	89.8	13.1	101.6	5.9	109.8	8.3	118.9	237
South Bedfordshire	213	69.7	27.0	88.5	19.7	105.9	0.8	108.9	1.8	110.9	521
Berkshire	1,259	516.8	22.2	631.4	6.3	671.3	6.2	734.2	7.7	791.0	628
Bracknell Forest	109	43.2	48.4	64.1	26.7	81.2	14.6	95.9	14.7	110.1	1,007
Newbury	704	82.5	26.5	104.4	14.0	119.0	12.5	136.7	5.1	143.7	204
Reading	40	126.8	10.3	139.8	–6.4	130.9	–5.1	128.9	10.8	142.9	3,536
Slough	27	93.5	6.4	99.5	–3.0	96.5	1.3	101.1	9.3	110.5	4,027
Windsor and Maidenhead	198	108.1	14.6	123.9	5.4	130.6	–1.9	132.5	6.9	141.5	713
Wokingham	179	62.7	59.0	99.7	13.4	113.1	20.1	139.2	2.3	142.4	795
Buckinghamshire	1,877	377.9	26.0	476.1	17.7	560.5	10.0	632.5	6.2	671.7	358
Aylesbury Vale	903	90.9	25.9	114.4	14.5	131.0	9.0	145.9	6.2	154.9	172
Chiltern	196	72.3	23.0	88.9	0.8	89.6	–2.1	89.8	3.0	92.5	471
Milton Keynes	309	49.3	35.5	66.8	84.6	123.3	39.2	176.3	11.8	197.1	639
South Buckinghamshire	145	55.5	14.6	63.6	–2.7	61.9	–2.1	62.5	0.9	63.1	436
Wycombe	325	109.9	29.6	142.4	8.7	154.8	–0.4	157.9	3.9	164.0	505
Cambridgeshire	3,400	436.5	15.8	505.6	12.3	567.9	10.6	645.1	9.0	703.3	207
Cambridge	41	95.5	3.5	98.8	–11.7	87.2	1.3	91.9	26.9	116.7	2,867
East Cambridgeshire	655	45.1	8.9	49.1	8.8	53.4	11.0	60.4	11.8	67.5	103
Fenland	546	62.8	3.0	64.7	2.1	66.0	10.6	74.4	6.4	79.2	145
Huntingdonshire	923	69.0	40.6	97.0	26.9	123.1	14.5	144.1	6.0	152.7	165
Peterborough	333	90.2	17.1	105.6	24.6	131.5	12.7	153.2	3.6	158.7	477
South Cambridgeshire	902	73.9	22.3	90.4	17.9	106.6	11.1	121.1	6.0	128.4	142
Cheshire	2,331	729.7	18.7	866.5	6.4	921.6	1.6	956.6	2.4	980.0	420
Chester	448	102.0	13.4	115.7	–1.0	114.5	–1.2	116.0	2.8	119.2	266
Congleton	211	55.3	28.4	71.0	11.2	78.9	5.2	84.5	2.4	86.6	410
Crewe and Nantwich	430	91.3	6.5	97.2	0.1	97.3	3.9	103.2	10.2	113.7	264
Ellesmere Port and Neston	87	56.6	38.7	78.5	4.7	82.2	–3.5	80.9	–0.3	80.7	930
Halton	74	82.1	16.8	95.9	27.1	121.9	–0.3	123.7	–0.5	123.0	1,667
Macclesfield	525	113.3	23.5	139.9	6.4	148.9	–0.8	151.6	0.7	152.6	291
Vale Royal	380	87.0	21.6	105.8	4.7	110.8	1.1	114.1	1.0	115.2	303
Warrington	176	142.1	14.4	162.5	2.9	167.1	7.1	182.7	3.5	189.0	1,074
Cleveland	597	526.5	7.8	567.7	–0.3	565.9	–4.3	550.3	1.8	560.1	939
Hartlepool	94	97.3	2.2	99.4	–5.0	94.5	–5.7	90.4	2.0	92.2	982
Langbaurgh-on-Tees	245	118.5	24.6	147.7	1.7	150.3	–5.1	145.1	–1.6	142.8	583
Middlesbrough	54	164.8	–4.6	157.3	–5.1	149.2	–7.1	140.8	4.3	146.9	2,728
Stockton-on-Tees	204	145.9	11.9	163.3	5.3	172.0	–0.6	173.9	2.4	178.2	874
Cornwall & Isles of Scilly	3,530	343.2	11.2	381.6	9.7	418.6	9.0	468.4	3.2	483.3	137
Caradon	665	48.5	11.5	54.1	23.9	67.0	11.4	76.5	4.2	79.7	120
Carrick	461	63.4	10.6	70.1	5.5	74.0	8.2	82.7	2.6	84.9	184
Kerrier	473	64.7	15.6	74.8	9.2	81.7	4.6	87.6	1.8	89.1	188
North Cornwall	1,179	52.4	7.8	56.5	13.4	64.1	12.2	73.8	6.6	78.7	67
Penwith	286	49.8	3.0	51.3	3.6	53.2	8.3	59.3	0.7	59.6	208
Restormel	451	62.1	16.6	72.4	6.1	76.8	10.1	86.5	3.4	89.5	198
Isles of Scilly	15	2.3	4.3	2.4	–22.8	1.9	7.9	2.0	–6.4	1.9	124
Cumbria	6,817	470.1	1.3	476.1	–0.9	471.7	0.4	483.2	1.5	490.6	72
Allerdale	1,251	95.4	–0.5	94.9	–0.7	94.2	–0.2	95.7	0.0	95.7	76
Barrow-in-Furness	78	75.2	0.1	75.3	–3.5	72.6	–1.3	73.1	–2.0	71.6	920
Carlisle	1,040	100.7	0.1	100.8	–1.3	99.5	–0.8	100.6	2.5	103.1	99
Copeland	741	73.5	–2.3	71.8	–0.5	71.5	–1.9	71.3	–0.8	70.7	95
Eden	2,156	42.5	–1.4	41.9	1.3	42.4	5.2	45.6	6.6	48.6	23
South Lakeland	1,550	82.8	10.4	91.4	0.0	91.4	3.1	96.9	4.1	100.9	65
Derbyshire	2,629	846.8	4.7	886.6	1.7	901.8	1.2	928.6	3.6	962.0	366
Amber Valley	265	102.8	2.4	105.3	3.2	108.6	1.7	111.9	3.0	115.2	435
Bolsover	160	75.4	–4.1	72.3	–2.7	70.3	–1.1	70.4	0.7	70.9	443
Chesterfield	66	94.1	2.2	96.2	1.0	97.1	0.5	99.4	1.3	100.7	1,525
Derby	78	212.7	3.2	219.6	–2.4	214.4	–0.4	218.8	6.8	233.7	2,995
Derbyshire Dales	795	62.6	4.0	65.1	0.9	65.7	1.2	67.6	3.1	69.6	88
High Peak	540	70.3	12.7	79.2	2.5	81.2	2.7	85.1	3.7	88.2	163

	Area sq km	1961 ('000s)	1961 to 1971 % change	1971 ('000s)	1971 to 1981 % change	Population 1981 ('000s)	1981 to 1991 % change	1991 ('000s)	1991 to 1996 % change	1996 mid-year pop. ('000s)	Density 1996 persons per sq km
North East Derbyshire	277	81.1	8.9	88.3	7.9	95.3	0.9	97.6	1.5	99.0	358
South Derbyshire	338	55.5	9.5	60.8	10.7	67.3	4.9	71.8	8.4	77.8	230
Erewash	109	92.3	8.1	99.8	2.1	101.8	2.4	106.1	0.7	106.8	977
Devon	**6,698**	**822.7**	**9.2**	**898.4**	**3.5**	**930.1**	**5.4**	**1,010.0**	**4.9**	**1,059.3**	**158**
East Devon	814	83.6	16.3	97.2	6.6	103.6	8.5	115.9	6.2	123.1	151
Exeter	47	88.6	8.0	95.7	-2.7	93.1	2.2	98.1	9.8	107.7	2,291
Mid Devon	915	47.1	11.0	52.3	9.9	57.5	9.4	64.3	2.8	66.0	72
North Devon	1,086	62.8	12.3	70.5	8.6	76.6	7.5	84.8	1.6	86.2	79
Plymouth	74	230.4	3.9	239.5	0.6	241.1	-2.3	243.4	5.1	255.8	3,445
South Hams	887	55.5	7.9	59.9	9.0	65.3	15.0	77.6	2.3	79.3	89
Teignbridge	674	80.4	11.9	90.0	4.0	93.6	12.7	108.3	7.8	116.7	173
Torbay	63	96.3	13.5	109.3	1.3	110.7	4.7	119.7	3.1	123.4	1,963
Torridge	979	40.5	10.4	44.7	4.5	46.7	9.1	52.1	4.4	54.4	56
West Devon	1,160	37.5	4.8	39.3	6.9	42.0	6.6	45.9	1.2	46.4	40
Dorset	**2,653**	**499.7**	**10.9**	**554.4**	**4.4**	**579.0**	**8.3**	**645.2**	**5.7**	**681.9**	**257**
Bournemouth	46	154.3	-0.3	153.9	-8.9	140.2	4.5	151.3	6.2	160.7	3,481
Christchurch	50	28.5	19.3	34.0	9.7	37.3	6.2	40.9	5.8	43.2	857
East Dorset	354	35.6	44.7	51.5	31.4	67.7	13.5	78.7	4.1	82.0	231
North Dorset	609	36.1	17.2	42.3	8.3	45.8	10.9	52.1	11.7	58.2	96
Poole	65	92.1	16.4	107.2	9.3	117.1	10.6	133.1	4.6	139.2	2,150
Purbeck	404	32.1	14.3	36.7	6.7	39.2	5.4	42.4	6.8	45.3	112
West Dorset	1,082	68.4	8.3	74.1	3.4	76.6	8.5	85.5	5.7	90.3	84
Weymouth and Portland	42	52.6	4.0	54.7	0.8	55.1	8.2	61.2	2.6	62.8	1,505
Durham	**2,429**	**605.3**	**0.3**	**607.1**	**-1.4**	**598.8**	**-2.3**	**593.4**	**2.5**	**608.1**	**250**
Chester-le-Street	68	42.7	13.1	48.3	7.9	52.1	-0.3	52.6	6.5	56.1	830
Darlington	197	95.1	2.9	97.9	-0.7	97.2	-0.4	98.9	2.4	101.3	513
Derwentside	270	99.9	-7.8	92.1	-4.9	87.6	-2.9	86.0	2.0	87.7	325
Durham	187	75.4	8.2	81.6	0.1	81.6	-2.6	80.7	11.7	90.1	483
Easington	145	110.9	-1.8	108.9	-7.6	100.6	-3.9	97.8	-2.7	95.2	658
Sedgefield	217	82.9	6.6	88.4	4.5	92.3	-3.3	90.5	-0.6	90.0	414
Teesdale	840	26.4	-6.8	24.6	-3.3	23.8	-0.3	24.1	1.6	24.5	29
Wear Valley	505	72.0	-9.3	65.3	-2.8	63.5	-2.4	62.7	0.8	63.3	125
East Sussex	**1,794**	**586.2**	**10.4**	**647.4**	**-1.0**	**641.0**	**3.7**	**690.4**	**6.4**	**734.9**	**410**
Brighton	57	163.1	-1.0	161.4	-11.2	143.3	-5.0	143.6	8.7	156.1	2,730
Eastbourne	44	60.9	16.4	70.9	4.5	74.1	6.1	81.4	9.3	89.0	2,014
Hastings	30	66.5	8.9	72.4	1.7	73.6	5.6	80.8	1.5	82.0	2,760
Hove	24	88.7	2.8	91.2	-8.5	83.4	-2.4	85.4	9.4	93.4	3,908
Lewes	292	56.6	27.6	72.2	6.3	76.8	10.5	87.4	-0.6	86.9	297
Rother	511	64.0	10.9	71.0	4.3	74.1	6.8	81.7	9.	89.5	175
Wealden	836	86.4	25.3	108.3	6.8	115.7	9.8	130.2	6.0	138.0	165
Essex	**3,662**	**1,103.6**	**23.1**	**1,358.1**	**7.6**	**1,461.8**	**2.2**	**1,528.6**	**3.8**	**1,586.2**	**433**
Basildon	110	88.7	45.9	129.4	16.9	151.3	4.1	161.1	1.3	163.3	1,484
Braintree	612	74.5	25.4	93.4	19.2	111.3	4.9	118.9	6.2	126.2	206
Brentwood	149	59.2	24.0	73.4	-2.0	71.9	-4.2	70.6	1.5	71.7	482
Castle Point	45	48.0	55.6	74.7	15.2	86.0	-1.4	86.6	-1.9	84.9	1,897
Chelmsford	342	93.0	32.3	123.0	11.7	137.4	8.7	152.4	2.7	156.6	458
Colchester	333	93.8	26.0	118.2	11.7	132.0	5.8	142.5	8.2	154.2	462
Epping Forest	340	107.0	6.7	114.2	1.3	115.7	-2.3	116.0	3.0	119.5	351
Harlow	30	53.7	45.4	78.1	1.5	79.3	-7.7	74.6	-1.0	73.4	2,437
Maldon	356	31.0	30.6	40.5	17.7	47.7	8.1	52.8	3.3	54.6	153
Rochford	165	49.4	38.7	68.5	6.8	73.1	1.3	75.4	1.4	76.5	465
Southend-on-Sea	42	165.1	-1.4	162.8	-4.3	155.8	-1.4	158.5	8.7	172.3	4,125
Tendring	333	80.4	27.4	102.4	10.1	112.8	8.9	125.8	5.1	132.3	397
Thurrock	164	114.1	9.6	125.0	1.0	126.3	-1.3	127.8	3.5	132.3	808
Uttlesford	641	45.7	19.3	54.5	12.4	61.2	4.4	65.4	4.8	68.5	107
Gloucestershire	**2,653**	**426.3**	**9.6**	**467.1**	**5.7**	**493.7**	**4.4**	**528.4**	**5.3**	**556.3**	**210**
Cheltenham	47	79.9	5.6	84.4	15.6	97.6	2.5	103.1	3.5	106.7	2,288
Cotswold	1,165	61.0	3.1	62.9	6.5	67.0	7.2	74.0	10.2	81.5	70
Forest of Dean	526	62.7	5.1	65.9	8.7	71.6	3.3	75.4	0.8	76.0	144
Gloucester	41	82.6	9.2	90.2	4.8	94.5	4.7	101.6	5.1	106.8	2,636
Stroud	461	82.3	9.1	89.8	8.6	97.5	4.1	103.6	4.2	108.0	234
Tewkesbury	414	57.8	27.9	73.9	-11.5	65.4	5.7	70.7	9.4	77.3	187
Hampshire	**3,777**	**1,150.6**	**19.3**	**1,373.0**	**5.1**	**1,443.3**	**4.2**	**1,541.5**	**5.6**	**1,627.4**	**431**
Basingstoke and Dean	634	68.3	51.4	103.4	25.4	129.6	9.3	144.8	2.2	147.9	233
East Hampshire	515	63.0	26.2	79.5	12.5	89.4	13.1	103.5	7.1	110.8	215
Eastleigh	80	61.0	28.5	78.4	17.5	92.1	12.4	106.0	5.4	111.7	1,401
Fareham	74	58.3	37.9	80.4	8.3	87.1	11.8	99.3	4.5	103.7	1,399
Gosport	22	62.4	22.0	76.1	0.9	76.8	-4.6	75.1	1.7	76.4	3,473
Hart	215	37.4	65.0	61.7	16.7	72.0	9.9	80.9	6.0	85.8	399
Havant	55	74.5	46.7	109.3	6.2	116.1	1.1	119.7	-2.0	117.3	2,122
New Forest	753	107.7	21.6	131.0	9.4	143.3	9.1	160.5	5.6	169.5	225
Portsmouth	42	215.1	-8.2	197.4	-11.2	175.4	-3.2	174.7	9.0	190.4	4,537
Rushmoor	39	63.1	18.7	74.9	8.0	80.9	-0.5	82.5	3.9	85.8	2,197
Southampton	50	205.0	4.9	215.1	-6.1	202.0	-5.3	196.9	9.1	214.9	4,311
Test Valley	637	61.5	29.9	79.9	12.9	90.2	9.9	101.4	5.7	107.2	168

Non-metropolitan Counties continued

	Area sq km	1961 ('000s)	1961 to 1971 % change	1971 ('000s)	1971 to 1981 % change	1981 ('000s)	1981 to 1991 % change	1991 ('000s)	1991 to 1996 % change	1996 mid-year pop.('000s)	Density 1996 persons per sq km
Hereford & Worcester	**3,923**	**491.9**	**13.8**	**560.0**	**11.5**	**624.4**	**6.5**	**676.7**	**2.9**	**696.6**	**178**
Bromsgrove	220	64.6	19.3	77.1	12.8	87.0	3.6	91.5	–6.9	85.2	388
Hereford	20	40.4	15.1	46.5	1.3	47.1	4.7	50.2	–2.7	48.9	2,403
Leominster	933	33.2	0.0	33.2	11.4	37.0	5.9	39.9	4.0	41.5	45
Malvern Hills	899	70.5	9.4	77.1	5.4	81.3	4.8	86.9	5.1	91.3	102
Redditch	54	34.3	19.0	40.8	62.7	66.4	15.8	78.1	–1.2	77.2	1,423
South Herefordshire	**905**	**42.6**	**4.2**	**44.4**	**4.2**	**46.2**	**9.6**	**51.8**	**7.2**	**55.5**	**61**
Worcester	33	66.1	11.3	73.6	2.3	75.3	6.4	81.8	12.9	92.3	2,773
Wychavon	664	69.8	17.8	82.2	13.0	92.9	7.6	101.7	6.2	108.0	163
Wyre Forest	195	70.4	20.9	85.1	7.1	91.2	2.5	94.8	2.0	96.7	495
Hertfordshire	**1,639**	**787.8**	**17.4**	**924.7**	**3.1**	**953.4**	**0.0**	**975.8**	**4.1**	**1,015.8**	**620**
Broxbourne	52	53.3	33.4	71.1	11.6	79.4	0.9	81.4	0.4	81.8	1,566
Dacorum	212	95.5	24.5	118.9	8.2	128.7	0.6	132.2	1.9	134.7	634
East Hertfordshire	**477**	**80.0**	**27.9**	**102.3**	**3.9**	**106.3**	**6.5**	**115.8**	**6.7**	**123.6**	**259**
Hertsmere	98	87.0	4.7	91.1	–4.1	87.3	–2.1	87.6	8.3	94.9	970
North Hertfordshire	**375**	**85.5**	**16.4**	**99.5**	**7.9**	**107.4**	**2.2**	**112.0**	**2.6**	**114.9**	**306**
St Albans	161	107.5	12.9	121.4	2.4	124.3	–1.1	126.2	3.2	130.3	808
Stevenage	26	43.0	56.0	67.1	10.1	73.8	–0.5	75.1	2.1	76.8	2,957
Three Rivers	89	78.6	2.8	80.8	–1.6	79.5	–3.7	78.5	7.8	84.6	952
Watford	21	75.6	3.8	78.5	–5.8	73.9	–2.4	74.6	5.9	78.9	3,685
Welwyn Hatfield	128	81.8	14.9	94.0	–1.4	92.7	–3.0	92.4	3.3	95.4	748
Humberside	**3,508**	**797.1**	**5.2**	**838.7**	**0.5**	**843.3**	**–0.3**	**858.0**	**3.7**	**889.5**	**254**
Beverley	404	81.4	24.4	101.3	3.6	104.9	4.3	111.7	5.7	118.0	292
Boothferry	646	54.0	2.2	55.2	8.5	59.9	5.0	64.2	1.8	65.3	101
Cleethorpes	164	49.2	35.8	66.8	2.3	68.3	–0.7	69.1	1.8	70.4	430
East Yorkshire	**1,043**	**63.7**	**2.8**	**65.5**	**12.9**	**74.0**	**11.4**	**84.1**	**6.0**	**89.1**	**85**
Glanford	580	46.3	24.2	57.5	14.7	66.0	7.1	71.8	2.1	73.3	126
Great Grimsby	28	98.0	–2.6	95.5	–4.1	91.5	–3.0	90.5	0.5	91.0	3,241
Holderness	538	33.2	20.5	40.0	14.7	45.9	9.3	51.0	3.1	52.6	98
Kingston-upon-Hull	71	304.0	–5.9	286.0	–6.7	266.8	–7.0	254.1	5.9	269.2	3,767
Scunthorpe	34	67.3	5.3	70.9	–6.8	66.0	–8.7	61.6	–1.3	60.7	1,800
Isle of Wight	**380**	**95.7**	**14.4**	**109.5**	**4.9**	**114.9**	**5.6**	**124.6**	**0.1**	**125.5**	**330**
Medina	117	56.3	14.4	64.4	3.3	66.5	4.2	71.1	0.2	71.2	609
South Wight	263	39.4	14.5	45.1	7.2	48.4	7.5	53.5	0.0	53.5	203
Kent	**3,728**	**1,198.5**	**16.8**	**1,399.4**	**3.5**	**1,448.4**	**1.7**	**1,508.9**	**3.2**	**1,557.3**	**418**
Ashford	581	61.9	27.8	79.1	7.1	84.7	6.6	92.3	6.0	97.9	169
Canterbury	309	91.2	20.7	110.1	3.8	114.3	5.9	123.9	10.1	136.5	442
Dartford	73	79.4	4.9	83.3	–3.7	80.3	–3.3	79.4	5.7	83.9	1,152
Dover	312	94.4	4.9	99.0	0.5	99.5	1.3	103.2	4.1	107.4	344
Gillingham	32	72.9	19.2	86.9	7.0	93.0	0.5	95.4	–0.4	95.0	2,926
Gravesham	99	83.5	15.7	96.6	–2.1	94.5	–4.5	92.5	–0.8	91.7	926
Maidstone	393	97.1	24.8	121.2	6.6	129.2	2.9	136.2	3.3	140.7	358
Rochester upon Medway	159	117.6	18.4	139.2	2.3	142.4	–0.6	144.9	–0.3	144.5	909
Sevenoaks	368	87.2	14.1	99.5	7.7	107.2	–0.8	108.8	1.5	110.5	300
Shepway	357	73.8	11.1	82.0	3.1	84.5	4.3	91.5	7.8	98.7	277
Swale	370	84.3	19.7	100.9	8.0	109.0	4.3	115.8	1.5	117.6	318
Thanet	103	103.7	10.7	114.8	3.1	118.3	1.3	123.7	1.5	125.5	1,215
Tonbridge and Malling	240	70.2	33.2	93.5	2.9	96.2	3.5	101.8	3.2	105.0	437
Tunbridge Wells	332	81.3	14.8	93.3	2.1	95.3	1.9	99.5	3.1	102.6	309
Lancashire	**3,070**	**1,261.1**	**6.6**	**1,344.7**	**1.3**	**1,362.9**	**–0.8**	**1,384.0**	**2.9**	**1,424.7**	**464**
Blackburn	137	143.4	–1.6	141.1	–0.1	140.9	–5.4	136.6	2.1	139.5	1,018
Blackpool	35	153.2	–0.8	151.9	–4.0	145.8	–2.6	146.1	4.4	152.5	4,366
Burnley	111	99.4	–2.8	96.6	–4.8	92.0	–3.1	91.1	–0.7	90.5	817
Chorley	203	67.0	16.1	77.8	16.4	90.5	4.5	96.5	0.1	96.6	476
Fylde	166	58.4	14.7	67.0	1.2	67.8	1.7	71.0	5.6	75.0	453
Hyndburn	73	80.0	0.7	80.6	–2.2	78.9	–2.8	78.4	1.9	79.9	1,094
Lancaster	576	114.8	7.7	123.6	–4.1	118.6	1.8	123.9	10.6	136.9	238
Pendle	169	85.8	–0.5	85.4	0.2	85.6	–2.8	85.1	–0.9	84.3	498
Preston	142	143.1	–5.9	134.7	–7.6	124.4	–1.0	126.1	6.9	134.8	947
Ribble Valley	584	44.5	15.7	51.5	3.0	53.0	–4.3	51.8	1.8	52.7	90
Rossendale	138	65.7	–5.9	61.8	4.3	64.4	0.0	65.7	–1.2	64.9	470
South Ribble	113	66.5	29.8	86.3	12.4	97.0	3.4	102.0	1.0	103.0	912
West Lancashire	338	61.5	48.9	91.6	16.2	106.4	–0.2	108.0	1.7	109.8	324
Wyre	284	77.8	21.9	94.8	2.9	97.5	1.9	101.8	2.5	104.3	367
Leicestershire	**2,551**	**706.1**	**13.2**	**799.6**	**4.5**	**835.6**	**1.7**	**867.5**	**6.9**	**927.5**	**364**
Blaby	130	50.5	46.9	74.2	3.3	76.7	6.4	82.7	3.5	85.6	656
Charnwood	279	104.0	20.8	125.6	5.8	132.9	4.8	141.8	9.8	155.7	558
Harborough	593	42.5	24.7	53.0	14.4	60.7	9.4	67.6	9.1	73.7	124
Hinckley and Bosworth	297	64.2	17.6	75.5	15.5	87.2	8.6	96.2	1.7	97.8	329
Leicester	73	288.1	–1.4	284.2	–2.8	276.2	–5.0	270.5	9.0	294.8	4,021
Melton	481	34.4	13.1	38.9	10.3	42.9	3.5	45.1	3.2	46.5	97
North West Leicestershire	279	65.3	8.6	70.9	10.6	78.4	1.3	80.6	4.6	84.3	302

	Area sq km	1961 ('000s)	1961 to 1971 % change	1971 ('000s)	1971 to 1981 % change	Population 1981 ('000s)	1981 to 1991 % change	1991 ('000s)	1991 to 1996 % change	1996 mid-year pop.('000s)	Density 1996 persons per sq km
Oadby and Wigston	24	33.6	48.2	49.8	1.8	50.7	−0.2	51.5	3.8	53.5	2,275
Rutland	394	23.5	17.0	27.5	8.7	29.9	2.8	31.5	12.2	35.3	90
Lincolnshire	**5,921**	**468.6**	**7.4**	**503.5**	**7.9**	**543.3**	**5.4**	**584.5**	**5.4**	**615.9**	**104**
Boston	362	47.3	3.2	48.8	7.0	52.2	0.3	53.2	1.8	54.2	150
East Lindsey	1,760	90.6	4.5	94.7	8.7	103.0	10.7	117.0	5.2	123.1	70
Lincoln	36	77.7	−4.4	74.3	1.8	75.6	5.9	82.0	1.8	83.5	2,340
North Kesteven	922	59.7	21.8	72.7	7.6	78.2	0.1	79.9	8.4	86.6	94
South Holland	742	56.0	1.6	56.9	8.3	61.6	7.4	67.3	6.1	71.4	96
South Kesteven	943	75.0	14.0	85.5	13.7	97.2	10.0	108.9	10.1	120.0	127
West Lindsey	1,156	62.3	13.3	70.6	6.9	75.4	−0.8	76.2	1.3	77.2	67
Norfolk	**5,385**	**565.9**	**10.6**	**625.7**	**9.7**	**686.3**	**6.3**	**745.6**	**4.2**	**777.0**	**144**
Breckland	1,291	62.0	23.2	76.4	25.5	95.9	9.7	107.2	6.1	113.7	88
Broadland	552	67.7	28.1	86.7	12.4	97.5	7.1	106.3	7.2	113.9	206
Great Yarmouth	174	70.2	7.7	75.6	6.0	80.1	6.7	87.7	1.8	89.3	514
Kings Lynn and West Norfolk	1,443	106.1	3.7	110.0	11.3	122.4	4.3	130.5	0.6	131.2	91
North Norfolk	987	74.0	0.3	74.2	7.9	80.1	10.3	90.5	7.1	96.9	98
Norwich	39	121.1	0.8	122.1	−1.9	119.8	−1.9	120.9	4.4	126.2	3,235
South Norfolk	900	64.3	25.5	80.7	14.7	92.6	8.9	102.6	3.1	105.8	118
Northamptonshire	**2,367**	**398.0**	**17.8**	**468.7**	**12.0**	**525.0**	**8.0**	**578.8**	**4.4**	**604.4**	**255**
Corby	80	40.0	31.5	52.6	−0.4	52.4	−0.6	53.0	−1.7	52.1	649
Daventry	666	37.3	29.0	48.1	19.2	57.3	7.5	62.9	3.8	65.3	98
East Northamptonshire	510	51.6	9.7	56.6	7.8	61.0	8.5	67.7	4.7	70.8	139
Kettering	233	59.9	9.8	65.8	7.4	70.7	6.1	76.2	6.1	80.8	346
Northampton	81	124.1	7.7	133.7	16.3	155.5	13.2	180.6	6.5	192.4	2,382
South Northamptonshire	634	40.9	36.4	55.8	14.7	64.0	8.2	70.7	6.2	75.0	118
Wellingborough	163	44.2	26.9	56.1	14.1	64.0	4.1	67.8	0.2	67.9	416
Northumberland	**5,026**	**274.3**	**1.9**	**279.5**	**5.7**	**295.4**	**1.4**	**304.7**	**0.9**	**307.4**	**61**
Alnwick	1,079	30.0	−7.0	27.9	0.4	28.0	5.4	30.1	3.4	31.1	29
Berwick-upon-Tweed	972	28.1	−8.2	25.8	−1.1	25.5	2.5	26.7	−0.5	26.6	27
Blyth Valley	70	54.5	11.4	60.7	26.7	76.9	2.0	79.6	0.5	80.0	1,139
Castle Morpeth	619	42.6	11.5	47.5	4.5	49.6	−0.5	50.3	−1.4	49.6	80
Tynedale	2,219	52.3	1.5	53.1	0.2	53.2	5.6	57.3	1.2	58.0	26
Wansbeck	67	66.8	−3.4	64.5	−3.7	62.1	−3.6	60.7	2.5	62.2	932
North Yorkshire	**8,309**	**575.2**	**9.0**	**627.2**	**4.2**	**653.6**	**4.8**	**702.2**	**4.6**	**734.7**	**88**
Craven	1,179	45.1	2.9	46.4	0.3	46.6	4.5	49.9	2.9	51.3	44
Hambleton	1,311	59.0	14.1	67.3	9.3	73.5	5.8	79.4	6.7	84.7	65
Harrogate	1,304	116.3	9.7	127.6	7.3	136.9	2.2	139.1	6.1	147.6	113
Richmondshire	1,319	39.4	7.9	42.5	−2.9	41.3	4.4	44.2	7.0	47.3	36
Ryedale	1,507	65.0	11.7	72.6	14.5	83.1	7.0	46.2	6.3	49.1	33
Scarborough	817	88.3	10.2	97.3	1.5	98.8	4.4	106.2	1.9	108.3	133
Selby	603	54.0	27.2	68.7	10.9	76.2	15.1	71.2	0.1	71.3	118
York	271	108.1	−3.1	104.8	−7.2	97.2	−1.3	166.0	5.5	175.1	646
Nottinghamshire	**2,160**	**901.0**	**8.2**	**974.5**	**0.2**	**976.6**	**−0.6**	**993.9**	**3.8**	**1,031.8**	**478**
Ashfield	110	96.3	5.6	101.7	4.1	105.9	0.8	108.4	0.2	108.6	988
Bassetlaw	637	90.0	8.3	97.5	3.7	101.1	1.3	104.0	2.2	106.3	167
Broxtowe	81	86.9	13.0	98.2	4.3	102.4	2.8	107.1	4.0	111.4	1,375
Gedling	120	80.8	19.1	96.2	12.0	107.7	0.4	110.1	1.9	112.2	935
Mansfield	77	85.0	12.4	95.5	4.0	99.4	−0.6	100.4	1.6	104.5	160
Newark and Sherwood	651	84.1	17.6	98.9	1.1	100.0	0.9	102.8	1.6	104.5	160
Nottingham	75	311.9	−3.6	300.6	−10.8	268.3	−5.6	263.5	7.8	284.0	3,806
Rushcliffe	409	66.0	30.2	85.9	7.1	92.0	3.9	97.6	6.1	103.5	253
Oxfordshire	**2,583**	**403.0**	**23.6**	**498.2**	**1.8**	**507.2**	**5.2**	**547.6**	**10.2**	**603.2**	**234**
Cherwell	589	70.1	34.7	94.4	12.0	105.7	8.5	117.8	12.6	132.7	225
Oxford	46	106.3	2.4	108.8	−0.9	107.8	−1.2	110.1	24.7	137.3	3,012
South Oxfordshire	655	94.3	34.4	126.7	−10.3	113.6	2.6	119.5	4.3	124.6	190
Vale of White Horse	579	76.4	22.3	93.4	7.5	100.4	7.3	109.9	2.4	112.5	194
West Oxfordshire	714	55.9	34.2	75.0	6.4	79.8	10.5	90.3	6.3	96.0	134
Shropshire	**3,488**	**297.7**	**13.2**	**337.1**	**9.9**	**370.4**	**7.6**	**406.4**	**3.7**	**421.3**	**121**
Bridgnorth	633	42.7	11.9	47.8	3.1	49.3	0.7	50.5	0.7	50.8	80
North Shropshire	679	45.2	4.2	47.1	4.3	49.1	5.6	52.9	2.2	54.1	80
Oswestry	256	29.7	2.0	30.3	−0.7	30.1	9.4	33.5	3.4	34.6	135
Shrewsbury and Atcham	602	72.9	13.0	82.4	3.3	85.1	5.3	91.7	5.8	97.1	161
South Shropshire	1,027	32.6	−0.6	32.4	3.2	33.4	11.9	38.2	5.9	40.5	39
The Wrekin	290	74.6	30.2	97.1	27.0	123.3	11.0	139.5	3.3	144.2	497
Somerset	**3,452**	**345.4**	**11.9**	**386.4**	**8.1**	**417.5**	**7.8**	**460.4**	**4.8**	**482.7**	**140**
Mendip	739	69.5	13.8	79.1	9.0	86.2	8.5	95.6	2.9	98.4	133
Sedgemoor	564	69.9	15.9	81.0	9.3	88.5	8.2	97.8	4.2	101.9	181
South Somerset (Yeovil)	959	104.3	9.7	114.4	13.0	129.3	7.1	141.7	6.4	150.7	157
Taunton Deane	462	73.0	12.5	82.1	3.4	84.9	8.0	93.7	5.5	98.9	214
West Somerset	727	28.6	4.2	29.8	−4.0	28.6	7.3	31.7	3.7	32.8	45
Staffordshire	**2,715**	**849.3**	**13.5**	**963.8**	**4.3**	**1,005.7**	**0.9**	**1,031.1**	**2.4**	**1,055.7**	**389**
Cannock Chase	79	60.7	30.1	79.0	7.1	84.6	3.6	88.8	2.2	90.8	1,151
East Staffordshire	390	86.9	8.6	94.4	0.1	94.5	1.1	97.1	3.4	100.4	257
Lichfield	329	51.4	56.8	80.6	9.3	88.1	3.3	92.7	0.5	93.2	283
Newcastle-under-Lyme	211	114.6	4.7	120.0	−2.3	117.2	−0.1	119.1	2.7	122.3	580

Non-metropolitan Counties continued

	Area sq km	1961 ('000s)	1961 to 1971 % change	1971 ('000s)	1971 to 1981 % change	Population 1981 ('000s)	1981 to 1991 % change	1991 ('000s)	1991 to 1996 % change	1996 mid-year pop. ('000s)	Density 1996 persons per sq km
South Staffordshire	408	62.1	33.3	82.8	16.2	96.2	8.2	105.5	−2.1	103.3	253
Stafford	599	92.9	19.7	111.2	4.1	115.8	−0.1	117.8	5.7	124.5	208
Staffordshire Moorlands	576	78.0	15.6	90.2	5.5	95.2	−1.3	95.5	−1.1	94.4	164
Stoke-on-Trent	93	277.3	−4.3	265.3	−5.8	249.8	−3.6	244.6	4.0	254.4	2,744
Tamworth	31	25.4	58.7	40.3	59.4	64.3	7.4	70.1	3.3	72.4	2,346
Suffolk	**3,798**	**467.1**	**15.2**	**538.0**	**9.7**	**590.2**	**5.3**	**636.3**	**4.0**	**661.6**	**174**
Babergh	595	47.0	34.7	63.3	14.4	72.4	7.8	79.6	−0.9	79.0	133
Forest Heath	374	31.7	24.9	39.6	29.3	51.2	4.2	54.8	25.1	68.6	184
Ipswich	39	117.4	5.0	123.3	−3.3	119.2	−3.9	117.0	−2.8	113.6	2,883
Mid Suffolk	871	54.1	12.2	60.7	14.2	69.3	10.9	78.4	2.6	80.4	92
St Edmundsbury	657	55.5	28.6	71.4	19.5	85.3	4.8	91.7	2.0	93.6	142
Suffolk Coastal	891	82.8	7.6	89.1	5.8	94.2	11.5	108.0	9.9	118.7	133
Waveney	370	78.6	15.3	90.6	8.7	98.5	5.9	106.8	0.9	107.7	291
Surrey	**1,677**	**905.6**	**10.7**	**1,002.2**	**−1.1**	**991.1**	**−0.2**	**1,018.0**	**2.9**	**1,047.1**	**624**
Elmbridge	97	106.2	8.8	115.5	−3.8	111.1	−0.6	114.5	8.8	124.5	1,289
Epsom and Ewell	34	71.2	1.5	72.3	−5.2	68.5	−4.6	67.0	3.4	69.3	2,032
Guildford	271	108.9	9.0	118.7	−0.2	118.5	0.3	122.4	1.8	124.6	460
Mole Valley	258	73.2	5.9	77.5	−1.9	76.0	1.5	79.2	0.2	79.4	307
Reigate and Banstead	129	114.6	4.5	119.7	−3.5	115.5	−1.3	117.8	1.3	119.3	924
Runnymede	78	71.0	6.6	75.7	−7.8	69.8	0.2	71.8	5.9	76.0	975
Spelthorne	57	83.3	16.3	96.9	−5.0	92.0	−4.9	90.0	−0.9	89.2	1,578
Surrey Heath	95	44.7	47.7	66.0	13.3	74.8	2.9	79.1	4.2	82.4	867
Tandridge	250	75.2	6.1	79.8	−5.1	75.7	−1.7	76.3	1.7	77.6	311
Waverley	345	89.8	15.9	104.1	3.6	107.8	2.1	113.2	0.8	114.1	331
Woking	64	67.5	12.6	76.0	7.0	81.3	4.2	86.8	4.5	90.7	1,426
Warwickshire	**1,979**	**386.8**	**17.8**	**455.5**	**3.1**	**469.7**	**1.0**	**484.2**	**3.4**	**500.6**	**253**
North Warwickshire	285	49.2	18.3	58.2	2.4	59.6	0.5	60.7	1.1	61.4	215
Nuneaton and Bedworth	79	88.5	21.6	107.6	5.0	113.0	2.0	117.1	1.1	118.3	1,498
Rugby	356	73.5	13.7	83.6	1.3	84.7	−2.2	84.6	3.0	87.1	245
Stratford-on-Avon	977	80.0	18.1	94.5	5.2	99.4	3.9	105.6	5.3	111.2	114
Warwick	282	95.6	16.7	111.6	1.4	113.1	0.2	116.3	5.3	122.5	434
West Sussex	**1,969**	**492.1**	**20.6**	**593.6**	**9.5**	**650.1**	**5.1**	**702.3**	**5.0**	**737.3**	**375**
Adur	42	48.6	13.6	55.2	4.3	57.6	−1.6	58.0	1.5	58.9	1,409
Arun	220	81.4	28.3	104.4	10.8	115.7	8.4	129.4	6.7	138.0	627
Chichester	786	80.6	13.2	91.2	4.8	95.6	3.1	101.4	2.7	104.1	132
Crawley	44	54.6	25.1	68.3	17.5	80.2	6.4	87.6	6.3	93.2	2,112
Horsham	511	67.0	27.8	85.6	13.7	97.3	8.6	108.6	9.2	118.6	232
Mid-Sussex	333	79.6	26.1	100.4	12.6	113.0	4.7	121.2	3.4	125.3	376
Worthing	32	80.3	10.2	88.5	2.5	90.7	2.9	96.2	3.2	99.2	3,055
Wiltshire	**3,476**	**423.0**	**15.1**	**487.0**	**5.3**	**512.6**	**7.5**	**564.5**	**5.1**	**593.3**	**171**
Kennet	957	54.8	17.5	64.4	−2.4	62.8	6.3	68.5	10.2	75.5	79
North Wiltshire	768	85.9	10.2	94.7	6.8	101.1	8.2	112.0	8.7	121.7	159
Salisbury	1,004	91.6	10.4	101.1	−1.8	99.3	3.6	105.3	6.9	112.5	112
Thamesdown	230	119.7	17.0	140.0	7.7	150.7	10.7	170.9	2.2	174.6	759
West Wiltshire	517	71.0	22.3	86.8	13.7	98.7	6.8	107.8	1.0	108.9	211
ENGLAND	**130,423**	**46,460.5**	**−1.0**	**46,018.4**	**−0.5**	**45,772.0**	**−0.1**	**47,055.2**	**4.3**	**49,089.1**	**376**

Wales

	Area sq km	1961 ('000s)	1961 to 1971 % change	1971 ('000s)	1971 to 1981 % change	1981 ('000s)	1981 to 1991 % change	1991 ('000s)	1991 to 1996 % change	1996 mid-year pop. ('000s)	Density 1996 persons per sq km
Clwyd	**2,430**	**322.3**	**11.3**	**358.6**	**7.5**	**385.6**	**3.6**	**408.1**	**2.3**	**417.4**	**172**
Alyn and Deeside	154	51.9	26.2	65.5	9.4	71.6	0.7	73.5	2.5	75.3	488
Colwyn	552	38.9	16.2	45.2	4.6	47.3	13.4	55.1	4.3	57.4	104
Delyn	281	50.7	12.2	56.9	14.9	65.4	1.8	67.9	3.1	70.0	249
Glyndwr	968	38.4	−1.8	37.7	3.3	38.9	5.0	41.9	1.0	42.3	44
Rhuddlan	109	42.0	13.1	47.5	8.2	51.4	3.2	54.6	0.8	55.0	507
Wrexham Maelor	367	100.4	5.4	105.8	4.9	111.0	1.9	115.3	1.9	117.4	320
Dyfed	**5,766**	**315.7**	**0.2**	**316.4**	**2.1**	**323.0**	**3.9**	**343.5**	**2.6**	**352.3**	**61**
Carmarthen	1,180	50.3	−1.4	49.6	2.5	50.8	6.1	55.1	3.0	56.8	48
Ceredigion	1,794	53.6	2.4	54.9	0.8	55.4	10.4	63.1	10.5	69.7	39
Dinefwr	972	38.8	−6.7	36.2	1.1	36.6	3.3	38.5	0.8	38.9	40
Llanelli	233	79.0	−2.7	76.9	−2.5	75.0	−2.1	74.7	−1.8	73.4	315
Preseli Pembrokeshire	1,151	61.3	2.4	62.8	7.8	67.7	1.4	70.2	1.4	71.2	62
South Pembrokeshire	436	32.7	10.1	36.0	4.4	37.6	8.8	41.9	1.2	42.4	97
Gwent	**1,377**	**424.0**	**4.1**	**441.4**	**−1.1**	**436.5**	**−1.0**	**442.2**	**2.3**	**452.3**	**329**
Blaenau Gwent	127	94.5	−9.4	85.6	−7.9	78.9	−5.5	76.1	1.6	77.3	609
Islwyn	102	65.4	1.4	66.3	−0.2	66.2	−1.9	66.2	0.9	66.8	655
Monmouth	831	54.2	18.8	64.4	10.2	71.0	4.8	76.1	5.4	80.2	96
Newport	190	128.6	6.4	136.8	−4.4	130.7	−1.0	133.3	3.1	137.4	722
Torfaen	126	81.3	8.6	88.3	1.6	89.7	−1.0	90.5	0.0	90.6	720
Gwynedd	**3,863**	**213.7**	**3.2**	**220.6**	**0.8**	**222.3**	**2.8**	**235.5**	**2.1**	**240.4**	**62**
Aberconwy	601	48.3	5.4	50.9	−2.5	49.6	3.3	53.0	3.7	55.0	91
Arfon	410	51.7	1.7	52.6	−4.4	50.3	2.3	53.3	7.6	57.4	140
Dwyfor	620	27.6	−6.5	25.8	−1.5	25.4	4.0	27.1	0.5	27.2	44
Meirionnydd	1,517	34.4	−8.4	31.5	−3.3	30.5	4.9	33.0	−1.8	32.4	21
Ynys Mon-Isle of Anglesey	715	51.7	15.7	59.8	11.2	66.5	1.3	69.1	−1.0	68.5	96

	Area sq km	1961 ('000s)	1961 to 1971 % change	1971 ('000s)	1971 to 1981 % change	Population 1981 ('000s)	1981 to 1991 % change	1991 ('000s)	1991 to 1996 % change	1996 mid-year pop.('000s)	Density 1996 persons per sq km
Mid Glamorgan	**1,017**	**519.5**	**2.3**	**531.6**	**0.4**	**533.6**	**-1.8**	**534.1**	**2.0**	**544.6**	**535**
Cynon Valley	176	72.6	-4.1	69.6	-3.6	67.1	-4.7	65.2	0.0	65.2	369
Merthyr Tydfil	111	66.9	-5.5	63.2	-5.4	59.8	-3.0	59.3	0.3	59.5	538
Ogwr	286	111.0	11.4	123.6	4.1	128.7	0.8	132.4	2.2	135.3	474
Rhondda	101	100.3	-11.3	89.0	-8.9	81.1	-5.2	78.3	-0.9	77.7	772
Rhymney Valley	177	94.4	7.7	101.7	2.7	104.4	-2.7	103.4	0.9	104.3	588
Taff-Ely	167	74.3	13.7	84.5	9.5	92.5	1.3	95.4	7.6	102.7	615
Powys	**5,077**	**102.3**	**-3.0**	**99.2**	**9.0**	**108.1**	**6.1**	**117.5**	**2.3**	**120.2**	**24**
Brecknock	1,791	39.6	-4.5	37.8	4.6	39.5	1.7	41.1	0.5	41.4	23
Montgomeryshire	2,059	44.2	-2.5	43.1	10.6	47.6	8.1	52.7	3.7	54.7	27
Radnorshire	1,228	18.5	-1.1	18.3	14.4	20.9	9.8	23.6	2.3	24.2	20
South Glamorgan	**416**	**380.3**	**2.6**	**390.3**	**-3.5**	**376.7**	**0.7**	**392.8**	**5.6**	**414.8**	**997**
Cardiff	120	289.9	-0.8	287.6	-6.3	269.5	-0.2	279.1	7.5	300.1	2,497
Vale of Glamorgan	296	90.4	13.6	102.7	4.5	107.3	3.0	113.7	0.9	114.8	388
West Glamorgan	**820**	**366.3**	**1.9**	**373.2**	**-2.5**	**363.8**	**-2.9**	**361.4**	**2.6**	**371.0**	**453**
Port Talbot	152	60.7	-2.1	59.4	-8.4	54.4	-8.1	51.0	0.7	51.4	338
Lliw Valley	218	55.7	1.1	56.3	5.4	59.3	4.4	63.1	2.4	64.6	297
Neath	204	69.9	-3.1	67.7	-2.2	66.2	-3.2	65.4	1.2	66.2	324
Swansea	246	180.0	5.4	189.8	-3.2	183.8	-3.6	181.9	3.8	188.8	768
WALES	**20,766**	**2,644.0**	**3.3**	**2,731.2**	**0.7**	**2,749.6**	**0.6**	**2,835.1**	**3.0**	**2,921.1**	**141**

Scotland

	Area sq km	1961 ('000s)	1961 to 1971 % change	1971 ('000s)	1971 to 1981 % change	1981 ('000s)	1981 to 1991 % change	1991 ('000s)	1991 to 1996 % change	1996 mid-year pop.('000s)	Density 1996 persons per sq km
Borders	**4734**	**102.2**	**-3.6**	**98.5**	**-1.2**	**97.3**	**4.3**	**103.9**	**2.1**	**106.1**	**22**
Berwickshire	876	18.4	-7.6	17.0	5.6	18.0	4.2	19.2	1.3	19.4	22
Ettrick and Lauderdale	1,355	33.4	-3.0	32.4	-4.4	31.0	7.3	34.0	4.3	35.5	26
Roxburgh	1,540	36.3	-2.5	35.4	-2.3	34.6	-0.1	35.3	-0.3	35.2	23
Tweeddale	899	14.1	-2.8	13.7	0.6	13.8	8.7	15.3	1.5	15.6	17
Central	**2652**	**244.6**	**7.5**	**263.0**	**2.0**	**268.2**	**-2.3**	**267.5**	**2.7**	**274.6**	**104**
Clackmannan	157	41.9	10.0	46.1	2.5	47.3	-0.9	47.7	2.4	48.8	311
Falkirk	299	132.3	6.2	140.5	2.4	143.8	-3.9	141.0	1.4	143	478
Stirling	2196	70.4	8.0	76.0	1.5	77.1	-0.2	78.9	5.0	82.8	38
Dumfries and Galloway	**6439**	**146.4**	**-2.2**	**143.2**	**-0.9**	**141.9**	**2.1**	**147.8**	**0.0**	**147.8**	**23**
Annandale and Eskdale	1,553	35.6	-2.8	34.6	1.2	35.0	3.9	37.1	0.0	37.1	24
Nithsdale	1,433	55.8	1.3	56.5	-2.8	54.9	1.9	57.0	0.5	57.3	40
Stewartry	1,671	23.3	-4.7	22.2	0.8	22.4	2.9	23.6	0.3	23.7	14
Wigtown	1,713	31.7	-5.7	29.9	-0.9	29.6	-0.4	30.1	-1.2	29.7	17
Fife	**1323**	**320.7**	**2.0**	**327.1**	**-0.6**	**325.1**	**2.6**	**341.2**	**2.4**	**349.3**	**264**
Dunfermline	302	119.5	0.8	120.5	1.3	122.1	1.9	127.3	2.2	130.1	431
Kirkcaldy	248	140.1	3.5	145.0	-1.6	142.7	0.9	147.1	1.0	148.5	598
North East Fife	758	61.1	0.8	61.6	-2.1	60.3	7.9	66.9	10.0	73.6	97
Grampian	**8,707**	**440.3**	**-0.4**	**438.6**	**5.5**	**462.9**	**4.7**	**503.9**	**5.7**	**532.5**	**61**
Aberdeen City	186	206.3	2.7	211.8	-5.7	199.8	-3.1	204.9	6.1	217.3	1,168
Banff and Buchan	1,528	75.4	-3.4	72.8	10.0	80.1	4.4	85.3	3.7	88.5	58
Gordon	2,214	49.2	-8.5	45.0	37.3	61.8	20.5	76.6	4.9	80.4	36
Kincardine and Deeside	2,550	34.1	-2.3	33.3	23.2	41.0	25.5	53.4	7.0	57.2	22
Moray	2238	75.3	0.5	75.7	5.9	80.1	1.7	83.6	3.4	86.5	39
Highland	**25784**	**163.9**	**7.1**	**175.6**	**6.5**	**187.0**	**6.2**	**204.0**	**2.3**	**208.7**	**8**
Badenoch and Strathspey	2,317	9.1	2.2	9.3	0.7	9.4	13.5	11.0	1.6	11.2	5
Caithness	1,776	27.4	1.5	27.8	-3.1	26.9	-3.5	26.7	-2.4	26.1	15
Inverness	2,789	45.8	8.7	49.8	9.0	54.3	11.5	62.2	3.4	64.3	23
Lochaber	4,468	15.9	20.1	19.1	-0.4	19.0	-1.1	19.3	0.5	19.4	4
Nairn	422	8.4	32.1	11.1	-13.2	9.6	6.8	10.6	3.0	10.9	26
Ross and Cromarty	4,976	32.8	6.1	34.8	28.9	44.9	7.1	49.2	2.6	50.5	10
Skye and Lochalsh	2,691	10.3	-3.9	9.9	0.5	9.9	14.9	11.8	1.8	12.0	4
Sutherland	5,865	14.2	-2.8	13.8	-6.3	12.9	-0.8	13.2	-0.3	13.2	2
Lothian	**1721**	**710.2**	**5.0**	**745.6**	**-3.0**	**723.2**	**-2.7**	**726.0**	**5.8**	**767.8**	**446**
East Lothian	678	74.8	3.5	77.4	1.9	78.9	4.3	84.1	4.7	88.1	130
Edinburgh City	262	483.9	-1.5	476.5	-10.8	425.2	-5.3	418.9	7.2	448.9	1,713
Midlothian	356	65.3	22.1	79.7	2.5	81.7	-5.2	78.8	1.5	80	225
West Lothian	425	86.2	29.9	112.0	22.7	137.4	2.7	144.1	4.6	150.8	355
Strathclyde	**13,529**	**2,584.0**	**-0.3**	**2,575.4**	**-7.8**	**2,375.0**	**-7.8**	**2,248.7**	**1.7**	**2,287.8**	**169**
Argyll and Bute	6,497	65.7	-1.1	65.0	-2.0	63.7	-1.1	65.1	-2.3	63.6	10
Bearsden and Milngavie	36	26.2	37.0	35.9	9.6	39.4	0.9	40.6	1.9	41.4	1,137
Clydebank	35	57.6	2.1	58.8	-11.4	52.1	-14.2	45.7	2.2	46.7	1,319
Clydesdale	1,322	54.6	-1.8	53.6	5.6	56.6	0.0	57.6	1.9	58.7	44
Cumbernauld and Kilsyth	103	18.7	143.9	45.6	34.9	61.5	-0.7	62.4	2.5	64.0	621
Cumnock and Doon Valley	800	53.2	-8.5	48.7	-8.0	44.8	-6.2	42.6	0.1	42.6	53
Cunninghame	884	111.1	13.3	125.9	8.3	136.3	-1.6	136.9	1.9	139.5	158
Dumbarton	472	70.7	11.3	78.7	-2.5	76.7	-2.2	77.2	1.5	78.3	166
East Kilbride	285	40.8	81.9	74.2	11.3	82.6	-1.7	82.8	2.9	85.2	299

Scotland continued

	Area sq km	1961 ('000s)	1961 to 1971 % change	1971 ('000s)	1971 to 1981 % change	Population 1981 ('000s)	1981 to 1991 % change	1991 ('000s)	1991 to 1996 % change	1996 mid-year pop. ('000s)	Density 1996 persons per sq km
Eastwood	115	43.8	13.9	49.9	7.2	53.5	9.7	60.0	4.5	62.7	544
Glasgow City	198	1,140.1	–13.8	982.3	–23.1	755.1	–15.5	662.9	2.6	680.0	3,438
Hamilton	131	95.2	9.6	104.3	3.5	107.9	–4.3	105.2	1.9	107.2	818
Inverclyde	162	112.5	–2.8	109.4	–9.0	99.6	–12.0	90.1	–3.3	87.1	538
Kilmarnock and Loudoun	373	79.0	2.5	81.0	0.9	81.7	–4.3	79.9	1.3	80.9	217
Kyle and Carrick	1202	104.9	5.4	110.6	1.4	112.2	–1.9	112.7	1.7	114.6	95
Monklands	164	111.5	1.9	113.6	–3.3	109.8	–8.3	102.4	0.1	102.5	626
Motherwell	172	157.1	0.3	157.6	–5.3	149.3	–6.1	142.6	0.8	143.7	835
Renfrew	307	182.5	11.2	202.9	1.2	205.3	–6.8	197.0	2.4	201.7	656
Strathkelvin	164	58.8	31.6	77.4	12.1	86.8	–3.6	85.2	0.7	85.8	523
Tayside	**7,502**	**397.8**	**–0.1**	**397.6**	**–3.7**	**382.8**	**–2.3**	**383.8**	**2.9**	**395.0**	**53**
Angus	2,031	85.1	–1.1	84.2	8.6	91.4	1.0	94.5	3.7	98.0	48
Dundee City	235	195.3	1.1	197.4	–10.1	177.5	–9.4	165.9	1.2	167.8	714
Perth and Kinross	5,236	117.4	–1.2	116.0	–1.9	113.8	6.0	123.5	4.6	129.2	25
Orkney	**992**	**18.7**	**–8.6**	**17.1**	**7.7**	**18.4**	**4.0**	**19.6**	**1.0**	**19.8**	**20**
Shetland	**1438**	**17.8**	**–2.8**	**17.3**	**31.6**	**22.8**	**–3.8**	**22.5**	**2.1**	**23**	**16**
Western Isles	**3134**	**32.6**	**–8.3**	**29.9**	**2.7**	**30.7**	**–5.7**	**29.6**	**–2.4**	**28.9**	**9**
SCOTLAND	**78133**	**5,179.2**	**1.0**	**5,228.9**	**–3.7**	**5,035.3**	**–3.4**	**4,998.6**	**2.6**	**5128**	**66**

Northern Ireland

	Area sq km	1961 ('000s)	1961 to 1971 % change	1971 ('000s)	1971 to 1981 % change	Population 1981 ('000s)	1981 to 1991 % change	1991 ('000s)	1991 to 1996 % change	1996 mid-year pop. ('000s)	Density 1996 persons per sq km
Antrim	578	–	–	34.0	32.4	45.0	–1.1	44.5	10.3	49.1	85
Ards	381	–	–	46.8	23.5	57.8	12.1	64.8	4.2	67.5	177
Armagh	671	–	–	46.4	6.1	49.2	5.3	51.8	2.3	53	79
Ballymena	632	–	–	49.0	11.9	54.8	3.3	56.6	2.6	58.1	92
Ballymoney	419	–	–	21.9	4.8	22.9	5.5	24.2	2.5	24.8	59
Banbridge	446	–	–	28.7	4.9	30.1	11.2	33.5	11.7	37.4	84
Belfast	115	–	–	416.7	–24.6	314.3	–11.1	279.2	6.5	297.3	2,588
Carrickfergus	82	–	–	27.0	6.0	28.6	14.4	32.8	8.1	35.4	432
Castlereagh	85	–	–	64.4	–5.6	60.8	0.0	60.8	5.6	64.2	755
Coleraine	486	–	–	44.6	4.8	46.7	7.9	50.4	8.1	54.5	112
Cookstown	622	–	–	26.1	8.3	28.3	10.0	31.1	2.0	31.7	51
Craigavon	379	–	–	67.7	8.2	73.3	2.4	75.0	4.7	78.5	207
Derry	387	–	–	84.9	4.9	89.1	7.0	95.4	9.5	104.4	269
Down	650	–	–	46.9	13.4	53.2	9.1	58.0	5.8	61.4	95
Dungannon	783	–	–	42.6	3.0	43.9	3.5	45.4	3.2	46.9	60
Fermanagh	1,877	–	–	51.0	1.2	51.6	4.7	54.0	2.2	55.2	29
Larne	336	–	–	29.9	–2.8	29.1	1.2	29.4	2.7	30.2	90
Limavady	586	–	–	23.8	13.3	27.0	9.7	29.6	5.5	31.2	53
Lisburn	446	–	–	70.7	18.8	84.0	18.4	99.5	9.0	108.4	243
Magherafelt	572	–	–	31.5	3.2	32.5	11.7	36.3	3.3	37.5	66
Moyle	494	–	–	14.0	2.8	14.4	2.7	14.8	0.8	14.9	30
Newry and Mourne	909	–	–	72.4	5.8	76.6	8.3	82.9	1.9	84.5	93
Newtownabbey	151	–	–	66.9	8.0	72.2	2.5	74.0	7.0	79.2	526
North Down	82	–	–	52.6	26.0	66.3	8.4	71.8	3.4	74.3	911
Omagh	1,130	–	–	41.2	7.5	44.3	3.4	45.8	3.0	47.2	42
Strabane	862	–	–	34.4	5.5	36.3	–0.4	36.1	1.0	36.5	42
NORTHERN IRELAND	**14,160**	**1,425.0**	**7.8**	**1,536.1**	**–0.3**	**1,532.2**	**3.0**	**1,577.8**	**5.4**	**1,663.3**	**117**
UNITED KINGDOM	**243,482**	**55,708.7**	**–0.3**	**55,514.6**	**–0.8**	**55,089.1**	**2.5**	**56,466.7**	**4.1**	**58,801.5**	**242**
ISLE OF MAN	**6**	**48.1**		**56.3**	**14.9**	**64.7**	**7.9**	**69.8**	**3.2**	**72**	**12,587**
CHANNEL ISLANDS	**192**	**106.4**	**18.1**	**125.7**	**5.1**	**132.1**	**10.4**	**145.8**	**0.5**	**146.5**	**763**
Jersey	116	59.5	21.0	72.0	5.7	76.1	10.4	84.0	0.8	84.7	730
Guernsey	63	44.9	14.5	51.4	3.7	53.3	10.5	58.9	0	58.8	933
Alderney	8	1.5	13.3	1.7	23.5	2.1	9.5	2.3	4.3	2.4	300
Sark	5	0.5	20.0	0.6	0.0	0.6	0.0	0.6		0.6	120

New Local authorities *

England – Unitary authorities

	Area			Population	Density
	hectares sq km	1991 ('000s)	'91 to '96 % change	1996 ('000s)	1996 persons per sq km
Bath & North East Somerset	351	158.7	3.8	164.7	469
Bristol	110	376.1	6.3	399.6	3,647
East Riding of Yorkshire	2,415	291.9	5.8	308.7	128
Hartlepool	94	90.4	1.9	92.1	982
Isle of Wight	380	124.6	0.7	125.5	330
Kingston upon Hull	71	254.1	5.0	266.8	3,734
Middlesborough	54	140.8	4.2	146.8	2,725
North East Lincolnshire	192	159.7	−0.7	158.5	826
North Lincolnshire	838	152.3	0.3	152.8	182
North Somerset	375	177.5	4.4	185.3	495
Redcar & Cleveland	245	145.1	−3.7	139.8	571
South Gloucestershire	497	220.4	6.7	235.1	473
Stockton-on-Tees	204	173.9	2.9	179.0	878
York	271	166	5.5	175.1	646

Wales – Unitary authorities

	Area			Population	Density
	hectares sq km	1991 ('000s)	'91 to '96 % change	1996 ('000s)	1996 persons per sq km
Anglesey, Isle of	719	68.2	−1.7	67.1	93
Blaenau Gwent	110	70.8	3.1	73.0	663
Bridgend	250	126.3	3.0	130.1	520
Caerphilly	277	166.7	1.5	169.1	610
Cardiff	140	283.3	11.2	315.0	2,250
Carmarthenshire	2,398	166.8	1.4	169.1	71
Ceredigion	1,797	63.9	8.8	69.5	39
Conwy	1,130	107.5	2.9	110.6	98
Denbighshire	840	90.0	2.5	92.2	110
Flintshire	436	138.5	4.6	144.9	332
Gwynedd	2,548	117.5	0.2	117.8	46
Merthyr Tydfil	111	58.6	−0.8	58.1	524
Monmouthshire	851	79.1	9.8	86.8	102
Neath Port Talbot	440	135.5	2.9	139.5	317
Newport	191	130.5	4.8	136.8	718
Pembrokeshire	1,595	112.2	1.2	113.6	71
Powys	5,200	118.3	5.2	124.4	24
Rhondda, Cynon, Taff	420	230.8	4.0	240.1	572
Swansea	380	223.1	3.2	230.2	606
Torfaen	126	88.8	1.9	90.5	719
Vale of Glamorgan	340	115.5	3.3	119.4	351
Wrexham	500	119.8	2.9	123.3	247
WALES	**20,766**	**2,811.9**	**3.9**	**2,921.1**	**141**

Scotland – Local authority areas

	Area			Population	Density
	hectares sq km	1991 ('000s)	'91 to '96 % change	1996 ('000s)	1996 persons per sq km
Aberdeen City	186	214.9	1.1	217.3	1,168
Aberdeenshire	6,318	216.5	5.0	227.4	36
Angus	2,181	108.7	1.9	110.8	51
Argyll & Bute	6,930	93.7	−3.1	90.8	13
Clackmannanshire	157	48.4	0.8	48.8	311
Dumfries & Galloway	6,439	147.7	−0.1	147.6	23
Dundee City	65	156.2	−3.8	150.3	2,312
East Ayrshire	1,252	124.3	−1.5	122.4	98
East Dunbartonshire	172	110.6	0.2	110.8	644
East Lothian	678	84.9	3.8	88.1	130
East Renfrewshire	173	86.1	2.3	88.1	509
Edinburgh, City of	262	439.5	2.1	448.9	1,713
Falkirk	299	143.1	−0.1	143	478
Fife	1,323	349.4	0.0	349.3	264
Glasgow City	175	631.7	−2.4	616.4	3,522
Highland	25,784	204.1	2.3	208.7	8
Inverclyde	162	91.6	−4.9	87.1	538
Midlothian	356	80.2	−0.2	80	225
Moray	2,238	84.2	2.7	86.5	39
North Ayrshire	884	139.1	0.3	139.5	158
North Lanarkshire	474	328.9	−0.9	325.9	688
Orkney Islands	992	19.6	1.0	19.8	20
Perth and Kinross	5,311	127.6	3.9	132.6	25
Renfrewshire	261	176.8	1.0	178.6	684
Scottish Borders	4,734	104.1	1.9	106.1	22
Shetland Islands	1,438	22.5	2.2	23	16
South Ayrshire	1,202	113.6	0.9	114.6	95
South Lanarkshire	1,771	304.4	1.0	307.5	174
Stirling	2,196	81.5	1.6	82.8	38

Scotland – Local authority areas continued

	Area			Population	Density
	hectares sq km	1991 ('000s)	'91 to '96 % change	1996 ('000s)	1996 persons per sq km
West Dunbartonshire	162	97.6	−1.8	95.8	591
West Lothian	425	146.3	3.1	150.8	355
Western Isles	3,134	29.4	−1.7	28.9	9
SCOTLAND	**78,133**	**5,107.0**	**0.4**	**5,128.0**	**66**

The population totals are of the people resident in the areas on the night of the census in early April in the year concerned. The 1996 figure is the estimate for June 1996. The intercensal change is not necessarily of these figures but measures the change in the populations of the area of the first year, and so accounts for any changes in boundary that occurred in the period. The area figure is the latest published figure and in many cases has varied in the period 1961–96.

* Beginning in 1996, changes were made to the local government areas of Scotland and Wales, and parts of England. The process is set to continue and further changes are due. As much data as is available at this time is shown in the second smaller table above. In the main table, data printed in italics is the last available for the former counties and districts and is for 1994.

UK trade 1996

Imports £ million
from (countries in order of total trade)

	Total trade	Percentage of world total	0 Food and live animals	01 Meat and meat preparations	04 Cereals and cereal preps	05 Fruit and vegetables	07 Coffee, tea, cocoa and spices	1 Beverages and tobacco	2 Crude materials (inedible)	24 Cork and wood	28 Metalliferous ores and scrap	3 Mineral fuels, lubricants etc.	33 Petrol and petrol products	4 Animal and veg. oils and fats	5 Chemicals	51 Organic chemicals	52 Inorganic chemicals	53 Dyeing and tanning materials
Germany	26,033.4	14.1	714.7	84.8	98.3	103.0	139.6	296.9	295.1	17.1	97.0	116.5	93.8	29.9	3,347.6	669.0	222.7	255.1
USA	23,011.5	12.5	633.5	13.9	43.9	232.4	11.7	177.2	799.8	77.7	232.7	286.0	63.2	22.2	2,154.9	500.9	201.8	125.2
France	16,898.6	9.2	1,547.4	272.5	294.0	443.5	94.1	789.7	258.5	11.4	50.2	567.2	169.9	30.0	2,526.0	610.8	139.0	91.6
Netherlands	11,954.8	6.5	1,799.1	662.8	99.3	548.0	119.6	118.0	424.3	15.4	34.7	226.3	206.9	223.4	2,092.2	568.8	152.1	131.6
Italy	9,345.7	5.1	684.9	33.7	143.7	372.5	11.3	263.0	107.0	19.1	4.4	22.9	20.5	32.3	755.5	108.7	11.9	43.5
Japan	8,994.3	4.9	21.2	0.2	1.1	1.3	1.0	5.9	40.2	0.1	9.5	0.7	0.7	0.9	433.9	200.6	34.0	25.6
Belgium–Lux.	8,249.6	4.5	633.7	84.0	70.6	234.4	52.0	70.5	140.3	3.4	24.1	177.3	168.8	39.9	1,483.8	344.4	56.4	73.4
Ireland	7,011.1	3.8	1,619.9	285.7	135.3	113.3	118.2	183.7	236.6	41.5	52.4	75.1	50.7	17.7	1,304.9	819.8	20.3	12.9
Switzerland	5,417.8	2.9	53.8	1.1	4.7	0.5	25.5	19.9	36.1	0.1	24.1	1.9	0.2	1.0	856.4	236.0	6.7	65.9
Norway	4,984.4	2.7	164.2	0.1	0.8	0.1	0.1	4.8	91.0	20.6	14.7	3,093.6	2,925.2	13.2	198.9	24.3	47.8	13.9
Spain	4,863.7	2.6	663.5	29.6	17.8	554.4	15.1	153.1	116.7	2.2	19.5	45.6	44.3	24.8	317.9	70.7	28.6	20.1
Sweden	4,580.1	2.5	28.0	4.5	6.2	2.3	6.5	2.7	458.3	354.6	25.9	131.3	129.1	2.3	436.1	63.0	23.6	19.1
Hong Kong	4,072.9	2.2	28.6	0.2	2.9	6.4	1.9	0.8	23.3	0.7	9.3	0.0	0.0	0.9	37.6	6.9	4.7	3.2
Singapore	2,572.6	1.4	34.1	0.3	3.5	3.9	4.3	1.5	60.6	3.8	3.9	0.1	0.1	1.4	195.9	176.6	0.6	0.9
Finland	2,490.4	1.4	20.3	0.9	5.3	0.7	8.6	10.1	280.3	187.2	14.3	25.5	25.2	5.3	137.4	47.4	13.6	11.3
Canada	2,484.0	1.3	188.3	0.2	35.9	38.9	0.8	30.3	549.4	73.5	314.9	60.7	6.2	0.8	100.8	8.9	32.3	3.2
Malaysia	2,380.1	1.3	40.8	0.0	0.9	2.7	5.4	0.3	61.5	32.8	0.2	1.1	1.1	60.1	39.6	22.7	0.1	0.7
Denmark	2,316.9	1.3	749.6	478.4	27.9	18.4	8.7	11.4	75.0	8.8	3.0	109.9	109.7	14.6	220.8	33.4	2.3	19.7
China	2,202.1	1.2	65.9	0.4	3.3	21.9	9.2	15.9	98.1	0.2	18.5	35.9	0.0	1.4	149.7	74.0	22.5	10.8
Taiwan	2,088.5	1.1	5.7	0.0	0.2	1.0	0.2	0.8	16.3	0.4	3.1	0.0	0.0	0.1	46.6	7.0	1.2	4.5
South Korea	2,038.4	1.1	4.7	0.1	0.1	0.3	0.3	0.4	10.4	0.1	3.0	0.5	0.5	0.0	100.4	30.4	4.1	13.8
Portugal	1,621.3	0.9	45.9	0.2	1.4	31.9	0.1	47.0	63.3	19.6	2.2	30.6	30.4	0.2	49.4	11.0	0.6	1.8
India	1,610.9	0.9	197.7	0.0	42.3	40.2	52.9	19.3	35.5	0.4	0.7	9.9	9.9	4.8	98.4	37.1	4.7	27.7
Australia	1,296.0	0.7	94.8	51.8	4.4	19.2	0.2	138.2	282.8	3.5	204.4	145.5	0.0	1.3	74.3	0.9	2.2	1.0
Russia	1,274.8	0.7	47.0	0	0.1	0.3	0.1	1.9	171.6	52.5	77.0	176.4	169.2		188.0	12.9	100.6	0.1
WORLD TOTAL	**184,112.6**	100	**14,576.1**	**2,604.5**	**1,137.7**	**4,302.9**	**1,281.5**	**2,920.3**	**6,298.2**	**1,272.2**	**1,616.3**	**7,025.7**	**5,716.1**	**720.0**	**18,506.9**	**4,850.7**	**1,284.6**	**1,020.7**
Percentage of world total		100	7.9	1.4	0.6	2.3	0.7	1.6	3.4	0.7	0.9	3.8	3.1	0.4	10.1	2.6	0.7	0.6

Exports £ million
from (countries in order of total trade)

	Total trade	Percentage of world total	0 Food and live animals	01 Meat and meat preparations	04 Cereals and cereal preps	05 Fruit and vegetables	07 Coffee, tea, cocoa and spices	1 Beverages and tobacco	2 Crude materials (inedible)	24 Cork and wood	28 Metalliferous ores and scrap	3 Mineral fuels, lubricants etc.	33 Petrol and petrol products	4 Animal and veg. oils and fats	5 Chemicals	51 Organic chemicals	52 Inorganic chemicals	53 Dyeing and tanning materials
Germany	20,165.8	12.0	610.6	158.9	146.8	39.8	53.5	238.2	213.1	3.9	41.5	1,653.6	1,630.0	22.8	2,469.6	719.2	155.8	190.8
USA	19,833.6	11.8	236.7	4.2	29.4	8.7	29.5	441.1	131.6	1.5	47.1	2,345.6	2,344.1	6.8	2,335.0	894.7	139.2	113.7
France	16,521.4	9.8	1,158.3	340.4	178.0	37.1	70.1	371.3	190.4	1.7	25.1	1,949.6	1,777.1	15.9	2,389.6	482.5	138.9	158.7
Netherlands	12,984.8	7.7	516.3	67.3	115.6	30.6	33.4	330.2	136.5	1.5	22.0	1,697.2	1,583.6	30.7	1,583.7	362.3	78.6	121.0
Ireland	8,938.4	5.3	992.5	117.6	221.8	130.4	114.2	133.2	134.8	19.3	18.0	468.2	396.9	50.3	1,190.4	199.2	50.9	71.4
Belgium–Lux.	8,263.9	4.9	315.1	39.0	58.8	16.3	12.8	172.0	205.2	1.2	60.0	212.7	187.8	7.8	1,515.3	601.5	94.5	48.0
Italy	7,819.8	4.7	366.3	64.3	120.7	32.9	15.6	94.3	256.5	1.0	42.0	374.0	347.1	4.0	1,150.7	260.3	32.4	120.2
Spain	6,506.7	3.9	404.2	25.0	148.8	28.5	22.8	234.3	218.3	0.8	125.8	318.9	274.6	1.1	937.1	193.8	112.7	65.2
Sweden	4,312.8	2.6	109.0	8.2	22.3	10.7	18.9	36.5	61.2	0.4	10.1	207.8	179.2	2.6	532.1	97.7	21.4	44.6
Japan	4,263.7	2.5	162.9	36.9	34.3	4.0	20.3	157.6	44.9	0.4	10.8	3.9	3.9	2.7	636.2	107.2	42.8	26.3
Switzerland	3,205.2	1.9	49.8	6.3	4.5	1.7	7.9	17.7	17.6	0.1	1.3	1.8	1.7	1.4	492.6	198.0	27.8	60.3
Hong Kong	2,923.4	1.7	81.8	27.0	6.6	4.3	3.5	164.2	43.3	0.6	19.7	4.9	4.8	1.0	246.0	23.1	11.8	49.2
Saudi Arabia	2,482.9	1.5	95.6	0.5	39.9	2.8	15.2	56.2	5.7	0.1	0.1	5.1	5.0	1.5	292.6	20.7	6.6	14.0
Australia	2,465.6	1.5	58.2	0	11.2	3.2	20.4	50.4	19.1	0.4	0.2	10.9	10.8	1.9	450.1	73.2	20.4	18.9
Denmark	2,200.3	1.3	155.0	28.9	47.8	9.0	12.0	20.5	31.1	0.2	2.2	39.9	38.6	2.0	314.4	35.9	13.5	18.5
Singapore	2,144.7	1.3	24.4	2.5	3.2	1.1	3.3	165.4	8.8	0.1	2.3	12.1	12.1	1.2	210.1	40.9	11.2	17.0
Norway	2,066.3	1.2	72.8	0.5	19.1	3.4	15.8	16.1	32.3	0.8	5.5	90.1	65.3	3.0	180.8	28.9	13.8	18.6
Canada	1,974.5	1.2	87.0	0.1	11.9	4.1	50.8	46.9	49.5	0.4	31.1	212.7	212.2	0.9	255.7	28.5	12.2	19.7
South Africa	1,880.8	1.1	40.1	12.6	13.0	1.7	3.3	58.5	21.0	0.1	1.8	79.2	79.2	1.3	290.1	44.2	17.4	21.2
Finland	1,767.6	1.1	36.3	2.5	8.9	2.3	7.6	9.1	63.3	0.3	0.8	337.5	335.7	1.4	184.3	15.0	11.1	16.2
India	1,706.6	1.0	4.5	0.0	0.2	0.6	0.1	8.2	65.2	0.9	47.1	27.9	27.9	0.8	132.8	52.2	4.6	14.9
Portugal	1,648.8	1.0	135.8	31.5	60.9	7.8	6.8	61.3	24.8	1.4	1.0	142.9	55.0	0.3	184.6	32.1	5.6	28.5
Turkey	1,565.9	0.9	16.3	0.6	1.7	0.7	1.7	46.6	155.4	0	61.1	5.2	5.2	0.9	220.0	28.3	6.8	31.4
Poland	1,350.9	0.8	46.7	2.1	18.5	3.2	7.3	4.6	29.8	0.1	0.1	332.5	332.1	2.9	189.8	8.2	3.8	17.8
South Korea	1,303.6	0.8	32.8	9.0	0.6	0.1	1.1	153.4	44.1	0.1	18.8	1.5	1.4	0.8	147.6	37.3	11.4	25.0
WORLD TOTAL	**167,734.0**	100	**6,991.8**	**1,084.1**	**1,591.4**	**467.3**	**682.7**	**4,382.1**	**2,610.2**	**44.6**	**668.1**	**10,937.7**	**10,282.1**	**206.0**	**22,364.3**	**5,209.6**	**1,212.5**	**1,648.9**
Percentage of world total		100	4.2	0.6	0.9	0.3	0.4	2.6	1.6	0.0	0.4	6.5	6.1	0.1	13.3	3.1	0.7	1.0

54 Medicinal and pharm. products	57 Plastics – primary	58 Plastics – non-primary	6 Manufactured goods	64 Paper, board and pulp	65 Textile yarns and fabrics	67 Iron and steel	68 Non-ferrous metals	7 Machinery and transport equip.	71 Power generating machinery	75 Office machinery and computers	76 Telecomm. and sound equip.	77 Electrical machinery and equip.	78 Road vehicles	8 Miscellaneous manufactures	82 Furniture	84 Clothing	85 Footwear Imports £ million	
646.4	346.5	3,654.0	700.5	511.8	754.2	444.1	15,3	41.9	754.0	1,393.8	679.9	2,084.6	7,324.2	2,215.4	144.0	291.7	73.4	Germany
471.3	209.4	151.8	2,054.1	277.8	318.9	105.2	469.8	12,534.9	1,391.3	2,398.4	1,469.0	3,025.9	446.8	3,820.0	73.6	113.8	1,140.6	USA
388.0	408.4	121.7	2,335.6	457.4	405.6	414.7	282.9	7,484.2	289.0	718.9	313.2	1,004.4	3,788.4	1,306.2	116.3	182.6	28.6	France
217.5	569.5	105.7	1,278.8	278.4	225.7	269.3	128.4	4,663.7	98.4	1,998.0	282.1	936.7	768.1	1,072.8	32.1	170.3	27.5	Netherlands
134.3	95.9	184.1	1,845.8	155.4	584.1	250.3	97.6	3,768.0	239.2	360.5	115.9	645.0	1,140.7	1,853.6	268.6	409.4	332.8	Italy
31.6	47.0	33.6	524.1	20.0	80.6	65.3	46.6	6,942.4	519.9	965.7	849.9	1,588.9	1,899.6	939.5	2.7	15.5	1.4	Japan
143.1	451.8	163.4	2,055.3	131.1	523.9	244.7	117.4	2,863.3	108.0	128.8	129.1	243.5	1,748.5	764.3	102.3	158.7	84.8	Belgium–Lux.
243.5	21.7	45.3	505.2	62.7	139.8	35.3	30.5	2,073.8	17.5	958.5	442.7	414.2	84.3	980.4	47.3	191.0	17.2	Ireland
349.6	49.7	27.6	2,542.3	39.4	79.7	24.7	90.5	1,081.5	160.6	80.6	44.6	190.9	20.6	819.9	9.5	24.3	5.3	Switzerland
6.1	43.9	12.9	772.5	254.3	6.6	143.5	303.2	388.9	32.5	20.5	62.8	36.1	19.2	149.5	10.7	2.3	0.4	Norway
52.5	63.7	19.8	812.8	76.8	150.0	157.9	55.9	2,295.0	267.0	53.7	126.9	163.2	1,516.6	433.2	28.4	21.7	135.5	Spain
201.8	52.9	36.7	1,624.1	864.7	31.3	447.0	115.4	1,662.2	116.1	32.0	289.1	205.5	594.1	233.6	53.3	11.6	1.1	Sweden
1.7	2.7	1.3	240.0	22.3	53.7	0.9	5.4	1,264.2	65.9	258.4	347.5	493.9	23.9	2,468.7	19.2	1,078.5	69.4	Hong Kong
5.1	2.4	1.3	48.0	7.6	7.9	2.7	3.4	1,857.9	36.8	973.2	181.7	601.3	10.6	349.9	10.9	52.3	3.5	Singapore
8.6	31.4	15.6	1,270.1	993.6	27.1	76.1	74.4	677.6	15.6	70.5	418.9	39.1	45.1	63.1	10.1	6.0	0.2	Finland
8.6	11.0	7.2	509.3	232.6	18.8	20.4	148.1	828.9	86.7	173.0	139.5	160.2	17.1	186.6	26.9	16.2	2.1	Canada
0.2	9.2	1.1	115.9	1.9	34.6	1.0	14.0	1,802.1	14.7	439.9	269.7	985.8	66.1	253.9	27.3	142.3	3.9	Malaysia
81.7	7.6	30.3	235.8	35.0	48.3	20.2	8.9	600.0	33.1	32.9	94.9	89.4	46.1	291.4	66.6	28.8	10.6	Denmark
10.0	1.9	2.1	342.9	12.9	115.6	16.2	19.4	485.8	19.0	99.3	130.8	154.4	10.3	1,004.6	37.5	341.4	90.3	China
0.4	20.9	7.4	312.9	2.8	72.9	5.9	17.6	1,300.4	19.5	583.9	132.7	358.7	79.8	404.2	30.7	73.5	38.0	Taiwan
8.2	26.5	11.5	209.6	3.4	79.8	12.7	1.0	1,491.9	27.2	452.2	215.2	437.2	257.5	218.2	0.9	62.8	14.5	South Korea
11.1	8.1	6.7	409.8	38.0	181.0	6.2	2.1	459.8	9.2	2.8	44.0	139.6	229.4	514.9	6.4	262.3	220.4	Portugal
8.8	1.1	8.1	480.5	3.4	317.7	23.3	1.9	192.7	68.4	16.4	12.6	19.1	27.1	569.1	5.7	314.4	98.1	India
58.9	0.1	3.9	177.0	0.6	19.5	5.6	124.3	281.1	84.6	31.4	29.5	24.9	10.1	85.2	1.5	6.9	0.8	Australia
1.3	0	0.1	626.1	17.3	2.1	30.3	507.4	34.6	3.0	4.4	5.0	3.5	4.6	26.7	2.5	8.6	0	Russia
3,110.0	**2,961.7**	**1,445.3**	**29,159.9**	**5,025.8**	**5,173.4**	**3,607.2**	**3,832.3**	**77,599.3**	**5,276.6**	**12,870.7**	**7,560.2**	**15,397.3**	**20,690.4**	**25,761.8**	**1,419.6**	**6,208.1**	**1,781.1**	**WORLD TOTAL**
1.7	1.6	0.8	15.8	2.7	2.8	2.0	2.1	42.1	2.9	7.0	4.1	8.4	11.2	14.0	0.8	3.4	1.0	
419.8	274.4	180.2	2,620.1	281.3	359.2	555.1	462.1	10,008.9	946.0	1,372.6	1,186.1	2,245.4	2,509.4	2,301.0	142.9	428.9	53.4	Germany
645.8	92.0	95.2	1,815.7	173.7	216.4	338.5	258.6	9,672.4	1,623.4	1,586.6	553.6	1,357.4	1,480.7	2,742.4	127.4	137.5	89.0	USA
648.1	189.5	153.2	1,825.5	297.4	336.1	271.7	221.2	6,714.7	472.2	1,107.9	713.2	1,247.5	1,383.1	1,890.1	98.8	386.6	58.2	France
430.7	247.1	92.5	1,326.1	166.8	331.9	204.8	110.8	6,092.4	203.4	3,029.8	554.7	638.8	926.5	1,245.9	76.6	176.4	23.2	Netherlands
281.5	117.1	114.1	1,576.3	327.3	261.6	234.8	159.7	2,834.9	75.3	498.1	256.0	831.9	544.0	1,540.5	105.5	445.8	109.5	Ireland
190.4	245.9	58.2	2,492.3	110.9	212.7	137.5	128.4	2,689.7	432.9	301.4	272.9	266.1	977.6	645.3	53.2	121.9	15.0	Belgium–Lux.
300.0	115.6	76.9	1,085.1	65.5	225.1	226.1	197.5	3,692.2	180.0	491.2	430.9	684.2	1,154.5	789.2	22.8	102.9	32.2	Italy
228.9	65.2	50.6	682.8	45.1	102.4	197.4	70.9	2,920.2	339.3	324.8	455.3	398.2	907.6	749.6	21.6	146.3	18.2	Spain
118.6	58.1	49.3	866.8	42.9	82.7	384.7	93.8	1,956.7	147.1	270.8	369.2	521.2	226.3	536.6	34.1	100.4	11.2	Sweden
273.7	21.0	15.7	439.9	19.0	85.6	22.3	98.2	2,033.4	97.0	623.8	59.7	294.7	615.4	743.1	35.0	134.5	22.0	Japan
67.6	25.9	23.6	832.0	35.8	38.8	60.2	178.0	1,061.9	71.8	241.1	105.5	146.5	169.8	719.6	13.8	58.6	5.1	Switzerland
55.5	27.5	20.4	483.1	43.3	96.5	105.7	48.8	1,484.2	303.5	61.0	267.4	394.1	105.2	400.6	21.3	61.3	16.6	Hong Kong
104.3	17.2	8.2	151.7	17.4	22.2	36.4	16.3	1,520.9	177.3	19.6	97.0	110.5	54.4	263.2	7.3	41.7	3.3	Saudi Arabia
188.9	22.2	24.7	254.1	40.6	47.6	35.7	13.7	1,199.5	167.6	99.9	202.1	122.9	180.9	384.6	10.8	12.6	8.7	Australia
80.1	31.1	37.1	338.5	27.1	75.7	84.8	29.4	968.5	47.9	257.6	145.3	133.2	159.3	322.8	15.3	76.9	8.3	Denmark
25.0	14.0	12.5	275.6	20.4	31.1	83.2	37.5	1,014.3	121.8	199.2	72.1	253.8	116.1	401.4	5.6	26.3	5.6	Singapore
25.4	14.8	12.3	358.0	21.6	37.7	150.8	20.0	877.0	52.7	124.4	94.3	98.9	123.9	322.1	14.3	47.0	9.1	Norway
84.7	28.2	12.8	220.0	25.4	24.8	55.4	19.9	878.5	169.5	87.8	51.0	141.4	75.2	209.0	6.1	19.9	14.7	Canada
48.3	32.7	18.0	211.6	39.3	27.3	38.1	15.0	964.5	44.1	149.1	138.3	142.3	168.6	207.4	7.4	8.4	3.5	South Africa
36.6	23.7	17.4	195.5	24.4	40.5	41.3	16.1	758.3	43.7	120.6	109.9	244.9	99.3	179.6	3.7	41.3	3.8	Finland
15.5	12.6	4.4	711.4	50.1	8.8	72.4	36.3	617.5	162.1	22.1	33.1	55.4	33.6	117.6	1.7	4.1	1.8	India
48.5	13.8	12.9	258.4	17.1	79.1	61.9	20.1	666.1	55.7	43.7	81.5	104.8	244.1	173.3	6.2	38.8	4.5	Portugal
54.7	19.8	11.9	166.5	14.8	29.0	48.6	11.0	815.6	145.5	73.3	51.3	58.5	180.1	132.4	6.2	12.1	1.6	Turkey
47.2	13.7	17.8	146.5	47.1	27.5	21.1	9.5	461.6	11.1	68.0	68.9	73.5	108.3	133.0	2.4	6.7	8.4	Poland
18.4	14.8	7.2	153.2	22.1	32.6	22.3	22.3	575.0	92.2	31.5	22.2	132.7	25.7	187.6	4.7	28.2	1.9	South Korea
5,360.4	**1,990.8**	**1,331.0**	**23,254.1**	**2,333.5**	**3,455.9**	**4,122.1**	**2,704.4**	**74,017.4**	**7,203.7**	**12,252.0**	**7,647.9**	**12,659.1**	**14,520.9**	**21,100.2**	**966.5**	**3,318.7**	**604.8**	**WORLD TOTAL**
3.2	1.2	0.8	13.9	1.4	2.1	2.5	1.6	44.1	4.3	7.3	4.6	7.5	8.7	12.6	0.6	2.0	0.4	

UK and Ireland agricultural data

	Total agricultural area (ha)	Number of agric. holdings	Av. farm size (ha)	Wheat as % of total agric. area	Barley as % of total agric. area	Potatoes as % of total agric. area	Sugar beet as % of total agric. area	Oilseed rape as % of total agric. area	Grassland as % of total agric. area	Cereals crops as % of total agric. area	Pigs per 100 ha of agric. land	Sheep per 100 ha of agric. land	Cattle per 100 ha of agric. land	Horticultural as % of total agric. area land	Dairy cows as % of cattle and calves	Agric. workers per 1,000 ha of agric. land
UNITED KINGDOM	16,999,244	234,921	72	10.8	6.9	18.4	1.0	1.1	2.1	1.08	55.2	69	22	44	250	34
ENGLAND	9,266,677	146,112	63	18.7	9.0	28.7	1.4	2.1	3.2	1.80	39.7	72	27	68	212	43
Avon	81,383	2,032	40	8.6	5.6	14.6	0.3	0	1.4	0.51	67.8	132	33	58	128	64
Bedfordshire	89,285	1,174	76	37.3	10.0	47.8	0.6	0.6	7.3	2.15	14.8	22	23	53	65	38
Berkshire	71,456	842	85	23.8	12.2	38.2	0.1	0	5.6	0.54	27.1	51	25	93	94	32
Buckinghamshire	123,870	1,853	67	21.9	7.4	30.6	...	...	5.3	0.35	42.6	72	18	34	190	36
Cambridgeshire	281,529	3,283	86	40.3	8.3	49.0	3.7	8.3	5.2	3.18	8.2	12	8	34	20	36
Cheshire	166,038	4,180	40	5.8	7.3	13.6	2.6	0.1	0.8	0.71	68.3	167	48	58	130	67
Cleveland	27,616	429	64	28.6	11.4	41.1	0.5	0	6.2	0.11	31.0	69	19	138	184	39
Cornwall & Isles of Scilly	276,045	6,679	41	2.2	9.6	12.9	1.5	0.1	0.4	1.31	67.9	143	25	23	229	54
Cumbria	461,830	6,270	74	0.4	3.8	4.3	0.1	0	...	0.04	64.1	117	25	14	577	31
Derbyshire	185,206	3,837	48	6.7	7.5	14.6	0.6	0.1	1.7	0.27	57.3	112	29	27	252	46
Devon	521,705	11,513	45	3.2	6.4	10.7	0.3	...	...	0.34	71.1	127	27	36	368	49
Dorset	196,627	2,949	67	13.1	7.0	21.2	...	...	...	0.26	54.5	117	41	80	108	40
Durham	156,081	2,169	72	12.8	7.1	20.5	0.5	0	3.0	0.08	47.5	74	14	29	447	30
East Sussex	112,718	2,227	51	11.6	4.5	18.1	0.2	0	2.2	1.30	52.0	63	25	19	265	50
Essex	263,693	3,554	74	38.3	9.8	48.7	1.9	1.6	6.8	1.97	11.9	18	21	47	30	44
Gloucestershire	204,613	3,389	60	16.9	9.5	27.5	0.5	0.1	4.0	0.70	44.6	79	28	27	202	40
Greater London	13,819	431	32	14.8	6.8	22.8	0.7	0	3.4	4.69	41.3	56	26	58	29	123
Greater Manchester	40,215	1,454	28	4.9	7.2	12.5	1.3	0.1	0.8	2.00	59.4	95	27	59	188	83
Hampshire	226,024	2,981	76	20.0	14.1	36.6	...	...	4.0	1.53	30.1	50	29	55	78	43
Hereford and Worcester	307,935	6,531	47	15.0	7.1	24.3	2.4	1.5	2.0	2.97	50.2	78	19	39	397	60
Hertfordshire	103,265	1,313	79	32.7	12.3	46.7	0.3	0.2	5.6	0.40	19.2	28	22	21	48	34
Humberside	284,561	3,391	84	37.9	15.1	53.8	2.8	3.4	6.0	4.57	11.3	25	14	259	49	38
Isle of Wight	25,859	487	53	17.0	5.8	24.5	1.3	0	3.0	1.75	44.2	77	28	16	141	58
Kent	246,643	4,078	60	22.2	5.6	29.4	...	...	5.5	7.71	30.3	30	21	14	223	78
Lancashire	215,116	5,307	41	3.5	3.1	7.0	1.4	0.1	0.3	2.46	65.8	126	34	69	361	68
Leicestershire	194,120	2,888	67	25.0	8.9	35.7	0.5	0.5	6.4	0.23	39.4	80	23	38	218	36
Lincolnshire	519,807	5,530	94	38.8	8.8	48.1	3.1	6.6	6.0	6.67	10.8	21	13	60	44	38
Merseyside	19,458	454	43	17.6	19.6	38.8	4.6	1.1	3.1	5.04	28.4	63	23	44	44	81
Norfolk	428,769	4,949	87	24.5	18.3	43.3	3.3	13.4	1.4	4.79	12.2	25	18	161	36	42
North Yorkshire	628,643	8,420	75	15.8	10.5	27.0	1.7	2.0	2.3	0.40	38.5	69	24	135	337	35
Northamptonshire	184,214	2,014	91	30.5	6.6	38.9	0.3	0.2	9.0	0.13	30.8	47	15	31	228	26
Northumberland	382,370	2,335	164	9.5	7.2	17.9	0.3	0	2.9	0.15	36.2	53	6	12	429	16
Nottinghamshire	149,672	1,987	75	29.3	13.8	44.3	3.2	5.4	6.4	2.09	19.8	43	22	89	59	39
Oxfordshire	203,110	2,077	98	25.4	12.9	39.6	0.3	0	7.3	0.37	29.0	47	24	106	110	28
Shropshire	283,205	4,728	60	12.6	11.1	25.6	2.8	3.6	0.9	0.30	53.2	106	31	45	337	43
Somerset	272,248	5,794	47	8.6	3.5	12.7	0.7	0.1	0.6	0.81	68.3	128	37	58	215	51
South Yorkshire	84,259	1,395	60	21.9	11.8	34.3	1.8	2.1	6.3	0.83	28.8	60	23	93	106	42
Staffordshire	195,244	4,640	42	10.0	8.0	18.9	2.0	1.2	1.8	0.73	61.6	135	37	58	158	56
Suffolk	304,483	3,443	88	33.1	13.9	47.6	1.8	7.6	3.6	3.71	10.8	19	20	220	25	41
Surrey	65,345	1,696	39	7.8	3.6	14.1	0.2	0	2.3	2.04	50.9	70	24	29	127	76
Tyne and Wear	13,485	271	50	28.1	11.1	40.2	0.3	0	...	0.52	32.9	58	15	26	80	44
Warwickshire	153,476	2,403	64	25.8	7.4	34.5	1.5	...	5.2	0.85	38.6	61	24	16	224	40
West Midlands	15,014	459	33	13.2	11.4	25.9	1.7	...	3.3	1.32	50.3	89	22	86	155	70
West Sussex	123,331	2,225	55	17.2	5.4	25.5	...	...	2.6	1.47	40.0	61	30	32	117	66
West Yorkshire	97,122	2,989	32	10.9	7.7	18.8	0.9	0.4	2.4	0.80	52.8	94	24	135	259	68
Wiltshire	266,171	3,052	87	20.1	10.1	31.5	...	...	3.7	0.21	39.2	79	35	50	86	30
WALES	1,476,708	28,076	53	0.8	2.1	3.2	0.2	0	0.1	0.11	70.2	90	22	6	752	40
Clwyd	177,401	3,506	51	1.2	2.7	4.2	0.1	0	0.1	0.21	76.6	111	28	13	877	44
Dyfed	446,912	10,580	42	0.4	3.1	3.8	0.4	...	...	0.10	77.0	118	31	3	508	49
Gwent	80,371	2,053	39	3.2	2.7	6.7	0.7	...	0.4	0.32	76.9	111	24	30	573	53
Gwynedd	297,304	4,490	66	0.1	1.0	1.2	0.1	...	...	0.04	53.9	60	10	4	718	28
Mid Glamorgan	48,352	891	54	0.7	2.2	3.2	0.1	0	...	0.12	63.9	62	13	4	801	40
Powys	368,569	5,286	70	0.8	1.2	2.2	0.1	...	0.1	0.02	71.7	68	10	3	1089	33
South Glamorgan	23,432	474	49	5.3	7.0	13.5	0.3	0	1.1	0.26	72.5	120	23	12	344	51
West Glamorgan	34,369	796	43	0.5	2.2	3.0	0.7	0	...	0.61	66.0	82	12	2	570	51
SCOTLAND	5,252,595	32,796	160	2.1	5.5	8.0	0.5	0	1.0	0.28	77.5	39	11	11	176	11
Borders	382,818	1,783	215	5.8	7.7	14.0	0.5	0	1.4	0.35	65.3	40	3	6	383	11
Central	195,324	1,120	174	1.4	3.3	5.1	0.1	0	0.7	0.04	83.6	33	10	1	225	10
Dumfries & Galloway	441,722	3,086	143	0.4	3.1	3.7	0.1	0	0	0.01	81.5	101	16	4	352	16
Fife	97,710	1,084	90	16.2	21.4	38.2	3.0	0	5.8	2.72	24.2	62	10	30	115	26
Grampian	633,107	6,703	94	3.1	16.5	20.9	1.0	0	3.1	0.39	47.9	63	6	47	117	18
Highland	1,640,197	4,794	342	0.2	1.3	1.7	0.1	0	0.1	0.01	91.6	9	3	2	78	4
Lothian	126,444	1,159	109	14.0	14.6	29.1	1.7	0	3.1	0.80	43.3	43	8	55	202	20

SCOTLAND continued

	Total agricultural area (ha)	Number of agric. holdings	Av. farm size (ha)	Wheat as % of total agric. area	Barley as % of total agric. area	Potatoes as % of total agric. area	Sugar beet as % of total agric. area	Oilseed rape as % of total agric. area	Grassland as % of total agric. area	Cereals crops as % of total agric. area	Pigs per 100 ha of agric. land	Sheep per 100 ha of agric. land	Cattle per 100 ha of agric. land	Horticultural as % of total agric. land	Dairy cows as % of cattle and calves	Agric. workers per 1,000 ha of agric. land
Shetland, Orkney & W. Isles	202,834	4,277	47	0	1.9	2.2	0.1	0	0	0.02	88.0	52	4	0	350	28
Strathclyde	905,849	5,854	155	0.2	1.9	2.2	0.1	0	0	0.04	88.2	54	20	2	209	12
NORTHERN IRELAND	**1,003,264**	**27,937**	**36**	**0.6**	**3.2**	**4.1**	**0.9**	**0**	**0**	**0.32**	**73.4**	**157**	**17**	**55**	**245**	**56**
Northern Antrim	213,133	4,926	43	0.4	3.2	3.8	1.2	0	0	0.09	76.0	153	19	51	320	52
Armagh	91,229	3,793	24	0.5	2.3	3.2	0.3	0	0.1	1.89	70.4	203	16	79	146	79
Down	174,821	5,347	33	2.1	7.0	9.8	1.6	0	0.2	0.52	62.0	176	20	61	264	67
Fermanagh	125,109	3,499	36	0	0	0	0	0	0	0.04	85.0	139	13	9	90	49
Londonderry	157,402	3,619	43	0.8	5.3	6.3	1.5	0	0	0.09	69.4	136	15	67	335	49
Tyrone	241,570	6,753	36	0.1	0	1.5	0.3	0	0	0.05	76.8	153	17	59	224	53
IRELAND	**4,388,500**	**152,667**	**29**	**1.6**	**4.1**	**6.2**	**0.5**	**0.8**	**0.09**	**0.19**	**80.4**	**162**	**21**	**35**	**191**	**52**
Carlow	79,100	1,906	41	4.7	11.5	16.7	0.4	5.1		0.13	68.6	128	16	17	430	37
Cavan	130,800	6,014	22	0	0.2	0.2	0.1	0	...	0	92.7	185	20	266	96	65
Clare	203,400	7,365	28	0	0.1	0.1	0.1	0	...	0	84.5	160	15	7	49	52
Cork	532,500	15,482	34	1.5	5.4	7.8	0.5	2.1	0.02	0.24	77.0	197	35	56	92	50
Donegal	197,100	9,154	22	0.1	2.4	3.0	1.6	0	0.05	0	60.9	101	10	15	369	58
Dublin	50,800	1,352	38	17.9	9.8	29.7	6.7	0.2	1.38	4.33	48.8	89	14	21	166	46
Galway	323,900	14,538	22	0	0.8	1.2	0.2	0.1	...	0.03	82.2	149	9	4	338	63
Kerry	285,600	9,738	29	0	0.6	0.6	0.1	0.1	...	0.04	71.5	138	33	20	192	51
Kildare	123,000	2,910	42	9.0	10.5	20.6	0.4	1.3	0.24	0.24	69.4	114	14	15	229	39
Kilkenny	165,000	3,972	42	2.3	6.7	10.1	0.5	1.0	0.06	0.30	82.8	195	22	38	162	41
Laoighis	118,300	3,517	34	1.4	10.5	12.3	0.2	2.5	...	0.17	78.6	186	17	28	137	48
Leitrim	79,900	4,042	20	0	0	0	0	0	...	0	91.0	114	7	20	164	64
Limerick	198,600	6,611	30	0.1	0.4	0.6	0.1	0	...	0.05	95.4	205	35	25	34	51
Longford	72,200	2,781	26	0	0.4	0.7	0.1	0	...	0	94.9	170	10	75	98	53
Louth	63,800	2,041	31	7.7	14.9	24.0	2.4	0	1.41	0.31	65.5	136	22	11	192	46
Mayo	241,000	13,344	18	0	0.2	0.3	0.2	0	...	0	82.6	134	10	12	272	78
Meath	190,600	5,055	38	6.1	5.0	13.0	2.3	0.2	0.73	0.26	78.8	166	20	11	189	38
Monaghan	90,300	4,757	19	0.1	0.6	0.6	0	0	...	0	94.7	210	23	40	56	72
Offaly	119,200	3,676	32	1.1	6.0	7.4	0.3	0.6	...	0.17	83.9	180	13	31	156	47
Roscommon	154,400	6,991	22	0	0.3	0.5	0.1	0.1	...	0	93.7	144	5	5	251	61
Sligo	104,500	4,944	21	0	0.2	0.2	0.1	0	...	0	85.7	131	12	4	178	61
Tipperary NR	142,900	3,983	36	0.1	5.5	5.9	0.2	0.6	...	0	86.5	206	22	21	129	44
Tipperary SR	166,900	4,436	38	2.0	4.4	6.7	0.1	0.9	...	0.06	88.1	203	25	72	142	45
Waterford	128,000	2,914	44	1.7	4.0	7.6	0.2	0.9	...	0.23	80.1	189	29	44	131	39
Westmeath	122,400	3,694	33	0.7	2.5	3.5	0.1	0.1	0.16	0	92.3	165	11	60	164	44
Wexford	195,500	5,009	39	2.2	16.0	19.3	0.8	3.8	...	0.41	70.0	143	24	37	312	47
Wicklow	108,700	2,443	44	3.9	5.9	10.6	0.6	0.6	0.09	0.09	70.9	121	19	17	493	36

The figures are for 1995. The grassland and labour figures for Ireland are not strictly comparable with those of the UK. The definitions of grassland are not the same, and a worker is an 'annual work unit'. In addition, the farm size, number of farms and workers are for 1991. Horticultural crops include vegetables, fruit, flowers and bulbs, in the open and under glass.

European statistics

	EUR 15	A	B	D	DK	E	EL	F	FIN	I	IRL	L	NL	P	S	UK
Area (sq km)	3,236,192	83,858	30,518	356,974	43,094	505,990	131,957	543,965	338,145	301,323	70,285	2,586	41,526	91,905	449,964	244,101
Population 1996 (thousands)	372,622	8,055	10,143	81,845	5,251	39,241	10,474	58,265	5,117	57,331	3,591	413	15,492	9,921	8,838	58,684
Density 1996 (persons/sq km)	115	96	332	229	122	78	79	107	15	190	51	160	373	108	20	240
Birth rate 1994 (births/1,000 pop.)	10.9	11.5	11.5	9.5	13.4	9.3	10	12.3	12.8	9.2	13.4	13.5	12.7	11	12.8	12.9
Death rate 1994 (deaths/1,000 pop.)	9.9	10	10.2	10.9	11.8	8.6	9.4	9	9.4	9.6	8.6	9.4	8.7	10.1	10.5	10.7
Infant mortality 1994 (deaths – 1 yr/1,000 births)	6.1	6.3	7.6	5.6	5.6	6	7.9	5.8	4.7	6.6	5.9	5.3	5.6	8.1	4.4	6.2
Migration rate 1993 (movements/1,000 pop.)	2.5	5	2.5	5.7	2.2	–1	5.4	1.2	1.8	3.2	–8.1	10.7	2.9	1.6	3.7	1.1
Population age –15 yrs male (% of total pop.)	9.1	9	9.3	8.4	8.5	8.8	8.9	10.1	9.8	7.8	13	9.3	9.4	9.3	9.6	10
Population age –15 yrs female (% of total pop.)	8.6	8.6	8.8	8	8.1	8.3	8.4	9.6	9.3	7.4	12.2	8.9	9	8.9	9.1	9.5
Population age 15–64 yrs male (% of total pop.)	33.7	34.1	33.4	34.8	34.3	33.9	33.7	32.7	33.8	34.1	31.8	34.5	34.8	32.9	32.4	32.6
Population age 15–64 yrs female (% of total pop.)	33.3	33.3	32.9	33.5	33.3	34	33.8	32.8	33.1	34.5	31.5	33.4	33.7	34.5	31.4	32.2
Population age 65+ yrs male (%of total pop.)	6	5.4	6.3	5.4	6.6	6.2	6.7	5.9	5.1	6.7	4.9	5.3	5.3	5.9	7.4	6.4
Population age 65+ yrs female (% of total pop.)	9.3	9.6	9.4	9.9	9.3	8.7	8.4	8.9	8.9	9.6	6.6	8.6	7.9	8.4	10.1	9.4
Employment 1994																
Agriculture as % of labour force	5	7	3	3	5	10	21	5	8	8	13	3	4	12	4	2
Industry as % of labour force	30	33	29	37	26	30	24	27	27	32	28	27	23	32	25	28
Services as % of labour force	64	59	68	60	68	60	56	68	65	60	59	70	71	56	72	70
Unemployment 1996 (% of labour force)	10.9	4.5	9.6	8.8	7.4	22.3	9.7	12	15.7	12.1	11.8	3.2	6.2	7.4	10	8.3
Unemployment male 1996 (% male labour force)	9.7	3.7	7.5	7.3	6.3	17.8	9.7	10.2	15.6	9.5	11.8	2.4	5	6.4	10.9	9.8
Unemployment female 1996 (% female labour force)	12.4	5.6	12.5	9.6	8.7	29.5	15.4	14.1	15.9	16.4	11.8	4.4	8	8.5	9	6.5
Unemployment < 25 yrs 1996 (% labour force –25)	21.5	6.4	20.8	9.6	11.8	41.9	31.2	26.1	31.4	33.9	18.3	8.7	10.9	17.2	22.1	14.9
Unemployment > 25 yrs 1996 (% labour force 25+)	9.2	4.2	8.3	8.7	6.4	18.4	6.8	10.4	13.9	8.6	10.3	2.5	5.3	5.8	8.5	7.1
Hourly labour costs in industry 1994 (ECU)	...	22.9	24.3	20	21.1	14.1	7.6	...	17.8	...	13.2	19.3	21.3	5.5	16.1	12.7
Agricultural land use 1995																
Total agricultural area (1,000 ha)	136,922	3,449	1,366	17,344	2,715	25,093	8,752	30,056	2,704	15,673	4,391	127	1,981	3,981	3,438	15,852
Arable land (1,000 ha)	70,513	1,403	847	11,835	2,502	10,118	2,250	18,102	2,142	8,329	958	58	915	2,317	2,767	5,970
Cereals (1,000 ha)	35,582	809	310	6,527	1,49	6,54	1,205	8,269	976	4,002	276	29	198	676	1,082	3,181
Wheat (1,000 ha)	16,510	266	209	2,579	608	2,03	852	4,742	101	2,478	71	9	135	252	256	1,859
Barley (1,000 ha)	11,024	229	54	2,109	714	3,54	133	1,386	516	391	181	13	36	53	444	1,192
Roots (1,000 ha)	4,000	80	164	857	163	442	120	721	71	380	74	1	297	97	91	436
Potatoes (1,000 ha)	1,501	27	56	316	42	211	52	171	36	89	23	1	179	96	33	171
Sugar beet (1,000 ha)	2,129	52	99	513	68	172	42	458	35	282	35	0	116	1	58	196
Permanent crops (1,000 ha)	10,814	76	15	209	7	4,716	1,083	1,183	4	2,663	3	1	38	772	3	41
Permanent grass (1,000 ha)	54,426	1,951	495	5,282	206	10,259	5,250	10,566	15	4,530	3,433	68	1,01	862	673	9,825
Woods (1,000 ha)	105,161	3,877	617	6,032	445	15,915	2,940	15,043	23,186	8,550	327	88	330	3,18	22,23	2,380
Crop yields 100 kg/ha																
Wheat 1975	...	...	38	...	51	16	23	39	...	27	44	25	49	13	...	43
Wheat 1995	53	49	70	69	76	14	25	65	38	33	83	57	87	14	61	78
Potatoes 1975	...	...	...	289	...	210	139	153	231	...	162	251	200	331	95	...	223
Potatoes 1995	300	268	352	314	377	199	216	337	221	238	275	285	410	150	328	368
Production (average 1993–95)																
Wheat (1,000 tonnes)	85,811	1,217	1,450	16,670	4,219	4,078	2,276	30,216	358	8,154	566	49	1,061	410	1,548	13,537
Barley (1,000 tonnes)	44,923	1,116	364	11,266	3,574	7,437	430	8,103	1,767	1,517	988	64	227	84	1,708	6,278
All cereals (1,000 tonnes)	176,841	4,459	2,129	37,247	8,391	14,386	4,592	54,094	3,351	18,250	1,682	144	1,486	1,397	4,767	20,468
Potatoes (1,000 tonnes)	47,276	735	1,928	10,609	1,561	3,958	1,050	5,691	767	2,083	599	23	7,376	1,334	938	6,631
Sugar beet (1,000 tonnes)	113,772	2,813	5,518	26,289	3,331	8,247	2,567	30,400	1,068	12,160	1,301	1	6,692	43	2,454	8,535
Wine (10,000 hl)	170,000	...	2	11,269	0	27,174	3,493	56,213	0	62,977	0	205	0	6,388	0	21
Cattle 1994 (1,000 head)	84,463	2,329	3,161	15,962	2,082	5,237	520	10,524	1,185	7,272	6,410	204	4,588	1,329	1,790	11,868
Dairy cows (% of all cattle)	40	39	38	42	37	39	51	83	38	40	43	38	40	48	37	38
Pigs 1994 (1,000 head)	117,594	3,729	6,984	24,698	10,864	18,296	951	14,593	1,332	8,023	1,498	76	13,931	2,416	2,324	7,878
Sheep and goats 1994 (1,000 head)	108,827	392	127	2,429	79	25,982	14,788	11,388	85	12,129	5,772	6	1,353	4,235	488	29,574
Meat production 1994 (1,000 tonnes)	35,152	829	1,765	6,105	1,971	4,096	572	6,679	344	4,225	961	...	3,040	746	529	3,634
Pig meat (% of total meat)	46	57	57	59	77	51	25	32	50	32	22	...	55	42	58	28
Beef meat (% of total meat)	22	26	20	23	10	12	13	24	31	28	46	...	0	13	27	25
Milk production 1994 (1,000 tonnes)	117,000	...	3,606	27,866	4,641	5,656	769	25,285	2,500	10,055	5,402	...	10,963	1,638	3,420	15,020
Cheese production 1994 (1,000 tonnes)	6,162	109	71	1,400	288	255	198	1,586	93	900	98	...	634	68	133	329
Butter production 1994 (1,000 tonnes)	1,822	43	70	461	78	19	3	448	45	93	142	...	184	17	65	154
Self-sufficiency 1994 %																
Wheat	...	125	74	116	144	85	99	206	84	73	69	...	45	32	...	110
Potatoes	...	98	172	98	97	96	87	100	92	78	72	...	148	78	...	89
Sugar	...	123	238	163	242	110	101	223	81	97	138	...	232	1	99	67
Holdings 1993 (1,000 holdings)	7,264	...	76	606	74	1,384	819	801	...	2,488	159	3	120	489	...	244
Holdings < 5 ha (% of all holdings)	59	...	35	31.6	2.6	58.1	75.7	27.6	...	77.5	10.4	26.5	34.1	78.1	...15.2	
Holdings > 100 ha (% of all holdings)	2.6	...	1.1	2.7	5.8	3.1	0.1	7.6	...	0.6	2.3	5.3	0.7	1.1		15.9
Agricultural labour force (1,000 people)	22,175	0	207	2,078	216	3,925	2,593	2,397	0	7,237	479	11.3	406	1,747	0	879
Roundwood production 1989 (1,000 cu. m)	251,139	16,255	4,832	35,060	2,101	17,047	2,491	44,076	46,460	8,780	1,500	...	1,325	10,205	54,580	6,427
Fish catches 1993 (1,000 tonnes)	6,985	5	36	315	1,651	1,201	200	702	139	557	272	...	418	281	345	866
GDP 1994 (million ECU pps)	6,192,000	146,890	191,480	1,492,110	99,150	495,940	112,590	1,037,580	77,140	993,650	52,510	11,340	268,360	110,880	143,770	958,030
GDP per head 1994 (ECU pps)	16,644	18,293	18,928	18,325	19,049	12,668	10,799	17,920	15,161	17,059	14,705	28,069	17,448	11,198	16,373	16,406
GDP change 1989–94 total (%)	1.9	2.5	1.6	4.5	1.9	1.5	0.7	1.1	–1.6	1.8	4.7	3.8	2.3	2	–0.3	0.8
GDP change 1989–94 per head (%)	0.5	1.5	1.2	–1.1	1.6	1.4	0.1	0.6	–2.1	0.8	4.4	2.4	1.5	2.2	–1	0.4

	EUR 15	A	B	D	DK	E	EL	F	FIN	I	IRL	L	NL	P	S	UK
Gross value added by sector 1993																
Agriculture (% of total)	2.4	2.5	1.7	1.1	3.6	3.8	13.7	2.4	5	3	7.7	1.5	3.3	5.1	2.9	1.6
Industry (% of total)	31.9	39	29.2	34.5	26.7	33.3	25.8	28.2	31.1	31.7	37.4	31	28.5	33.6	39.6	31.1
Services (% of total)	65.7	58.6	69.1	64.4	69.7	62.9	60.5	69.4	63.7	65.3	54.9	67.5	68.1	61.2	57.6	67.3
Industrial production indices (1990 = 100)	103.1	1123	98.7	95.9	1158	1033	97.4	99.1	1158	1078	1585	1019	1056	99.4	1138106	
Aluminium production 1994 (1,000 tonnes)	2,087	...	...	505	...	338	138	384	...	176	...	...	231	...	84	231
Coal production 1994 (1,000 tonnes)	131,220	...	...	57,623	...	18,194	...	7,538	...	...	1	...	...	147	...	47,717
Copper production 1994 (1,000 tonnes)	1,564	51	371	592	...	188	...	59	69	84	...	...	...	...	103	47
Crude oil production 1994 (1,000 tonnes)	151,022	1,147	...	2,938	9,118	948	531	2,769	...	4,895	...	...	4,323	...	5	124,348
Crude oil imports 1994 (1,000 tonnes)	507,407	7,790	28,372	106,262	5,263	53,796	12,914	74,644	9,899	75,225	2,292	...	56,741	13,454	18,016	42,739
Petroleum products 1994 (1,000 tonnes)	629	9.8	32	120	9	56	16	80	12	93	2.3	...	75	14	18	93
Natural gas production 1994 (10,000 TJ)	7,425	54	0	664	200	8.4	2.2	134	...	770	102	...	,2785	...	...	2705
Natural gas – consumption 1994 (1,000 TJ)	11,89	272	450	2,847	125	293	2.2	1,294	132	1,886	102	23	1,552	...	30	2,801
Iron ore production 1995 (1,000 tonnes)	27,121	2,107	...	...	...	1,859	...	1,497	...	...	...	...	...	...	21,658	...
Lead production 1994 (1,000 tonnes)	1,492	17	124	332	...	75	...	261	...	204	10	...	25	8	83	353
Zinc production 1994 (1,000 tonnes)	1,926	...	211	360	...	299	...	309	173	256	...	...	213	4	...	101
Cement 1994 (million tonnes)	173	4.6	8.8	36.1	1.8	26.7	13.9	21.2	1.1	33.1	1.5	...	3.1	7.6	2.2	11.1
Cars 1994 (1,000)	13,882	45	1,492	4,094	1	1,822	...	3,175	...	1,341	...	...	92	...	353	1,467
Commercial vehicles 1994 (1,000)	1,643	7	61	262	...	321	...	383	...	194	...	...	12	...	82	321
Ships launched 1993 (1,000 gross tonnes)	3,472	0	2.6	963	960	556	1.5	41	182	469	...	0	152	98	0.9	230
Ships under construction June 1994 (1,000 gross t.)	2,775	465	30	673	355	282	17	388	0.2	740	...	0	153	120.1	134	296e
Man-made fibres cellulosic 1993 (1,000 t.)	574	0	45	178	0	8.5	5	0	57	32	0	0	...	131	19	98
Man-made fibres non-cellulosic 1993 (1,000 t.)	2,661	67	269	815	49	262	6.9	118	71	624	109	0	0	37	0	232
Cotton yarns 1994 (1,000 tonnes)	950	23	41	152	3	86	98	164	1	254	...	0	3	111	...	14
Cotton fabrics 1994 (1,000 tonnes)	739	16	39	136	3	69	55	94	2	168	...	0	9	68	...	80
Woollen yarns 1994 (1,000 tonnes)	876	5	70	34	2	71	25	46	...	529	...	0	2	25	2	65
Woollen fabrics 1994 (1,000 tonnes)	285	1	3	27	1	...	...	37	1	165	...	0	2	9	1	38
Pulp and paper 1993 (1,000 tonnes)	63,586	3,301	1,266	12,793	328	3,348	750	7,824	9,993	6,019	...	0	2,855	998	8,868	5,243
Cigarettes 1993 (thousand million)	700	16.1	25.5	205	6.5	70	29.4	46.8	7	85.5	5.1	...	77	16.2	9.6	96.9
Energy total 1994 (million tonnes of oil equiv.)	725	8.8	10.9	141.1	14.8	32.2	9.7	120.7	12.7	31.2	3.6	0.1	66.3	3.3	30.8	239.1
Energy source – coal (mtoe)	136	0.3	0	80.9	0	10.5	7.4	5.2	2.2	0.1	1.2	0	0	0.1	0.3	27.9
Energy source – oil (mtoe)	153	1.1	0	3	9.2	0.9	0.5	2.8	0	4.9	0	0	4.4	0	0	126.2
Energy source – natural gas (mtoe)	187	1.2	0	14.3	4.3	0.2	0	2.9	0	16.5	2.2	0	59.9	0	0	58.2
Energy source – nuclear (mtoe)	202	0	10.5	36.8	0	14.3	0	92.9	5	0	0	0	1	0	18.9	22.8
Energy source – primary electricity (mtoe)	25.8	3.1	0	1.6	0.1	2.4	0.2	6.8	1	3.8	0.1	0	0	0.9	5.1	0.5
Energy consumption per head (toe)	3,602	3,246	4,972	4,101	3,874	2,488	2,314	3,947	5,966	2,671	3,072	9,300	4,599	1,921	5,529	3,761
Energy trade (mtoe)	634	17	43	193	6.2	68	16	110	20	126	7	4	17	16	19	−29
Electricity production 1994 (1,000-mill kWh)	2,146	53	69	490	38	154	37	454	62	220	16	1.1	77	30	139	306
Pig iron 1995 (1,000 tonnes)	97,279	3,877	9,198	30,013	0	5,108	0	12,860	2,271	11,684	0	1,030	5,530	411	3,035	12,262
Crude steel 1995 (1,000 tonnes)	155,744	5,004	11,557	42,051	653	13,796	940	18,105	3,216	27,687	309	2,613	6,409	829	4,898	17,677
Crude steel consumption per head 1993 (kg)	318	401	423	423	284	266	182	249	290	420	109	...	274	171	381	239
Finished roll products 1995 (1,000 tonnes)	134,594	4,213	11,033	34,316	631	12,771	1,436	15,109	3,331	24,034	276	2,407	4,702	703	4,461	15,171
Trade Imports 1995 (million ECU)	544,725	50,292	123,331	338,647	33,738	84,090	18,952	221,245	22,530	155,948	24,196	...	141,612	24,931	49,681	207,804
% of GDP	9.1	28	60	18	26	20	22	19	24	19	49	...	48	30	29	25
per head (1,000 ECU)	1.5	6.2	12.2	4.1	6.5	2.1	1.8	3.8	4.4	2.7	6.8	...	9.2	2.5	5.6	3.5
Trade Exports 1995 (million ECU)	569,035	43,729	133,255	389,265	37,760	72,913	8,246	230,245	30,955	176,654	33,412	...	155,328	17,418	61,069	181,250
% of GDP	9.5	25	65	21	29	17	10	20	32	21	68	...	51	21	35	22
per head (1,000 ECU)	1.5	5.4	13.1	4.8	7.2	1.9	0.8	4	6.1	3.1	9.3	...	10	1.8	6.9	3.1
Trade balance 1995 (million ECU)	24,310	−6,563	9,924	50,618	4,022	−11,177	−10,706	9,000	8,425	20,706	9,216	...	13,716	−7,513	11,388	−26,554
Television sets/1,000 inhabitants 1993	489	498	452	558	530	405	346	580	633	429	298	354	544	305	668	433
Telephone lines/1,000 inhabitants 1993	462	450	437	457	591	365	458	537	546	423	329	544	501	330	680	471
Railways line-length 1993 (km)	155,558	5,600	3,410	40,397	2,349	12,601	2,474	32,579	5,885	15,942	1,944	275	2,757	3,063	9,746	16,536
Railways passenger-km 1993 (million)	262,547	9,342	6,694	58,003	4,700	15,457	1,726	58,603	3,007	47,101	1,274	262	14,788	5,397	5,830	30,363
Railways net tonne-km 1993 (million)	204,396	11,798	7,583	64,626	1,797	7,558	524	45,033	9,259	18,792	575	607	2,681	1,665	18,133	13,765
Inland waterways length 1993 (km)	27,382	351	1,513	6,902	...	...	...	5,822	6,245	1,466	...	37	5,046	...	...	...
Inland waterways tonnes carried 1993 (1,000 t.)	621,915	6,452	67,582	218,012	...	...	...	64,864	1,647	606	...	10,224	252,528	...	...	...
Air passenger-km 1993	352,884	5,629	6,484	52,941	4,403	26,729	7,899	59,604	5,317	29,634	4,209	291	38,544	7,868	9,332	94,000
Maritime fleets 1994 (1,000 gross tonnes)	72,090	134	233	5,696	5,799	1,560	30,162	4,348	1,404	6,818	190	1,143	4,396	884	2,797	6,526
Motorways 1994 (km)	44,044	1,589	1,665	11,143	796	6,485	280	7,956	318	6,397	72	121	2,208	587	1,141	3,286
Other roads 1994 (km)	3,761,252	104,720	140,890	628,792	70,374	153,244	81,000	908,121	77,728	809,701	91,450	5,113	103,683	67,390	133,859	385,187
Cars 1994 (1,000)	156,748	3,479	4,210	39,765	1,610	13,734	2,074	24,900	1,873	29,430	939	229	5,884	3,532	3,594	21,740
Cars/1,000 inhabitants	423	433	416	488	309	351	199	430	368	518	263	567	383	357	409	373
Water abstractions 1990 (cu. m per inhabitant)	555	327	...	744	234	951	...	667	472	991	...	125	524	735	348	249
CO_2 emissions from fossil fuels 1994 (mill t.)	3,103	57	117	897	63	229	78	349	61	393	32	12	164	45	56	550
Generation of waste 1990 (kg/capita)	388	622	231	345	...	323	296	534	623	353	...	449	499	302	375	348
Commercial fertilizers used 1993 (1,000 tonnes)	16,141	262	320	2,672	485	1,826	...	4,611	...	1,750	710	...	523	237	333	2,071

The country abbreviations at the top of the columns are those used by Eurostat and are also referred to on the map on page 128: EUR 15 (the 15 member states of the EU), A (Austria), B (Belgium), D (Germany), DK (Denmark), E (Spain), EL (Greece), F (France), FIN (Finland), I (Italy), IRL (Ireland), L (Luxembourg), NL (Netherlands), P (Portugal), S (Sweden) and UK (United Kingdom).

The following abbreviations are used in the table: pps = purchasing power standard, enabling values to be compared in real terms; in 1995, 1 ECU pps = £1.42 : ECU = the currency of the EU
GDP = Gross Domestic Product : kWh = kilowatt hours : mtoe = million tonnes of coal equivalent : t. = tonnes : TJ = Tera Joule (a measure of energy equivalent to 23.88 tonnes of oil)

European Union 1998

ICELAND
NORWAY
FIN FINLAND
S SWEDEN
DENMARK
DK
IRELAND IRL
UNITED KINGDOM
UK
NL NETHERLANDS
D GERMANY
B BELGIUM
L
ESTONIA
LATVIA
LITHUANIA
RUSSIA
BELARUS
POLAND
CZECH REPUBLIC
SLOVAK REP.
UKRAINE
F FRANCE
SWITZERLAND
A AUSTRIA
SLOVENIA
HUNGARY
CROATIA
MOLDOVA
ROMANIA
PORTUGAL
P
E SPAIN
I
BOSNIA-HERZEGOVINA
YUGOSLAVIA
BULGARIA
ALBANIA
MACEDONIA
TURKEY
ITALY
EL GREECE
CYPRUS

European Union 1998

- European Union 1998
- Possible new members by 2003*
- European Free Trade Association

CARTOGRAPHY BY PHILIP'S © GEORGE PHILIP LIMITED

The EU in the global context

Grouping/country	Land area thousand sq km	Population 1997 millions	Population density persons per sq km	Population growth 1970–90 av. annual %	GNP 1995 thousand-million $US	GNP 1995 per person $US	Origin of GNP 1995		
							Agric.	Industry	Services
Europe 15 (1998)	3,132	375	120	0.3	7,980	21,250	2	30	67
Possible new members by 2003	539	63	117	0.6	175	2,775	6	37	56
Europe 20 (2003)	3,671	438	119	0.4	8,154	18,600	2	30	67
Rest of Western Europe (1)	447	11.8	27	0.4	429	36,250	3	33	64
Rest of Eastern Europe (2)	1,628	135	83	0.6	234	1,750	17	38	45
Cyprus	9.2	0.8	83	0.7	8.5	11,000	6	43	51
Turkey	770	64	83	2.6	169	2,650	16	31	53
Russia	16,996	148	8.7	0.7	332	2,250	7	38	55
Canada	9,221	30	3.3	1.1	574	39,400	3	30	67
China	9,326	1,210	130	1.6	745	600	21	48	31
Japan	377	126	334	0.9	496	39,400	2	38	60
USA	9,573	268	28	0.9	7,100	26,500	2	26	72

(1) = Iceland, Norway and Switzerland.
(2) = Albania, Belarus, Bosnia-Herzegovina, Bulgaria, Croatia, Latvia, Lithuania, Macedonia, Malta, Moldova, Romania, Slovak Republic, Ukraine and Yugoslavia.

* Please note that at the time of going to press, the five countries highlighted above (Czech Republic, Estonia, Hungary, Poland and Slovenia) were deemed the most likely to make up the first wave of new entrants into an expanded European Union. In addition, Bulgaria, Cyprus, Latvia, Lithuania, Romania and the Slovak Republic have all applied for membership. Turkey has had its application suspended.